A FIRST COURSE IN
NUMERICAL ANALYSIS

INTERNATIONAL SERIES IN
PURE AND APPLIED MATHEMATICS

William Ted Martin and E. H. Spanier
CONSULTING EDITORS

A FIRST COURSE IN NUMERICAL ANALYSIS

ANTHONY RALSTON

Professor of Mathematics
State University of New York
at Buffalo

McGRAW-HILL BOOK COMPANY

New York • St. Louis • San Francisco

Toronto • London • Sydney

TO MY PARENTS, RUTH AND ALFRED RALSTON

PREFACE

This book is based on a course I have been giving in the graduate school of the Stevens Institute of Technology. The course has been taken by both graduate students and advanced undergraduates in mathematics as well as by a sprinkling of nonmathematics students.

Because of the extremely rapid growth in the past decade and a half of all areas of science and technology related to digital computers, there is quite reasonably some controversy about how digital computers and related fields should fit into the pattern of higher education. This is particularly true in the area of numerical analysis. Many undergraduates, as freshmen or sophomores, now take a course which introduces them to digital computers and numerical methods. Although such a course is extremely valuable, I think the emphasis should be on the digital computer and not the numerical methods aspect. The reasons for this are twofold. In the first place, the ability to use a digital computer, even if this means no more than knowing how to use an algebraic language, should be of great value to the student in advanced undergraduate courses in science and engineering. On the other hand, at a low undergraduate level the student's mathematical background is not sufficiently sophisticated to enable him to be taught more than quite superficial aspects of numerical methods. (This is not to say that numerical methods should play no role in such a course. As examples with which to impress the student with the usefulness and power of the computer, they can serve a valuable purpose.)

Therefore, the title of this book means that I expect a course taught from it to be the student's first introduction to numerical analysis as a full-fledged branch of applied mathematics. Major portions of this book require no more than the usual two-year calculus sequence as prerequisite. However, the level of mathematical sophistication assumed is more appropriate to a student who has had advanced calculus. Indeed, where convenient I have assumed a knowledge of advanced calculus as well as some acquaintance with such topics as Fourier series, orthogonal polynomials, and complex variables. Chapters 9 and 10 assume that the student has had at least a semester course in matrix algebra.

The orientation of this book is almost entirely toward the use of numerical analysis on digital computers (although hand computation has by no means been ignored). Modern numerical analysis can be appreciated only within the context of some minimum knowledge of digital computers. While I have tried to include this minimum knowledge in Sec. 1.5, I would expect that few students would take a course from this book without some prior experience with digital computers, particularly with the use of some algebraic language. Many of the problems which require numerical work can be reasonably done only if the student has a computer available. Moreover, I am convinced that the value of a numerical analysis course is significantly increased if the student solves problems of some complexity either by hand or on a computer. I fully agree with R. W. Hamming that " . . . the purpose of computing is insight, not numbers . . . ," but, for the student, numbers are often the best road to insight.

Most of the topics in this book are approached non-algorithmically, partly because in a number of cases no good algorithmic approach exists and partly because a too formal approach to numerical analysis has a tendency to obscure the essentials of the subject. Problem solving on a computer provides an excellent opportunity for the student to think algorithmically.

As is common in numerical analysis texts, Chap. 1 contains a potpourri of introductory material with emphasis on the sources, types, and analysis of errors. Chapter 2 is an introduction to the central problem of numerical analysis—approximation—with emphasis on the reasons why polynomial approximation is dominant in numerical analysis.

In Chap. 3 on interpolation, there is relatively less emphasis on finite-difference techniques than is usual in books on numerical analysis because such techniques are less useful on digital computers than for hand computation. In Chap. 4 the Gaussian approach to numerical quadrature is emphasized for the purpose of presenting a unified approach to the subject. Within this context, Newton-Cotes techniques are introduced and their relatively greater usefulness is indicated. The approach to the solution of ordinary differential equations in Chap. 5 stresses the use of predictor-corrector techniques and the importance of stability. Runge-Kutta methods are considered in the context of their use as starting methods.

The method of least squares in its application to discrete data is the subject of Chap. 6. The emphasis in this chapter is on the use of orthogonal polynomials in the generation of least-squares approximations. Chapter 7 is concerned with the approximation of functions by polynomials and rational functions and concludes with an algorithm for the generation of the best approximation in the Chebyshev sense.

Chapters 8 and 9 treat, respectively, the solution of nonlinear equations and systems of linear equations. In the former both transcendental and polynomial equations are considered. In both chapters the stress is on efficient techniques for machine computation.   Chapter 10 is concerned with techniques for the calculation of the eigenvalues and eigenvectors of a matrix, again with the emphasis on the usefulness of the methods on digital computers.

It will ordinarily not be possible to cover all the material in this book in a full-year course in numerical analysis.   Rather than suggest topics for inclusion or exclusion, I would leave this to the instructor's own taste and experience.   The fact that the subjects of each of Chaps. 3 through 10 have themselves been the subjects of at least one book apiece should serve to emphasize to the student that a course taught from this book is indeed a first course in numerical analysis.   Moreover, little or no mention is made of the numerical solution of partial differential equations, integral equations, or boundary-value problems, or of linear programming. These topics properly fall in the domain of advanced numerical analysis. Since the basis of much of advanced numerical analysis is the solution of systems of linear equations and the calculation of eigenvalues, these topics have been purposely placed at the end of this volume.

In each of Chaps. 3 through 10 there are a number of illustrative examples whose purpose is to enhance the student's understanding of the relevant numerical method.   Since a morass of numbers is more likely to impede this aim than otherwise, the numbers in these examples have, where possible, been kept simple.

The problems themselves fall into four categories:
1. Simple proofs of topics considered in the text.
2. Algebraic manipulations and derivations, which would not add materially to the understanding of the student if included in the text, but which may nevertheless be instructive.
3. Computational problems.
4. Proofs and derivations of results which are an extension of the subject matter in the text.

Although the especially difficult problems have been starred (*), the student will find few really easy problems.   One of the major purposes of the appendix containing hints and answers to the problems is to help the student in solving problems which he finds difficult.   The student should be prepared to find minor discrepancies between his numerical answers and those in this appendix.   These will generally be the result of the idiosyncrasies of roundoff error on the computer on which he has performed his calculations.†

The few bibliographic references in the text itself are to topics outside

† All the calculations for this book were performed on the IBM 1620 computer at the Computer Center of the Stevens Institute of Technology which is partially supported by the National Science Foundation.

the scope of numerical analysis or to topics not suitable for problems. The bibliographic notes and references at the end of each chapter are meant to guide the student to basic sources from which he may usefully extend his knowledge. For this reason no attempt has been made to make the bibliography exhaustive, and comparatively few foreign-language references have been included.

As a final word, the student should not expect the result of a numerical analysis course to be the ability to choose infallibly the "best" method for a particular problem. Because the application of numerical analysis to actual problems is an art as well as a science such certain choices seldom exist. Therefore, the guidance that I have attempted to give the reader in various places in this book as to the selection of a method should be taken as generalizations and not as rules.

Since the material from this book has been drawn from many sources, I have a debt to many numerical analysts both past and present. But my debt is particularly great to three men, each the author of a standard text in numerical analysis. I have had the privilege of being a student of two of them—Zdenek Kopal and F. B. Hildebrand—and a colleague of the third—R. W. Hamming. To anyone familiar with their books, my debt will be particularly clear.

The errors that remain in this book are, of course, entirely my own responsibility. But the fact that errors are not more prevalent than they are is due to the efforts of a number of colleagues and friends who have read this manuscript. In particular, I must express my appreciation to E. Bareiss, E. W. Cheney, Phyllis Fox, R. W. Hamming, B. Parlett, W. G. Strang, and J. F. Traub for reading and commenting on all or parts of the manuscript. To Marie Scarpato goes my thanks not only for her accurate typing, typing, and retyping of the manuscript but also for her operation of the computer for almost all the calculations required for this book. And finally my greatest debt is to my wife and children for their cheerful acceptance of a part-time husband and father during the writing of this book.

ANTHONY RALSTON

CONTENTS

NOTATION

The table below is a list of symbols and notation used in this book. Amplified explanations are given when necessary at the first use of the symbol or notation. The reader is cautioned that some symbols may have more than one meaning but, hopefully, these are unambiguous [e.g., $P_n(x)$ is used as the notation for the Legendre polynomial of degree n in Chap. 4 and thereafter, but in Chap. 2 this notation is also used for a general polynomial of degree n].

A. PROBLEMS AND REFERENCES

Meaning	Example	Page First Used
1. References in text to problems at end of each chapter—numbers in braces	{2}	5
2. References to bibliography at end of each chapter—name followed by date in parentheses	Feller (1950)	10
3. Problems of more than ordinary difficulty—asterisk next to problem number	*10	20

B. GENERAL MATHEMATICAL NOTATION

Meaning	Symbol or Example	Page First Used
1. Approximately equal	$\approx$	8
2. Binomial coefficient	$\binom{n}{k}$	28
	$(m)_k$	48
3. Closed interval	$[a,b]$	1
4. Conjugate transpose of vector or matrix—superscript asterisk*	$\mathbf{v}^*$	432
5. Continued fraction	$\dfrac{C_1|}{|x + D_1} + \dfrac{C_2|}{|x + D_2} + \cdots$	277
6. Derivatives:		
(a) Single, double, or triple prime	$f''(\xi_1)$	1
(b) Lowercase Roman superscript	$f^{\mathrm{iv}}(\xi_2)$	1
(c) Letter or number in parentheses	$f^{(k)}(x)$	32

	Meaning	Symbol or Example	Page First Used
7.	Determinant of a matrix	$\lvert A \rvert$	396
8.	Divided difference	$f[a_1, a_2, \ldots, a_k]$	72
9.	Evaluation of quantity		
	(a) At one point	$\big\vert_n$	193
	(b) Difference at two end points	$\big\vert_{i=0}^{i=N+1}$	237
10.	Factorial function	$x^{(n)}$	136
11.	Inner product (T for transpose)	$(\mathbf{u}, \mathbf{v})$	6
		$\mathbf{x}^T \mathbf{x}$	418
12.	Norm of		
	(a) Matrix (spectral)	$\lVert A \rVert$ or $\lVert A \rVert_S$	417
	(b) Matrix (Euclidean)	$\lVert A \rVert_E$	417
	(c) Vector	$\lVert \mathbf{x} \rVert$	418
13.	Open interval	$(-1,1)$	89
14.	Order of magnitude	$O(h^2)$	169
15.	Sequences of functions or numbers—indexed quantity in braces (cf. A1 above)	$\{x^n\}$	25
16.	Spectral radius of a matrix	$\rho(A)$	418
17.	Union of sets	$\cup$	467
18.	Vectors—boldface English or Greek letters		
	(a) Column	$\mathbf{u}$	6
	(b) Row (T for transpose)	$\mathbf{x}^T$	394

C.   SPECIFIC MATHEMATICAL SYMBOLS

	Symbol	Meaning	Page First Used
1.	$B_n(x)$	Bernstein polynomial	28
2.	$B_n(x)$	Bernoulli polynomial	131
3.	B_n	Bernoulli number	132
4.	D	Differentiation operator	141
5.	E	Shifting operator	69
6.	EI	Efficiency index	323
7.	$\mathrm{erf}(x)$	Error function	20
8.	$H_n(x)$	Hermite polynomial	96
9.	I	Identity matrix	417
10.	$I_a^b R(x)$	Cauchy index	352
11.	$I_n(x)$	Modified Bessel function of first kind	287
12.	$I_{pq}(x_i)$	Iteration function	334
13.	$J_p(x)$	Bessel function of first kind	68
14.	$J_n(x; a, \beta)$	Jacobi polynomial	97

Symbol	Meaning	Page First Used
15. $l_j(x)$	Lagrangian interpolation polynomial	41
16. $L_n(x)$	Laguerre polynomial	95
17. $P_n(x)$	Legendre polynomial	88
18. $S_n^{(k)}$	Stirling number of first kind	79
19. $S_n(x)$	Chebyshev polynomial of second kind	100
20. $s_n^{(k)}$	Stirling number of second kind	157
21. T	Transpose of matrix or column vector	394
22. $T_n(x)$	Chebyshev polynomial	98
23. $T_r^*(x)$	Shifted Chebyshev polynomial	313
24. $\text{tr}(A)$	Trace of a matrix	418
25. $\mathbf{x}_c$	Computed solution of linear system	397
26. $\mathbf{x}_t$	True solution of linear system	397
27. ∇	Backward-difference operator	47
28. Δ	Forward-difference operator	46
29. δ	Central-difference operator	47
30. δ_{jk}	Kronecker delta	42
31. $\Gamma(x)$	Gamma function	97
32. μ	Mean central-difference operator	70

chapter 1

INTRODUCTION AND PRELIMINARIES

1.1 WHAT IS NUMERICAL ANALYSIS?

That numerical analysis is both a science and an art is a cliché to specialists in the field but is often misunderstood by nonspecialists. Is calling it an art and a science only a euphemism to hide the fact that numerical analysis is not a sufficiently precise discipline to merit being called a science? Is it true that "numerical analysis" is something of a misnomer because the classical meaning of analysis in mathematics is not applicable to numerical work? In fact, the answer to both these questions is "no." Rather the science and art juxtaposition is due to an uncertainty principle which often occurs in solving problems, namely, that to determine the best way to solve a problem may require the solution of the problem itself. In other cases, the best way to solve a problem may depend upon a knowledge of the properties of the functions involved which is unobtainable either theoretically or practically. A simple example will illustrate this. Two common methods for estimating the

$$\int_a^b f(x)\,dx$$

are the trapezoidal rule and the parabolic rule. The error incurred (i.e., the difference between the true value of the integral and the approximation) in the former is $-(b-a)^3 f''(\xi_1)/12n^2$ where $n+1$ is the number of points at which we evaluate $f(x)$ in $[a,b]$ and ξ_1 is some (unknown) point in $[a,b]$. For the parabolic rule the error is $-(b-a)^5 f^{\mathrm{iv}}(\xi_2)/180n^4$ where again $n + 1$ is the number of points at which $f(x)$ is evaluated and ξ_2 is an unknown point in $[a,b]$. Which do we use, especially when $f(x)$ is such that its derivatives are not reasonably calculable? As numerical analysis is a science, it has provided us with these two methods and the errors incurred when we use them, but as it is an art, it requires us to use our intuition, experience, and knowledge of functions "like" $f(x)$ to choose that method best suited to our particular problem.

As a science then, numerical analysis is concerned with the processes by which mathematical problems can be solved by the operations of arithmetic. Sometimes this will involve the development of algorithms to solve a problem which is already in a form in which the solution can be found by arithmetic means (e.g., simultaneous linear equations). Often it will involve replacing quantities which cannot be calculated arithmetically (e.g., derivatives or integrals) by approximations which enable an approximate solution to be found. In this case, we shall naturally be interested in the errors incurred in our approximation. But in any case, the tools we shall use in developing the processes of numerical analysis will be the tools of exact mathematical analysis as classically understood.

As an art, numerical analysis is concerned with choosing that procedure (and suitably applying it) which is "best" suited to the solution of a particular problem. This implies the need for anyone who wishes to practice numerical analysis to develop experience and with it, hopefully, intuition. We have therefore provided numerous examples to illustrate the numerical methods discussed. The purpose of these examples is to help the reader to understand principles and develop an insight into computational processes. To further these aims, the numbers, where possible, have been kept simple.

Numerical analysis is a very different discipline today from what it was only fifteen years ago at the advent of the high-speed digital computer. High-speed computation has revolutionized numerical analysis as an art and given enormous impetus to its development as a science. Our orientation in this book will be strongly toward methods which are particularly useful on digital computers. To do this is not to ignore methods for desk calculators. Most of the methods to be discussed are applicable to both hand and automatic computation. But we recognize the fact that today the overwhelming majority of significant computations are performed on digital computers.

The reader with no experience with digital computers should not feel dismayed at this point. Very few sections of this book require any definitive knowledge of digital computers. Moreover, those facets of digital computers which are necessary for the understanding of some sections are discussed in Sec. 1.5.

1.2 SOURCES OF ERROR

Numerical answers to problems generally contain errors which arise in two areas—those inherent in the mathematical formulation of the problem and those incurred in finding the solution numerically.   The former category includes the error incurred when the mathematical statement of a problem is only an *approximation to the physical situation*.   Such errors are often negligible, as in the case of neglecting relativistic effects in problems in classical mechanics.   If they are not negligible, then, no matter how accurate the numerical computations, there will be a significant error in the result.   Another source of inherent error is the *inaccuracies in the physical data*.   Such errors are also generally negligible when they are caused by inaccuracies in physical constants (e.g., the gravitational constant).   But when they are the result of errors in empirical data, the worth of a computed solution must be carefully weighed against these errors.   Moreover, because such errors are usually random, treating them analytically may be quite difficult.   Such errors will play significant roles in Chaps. 6 and 9.

There are three main sources of computational error.   The first, familiar to all users of desk calculators or just pencil and paper, is the gross error, or *blunder*.   Digital computers have enormously reduced the probability of such errors, but where the correctness of a computed solution cannot be readily verified, their possibility should not be ignored. It is the other two sources of computational error which will chiefly interest us here, however.

The first of these sources is that caused by solving not the problem as formulated, but rather some approximation to it.   This is usually caused by the replacement of an infinite (i.e., summation or integration) or infinitesimal (i.e., differentiation) process by a finite approximation. Some examples of this are:

1. Calculation of an elementary function (e.g., $\sin x$) by using the first n terms of its infinite Taylor-series expansion.
2. Approximation of the integral of a function by a finite summation of functional values as in the trapezoidal rule.
3. Solution of a differential equation by replacing the derivatives by approximations to them (e.g., difference quotients).
4. Solution of the equation $f(x) = 0$ by the Newton-Raphson method, an iterative process which in general converges only in the limit as the number of iterations goes to infinity.

We shall denote this type of error in all its various forms as *truncation* error, since it often is the result of truncating an infinite process to get a finite process.   In all the numerical procedures considered in this book, we shall be interested in estimating, or at least bounding, this error (to know it would, of course, be to eliminate it!).

The other source of error of importance to us is that caused by the fact that arithmetic calculations can almost never be carried out with complete accuracy. Most numbers have infinite decimal representations which must be rounded. But even if the data of a problem can be expressed exactly by finite decimal representations, division may introduce numbers which must be rounded and multiplication may produce more digits than can be reasonably retained. The error we introduce by rounding a number will be called *roundoff* error. As with the errors in empirical data, roundoff error has a random character which makes it difficult to deal with. We shall consider these difficulties in more detail in Sec. 1.4.

1.3   ERROR DEFINITIONS AND RELATED MATTERS

In the previous section, we relied upon the fact that the reader undoubtedly has a good intuitive notion of error. Here we shall formalize the concept of error. The two basic definitions are

(1)   True value = approximate value + error

(2)   Relative error $= \dfrac{\text{error}}{\text{true value}}$

Thus, denoting error by E and relative error by RE, if we approximate $\frac{1}{3}$ by .333, we have

$$E = \tfrac{1}{3} \times 10^{-3}$$

and

$$RE = 10^{-3}$$

Generally, we shall be interested in E (which is sometimes called absolute error) rather than RE, but when the true value of a quantity is very small or very large, relative errors are more meaningful. For example, if the true value of a quantity is 10^{15}, an error of 10^{6} is probably not serious, but this is more meaningfully expressed by saying that $RE = 10^{-9}$. In actual computation of the relative error, we shall often replace the unknown true value by the computed approximate value.

1.3-1   Significant digits and the ordering of a computation

Let x be a real number which, in general, has an infinite decimal representation. We shall say that x has been correctly rounded to a d-decimal-place number, which we denote by $x^{(d)}$, if the *roundoff error* ϵ is such that†

$$|\epsilon| = |x - x^{(d)}| \leq \tfrac{1}{2} \times 10^{-d} \tag{1.3-1}$$

Thus, if $x = 6.74399666 \cdots$, $x^{(3)} = 6.744$ and $x^{(7)} = 6.7439967$.

If y is any approximation to a true value x, then the kth decimal place of y is said to be *significant* if

$$|x - y| \leq \tfrac{1}{2} \times 10^{-k} \tag{1.3-2}$$

Therefore, every digit of a correctly rounded number is significant.‡

It might seem natural now to define the number of significant digits in y to be all the digits of y satisfying the definition of significant digit. Thus, if $y_1 = .9863$ is an approximation to $x_1 = .98632$ and if $y_2 = .0028$ is an approximation to $x_2 = .00278$, we would say y_1 and y_2 both have four significant digits. But are y_1 and y_2 equally "significant"? If they are the final answers to a computation and we are interested in absolute error, then they certainly are. But if they are intermediate numbers in a calculation which are to be used later as divisors, then they most certainly are not. For the magnitude of the error in $1/y_1$ is much less than that in $1/y_2$ {2}. We shall therefore avoid the use of the notion of the number of significant digits in a number.

The example above indicates that numbers with leading zeros can cause substantial magnification of error when used as divisors. In numerical calculations subtraction (or addition of numbers of opposite sign) is the most common source of numbers with leading zeros. Suppose all the digits in $y_1 = 2.78493$ and $y_2 = 2.78469$ are significant. Then the error in $y_1 - y_2 = .00024$ is in magnitude at most 10^{-5} (the sum of the maximum magnitudes of the errors in y_1 and y_2). But, if $y_1 - y_2$ is later used as a divisor, the magnitude of the error will be greatly magnified. Note that the relative error in y_1 is less than $\tfrac{1}{2} \times 10^{-5}/2.784925 \approx 1.8 \times 10^{-6}$, while that in $y_1 - y_2$ may be as much as $10^{-5}/.00023 \approx 4.3 \times 10^{-2}$. Thus we may say that, if the sum or difference of two numbers causes a large increase in relative error, then, if this result is later used as a divisor, substantial magnification of error may occur. This phenomenon is one of which the numerical analyst must continually be aware.

† When $|\epsilon| = \tfrac{1}{2} \times 10^{-d}$, we have the choice of rounding "up" or "down." That is, the number $.2775500 \cdots$ rounded to four decimal places may be either $.2776$ or $.2775$. Commonly, such numbers are always rounded "up" or always "down," but, since it is usually desirable to avoid any bias in roundoff, a rule such as rounding so that the last digit is always even (or always odd) is desirable in lengthy computations.

‡ It is not satisfactory to define the kth digit of y as significant only if x and y are identical when rounded to k digits. For suppose $x = 3.76512$ and $y = 3.7648$. Then the 6 would not be significant, but the 4 would be. By our definition, both are significant.

A common fallacy that is spread about arithmetic computations is that, if the lowest-order significant digit in the numbers in the data is in the kth position, then the accuracy (i.e., absolute error) in the computation cannot be improved by carrying lower-order digits than the kth at any point. That this is false in general we shall illustrate with an example whose importance we shall see in Chap. 9. Let $\mathbf{u}$ and $\mathbf{v}$ be two vectors with components

$$\mathbf{u} = (u_1, \ldots, u_n) \qquad \mathbf{v} = (v_1, \ldots, v_n)$$

each correctly rounded to k digits, the true vectors being $\mathbf{U}$ and $\mathbf{V}$. Suppose we wish to calculate the inner product

$$(\mathbf{u},\mathbf{v}) = \sum_{i=1}^{n} u_i v_i \tag{1.3-3}$$

and retain k digits. The question is: Is the error in the result affected by whether we round each product $u_i v_i$ to k digits and then sum them or first sum and then round? Let U_i and V_i be the true values of u_i and v_i, respectively, and let ϵ_i and δ_i be their respective errors. Then

$$u_i v_i = (U_i - \epsilon_i)(V_i - \delta_i) = U_i V_i - \delta_i U_i - \epsilon_i V_i + \delta_i \epsilon_i \tag{1.3-4}$$

If we round each product to k digits and denote the result by $(u_i v_i)_R$, we have

$$(u_i v_i)_R = U_i V_i - \delta_i U_i - \epsilon_i V_i + \delta_i \epsilon_i + \gamma_i \tag{1.3-5}$$

where $|\gamma_i| \leqq \frac{1}{2} \times 10^{-k}$. In the first method proposed above, we sum the $(u_i v_i)_R$ to get

$$(\mathbf{u},\mathbf{v}) = \sum_{i=1}^{n} (u_i v_i)_R = \sum_{i=1}^{n} U_i V_i - \sum_{i=1}^{n} (\delta_i U_i + \epsilon_i V_i - \delta_i \epsilon_i - \gamma_i) \tag{1.3-6}$$

so that the error in the result is given by

$$(\mathbf{U},\mathbf{V}) - (\mathbf{u},\mathbf{v}) = \sum_{i=1}^{n} (\delta_i U_i + \epsilon_i V_i - \delta_i \epsilon_i) - \sum_{i=1}^{n} \gamma_i \tag{1.3-7}$$

In the second method, we calculate each product without rounding (that is, we carry double the number of digits in each component; see Sec. 1.5-3 on double precision) and then round the result. Thus we calculate

$$(\mathbf{u},\mathbf{v}) = \sum_{i=1}^{n} u_i v_i + \gamma = \sum_{i=1}^{n} U_i V_i - \sum_{i=1}^{n} (\delta_i U_i + \epsilon_i V_i - \delta_i \epsilon_i) + \gamma \tag{1.3-8}$$

where $|\gamma| \leqq \frac{1}{2} \times 10^{-k}$. Thus

$$(\mathbf{U},\mathbf{V}) - (\mathbf{u},\mathbf{v}) = \sum_{i=1}^{n} (\delta_i U_i + \epsilon_i V_i - \delta_i \epsilon_i) - \gamma \qquad (1.3\text{-}9)$$

Since u_i and v_i are both correctly rounded to k digits

$$\left| \sum_{i=1}^{n} (\delta_i U_i + \epsilon_i V_i - \delta_i \epsilon_i) \right| \leqq \frac{1}{2} \times 10^{-k} \sum_{i=1}^{n} (|U_i| + |V_i| + \frac{1}{2} \times 10^{-k})$$
$$(1.3\text{-}10)$$

Also

$$\sum_{i=1}^{n} |\gamma_i| \leqq \frac{n}{2} \times 10^{-k} \qquad (1.3\text{-}11)$$

In (1.3-7) and (1.3-9) only the last term in each equation is the result of roundoff in the calculation.   The other terms in these equations are the result of the inherent roundoff error in $\mathbf{u}$ and $\mathbf{v}$.   Now let us assume that U_i and V_i are, for all i, less than 1 in magnitude (which is a common requirement for fixed-point numbers in a digital computer; see Sec. 1.5-2).†
Then the second term on the right-hand side of (1.3-7) is of the same order of magnitude as the first term.   But the second term on the right-hand side of (1.3-9), consisting as it does of a single roundoff term, is small compared with the first term.   Therefore, the second method generally leads to a smaller error in the computed scalar product than the first. Considerations of this kind, which are seldom significant in computations done on a desk calculator, can be of great significance on a digital computer where the number of computations performed may make roundoff, and thus the order in which a computation is performed, a very significant factor.

1.3-2   Error in functional evaluation

Equation (1.3-4) is a special case of the general problem of estimating the error in the evaluation of $f(y_1, \ldots, y_n)$ where

$$y_i = x_i - \epsilon_i \qquad (1.3\text{-}12)$$

† In fact, our previous assumption that the scalar product as well as the components are rounded to k digits is not reasonable unless all numbers are less than 1 in magnitude.   For, if some components were 1 or greater in magnitude, then the scalar product would in general contain more digits to the left of the decimal point than the components.   Thus, keeping k decimal places in each would be equivalent to keeping more *digits* in the scalar product than in the components.

with x_i the true value of the ith variable and ϵ_i the error.   Then

$$f(x_1, \ldots ,x_n) - f(y_1, \ldots ,y_n) = \sum_{i=1}^{n} \epsilon_i \frac{\partial f}{\partial x_i} + \frac{1}{2}\left(\sum_{i=1}^{n} \epsilon_i \frac{\partial}{\partial x_i}\right)^2 f$$
$$+ \cdots \quad (1.3\text{-}13)$$

where the partial derivatives are to be evaluated at $(y_1, \ldots ,y_n)$.   Since we shall usually be able to assume that terms containing products of the errors are small compared with the first term on the right-hand side of (1.3-13), we may write

$$f(x_1, \ldots ,x_n) - f(y_1, \ldots ,y_n) \approx \sum_{i=1}^{n} \epsilon_i \frac{\partial f}{\partial x_i} \qquad (1.3\text{-}14)$$

Note that the assumption made here is equivalent to ignoring the last term on the right-hand side of (1.3-4).   Equation (1.3-14) can serve as a convenient tool in estimating errors in functional evaluation, although in special cases more terms in (1.3-13) may need to be retained.

1.4   ROUNDOFF ERROR

If the solution of a problem requires many thousands or even millions of arithmetic operations, each of which is performed using rounded numbers, then it is intuitively clear that the accumulated roundoff error may significantly affect the result.   It is true that, given the computation to be performed and the roundoff rules that will be applied, the roundoff error at each step is determined.   Thus roundoff is not a random process.   But a priori it is essentially impossible to determine what the roundoff error will be in the millionth or even the hundredth step of the computation. Therefore, a probabilistic approach to roundoff error is helpful in understanding how this error accumulates.

1.4-1   The probabilistic approach to roundoff.   A particular example

Consider the addition of n numbers $\{a_i\}$ each correctly rounded to d decimal places.   Since the error in each number is no greater than $\frac{1}{2} \times 10^{-d}$, the accumulated error in the sum is no greater than $n/2 \times 10^{-d}$. But since most errors will be less in magnitude than $\frac{1}{2} \times 10^{-d}$, and since the differing signs in the errors will cause some cancellation of error, we expect the accumulated error to be substantially less than $n/2 \times 10^{-d}$ in general.   Our object here is to consider just what the distribution of this error is.

Denote by ϵ_i the roundoff error in a_i, and for convenience, let us, without loss of generality, take $d = 0$ in what follows.   Then ϵ_i takes on

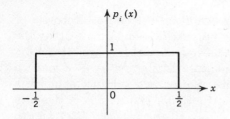

Fig. 1.1 Graph of $p_i(x)$, the probability density of ϵ_i.

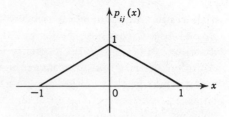

Fig. 1.2 Graph of $p_{ij}(x)$, the probability density of ϵ_{ij}.

values in the interval $[-\frac{1}{2},\frac{1}{2}]$, and if we assume each value in this range is equally likely, then the probability density of ϵ_i is shown in Fig. 1.1, which indicates that

$$\Pr\,(x_1 \leqq \epsilon_i \leqq x_2) = \begin{cases} x_2 - x_1 & -\frac{1}{2} \leqq x_1,\, x_2 \leqq \frac{1}{2} \\ x_2 + \frac{1}{2} & x_1 < -\frac{1}{2},\, -\frac{1}{2} \leqq x_2 \leqq \frac{1}{2} \\ \frac{1}{2} - x_1 & -\frac{1}{2} \leqq x_1 \leqq \frac{1}{2},\, x_2 > \frac{1}{2} \\ 1 & x_1 < -\frac{1}{2},\, x_2 > \frac{1}{2} \end{cases}$$

$$(1.4\text{-}1)$$

Now let us consider what happens when a_i is added to a_j, assuming that the roundoff errors in the two numbers are independent. Then {11} the probability density of the error $\epsilon_{ij} = \epsilon_i + \epsilon_j$ in $a_i + a_j$ is shown in Fig. 1.2.

From Fig. 1.1 we may calculate the variance σ_i^2 of $p_i(x)$ as

$$\sigma_i^2 = \int_{-\frac{1}{2}}^{\frac{1}{2}} x^2\,dx = \frac{1}{12} \tag{1.4-2}$$

and from Fig. 1.2, the variance of $p_{ij}(x)$ is†

$$\sigma_{ij}^2 = \int_{-1}^{0} x^2(1 + x)\,dx + \int_{0}^{1} x^2(1 - x)\,dx = \frac{1}{6} \tag{1.4-3}$$

Corresponding results for the sum of three {11} and four numbers would suggest a result which is only hinted at by the results for one and two numbers. This is that, in the limit as $n \to \infty$, the density function for the sum of n numbers approaches the normal density function with zero mean and variance $n\sigma_i^2$ with σ_i given by (1.4-2). Thus, if ϵ is the accumulated roundoff error for n additions

$$\Pr\,(x \leqq \epsilon \leqq x + dx) \to \frac{1}{(\pi n/6)^{\frac{1}{2}}}\, e^{-6x^2/n}\,dx \tag{1.4-4}$$

as $n \to \infty$ where the function on the right-hand side of (1.4-4) is the normal density function with zero mean and standard deviation $\sigma = (n/12)^{\frac{1}{2}}$.

† Or we may calculate σ_{ij} using the result that the variance of the sum of independent distributions with zero mean is the sum of the variances.

This result may be derived rigorously using the central-limit theorem of probability theory [see Feller (1950), pp. 191ff.], which states that the distribution of a sum of n mutually independent random variables with a common distribution approaches a normal distribution as $n \to \infty$ with mean equal to that of the common distribution and variance equal to n times the variance of the common distribution. [When $d \neq 0$, the only changes that must be made are to multiply all variances by 10^{-2d} and to multiply x and dx on the right-hand side of (1.4-4) by 10^d.]

In actual fact the normal density function gives a very good approximation to the distribution of $\epsilon_1 + \cdots + \epsilon_n$ for quite small n; so let us suppose we can use the right-hand side of (1.4-4) as the probability density for the error in our sum of n numbers. The *probable error*, which is defined as that positive value of x for which the probability is $\frac{1}{2}$ that the magnitude of ϵ will exceed x, is given by

$$.6745\sigma = (.6745/\sqrt{12})\,\sqrt{n} \tag{1.4-5}$$

Thus, while the error cannot exceed $n/2$ in magnitude, the probable error is proportional to the square root of n. For the sum of n numbers then, the probable error is substantially less than the maximum error, for lengthy computations (i.e., large n) by an order of magnitude or more. This is a general result which we would intuitively expect to hold also for more complicated computations where the analysis of roundoff error is too complex to carry out.

This result leads to what seems like a paradoxical situation in error analysis. On the one hand, in numerical computations we are usually interested in bounding the error incurred. That is, when we finish a computation, we like to be able to say that the computed result differs by *no more than* the error bound from the true result. In deriving such error bounds, we shall then, for the roundoff component of the error, choose its maximum value. On the other hand, we now realize that, by so doing, we are generally being unduly conservative. This paradox can be resolved only in the context of a particular situation. If roundoff error is small compared with truncation error, then using its maximum value will not make the error bound unrealistic. But if roundoff is the dominant error, the unrealistic error bound may have to be replaced by an estimate—generally a conservatively high estimate—of the expected error in order to get a usable result. Because $\sqrt{n}$ appears in the probable error while n appears in the maximum error in the above example, a common way to estimate the roundoff error in a long computation is to find a bound on the error and then to replace n (where n is a measure of the number of computations) by $\sqrt{n}$.

A problem closely related to that considered above is forming the

weighted sum of the n numbers

$$\sum_{i=1}^{n} \alpha_i a_i \tag{1.4-6}$$

If the roundoff errors in the a_i's all have the density function shown in Fig. 1.1, the result, analogous to the one above, is that the density function of the error in the sum approaches a normal density function with zero mean and variance

$$\sigma^2 = \frac{1}{12} \sum_{i=1}^{n} \alpha_i^2 \tag{1.4-7}$$

Linear combinations of the form (1.4-6) occur often in numerical analysis, as we shall see.   The coefficients α_i may often be chosen arbitrarily except for a constraint of the form

$$\sum_{i=1}^{n} \alpha_i = \alpha > 0 \tag{1.4-8}$$

An obvious question then is: What values of the α_i lead to the best roundoff behavior in the sum?   The answer depends on what we mean by best. If we only wish to minimize the bound on the roundoff error, then all sets of α_i which are all positive are equally good.   But if $\alpha_1 = \alpha$ and all the other α_i are zero, then the worst case will often be realized.   A more reasonable definition of "best" would be that set of α_i which minimizes σ^2 in (1.4-7), since this will lead to good roundoff behavior on the average (why?).   Minimizing σ^2 subject to the constraint (1.4-8) is a problem easily solved using the Lagrangian-multiplier technique {15}.   The answer is that the α_i are all equal to α/n.   Therefore, the roundoff properties of any sum of the form (1.4-6) may be judged by comparing the sum of the squares of the α_i with α^2/n.

1.4-2   Most-significant-digit theory

If we were to analyze more complex roundoff situations than those considered in the previous section, we would have to consider the effects of multiplication and division also.   In fact, in Sec. 1.3-1, we did consider the case of the multiplication of two rounded numbers.   Making the reasonable assumption that the errors ϵ_i and δ_i are small in comparison with U_i and V_i, the error in the product is determined by $U_i \delta_i$ and $V_i \epsilon_i$ and, therefore, by the leading digit of U_i and V_i.   A natural assumption in the analysis of this error would seem to be that the leading digits are uniformly distributed.   But Hamming (1962, p. 35) has pointed out that

this is not so.   As an example to illustrate this, consider the leading digits produced by the product of all possible combinations of one-digit numbers as shown in Table 1.1.   This illustrates that, starting with a flat distribution of leading digits, products of such numbers have leading digits heavily biased toward the lower digits.   Similar results may be shown for division and for calculations involving sequences of multiplications and divisions.   These results then affect the analysis of errors in later multiplications such as those in (1.3-5) {16}.

Table 1.1   Distribution of leading digits of products of one-digit numbers

Leading digit	No. of products
1	18
2	15
3	11
4	12
5	6
6	7
7	4
8	5
9	3

Now the above does not help us in finding roundoff-error *bounds*. But it does indicate one more reason why such bounds (which must assume the worst case of the leading digit) are likely to be very conservative.   In fact, the reader will have been well served if he has got the impression from this section that analysis of roundoff error can be both tricky and treacherous and that a proper evaluation of its effect on a given computation can be extremely difficult.

We conclude this section by noting that even our sometimes implicit assumption that roundoff errors in different numbers are independent is often not correct.   We made this assumption from necessity; the analysis of correlated roundoff errors is very difficult and almost no results are known.   But it is known from empirical computational evidence that frequently there is such correlation.

1.5   AUTOMATIC DIGITAL COMPUTERS

If a choice had to be made about the order in which to take two courses, one on the fundamentals of digital computers and the other on numerical analysis, certainly the course in digital computers should be taken first. But in fact, the interaction between two such courses is not great.   In

particular, no knowledge whatever of programming digital computers is necessary to understanding the remainder of this book.   However, certain aspects of digital computers to be presented in the next few pages, particularly in relation to how they perform arithmetic, will help the reader considerably at various places in this book.

1.5-1   Basic ideas

Figure 1.3 illustrates the basic functional parts of a digital computer and their relations.   The functions of the *input* and *output* boxes are self-explanatory.   Information to be entered into the computer is most typically on punched cards, magnetic tape, or punched paper tape.   Output information is often on these media, but also in common use is direct printed output.

Inside the dotted lines is the electronic heart of the computer.   In the *memory* two types of information are stored, the numbers relevant to the problem and the instructions which tell the computer what operations to perform.   These operations are conveniently divided into the following categories:

1. Arithmetic operations.   Digital computers can generally take any two numbers in the memory and perform any of the four arithmetic operations on them.   The actual performance of the operations is done in the *arithmetic unit*.
2. Logical operations.   On the basis of such criteria as the sign of a number or the comparative magnitude of two numbers, either of two instructions may be performed next.   For example, if a par-

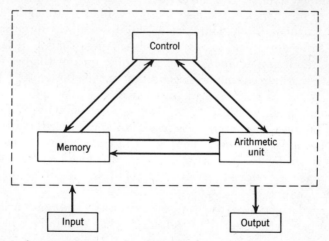

Fig. 1.3 Basic functional parts of a digital computer.   Arrows indicate information flow or control signals.

ticular number is positive, one may wish to perform one computation, while if it is negative, one may wish to perform another computation or, perhaps, stop the computation.
3. Transfer of data operations. These operations move data from one location in memory to another.
4. Input-output operations. These control the reading of information into and out of the computer.

The determination of which operations are to be performed on what numbers at a given time is the function of the *control unit*. In other words, the control unit determines which instruction is to be obeyed and, for example, if it is an arithmetic instruction, which numbers are to be used. The control unit also signals the other units of the computer to see that the instruction is carried out.

Of particular interest to us here are the forms in which numbers appear in the computer and some details of how the arithmetic operations are carried out.

1.5-2   Fixed- and floating-point arithmetic

The memory of a digital computer is usually divided up into a number of separate slots called *words*. Each word holds the same number, say d, of decimal digits plus a sign.† Negative numbers may be stored as absolute value plus sign or in complement form, but this need not concern us here. Thus, for example, a computer might be able to store 5000 ten-digit numbers. Typically, the computer will be designed so that each d-digit number is assumed to have its decimal point at the left-hand end of the word. That is, all numbers are assumed to be less than 1 in magnitude. This requires that in addition, subtraction, and division, the numbers be such that the sum, difference, or quotient also be less than 1 in magnitude. When the result of a computation is a number greater than or equal to 1 in magnitude, the resulting error condition is called *overflow*. When the computer performs arithmetic on numbers as described here, this mode of arithmetic is called *fixed-point* (i.e., fixed *decimal* point) arithmetic. We note that on most computers, it is possible to preserve all digits of the $2d$ digits in a product by storing the product in two separate memory words. Also, it is generally possible to use a $2d$-digit dividend by taking two words in memory as the dividend. The ability of most computers to do this will be used in Chap. 9.

The reader may already have surmised that fixed-point arithmetic is tedious to plan because of the requirement that all numbers be less than

---

† Many computers store numbers in binary rather than decimal form, but our discussion carries over to binary computers with just a change of minor details.

1 in magnitude. Indeed the necessity of *scaling* the numbers so that nowhere in the calculation will any result be greater than or equal to 1 in magnitude is generally extremely difficult a priori. For this reason, virtually all computers can, either by proper programming or with built-in equipment, perform *floating-point* arithmetic as well as fixed-point arithmetic. In this mode, the d-digit number in a word is not a number as such but rather has two distinct parts x and y of m and $d - m$ digits, respectively. In floating-point arithmetic, the number is then interpreted by the computer to be of the form $x \times 10^y$, where the magnitude of x is again assumed less than 1 and y is interpreted as an integer. (For binary computers the 10 becomes a 2.) Thus, with $d = 10$ and $m = 8$, the number

$$\underbrace{4637000}_{x}\underbrace{007}_{y} \qquad (1.5\text{-}1)$$

would be interpreted as

$$.4637 \times 10^7 \qquad (1.5\text{-}2)$$

It is necessary to have both x and y signed numbers, but only one sign is usually available. To overcome this difficulty, one device which is often used is, in the case $d - m = 2$, the excess-50 notation in which the number is interpreted as $x \times 10^{y-50}$. Thus the number in (1.5-1) would be .4637 $\times$ 10^{-43} and the number in (1.5-2) would be represented by

$$\underbrace{4637000}_{x}\underbrace{057}_{y}$$

Because of the obvious analogy to logarithms, x is often called the mantissa of the number and y the characteristic or exponent.

Floating-point arithmetic then provides a great deal of flexibility in number size and therefore virtually eliminates scaling. It is used in the great majority of all scientific computations although floating-point addition and subtraction are substantially slower than the corresponding fixed-point operations. (For multiplication and division floating- and fixed-point operations generally require about the same amounts of time.) Our definitions of errors are applicable to both fixed- and floating-point computations. Relative error is more likely to be of interest in floating- than in fixed-point computations because of the possible appearance of large positive or negative exponents. We have restricted our specific analyses of roundoff error to the fixed-point case because the details of fixed-point error analysis are generally somewhat easier to follow than those for floating-point. Fixed-point error analysis therefore leads to a better intuitive feeling for the problems involved. Analyses similar to those in Secs. 1.3 and 1.4 may also be carried out for floating-point computations, but the results are generally not so clean, particularly in the probabilistic case. It is worth noting, however, that the conclusion of Sec. 1.3-1, that double-precision accumulation of scalar products is desirable, is also true for floating-point calculations.

On a few computers, called variable word length computers, the number of digits in a number may vary. Even on such computers, however, fixed- and floating-point arithmetic is possible and the variations in details are not important enough to concern us here.

1.5-3   Single- and double-precision arithmetic

Arithmetic performed in either fixed- or floating-point mode on numbers the length of one word (i.e., d-digit numbers) is called *single-precision* arithmetic. We have mentioned that products the length of two words may be obtained. In order to use such products in later calculations, it must be possible to perform arithmetic on these double-length numbers. It is always possible to program the computer to perform the ordinary arithmetic operations on these double-length numbers. Such arithmetic is called *double-precision* arithmetic.

Double-precision arithmetic is also possible with floating-point numbers by, for example, letting the mantissa have $m + d$ digits and the exponent $d - m$ digits as before.

On variable word length computers, the distinction between single and double precision is not meaningful since numbers may have virtually any number of digits and the computer is built to perform arithmetic on these variable length numbers.

1.5-4   Roundoff

To get a d-digit product when two d-digit numbers are multiplied, the computer rounds the $2d$-digit product in a manner entirely analogous to the procedure outlined in Sec. 1.3-1. In division, the quotient must be rounded in general. In floating-point arithmetic, roundoff also occurs in addition and subtraction when two numbers with different exponents are added {17}.

Still another kind of roundoff occurs when a fixed-point number is scaled. Suppose $d = 10$ so that the number 3.674953×10^{-4} is stored as

   0003674953

In order to multiply this number by 10^3, we need merely to shift it left three places to obtain

   3674953000

But why should we introduce zeros on the right-hand end?   If this number was a previously rounded number, then introducing zeros minimizes the maximum error we can make (why?).   If, on the other hand, this number was previously truncated instead of rounded, then the introduction of 500 minimizes the maximum error.   On some computers where scaling is done automatically in floating-point arithmetic, the user can specify the digit to be introduced on the right and, in this way, test the effect of using two different digits when the same computation is performed twice.

1.5-5   Speed of computation

We are interested here not in the absolute speed of digital computers but rather in the relative speed with which they perform various computations.   If two methods for computing the solution to the same problem differ only in the number and type of computations to be performed (and not, therefore, significantly in the computed result), then we should use that method which requires the least computing time.   But how are we to estimate this?   The general answer is that all the non-input-output operations described in Sec. 1.5-1 require approximately the same amount of time except for the floating-point arithmetic operations and fixed-point multiplication and division.   Floating-point addition and subtraction are equally time-consuming but are usually substantially more time-consuming than their fixed-point counterparts because of the need to match the exponential parts of the numbers.   On large, fast computers fixed-point division is little if at all slower than fixed-point multiplication and the same is true for the corresponding floating-point operations.   On some smaller, slower computers division may be slower than multiplication by a factor of 3 or more, but most computations require many more multiplications than divisions.

Typically—and we emphasize that this varies from computer to computer—fixed-point multiplication and division are substantially slower than fixed-point addition and subtraction, often by a factor of 5 or more.   Floating-point multiplication and division may, however, be as fast or nearly as fast as the corresponding fixed-point operations.   Nevertheless, on all but the most modern high-speed computers, floating-point multiplication and division are still slower than floating-point addition and subtraction by a factor of 2 or more.

On some of the highest-speed computers available today and on some being designed for the future, floating-point arithmetic is almost as fast as fixed-point arithmetic and, more significantly, all the floating-point operations require similar amounts of time.   Nevertheless, for simplicity and because it is reasonable on most computers, we shall at various places in this book evaluate the relative merits of different computational processes by counting the number of multiplications and divisions they require. The conclusions we shall draw will usually be valid even for floating-point computations on computers on which floating-point addition and subtraction are as time-consuming as floating-point multiplication and division.

With this potpourri of preliminaries behind us, we are ready to get into the heart of our subject. In the pages that follow, we shall discuss many of the basic topics in the numerical analysis of problems involving functions of a single real variable (and all numbers will be real unless otherwise stated). Only in discussing simultaneous linear and nonlinear equations shall we consider functions of more than one variable. The functions we shall consider will generally be assumed—and this assumption will usually be implicit—to be continuous, although when this assumption is not necessary it will usually be clear from the context. Often, and again implicitly, we shall assume that the functions we deal with have as many derivatives as required by the analysis.

BIBLIOGRAPHIC NOTES

1.1–1.4 Many of the texts on numerical analysis contain an introductory chapter with material in some degree similar to this. In particular, Hamming (1962) devotes a chapter to roundoff error. Valuable general material is also contained in Hildebrand (1956), Householder (1953), and Scarborough (1962).

The only alternative to ignoring roundoff error—which can be fatal—is to understand it and particularly the basis of the probabilistic theory. For this, Feller (1950) is a good reference. The recent book by Wilkinson (1964) is an excellent source on the subject of error analysis in numerical analysis. In particular, this book contains analyses of errors in both fixed- and floating-point arithmetic.

1.5 More detailed introductions to digital computers and programming can be found in Sherman (1963), McCracken (1957), and Leeds and Weinberg (1961), among others. For more details about how arithmetic is performed on computers, see Flores (1960, 1963) and Richards (1955).

BIBLIOGRAPHY

Feller, W. (1950): *Probability Theory and Its Applications*, John Wiley & Sons, Inc., New York.

Flores, I. (1960): *Computer Logic*, Prentice-Hall, Inc., Englewood Cliffs, N.J.

Flores, I. (1963): *The Logic of Computer Arithmetic*, Prentice-Hall, Inc., Englewood Cliffs, N.J.

Hamming, R. W. (1962): *Numerical Methods for Scientists and Engineers*, McGraw-Hill Book Company, New York.

Henrici, P. (1964): *Elements of Numerical Analysis*, John Wiley & Sons, Inc., New York.

Hildebrand, F. B. (1956): *Introduction to Numerical Analysis*, McGraw-Hill Book Company, New York.

Householder, A. S. (1953): *Principles of Numerical Analysis*, McGraw-Hill Book Company, New York.

Leeds, H. D., and G. M. Weinberg (1961): *Computer Programming Fundamentals*, McGraw-Hill Book Company, New York.

McCracken, D. D. (1957): *Digital Computer Programming*, John Wiley & Sons, Inc., New York.

Richards, R. K. (1955): *Arithmetic Operations in Digital Computers*, D. Van Nostrand Company, Inc., Princeton, N.J.

Scarborough, J. B. (1962): *Numerical Mathematical Analysis*, 5th ed., The Johns Hopkins Press, Baltimore.

Sherman, P. M. (1963): *Programming and Coding Digital Computers*, John Wiley & Sons, Inc., New York.

Wilkinson, J. H. (1964): *Rounding Errors in Algebraic Processes*, Prentice-Hall, Inc., Englewood Cliffs, N.J.

PROBLEMS

Section 1.3

1. Let all the numbers in the following calculations be correctly rounded to the number of digits shown: (a) $1.1062 + .947$; (b) $23.46 - 12.753$; (c) $(2.747)(6.83)$; (d) $8.473/.064$. For each calculation, determine the smallest interval in which the result, using true instead of rounded values of the quantities, must lie.

2. Let $y_1 = .9863$ and $y_2 = .0028$ be correctly rounded approximations to x_1 and x_2, respectively. Find the maximum magnitude of the difference between the calculated values of $1/y_1$ and $1/y_2$ and the true values.

3. (a) Suppose you are given n numbers, $a_1, \ldots, a_n$, where a_i is correctly rounded to d_i decimals. You wish to compute the sum of these n numbers and to retain $d = \min_i d_i$ decimals. Does it matter whether all the numbers are first rounded to d decimals and then added or whether they are first added and then rounded? Why?

(b) Let x and y be numbers less than 1 in magnitude which are correctly rounded to $2d$ and d decimals, respectively. Let $|x| < |y|$ and suppose you wish to compute x/y as a d-digit quotient. Show that using a $2d$-digit dividend is preferable to first rounding x to d digits and then dividing.

4. (a) Let $a_i = 1/i, i = 2, \ldots, 10$ be correctly rounded to four decimal places. Compute $\sum_{i=2}^{10} a_i^2$ by both the methods discussed in Sec. 1.3-1. Which result is more accurate? How do you *know*?

(b) Using the result of Prob. 3b and Sec. 1.3-1, what is the best way to calculate x defined by the equation

$$ax + \sum_{i=1}^{n} b_i c_i = 0$$

5. Use (1.3-14) to approximate the error incurred when correctly rounded numbers are used to compute (a) the product of n numbers; (b) the quotient of two numbers; (c) a power of a number where the power is known exactly; (d) a power of a number where the power is also in error.

6. (a) Use the results of parts a and b of the previous problem to get estimates of the errors in the computations of Prob. $1c$, d. Where there are discrepancies between these bounds and those calculated in Probs. 1 and 2, what causes them?

(b) Repeat part a on the computations of Prob. 2.

7. Use the results of Prob. $5c$ and d to get estimates of the errors in (a) $(6.45)^{1/32}$; (b) $(8.47)^{.643}$, if $1/32$ is exact and all other numbers are correctly rounded as shown.

8. (a) Suppose you wish the values of (i) $\cos 1.473$, (ii) $\tan^{-1} 2.621$, (iii) $\ln 1.471$, (iv) $e^{2.653}$, but in each case have a table at an interval of .01 in the argument. Use (1.3-14) to get an estimate of the error made by using the nearest values in the tables to the given arguments.

(b) Suppose each of the values in part a is a correctly rounded value. Estimate the maximum error incurred using the nearest tabular values.

9. (a) If $v = 16t^2$, find Δt, the allowable error in t, as a function of t in order that v will have a relative error of less than .01 in magnitude. Use the approximate value in the denominator of the expression for RE.

(b) Let $f(x) = \dfrac{2.5132x - .0476}{4.2715x - 6.3120}$. Find bounds for the absolute and relative errors in $f(x)$ for the exact value $x = 1.62$ if all the coefficients are correctly rounded numbers. Why is the problem substantially more difficult if x is also a rounded number?

Section 1.4

*10. (a) Let ϵ have a probability density $p(x)$ on $(-\infty, \infty)$. Show that the probability that ϵ does not exceed x is given by

$$P(x) = \int_{-\infty}^{x} p(x)\, dx$$

$P(x)$ is called the probability distribution of ϵ.

(b) Use this result to show that, if ϵ_1 and ϵ_2 are independently distributed variables with probability densities $p_1(x)$ and $p_2(x)$, the probability distribution of $\epsilon_1 + \epsilon_2$ is given by

$$\iint_{s+t<x} p_1(s) p_2(t)\, ds\, dt$$

(c) Manipulate this integral to show that the probability density of $\epsilon_1 + \epsilon_2$ is given by

$$\int_{-\infty}^{\infty} p_1(x - t) p_2(t)\, dt$$

*11. (a) Use the result of the previous problem to verify Fig. 1.2.

(b) Use this result to find the probability density of $\epsilon_1 + \epsilon_2 + \epsilon_3$ when each of these variables is independently distributed as shown in Fig. 1.1.

(c) Compare the results of a and b with the corresponding normal density functions given by (1.4-4) with $n = 2$ and 3 by plotting the graphs of the functions.

12. The error function is defined by

$$\mathrm{erf}(x) = \frac{2}{\sqrt{\pi}} \int_{0}^{x} e^{-t^2}\, dt$$

(a) Show that

$$\lim_{x \to \infty} \text{erf } (x) = 1$$

[*Hint:* Consider erf (x) erf (y) and use polar coordinates.]

(b) Use this result and (1.4-4) to show that the normal distribution function corresponding to the normal density function with zero mean and variance $n/12$ is given by $\frac{1}{2} + \frac{1}{2}$ erf $[(6/n)^{\frac{1}{2}}x]$.

(c) Finally deduce that the probability that ϵ in (1.4-4) is less than x in magnitude is given by erf $[(6/n)^{\frac{1}{2}}|x|]$.

13. (a) Use a table of the error function to verify Eq. (1.4-5).

(b) How large must n be so that the probable error is less than $\frac{1}{10}$ the maximum error $n/2$? For this n, use part c of the previous problem to estimate the probability that the error is greater in magnitude than three-quarters of the maximum error.

*14. Consider the iteration

$$x_{i+1} = \alpha x_i + \beta \qquad x_0 = a \qquad \beta \neq 0 \text{ or } a(1 - \alpha)$$

(a) Show that $|\alpha| < 1$ in order for the iteration to converge (i.e., in order that $\lim_{i \to \infty} x_i$ will exist).

(b) Let ϵ_i be the accumulated roundoff error in x_i, and let δ_i be the roundoff error introduced in the calculation of x_i from x_{i-1} (with δ_0 the roundoff error in x_0). Assume α and β are known exactly and that all x_i are correctly rounded to d decimals. Find a bound δ on δ_i assuming the arithmetic is performed as efficiently as possible.

(c) Use the iteration equation to derive a difference equation relating ϵ_i, ϵ_{i-1}, and δ_i.

(d) Use this result to show by induction that

$$\epsilon_i = \sum_{j=0}^{i} d_{ij}\delta_j$$

where $d_{ii} = 1$ and

$$d_{ij} = \alpha d_{i-1,j} \qquad i > j \geqq 0$$

(e) Thus, deduce that

$$d_{ij} = \alpha^{i-j}$$

and, therefore, that

$$|\epsilon_i| \leqq \frac{1}{1 - |\alpha|} \delta$$

(f) Use the results of parts b, d, and e and Eq. (1.4-7) to show that the variance of the probability density of ϵ_i is given by

$$\sigma^2 = \frac{10^{-2d}}{12} \frac{1 - \alpha^{2i+2}}{1 - \alpha^2} \leqq \frac{10^{-2d}}{12} \frac{1}{1 - \alpha^2}$$

[Ref.: Henrici (1964), pp. 309–314.]

15. Use a Lagrangian multiplier to show that σ^2 in (1.4-7) is minimized subject to the constraint (1.4-8) when all the α_i's are equal.

16. Suppose the components of **u** and **v** in Sec. 1.3-1 are the results of previous computations involving multiplications. Further, suppose that we bound the right-hand side of (1.3-10) by replacing each U_i and V_i by 1.   Explain why Table 1.1 indicates that this leads to an even more conservative bound than might be expected.

Section 1.5

17. Consider a computer where floating-point numbers have eight-digit mantissas followed by two-digit exponents in which the exponents are expressed in excess-50 form.   Let two such numbers be

$$4735821653 \ (.47358216 \times 10^3) \text{ and } 3294175251 \ (.32941752 \times 10^1)$$

(a) Add these two numbers and put the result in the same floating-point form.

(b) If both numbers are exact as given, what is the error in the sum?

(c) If both mantissas are correctly rounded as shown, compute a bound for the error in the sum found in part a.

18. (a) In fixed-point arithmetic with the magnitude of all numbers less than 1, show that all arithmetic operations except multiplication may result in overflow. Give an example of overflow with each of the other three arithmetic operations.

(b) In floating-point arithmetic, with numbers having an m-digit mantissa and $(d - m)$-digit exponent, show that all arithmetic operations may lead to numbers which are too large to be expressed in the $(m, d - m)$ format.   Give examples.

(c) Underflow is a condition that occurs in floating-point arithmetic when a number too small to be represented occurs.   Show that underflow may occur as the result of any floating-point arithmetic operation.   Give examples.

*19. Consider a double-precision arithmetic scheme where a $2d$-digit number is held in two d-digit words.   Suppose that the computer can add two d-digit numbers at a time and can recognize when overflow occurs.

(a) Devise an algorithm for adding two such double-precision numbers assuming all numbers are positive.

(b) If both halves of the double-precision number have a sign associated with them, and if the signs are required to be the same, modify this algorithm so that it can handle addition of positive and negative numbers so that the sum will also have the same sign in both halves.

In both parts assume there is no overflow in the overall sum.

20. If multiplication is ten times as slow as addition on a computer, what is the most efficient way of evaluating the polynomial

$$f(x) = \sum_{i=0}^{n} a_i x^i$$

for a given value of x?   (See Sec. 7.2.)

chapter 2

POLYNOMIAL APPROXIMATION

2.1 APPROXIMATION

We have said that numerical analysis is concerned with the solution of mathematical problems by arithmetic processes. Clearly then, the need to approximate nonarithmetic quantities by arithmetic quantities—and to ascertain the errors associated with such approximations—lies at the heart of much of numerical analysis. In a given situation there will usually be several possible methods of obtaining the desired approximation. Which of these to choose depends upon which of various possible criteria are used to judge how efficacious a given approximation is. The following simple example will illustrate what these criteria are and how they affect the choice of an approximation.

Suppose that we are given a value of x and we wish to calculate $\sqrt{x}$. The following are among the possibilities open to us:

1. Use the classic method learned by most people in grammar school which begins by pairing off digits on either side of the decimal point.
2. Look up x in a table of square roots and, if x lies between two arguments in the table, interpolate (see Chap. 3) to find the $\sqrt{x}$.
3. Use any one of a number of iterative techniques (see Chap. 8) to compute $\sqrt{x}$.

Our object here is not to decide which of these methods should be used but rather to discuss the considerations that must precede any such decision. We naturally assume that all the methods "work," that is, that they all lead to a result which can reasonably be considered an approximation to $\sqrt{x}$. The basic question we must answer is

What error can we tolerate in the result?

This question not only recognizes the importance of the error incurred in an approximation but, more subtly, implies the importance of being able to estimate or bound this error. The latter is a consideration of first importance in choosing a method for the solution of a problem. Only when we have methods where it is possible to estimate or bound the error can we then try to compare these methods on the basis of the magnitudes of the errors to which they lead. Each of the above methods for computing the square root has an error which can be estimated or bounded and which can be made arbitrarily small by carrying the computation far enough (e.g., by computing as many decimal places as desired in the first method). Therefore, on the basis of error considerations, each is a reasonable candidate for computing the square root.

The reader may have noted that the question above is ambiguous. What do we mean by error in the result? Absolute error or relative error? Do we wish to bound the error for all x in some interval or will we be satisfied with a small average error (where now "average" is ambiguous)? These queries need to be answered in practice, but our purpose here has been to point out *that the primary aim of any approximation is to achieve some desired degree of accuracy* and implicit in this aim is the assumption that the accuracy can indeed be estimated.

In one important sense our approach to numerical analysis in this book will be basically pragmatic; that is, except for techniques of special theoretical interest, we shall concentrate on methods which are, in fact, usable in practice. Thus, for a given method, we shall usually also wish to answer the question

How fast can a solution be computed using a given method?

In the case of the first method above for the calculation of $\sqrt{x}$, this question is easily answered since, given the number of decimal places desired in the square root, this is a finite process with the number and type of calculations strictly determined. Using the second method, interpolation, we must first choose an interpolation formula which will achieve the desired accuracy. Having done this, however, the amount of calculation is again strictly determined.† But using iterative processes, the situation is different. Our assumption that the method would "work" is equivalent to assuming that the iteration converges. But the amount of computation required to achieve the desired degree of accuracy depends on the rate of convergence. Therefore, determining rates of convergence in iterative processes will always be of importance to us.

---

† This is really a simplification of the truth; see Sec. 3.6.

Generalizing then from our example of the $\sqrt{x}$, we conclude that the primary aim of an approximation is to achieve some desired degree of accuracy and to be such that the accuracy can be estimated. Secondly, we are also interested in the amount of computation required to achieve the approximation. With these heuristic notions behind us, we may now proceed to consider the general problem of approximation.

2.1-1 Classes of approximating functions

Much of the approximation done in numerical analysis consists of approximating a function $f(x)$ by some combination—most often a linear combination—of functions drawn from some particular class of functions. The most familiar example of this is the approximation of $f(x)$ by the first N terms of its Taylor-series expansion. Another familiar example occurs in the trapezoidal rule in which $f(x)$ is approximated by a sequence of straight lines. In the former example and for each straight line in the trapezoidal rule, the approximation is a linear combination of functions from the class $\{x^n\}$, $n = 0, 1, \ldots$. More generally, we may consider the class $\{p_n(x)\}$ where $p_n(x)$ is a polynomial of degree n. Another class which is suggested by the importance of periodic functions is the class of Fourier functions $\{\sin nx, \cos nx\}$, $n = 0, 1, \ldots$. There are, of course, a number of other classes of functions—exponential functions are an obvious example—which would lead to useful approximations in particular cases. But for general application, polynomials and the Fourier functions are by far the most important, with the former predominating. Since this assertion about polynomial approximations is basic to our study of numerical analysis, we shall, in the next few pages, attempt to justify it.

2.1-2 Types of approximations

Let $f(x)$ be a function which we wish to approximate using the class of functions $\{g_n(x)\}$, $n = 0, 1, \ldots$. Suppose we approximate $f(x)$ by the linear combination

$$f(x) \approx a_0 g_0(x) + a_1 g_1(x) + \cdots + a_m g_m(x) \tag{2.1-1}$$

where the a_i, $i = 0, 1, \ldots, m$ are constants. We shall call (2.1-1) an approximation of *linear* type to $f(x)$. Because the analysis of approximations involving nonlinear combinations of the approximating functions is, like most nonlinear analysis, very difficult, we shall be concerned almost entirely with approximations of linear type. In Chap. 7, however, we shall make extensive use of approximations of *rational* type which have the form

$$f(x) \approx \frac{a_0 g_0(x) + a_1 g_1(x) + \cdots + a_m g_m(x)}{b_0 g_0(x) + b_1 g_1(x) + \cdots + b_k g_k(x)} \tag{2.1-2}$$

The crux of the approximation problem is the criterion to use in choosing the constants in (2.1-1) and (2.1-2). Three methods of doing this lead to three types of approximations of major importance:

1. *Exact* or *interpolatory* approximations in which the constants are chosen so that at the points x_i, $i = 1, \ldots, p$ the approximation and its first r_i derivatives (where r_i is a nonnegative integer) agree with $f(x)$ (except for roundoff).
2. *Least-squares* approximations in which the object is to minimize the integral of the square of the difference between $f(x)$ and its approximation (perhaps multiplied by a suitable weighting function) over an interval $[a,b]$ or, more commonly, to minimize the weighted sum of the squares of the error over a discrete set of points of $[a,b]$.
3. *Minimum maximum error* approximations where the aim is to minimize the maximum magnitude of the difference between $f(x)$ and its approximation (again perhaps suitably weighted) on an interval $[a,b]$.

These heuristic definitions have been given here in order to orient the reader to what follows. They will be made properly precise in later chapters. Of the three types, exact approximations are generally easier to derive and analyze (i.e., errors can be more easily estimated) than the other two. Chapters 3 through 5 will be exclusively concerned with exact approximations. Because of their particular advantages in certain applications, we shall discuss least squares and minimum maximum error approximations in Chaps. 6 and 7, respectively.

2.1-3 The case for polynomial approximation

By a polynomial approximation, we mean one of the form (2.1-1) where each $g_i(x)$ is a polynomial. The computational case for the use of polynomials as the approximating functions follows directly from the fact that a digital computer can perform only the computational operations of arithmetic. A piecewise rational function is then the *most general kind of function that can be evaluated directly on a digital computer*.† Thus, in

---

† This is a slight exaggeration. Somewhat more general functions can be evaluated using the logical operations or operations on the magnitude of a number which are available on many computers. But for all practical purposes, the statement above is true.

approximating a function $f(x)$ using any other class of functions $\{g_n(x)\}$, we must first evaluate the functions $g_n(x)$ using some approximation of each $g_n(x)$ as a polynomial in x or rational function of x. As a word of caution, though, it is easy to overemphasize this advantage of the class $\{x^n\}$. Thus, for example, in Chap. 6 we shall indicate how Fourier approximations can be calculated with only a single evaluation of a sine and a cosine.

One property that the powers of x and the trigonometric functions (as well as exponential functions) have in common is that an approximation using either of these classes changes its coefficients but not its form if the origin of the coordinate system is changed. Thus, if $P(x)$ is a polynomial or rational function, so is $P(x + \alpha)$, and if $T(x)$ is a linear or rational approximation using sines and cosines, so is $T(x + \alpha)$. Approximations using powers of x have the further advantage that, if the scale of the variable is changed, again the coefficients but not the form of the approximation are changed. Thus $P(kx)$ is still a polynomial in x. But this property does not hold for approximations using sines and cosines. That is, in general, for noninteger $k \sin nkx$ is not a member of the class $\{\sin nx\}$.

One further obvious analytic advantage of polynomials is the ease with which they may be manipulated in general and differentiated and integrated in particular. In classical analysis, this enables us, for example, to express the remainder term in a Taylor series in closed form, and as we shall see, there are analogous advantages in numerical analysis. A similar analytic advantage is also possessed by the Fourier functions.

All the advantages of the class $\{x^n\}$ that we have mentioned would be for naught if there were no analytic basis for our hope that we can achieve arbitrarily high accuracy with this class. We assume the reader is familiar with the result [Courant and Hilbert (1953), p. 65] that the set of functions $\{x^n\}$ is complete over any interval $[a,b]$; that is, for any piecewise continuous function $f(x)$, given any $\epsilon > 0$, there exists an n and coefficients $a_0, \ldots, a_n$ such that

$$\int_a^b \left[f(x) - \sum_{i=0}^n a_i x^i \right]^2 dx < \epsilon \tag{2.1-3}$$

Since sines and cosines also form a complete set, there is a result analogous to (2.1-3) for them. This result assures us that we can achieve arbitrarily good least-squares approximations using linear combinations of polynomials. To show that we can achieve arbitrarily small minimum maximum error with linear combinations of polynomials, we shall now prove the classical theorem of Weierstrass on polynomial approximation. As a corollary of this theorem, we shall then obtain a similar result for Fourier approximations.

2.1-3-1   The Weierstrass approximation theorem

Theorem 2.1 (Weierstrass)   If $f(x)$ is continuous on a finite interval $[a,b]$, then, given any $\epsilon > 0$, there exists an $n[= n(\epsilon)]$ and a polynomial $P_n(x)$ of degree n such that

$$|f(x) - P_n(x)| < \epsilon \tag{2.1-4}$$

for all x in $[a,b]$.

Thus, by requiring continuity instead of piecewise continuity, we achieve uniform approximation instead of approximation in the mean as in (2.1-3).

Proof   Our proof of this theorem is due to Bernstein (1912).   It is achieved by constructing a sequence of polynomials which converges uniformly to $f(x)$.   Without loss of generality, we let $a = 0$, $b = 1$ since any other interval may be reduced to $[0,1]$ by a simple change of variable $\{11\}$.   On this interval, the Bernstein polynomial of degree n is defined by

$$B_n(x) = \sum_{k=0}^{n} \binom{n}{k} x^k (1 - x)^{n-k} f\left(\frac{k}{n}\right) \tag{2.1-5}$$

We shall show that

$$\lim_{n \to \infty} B_n(x) = f(x) \tag{2.1-6}$$

uniformly in $[0,1]$.   To prove this theorem, we require the following

Lemma 2.1   The following identities are true:

$$\sum_{k=0}^{n} \binom{n}{k} x^k (1 - x)^{n-k} = 1$$

$$\sum_{k=0}^{n} \frac{k}{n} \binom{n}{k} x^k (1 - x)^{n-k} = x \tag{2.1-7}$$

$$\sum_{k=0}^{n} \frac{k^2}{n^2} \binom{n}{k} x^k (1 - x)^{n-k} = \left(1 - \frac{1}{n}\right) x^2 + \frac{1}{n} x$$

Proof   To derive all three identities, we use the binomial expansion

$$(p + q)^n = \sum_{k=0}^{n} \binom{n}{k} p^k q^{n-k} \tag{2.1-8}$$

The first identity follows immediately when $p + q = 1$.   The other two follow by differentiating (2.1-8), respectively, once and twice with respect to p and then setting $p + q = 1$ {12}.

Combining the identities in (2.1-7) we have

$$\sum_{k=0}^{n} \left(\frac{k}{n} - x\right)^2 \binom{n}{k} x^k (1 - x)^{n-k} = \frac{x(1 - x)}{n} \qquad (2.1\text{-}9)$$

Multiplying the first identity in (2.1-7) by $f(x)$ and subtracting $B_n(x)$ we have

$$f(x) - B_n(x) = \sum_{k=0}^{n} \left[f(x) - f\left(\frac{k}{n}\right)\right] \binom{n}{k} x^k (1 - x)^{n-k} \qquad (2.1\text{-}10)$$

Since $f(x)$ is continuous on [0,1], it is both uniformly continuous and bounded. Therefore, there exist δ and M such that

$$\begin{aligned} |f(x_1) - f(x_2)| &< \epsilon/2 &&\text{if } |x_1 - x_2| < \delta &&x_1, x_2 \; \epsilon \; [0,1] \\ |f(x)| &< M &&x \; \epsilon \; [0,1] \end{aligned} \qquad (2.1\text{-}11)$$

where ϵ is as given in the statement of the theorem.

For any x, we divide the points k/n, $k = 0 , \ldots , n$ into two sets A and B such that

$$\begin{aligned} k/n \text{ is in } A &&\text{if } |k/n - x| < \delta \\ k/n \text{ is in } B &&\text{otherwise} \end{aligned}$$

Then, using the first of the relations (2.1-11) and the first of the identities (2.1-7)

$$\left| \sum_A \left[f(x) - f\left(\frac{k}{n}\right)\right] \binom{n}{k} x^k (1 - x)^{n-k} \right| < \frac{\epsilon}{2} \sum_A \binom{n}{k} x^k (1 - x)^{n-k} \leq \frac{\epsilon}{2}$$

$$(2.1\text{-}12)$$

Using the second of the relations (2.1-11) and (2.1-9)

$$\left| \sum_B \left[f(x) - f\left(\frac{k}{n}\right)\right] \binom{n}{k} x^k (1 - x)^{n-k} \right| \leq 2M \sum_B \binom{n}{k} x^k (1 - x)^{n-k}$$

$$= 2M \sum_B \frac{(k/n - x)^2}{(k/n - x)^2} \binom{n}{k} x^k (1 - x)^{n-k}$$

$$\leq \frac{2M}{\delta^2} \frac{x(1 - x)}{n} \leq \frac{M}{2n\delta^2} \qquad (2.1\text{-}13)$$

since $0 \leq x(1 - x) \leq \frac{1}{4}$ on [0,1]. Now choosing n so that

$$M/2n\delta^2 < \epsilon/2 \qquad (2.1\text{-}14)$$

and combining (2.1-12) and (2.1-13) in (2.1-10), the theorem is proved by identifying $P_n(x)$ with $B_n(x)$.

For periodic functions, we have the analogous theorem

Theorem 2.2 (Weierstrass) If $F(t)$ is a periodic continuous function of period 2π, then, given any $\epsilon > 0$, there exists an $n[= n(\epsilon)]$ and a trigonometric sum

$$S_n(t) = a_0 + \sum_{k=1}^{n} (a_k \cos kt + b_k \sin kt) \qquad (2.1\text{-}15)$$

such that

$$|F(t) - S_n(t)| < \epsilon \qquad (2.1\text{-}16)$$

for all t.

Using Theorem 2.1, this theorem is not hard to prove; we leave the proof to a problem {13}.

In a sense then, Theorem 2.1 justifies the use of polynomial approximations since it guarantees that a polynomial *can* be found with an arbitrarily small maximum deviation from $f(x)$ on $[a,b]$. In fact, since the proof is constructive, the reader may well think that we have solved the problem of minimum maximum error approximations. Furthermore, our reasons for preferring exact approximations—ease of derivation and error analysis—may seem to be weak in the light of Theorem 2.1. But, unfortunately, we have neither solved the minimum maximum error problem nor have we really weakened the case for exact approximation. The reasons for this are as follows:

1. In deriving minimum maximum error approximations, we shall be concerned with finding, for example, that polynomial of degree n which has the minimum maximum error as an approximation to $f(x)$. The Bernstein polynomial of degree n is by no means this polynomial.
2. The usual situation with exact approximations is that we are given only a sequence of points x_i and the corresponding $f(x_i)$ (i.e., a table). But, using Bernstein polynomials, we are forced to use particular values of $f(x)$ which may not be available. Moreover, the Bernstein polynomial of degree n is no help in deriving the polynomial of degree $n + 1$. This is a serious drawback, as will be made clearer in Chap. 3.
3. The ease with which it appears possible to bound the error in a Bernstein polynomial is a mirage, because the error bound tends to be extremely conservative. The following example will illustrate this.

Example 2.1 What degree Bernstein polynomial will guarantee an error of less than .2 in approximating e^x on $[0,1]$?

We have the inequality on [0,1]

$$|e^{x_1} - e^{x_2}| < e|x_1 - x_2|$$

which follows from the mean-value theorem.   Therefore, with $\epsilon = .2$, taking $\delta < .2/2e$ satisfies the first relation of (2.1-11).   Since $M = e$, in order to satisfy (2.1-14) we need

$$n > \frac{M}{\epsilon\delta^2} > \frac{e^3}{2 \times 10^{-3}} > 10,000$$

However, if we compute the Bernstein polynomial of degree 2, we find

$$B_2(x) = (1 - x)^2 + 2x(1 - x)e^{\frac{1}{2}} + x^2 e$$

and by direct calculation

$$|e^x - B_2(x)| < .11$$

on [0,1].   Therefore, the estimate resulting from the proof of Theorem 2.1 is extremely conservative.   Moreover, using the techniques of Chap. 7, we can achieve a substantially smaller maximum error than .11 with a quadratic approximation to e^x on [0,1].

Our conclusion then is that the Bernstein polynomials, while they lead to an elegant constructive proof of the Weierstrass theorem, do not in themselves generally give useful polynomial approximations.

The assurance that Theorem 2.1 gives us that we can find polynomial approximations which have arbitrarily small error, combined with the computational and other analytic advantages mentioned previously in this section, make a strong case for polynomial approximations.   Their dominance in the next four chapters will then not surprise the reader.

The case for polynomial approximation is, however, not so good as to rule out all other types.   In Chap. 7 our approximating functions will always be polynomials, but we shall make extensive use of rational approximations of the form (2.1-2).   Approximations using functions other than polynomials are of considerable importance also.   We have already noted the importance of periodic functions and the fact that the Fourier functions satisfy results analogous to those discussed in this section for polynomials.

The importance of "band-limited functions," functions whose constituent periodicities are known to be bounded, in many servomechanism and related problems is another indication of the importance of approximations using the Fourier functions.   We shall touch on such approximations briefly in Sec. 6.8, but for a more extensive treatment of this area, we refer the reader to Hamming (1962).

2.2   THE BASIC OPERATOR

In Chaps. 3, 4, and 5 we shall consider methods for interpolation, extrapolation, numerical differentiation, numerical quadrature, and the

numerical solution of ordinary differential equations, all of which will
be based on polynomial approximations. In textbooks on classical
numerical analysis the interrelation between these various subjects can
be clearly seen because interpolation methods are used as the basis from
which to derive methods for numerical differentiation, numerical quadrature, and numerical integration. Modern numerical analysis is not quite
so tidy. In some instances we shall use a method for one type of computation (e.g., interpolation) to derive a method for another type (e.g., numerical differentiation). But more often than not different approaches in
deriving methods for different computations are more instructive than
the approach which emphasizes the relationship among various methods.
However, so that the student does not lose sight of the basic unity of the
subject matter of the next three chapters, we shall, in this section, introduce a linear operator which is the basis of all the methods of the next
three chapters with the exception of those in Sec. 5.6-3.

This linear operator is to be such that, by properly choosing the
parameters in it, representations of methods of interpolation, extrapolation, numerical differentiation, numerical quadrature, and numerical
integration can be obtained. In this section we shall describe this basic
operator generally and then, in Sec. 2.2-1, we shall indicate how the
operator can be specialized to obtain methods of various types.

Remembering that our interest is in polynomial approximation, we
define the basic operator by

$$L[f(x)] \equiv \delta_k f^{(k)}(x) + \sum_{i=0}^{m} \sum_{j=1}^{n} A_{ij}(x) f^{(i)}(a_{ij})$$
$$0 \leq k \leq m \qquad f^{(0)}(a_{0j}) = f(a_{0j}) \quad (2.2\text{-}1)$$

where the superscripts denote differentiation, the a_{ij} are constants, and
the $A_{ij}(x)$ are polynomials in x. The value of δ_k will be 0 or 1 depending
upon whether the operator in question is concerned with specific values of
the independent variable x (as it will be in the cases of numerical quadrature and integration) or with a general value of x (as it will be in the cases
of interpolation, extrapolation, and numerical differentiation). The
value of k will be zero except in the case of numerical differentiation. By
choosing the a_{ij}, $A_{ij}(x)$, and k, m, and n in varying ways, we may derive
many different numerical methods. The general procedure is as follows:

1. Replace that portion of $L[f(x)]$ that we wish to approximate by its
   approximation. Examples: (i) replace $f^{(k)}(x)$ by $y^{(k)}(x)$, $k > 0$ in
   the case of numerical differentiation of $f(x)$. (ii) replace $f(a_{0j_2}) -$
   $f(a_{0j_1})$ by the approximate integral I in the case of the numerical

evaluation of

$$\int_{a_{0j_1}}^{a_{0j_2}} f'(x)\, dx$$

Call the resulting operator $\bar{L}$.   Then

2. Solve for this approximation in the equation $\bar{L}[f(x)] = 0$.   This results in the desired approximation.

In order that the resulting approximation should have coefficients of values of $f(x)$ and its derivatives which are polynomials, it is desirable to require that the coefficient of the quantity to be approximated in (2.2-1) be a constant which, for convenience, we shall always take to be 1.   With this convention the error in any approximation derived by the above procedure is given by

$$E(x) = L[f(x)] - \bar{L}[f(x)] = L[f(x)] \tag{2.2-2}$$

since $\bar{L}[f(x)] = 0$.   A more correct notation would be $E[f(x)]$ since the error will depend on the function $f(x)$, but for simplicity we shall generally use the notation of (2.2-2).   In the following section we shall illustrate the above procedure with some examples in order to give the student some insight into the aforementioned unity of the subject matter of Chaps. 3 to 5.

2.2-1   Specialization of the basic operator

By suitably restricting some of the quantities in (2.2-1), we shall in this section specialize the operator L and thereby define operators for interpolation, extrapolation, numerical differentiation, numerical quadrature, and numerical integration.

1. If $\delta_0 = 1$ and at least one $A_{0j}(x) \neq 0$, then L is an interpolation operator if $x \,\varepsilon\, [\min\,(a_{ij}),\ \max\,(a_{ij})]$ and an extrapolation operator otherwise.

Example

$$L_1[f(x)] = f(x) - \frac{x - x_1}{x_0 - x_1} f(x_0) - \frac{x - x_0}{x_1 - x_0} f(x_1) \tag{2.2-3}$$

To get $\bar{L}_1[f(x)]$ we replace $f(x)$ in (2.2-3) by an approximation $y(x)$.   Then

$$\bar{L}_1[f(x)] = y(x) - \frac{x - x_1}{x_0 - x_1} f(x_0) - \frac{x - x_0}{x_1 - x_0} f(x_1) = 0 \tag{2.2-4}$$

is an equation for linear interpolation (or extrapolation) when solved for $y(x)$.   From (2.2-2) the error is given by $E(x) = f(x) - y(x)$.

2. If $\delta_k = 1$, $k > 0$ and at least one $A_{0j}(x) \neq 0$, then L is a numerical differentiation operator of order k.

Example

$$L_2[f(x)] = f'(x) + \frac{f(x_0) - f(x_1)}{x_1 - x_0} \tag{2.2-5}$$

is a numerical differentiation operator of order 1. Replacing $f'(x)$ by $y'(x)$ the equation

$$\bar{L}_2[f(x)] = y'(x) + \frac{f(x_0) - f(x_1)}{x_1 - x_0} = 0 \tag{2.2-6}$$

when solved for $y'(x)$, leads to an approximation for the first derivative of $f(x)$. Note that $L_2[f(x)]$ is just the derivative of $L_1[f(x)]$.

3a. If $\delta_k = 0$, if all $A_{0j}(x) = 0$ except for two, $A_{0,j_1}(x)$ and $A_{0,j_2}(x)$, which equal $+1$ and -1, respectively, and if all $A_{ij}(x), i \geqq 1$ are constants, then L is a numerical quadrature operator.

Example

$$L_3[f(x)] = f(b) - f(a) - \frac{b - a}{2}[f'(b) + f'(a)] \tag{2.2-7}$$

Then

$$\bar{L}_3[f(x)] = I - \frac{b - a}{2}[f'(b) + f'(a)] = 0 \tag{2.2-8}$$

when solved for the constant I, is the familiar trapezoidal rule for approximating $\int_a^b f'(x)\, dx$.

3b. If $\delta_k = 0$, if all $A_{ij}(x)$ are constants, and if at least two $A_{0j}(x)$ are not equal to zero, then L is a numerical integration operator.

Example

$$L_4[f(x)] = f(x_1) - f(x_0) - hf'(x_0) \tag{2.2-9}$$

where $h = x_1 - x_0$. Replacing $f(x_2)$ by $y(x_2)$ and solving for $y(x_2)$ in

$$\bar{L}_4[f(x)] = y(x_1) - f(x_0) - hf'(x_0) \tag{2.2-10}$$

we get an equation for the numerical integration of an ordinary differential equation $z' = F(x,z)$ where $f(x)$ in (2.2-10) is identified with $z(x)$ {20} [cf. Eq. (5.5-13)].

Remarks

1. Numerical quadrature operators are clearly a subset of numerical integration operators. But only the former can be used to evaluate $\int_a^b g(x)\, dx$ with $g(x) = f'(x)$. We note that in practice, in using methods of the type 3b for the numerical solution of ordinary differential equations, not one but all the functional values in (2.2-9) would be replaced by approximate values. Thus, for the differential equation $z' = F(x,z)$, $y(x_2)$ in (2.2-10) would be an approximation to $z(x_2)$ expressed as a linear combination of approximations to $z(x)$ and $z'(x)$ at other points {20}. This means we have to consider not only the error $E(x) = L_4[z(x)] - \bar{L}_4[z(x)]$

but the error introduced by replacing the other values of $z(x)$ and $z'(x)$ in (2.2-10) by approximate values. The significance of this remark will become clear in Chap. 5.

2. To tabulate

$$f(t) = \int_a^t g(x)\, dx \tag{2.2-11}$$

at a sequence of values of t, we may use a numerical quadrature operator repetitively. Also, since (2.2-11) is equivalent to the differential equation $f'(t) = g(t)$, numerical integration operators may be used [but note the difficulty in starting the integration because, for example, (2.2-10) requires knowledge of $f(x)$ at x_0 and x_1 to get a value at x_2].

3. The relation between L_1 in (2.2-3) and L_2 in (2.2-5) illustrates the ability to derive a method for one type of computation from a method for another type of computation. Some other examples of this are considered in {16 to 18}. But, as we mentioned previously, we shall in the chapters that follow make comparatively little use of this ability.

BIBLIOGRAPHIC NOTES

2.1   There are a number of works which treat the general problem of approximation in much greater depth than we have here. In particular, we recommend Achieser (1956) and Natanson (1955). A number of articles on approximation theory are found in Langer (1959), including general articles by Buck (1959) and Sard (1959). Many of the more specific works on approximation will be referred to in later chapters.

The cases for and against polynomial approximation as well as the case for trigonometric approximation are well presented in Hamming (1962). Our proof of the Weierstrass theorem is due to Bernstein (1912) and can also be found in Achieser (1956) and Macon (1963). For a quite different proof, see Courant and Hilbert (1953).

2.2   The operational notation is not generally found in numerical analysis texts. An example of a similar notation used for a specific case can be found in Daniell (1940).

BIBLIOGRAPHY

Achieser, N. I. (1956): *Theory of Approximation* (translated by C. J. Hyman), Frederick Ungar Publishing Co., New York.

Bernstein, S. N. (1912): Démonstration du théorème de Weierstrass fondée sur le calcul de probabilité, *Proc. Kharkov Math. Soc.*, vol. 13.

Buck, R. C. (1959): Survey of Recent Russian Literature on Approximation in *On Numerical Approximation* (R. E. Langer, ed.), The University of Wisconsin Press, Madison, Wis.

Courant, R., and D. Hilbert (1953): *Methods of Mathematical Physics*, vol. 1 (translated), Interscience Publishers, Inc., New York.

Daniell, P. J. (1940): Remainders in Interpolation and Quadrature Formulae, *Math. Gaz.*, vol. 24, pp. 238–244.

Hamming, R. W. (1962): *Numerical Methods for Scientists and Engineers*, McGraw-Hill Book Company, New York.

Langer, R. E. (ed.) (1959): *On Numerical Approximation*, The University of Wisconsin Press, Madison, Wis.

Macon, N. (1963): *Numerical Analysis*, John Wiley & Sons, Inc., New York.

Natanson, I. P. (1955): *Konstructive Funktionentheorie* (German translation by K. Bogel), Akademie-Verlag GmbH, Berlin.

Sard, A. (1959): The Rationale of Approximation in *On Numerical Approximation* (R. E. Langer, ed.), The University of Wisconsin Press, Madison, Wis.

PROBLEMS

Section 2.1

1. Find a first-degree polynomial approximation $P(x) = ax + b$ to $\sin x$ on $[0, \pi/2]$.

  (*a*) using the first nonzero term of the Maclaurin expansion of $\sin x$.

  (*b*) which minimizes $\int_0^{\pi/2} [P(x) - \sin x]^2 \, dx$.

  (*c*) which minimizes $\int_0^{\pi/2} x[P(x) - \sin x]^2 \, dx$.

For all three approximations, draw a graph of the error $E(x) = \sin x - P(x)$. In what sense is the approximation *a* an exact approximation in the terminology of Sec. 2.1? What are the significant characteristics of the error in *a* compared with those in the least-squares approximations *b* and *c*?

*2. Now consider the problem of finding an approximation to $\sin x$ of the form $P(x) = ax + b$ which minimizes

$$\max_{x \in [0, \pi/2]} |P(x) - \sin x|$$

  (*a*) Prove that any such $P(x)$ must be such that $E(x) = \sin x - P(x)$ has at least two zeros in $[0, \pi/2]$.

  (*b*) Starting from the result of Prob. 1*c*, derive an approximation to $\sin x$ of the form $ax + b$ with a smaller maximum error.

3. For parts *b* and *c* of Prob. 1, derive the equations for a and b when $\sin x$ is replaced by $f(x)$.

4. Do Probs. 1 and 3 when $P(x)$ is replaced by the quadratic approximation $Q(x) = ax^2 + bx + c$.

5. Consider the continued-fraction expansion for the inverse tangent

$$\tan^{-1} t \approx \cfrac{t}{1 + \cfrac{t^2}{3 + \cfrac{t^2}{5 + {}}}}$$

$$\cdots$$

$$\cfrac{t^2}{2n + 1}$$

(a) Show that for any n, this is equivalent to approximating $\tan^{-1} t$ by a rational function.

(b) For $n = 1$ and 2 compute the rational approximations and draw the graph of the error in the approximations on the interval $[0,1]$.

(c) For each of the approximations of part b, consider the analogous approximation derived by truncating the Maclaurin-series expansion for $\tan^{-1} t$ after the term of degree equal to the sum of the degrees of numerator and denominator in b. Draw the graphs of the errors and compare with those in b.

6. Derive an approximation to e^x of the form

$$e^x \approx \frac{ax + b}{x + c}$$

which at $x = 0$ has the same value and the same first two derivatives as e^x. Draw the graph of the error for $-1 \le x \le 1$ (cf. Sec. 7.4).

*7. Let $\sin x$ be approximated by the first three nonzero terms of its Maclaurin expansion.

(a) For any x find a bound on the magnitude of the truncation error.

(b) Convert the coefficients to correctly rounded 10-decimal-digit numbers and write the approximation in the form derived in Prob. 20, Chap. 1.

(c) If $|x| < 1$ is correctly rounded to 10 decimal digits, find a bound on the error in the correctly rounded value of x^2.

(d) Use this bound to derive an approximate bound on the roundoff error incurred in evaluating the approximation in b if all intermediate quantities are rounded to 10 decimals. Again assume $|x| < 1$ and neglect all quantities with order of magnitude less than 10^{-d}.

(e) For $x = \pi/4$ perform the calculation carrying 10 decimals at every stage. Compare the result with the correct value. Is the error caused by truncation and roundoff within expected limits?

8. Neglecting roundoff error, how many terms of the Maclaurin expansion for $\sin x$ are required to obtain a maximum error of less than 10^{-7} in the range $[0,\pi/2]$? In the range $[0,\pi]$?

9. Let $f(x)$ be approximated by

$$f(x) \approx P_1(x)f(a_1) + P_2(x)f(a_2)$$

where $P_1(x)$ and $P_2(x)$ are linear polynomials.

(a) Find $P_1(x)$ and $P_2(x)$ if the approximation is to have no error at $x = a_1$ and a_2 independent of the function $f(x)$. What is the advantage of having $P_1(x)$ and $P_2(x)$ independent of $f(x)$?

(b) Find an expression for the error in the approximation when $f(x) = x^2 + ax + b$. How do you explain the dependence of the result on a and b?

*10. A common iterative method for calculating the square root of a number a uses the formula

$$x_{n+1} = \frac{1}{2}\left(x_n + \frac{a}{x_n} \right) \qquad n = 1, 2, \ldots$$

where x_1 is an arbitrary positive number.

(a) Prove that, if $\lim_{n \to \infty} x_n$ exists, then this limit is $\sqrt{a}$.

(b) Prove that if $a \le x_n \le 1$ then $a \le x_{n+1} \le 1$.

(c) Prove that, if $0 < a < 1$, then the iteration does converge (i.e., $\lim_{n \to \infty} x_n$ does exist).

11. (*a*) Derive the change of variable which transforms any finite interval $[a,b]$ to $[0,1]$.

(*b*) By making the appropriate change of variable in (2.1-5), calculate the Bernstein polynomials of degree 1, 2, and 3 for $f(x) = \sin x$ on the interval $[0,\pi/2]$. Draw the graph of $\sin x - B_n(x)$ in each case and for $n = 1$ and 2 compare these errors with the corresponding errors in Probs. 1 and 4.

(*c*) Using the inequality (2.1-14), what value of n *guarantees* a smaller maximum error than that found in part *b* for $n = 1$?

12. (*a*) Derive the identities (2.1-7).   (*b*) Using these identities, derive (2.1-9).

*13. Let $F(t)$ be a periodic continuous function of period 2π and define

$$\phi(t) = \frac{F(t) + F(-t)}{2} \qquad \psi(t) = \frac{F(t) - F(-t)}{2} \sin t$$

(*a*) Use Theorem 2.1 to show that, given any $\epsilon > 0$, there exist polynomials $P(x)$ and $Q(x)$ such that

$$|\phi(t) - P(\cos t)| \leq \epsilon/4 \qquad |\psi(t) - Q(\cos t)| \leq \epsilon/4$$

for *all t*.

(*b*) Thus deduce that

$$|F(t) \sin t - U(t)| \leq \epsilon/2$$

where

$$U(t) = Q(\cos t) + P(\cos t) \sin t$$

is a trigonometric sum.   Similarly, show that there is another trigonometric sum $V(t)$ such that

$$|F(\pi/2 - t) \sin t - V(t)| \leq \epsilon/2$$

(*c*) Use the two inequalities of part *b* to deduce that

$$|F(t) - U(t) \sin t - V(\pi/2 - t) \cos t| \leq \epsilon$$

and, from this, complete the proof of Theorem 2.2.   [Ref.: Achieser (1956), pp. 32–33.]

*14. (*a*) If $F(t)$ in the previous problem is also even, show how the proof can be considerably simplified.

(*b*) For the function

$$F(t) = \begin{cases} t - 2m\pi & 2m\pi \leq t < (2m + 1)\pi \\ 2m\pi - t & (2m - 1)\pi \leq t < 2m\pi \end{cases}$$

where m takes on all positive and negative integral values, use this simplification to derive an approximation of the form (2.1-15) to $F(t)$ using first- and second-degree Bernstein polynomials.   How do you explain the relation between the two results? Draw the graph of the error.

15. For $f(x) = 1/(1 + x^2)$ calculate the Bernstein polynomials for $n = 2, 3, 4$ on the interval $[-1,1]$ and draw the graph of the error in each case.   (This function is an example of a case where *exact* polynomial approximation leads to certain difficulties; see p. 57n.)

Section 2.2

16. Show that an interpolation (or extrapolation) operator results by taking the difference between $f(x)$ and a Taylor-series expansion for $f(x)$ about $x = x_1$, truncated after the term in the $(N - 1)$st derivative (see Prob. 1, Chap. 3).

17. When the operator of the previous problem is differentiated, does a differentiation operator result?   Why?

18. By setting $x = b$ and then $x = a$ in the operator of Prob. 16 and then subtracting, show that a numerical quadrature operator results.

19. If L is a numerical quadrature operator, show how it might be used to get an approximate value of the iterated integral

$$\int_c^d dy \int_a^b f(x,y) \, dx$$

(cf. Sec. 4.14).

20. Consider the first-order differential equation

$$z' = F(x,z) \qquad z(x_0) = z_0$$

(a) Show how (2.2-10) may be used to get an approximate value for $z(x_1)$.

(b) Thus show how (2.2-10) could be used to generate an approximate solution to the differential equation at a sequence of points.

chapter 3

INTERPOLATION

3.1 INTRODUCTION

Interpolation lies at the heart of classical numerical analysis. There are two main reasons for this. The first is that in hand computation there is continual need to look up the value of a function in a table. In order to find the value of the function at nontabulated arguments, it is necessary to interpolate. Moreover, the highly accurate tables at small increments of the argument that we take for granted today are mostly of comparatively recent origin. Therefore, classical numerical analysts developed an extremely sophisticated group of interpolation methods. Today the need to interpolate arises comparatively seldom; for example, on digital computers we almost always generate directly the value of a function rather than interpolate in a table of values (see Chap. 7). And when the need to interpolate in a table does arise, the small increments in the arguments in most tables mean that quite simple techniques (e.g., linear or quadratic interpolation) will usually suffice. Thus, while every numerical analyst must know how to interpolate, he will seldom, if ever, have use for the more sophisticated interpolation techniques.

Why then commence the main body of this book with a chapter on interpolation? The answer to this question is provided by the second of the reasons mentioned at the beginning of this section. This is that interpolation formulas are the starting points in the derivations of many methods in other areas of numerical analysis. Almost all the classical methods of numerical differentiation, numerical quadrature, and numerical integration are directly derivable from interpolation formulas. While modern numerical analysis does not rely so heavily on interpolation formulas in these areas, their importance and usefulness are still great, as we shall see in Chaps. 4 and 5. This then is ample motivation for treating interpolation at the outset of this book.

Because we are especially interested in digital computer applications, our approach to interpolation will differ substantially from that in most texts. In particular, we shall not emphasize interpolation formulas based on difference techniques since these are seldom used on computers. Nevertheless, we shall not ignore finite differences because of their great usefulness in hand computation and, even on digital computers, for certain applications (see Secs. 4.3 and 4.15-1).

Suppose we have a function $f(x)$ which is known (perhaps along with certain of its derivatives) at a set of points. These points will hereafter be called the *tabular* points because interpolation so often takes place in a table of functional values. The object of interpolation is to *estimate* values of the function at nontabular points and—at least—to *bound* the error between the estimated and true values. Our approach will be to approximate $f(x)$ by a function $y(x)$ which, at the tabular points, has the same values as $f(x)$ (and perhaps the given derivative values, if any). Thus, in the language of the previous chapter, we shall be using exact approximations. In this chapter we shall consider only the case where $y(x)$ is a polynomial. In the last section of Chap. 6 we shall consider the case in which $y(x)$ is a linear combination of trigonometric functions.

In Sec. 2.2-1 the form of the general interpolation operator was given as

$$L[f(x)] = f(x) + \sum_{j=1}^{n} \sum_{i=0}^{m} A_{ij}(x) f^{(i)}(a_{ij}) \tag{3.1-1}$$

Except in Sec. 3.8 we shall be concerned only with the case $m = 0$; that is, we shall use only the functional values of $f(x)$. When $m = 0$ we replace $A_{0j}(x)$ by $-l_j(x)$ in order to conform to standard notation. Thus (3.1-1) becomes

$$L[f(x)] = f(x) - \sum_{j=1}^{n} l_j(x) f(a_j) \tag{3.1-2}$$

Our object is to determine the $l_j(x)$ so that

$$L[f(a_j)] = 0 \qquad j = 1, \ldots, n \tag{3.1-3}$$

independent of the function $f(x)$. In general, however, for nontabular points

$$L[f(x)] = E(x) \tag{3.1-4}$$

That is, $l_j(x)$ is a polynomial!

$$f(x) = \sum_{j=1}^{n} l_j(x)f(a_j) + E(x) = y(x) + E(x) \tag{3.1-5}$$

where $y(x)$ is our approximation to $f(x)$, and $E(x)$ is the error in the approximation. In the notation of the previous chapter, the operator $\bar{L}[f(x)]$ is obtained by replacing $f(x)$ in (3.1-2) by its approximation

$$y(x) = \sum_{j=1}^{n} l_j(x)f(a_j) \tag{3.1-6}$$

In terms of $y(x)$ and $E(x)$ the requirement (3.1-3) becomes

$$E(a_j) = f(a_j) - y(a_j) = 0 \qquad j = 1, \ldots, n \tag{3.1-7}$$

Our two aims then are to determine the $l_j(x)$ so that (3.1-7) is satisfied and to find a representation for $E(x)$ which will enable us to estimate or at least bound the error for values of $x \neq a_j, j = 1, \ldots, n$.

3.2 LAGRANGIAN INTERPOLATION

In this section we consider the case where there are no restrictions on the spacing of the tabular points. In Sec. 3.3 we shall then consider the case of equally spaced abscissas. Even in the general situation we consider here, however, the determination of the polynomials $l_j(x)$ is straightforward. Since we wish the error at the tabular points to be zero independent of $f(x)$, it follows using (3.1-5) that

$$l_j(a_k) = \delta_{jk} \qquad j, k = 1, \ldots, n \tag{3.2-1}$$

where δ_{jk} is the *Kronecker delta*.† Since $l_j(x)$ is to be a polynomial, this requires that it have a factor

$$(x - a_1)(x - a_2) \cdots (x - a_{j-1})(x - a_{j+1}) \cdots (x - a_n) \tag{3.2-2}$$

and since $l_j(a_j) = 1$ we may write

$$l_j(x) = \frac{(x - a_1) \cdots (x - a_{j-1})(x - a_{j+1}) \cdots (x - a_n)}{(a_j - a_1) \cdots (a_j - a_{j-1})(a_j - a_{j+1}) \cdots (a_j - a_n)} \tag{3.2-3}$$

Note that there are other possible polynomial representations of $l_j(x)$, but (3.2-3) is the only possible polynomial of degree $n - 1$ and no polynomial of lesser degree is possible (why?). It is notationally convenient to write

†$\delta_{jk} = 0$ unless $j = k$, in which case $\delta_{jk} = 1$.

$l_j(x)$ as

$$l_j(x) = \frac{p_n(x)}{(x - a_j)p_n'(a_j)} \qquad p_n'(a_j) = \frac{dp_n}{dx}\Big|_{x=a_j} \tag{3.2-4}$$

where

$$p_n(x) = \prod_{i=1}^{n} (x - a_i) \tag{3.2-5}$$

To find an expression for $E(x)$, we consider the function

$$F(z) = f(z) - y(z) - [f(x) - y(x)][p_n(z)/p_n(x)] \tag{3.2-6}$$

with $y(x)$ as in (3.1-6). The function $F(z)$ *as a function of z* has $n + 1$ zeros at the points $a_1, \ldots, a_n$ and x [assume for now that x in (3.2-6) is not one of the tabular points]. Therefore, by applying Rolle's theorem n times ·

$$F^{(n)}(z) = f^{(n)}(z) - y^{(n)}(z) - [f(x) - y(x)][n!/p_n(x)] \tag{3.2-7}$$

has at least one zero in the interval spanned by $a_1, \ldots, a_n$ and x. Calling this zero $z = \xi$ and noting that $y^{(n)}(z) = 0$ since $l_j(z)$ is a polynomial of degree $n - 1$, we have

$$0 = F^{(n)}(\xi) = f^{(n)}(\xi) - [f(x) - y(x)][n!/p_n(x)] \tag{3.2-8}$$

from which, using (3.1-5), it follows that

$$E(x) = [p_n(x)/n!]f^{(n)}(\xi) \tag{3.2-9}$$

where ξ, which is an unknown function of x, lies in the interval spanned by $a_1, \ldots, a_n$ and x. Although x in (3.2-6) was restricted to be a non-tabular point, $E(x)$, as given by (3.2-9), holds for both tabular and non-tabular points (why?).

Equation (3.1-5) with the $l_j(x)$ given by (3.2-4) and $E(x)$ by (3.2-9) is called the *Lagrangian interpolation formula*. When $n = 2$, $y(x)$ is the familiar formula for linear interpolation [cf. (2.2-4)]

$$y(x) = \frac{x - a_2}{a_1 - a_2} f(a_1) + \frac{x - a_1}{a_2 - a_1} f(a_2) \tag{3.2-10}$$

The polynomials $l_j(x)$ are called *Lagrangian interpolation polynomials*. Our derivation of the Lagrangian formula has been equivalent to finding that polynomial of degree $n - 1$ which passes through the points $[a_j, f(a_j)]$, $j = 1, \ldots, n$ {4}. Therefore, as we would expect, (3.2-9) indicates that this formula is *exact* [i.e., $E(x) = 0$ for all x] for polynomials of degree $n - 1$ or less. In general, an interpolation formula which is exact for polynomials of degree r is said to have an *order of accuracy* r or to be of *order* r.

The use of the Lagrangian interpolation formula is straightforward. To estimate $f(x)$ at a nontabular point, we merely compute $y(x)$ as given by (3.1-6) using (3.2-4) and (3.2-5) to compute the polynomials $l_j(x)$. If we can estimate or bound the nth derivative of $f(x)$, then the error can be estimated or bounded using (3.2-9).

Example 3.1   Let $f(x) = \ln x$.   Given the table of values

x:	.40	.50	.70	.80
$\ln x$:	$-.916291$	$-.693147$	$-.356675$	$-.223144$

estimate the value of $\ln .60$.

With $a_1 = .40$, $a_2 = .50$, $a_3 = .70$, and $a_4 = .80$, we calculate from (3.2-4)

$$l_1(.60) = -\tfrac{1}{6} \qquad l_2(.60) = \tfrac{2}{3}$$
$$l_3(.60) = \tfrac{2}{3} \qquad l_4(.60) = -\tfrac{1}{6}$$

and from (3.1-5) we get the approximation

$$\ln .60 \approx -.509975$$

The true value is $\ln .60 = -.510826$. From (3.2-9) we get

$$E(.60) = \frac{p_4(.60)}{4!}\left(\frac{-6}{\xi^4}\right) = \frac{-.0004}{4}\frac{1}{\xi^4}$$

In the interval $(.4,.8)$, $\dfrac{10^4}{4096} < \dfrac{1}{\xi^4} < \dfrac{10^4}{256}$ so that

$$\tfrac{1}{4096} < |E(.60)| < \tfrac{1}{256}$$

and indeed the difference between the approximate and true values lies within this error.

3.3   INTERPOLATION AT EQUAL INTERVALS

In most applications of interpolation, the tabular points are equally spaced. For this reason it is worthwhile to consider the simplifications of the Lagrangian formula that can be made in this case.

3.3-1   Lagrangian interpolation at equal intervals

Let the equal spacing be h so that

$$a_{j+1} - a_j = h \qquad j = 1, \ldots, n-1 \tag{3.3-1}$$

For reasons of symmetry and computational convenience, it is common to take n odd and let

$$x = a_r + hm \tag{3.3-2}$$

where $r = (n+1)/2$. Thus $m = 0$ corresponds to the center of the

Table 3.1   Values of the Lagrangian interpolation polynomials for $n = 5$ $(x = a_3 + hm)$

m	$l_1(m)$	$l_2(m)$	$l_3(m)$	$l_4(m)$	$l_5(m)$	
0	.0000	.0000	1.0000	.0000	.0000	0
.2	.0144	−.1056	.9504	.1584	−.0176	−.2
.4	.0224	−.1536	.8064	.3584	−.0336	−.4
.6	.0224	−.1456	.5824	.5824	−.0416	−.6
.8	.0144	−.0896	.3024	.8064	−.0336	−.8
1.0	.0000	.0000	.0000	1.0000	.0000	−1.0
1.2	−.0176	.1024	−.2816	1.1264	.0704	−1.2
1.4	−.0336	.1904	−.4896	1.1424	.1904	−1.4
1.6	−.0416	.2304	−.5616	.9984	.3744	−1.6
1.8	−.0336	.1824	−.4256	.6384	.6384	−1.8
2.0	.0000	.0000	.0000	.0000	1.0000	−2.0
	$l_5(m)$	$l_4(m)$	$l_3(m)$	$l_2(m)$	$l_1(m)$	m

interval spanned by the tabular points. Using (3.3-2), $p_n(x)$ and $l_j(x)$ can be expressed as functions of m. In particular, from (3.2-3) it follows that $l_j(m)$ is independent of h and can thus be tabulated as a function of m. Using (3.3-2) the Lagrangian interpolation formula becomes, writing $f(a_r + hm)$ as $f(m)$,

$$f(m) = \sum_{j=1}^{n} l_j(m)f(a_j) + [h^n p_n(m)/n!] f^{(n)}(\xi) \tag{3.3-3}$$

where

$$p_n(m) = (m - r + 1)(m - r + 2) \cdots m(m + 1)$$
$$\cdots (m + r - 1) \quad (3.3\text{-}4)$$

Table 3.1 is a short tabulation of the Lagrangian interpolation polynomials $l_j(m)$ for $n = 5$. Clearly, when m and n are such that the $l_j(m)$ are tabulated, the use of (3.3-3) is quite straightforward on a desk calculator. On a digital computer, it will seldom be convenient to store such a table but rather will be easier to generate the values of $l_j(m)$ using (3.2-4).

Example 3.2   Using the same data as in Example 3.1 plus the true value of ln .60, estimate the value of ln .54.

We have $h = .1$; using Table 3.1 with $m = -.6$, we get from (3.3-3)

$$\ln .54 \approx -.0416 \ln .40 + .5824 \ln .50 + .5824 \ln .60 - .1456 \ln .70 + .0224 \ln .80$$
$$= -.616143$$

whereas the true value is −.616186.

When the values of $l_j(m)$ are not tabulated, then, for hand computation, instead of (3.3-3) it is preferable to use the finite-difference interpolation formulas which we shall discuss in Sec. 3.4. Before proceeding to discuss finite differences, however, we emphasize that *there is one and only one polynomial of degree n − 1 that takes on the values of f(x) at the n tabular points* (why?). In what follows, we shall write interpolation formulas in a form very different from (3.1-5) or (3.3-3). But as long as these formulas involve polynomials passing through the same n tabular points, they will be identical to the Lagrangian interpolation formula.

3.3-2 Finite differences

In textbooks on classical numerical analysis, the calculus of finite differences and the interpolation, differentiation, and integration formulas based on it were always of central importance. This is because, for work on desk calculators, finite differences are a wonderfully convenient tool. Aside from their advantages for hand computation, there are certain special applications for which finite differences are invaluable (see Sec. 3.3-2-3). Also they are used extensively—although generally in a quite simple form—in the numerical solution of partial differential equations and boundary-value problems of ordinary differential equations on digital computers (see Sec. 4.3).

3.3-2-1   Definitions

As in Sec. 3.3-1 let the interval between successive tabular points be h. Then we define:

1. The kth *forward difference* of $f(x)$ as

$$\Delta^k f(x) = \Delta^{k-1} f(x + h) - \Delta^{k-1} f(x) \quad k = 1, 2, \ldots$$
$$\Delta^0 f(x) = f(x)$$

(3.3-5)

Thus, for example,

$$\Delta^1 f(x) \equiv \Delta f(x) = f(x + h) - f(x)$$

(3.3-6)

$$\Delta^2 f(x) = \Delta f(x + h) - \Delta f(x) = f(x + 2h) - 2f(x + h) + f(x)$$

(3.3-7)

In fact, it should be clear from this definition that any order difference can be written as a linear combination of functional values as in (3.3-6) and (3.3-7). The general form of this linear combination, whose derivation we leave to a problem {8}, is

$$\Delta^j f(x) = \sum_{k=0}^{j} (-1)^{j-k} \binom{j}{k} f(x + kh)$$

(3.3-8)

where the binomial coefficient $\binom{j}{k} = \dfrac{j!}{k!(j-k)!}$.

2. The kth *backward difference* as

$$\nabla^k f(x) = \nabla^{k-1} f(x) - \nabla^{k-1} f(x - h) \qquad k = 1, 2, \ldots$$
$$\nabla^0 f(x) = f(x) \tag{3.3-9}$$

3. The kth *central difference* as

$$\delta^k f(x) = \delta^{k-1} f(x + \tfrac{1}{2}h) - \delta^{k-1} f(x - \tfrac{1}{2}h)$$

$$\delta^0 f(x) = f(x) \qquad\qquad k = 1, 2, \ldots \tag{3.3-10}$$

Note that if x is a tabular point then only even central differences involve tabular points (why?).

A property of differences that we shall have use for later is that the first difference of a polynomial of degree n is a polynomial of degree $n - 1$ {9}. Therefore, *the nth difference of a polynomial of degree n is a constant, and the $(n + 1)$st difference is identically zero.* The properties of finite differences and the formulas based upon them may be derived by operational calculus using the difference operators Δ, ∇, and δ; we leave a consideration of this approach to a problem {10}.

3.3-2-2 *The lozenge diagram*

In the remainder of this section, we shall denote $\Delta^i f(a_k)$ by $\Delta^i f_k$ with a corresponding notation for backward and central differences. Furthermore, we shall change our previous notation slightly and let the tabular points have both positive and negative subscripts. When we calculate differences, it is convenient to set up a *difference table* as in Fig. 3.1 in

a_{-4}	f_{-4}		$\Delta^2 f_{-5}$		$\Delta^4 f_{-6}$	
		Δf_{-4}		$\Delta^3 f_{-5}$		$\Delta^5 f_{-6}$
a_{-3}	f_{-3}		$\Delta^2 f_{-4}$		$\Delta^4 f_{-5}$	
		Δf_{-3}		$\Delta^3 f_{-4}$		$\Delta^5 f_{-5}$
a_{-2}	f_{-2}		$\Delta^2 f_{-3}$		$\Delta^4 f_{-4}$	
		Δf_{-2}		$\Delta^3 f_{-3}$		$\Delta^5 f_{-4}$
a_{-1}	f_{-1}		$\Delta^2 f_{-2}$		$\Delta^4 f_{-3}$	
		Δf_{-1}		$\Delta^3 f_{-2}$		$\Delta^5 f_{-3}$
a_0	f_0		$\Delta^2 f_{-1}$		$\Delta^4 f_{-2}$	
		Δf_0		$\Delta^3 f_{-1}$		$\Delta^5 f_{-2}$
a_1	f_1		$\Delta^2 f_0$		$\Delta^4 f_{-1}$	
		Δf_1		$\Delta^3 f_0$		$\Delta^5 f_{-1}$
a_2	f_2		$\Delta^2 f_1$		$\Delta^4 f_0$	
		Δf_2		$\Delta^3 f_1$		$\Delta^5 f_0$
a_3	f_3		$\Delta^2 f_2$		$\Delta^4 f_1$	
		Δf_3		$\Delta^3 f_2$		$\Delta^5 f_1$
a_4	f_4		$\Delta^2 f_3$		$\Delta^4 f_2$	

Fig. 3.1 Forward difference table.

which each entry after the second column is the difference of the two immediately to its left. The use of forward differences in the table is arbitrary; backward differences could just as easily have been used (but not central differences—why?).

Example 3.3   Using the data of Example 3.2 with one point added at either end, compute the difference table.

The result is

x	$\ln x$	Δ	Δ^2	Δ^3	Δ^4	Δ^5	Δ^6
.30	-1.203973						
		.287682					
.40	$-\ .916291$		$-.064538$				
		.223144		.023715			
.50	$-\ .693147$		$-.040823$		$-.011062$		
		.182321		.012653		.005959	
.60	$-\ .510826$		$-.028170$		$-.005103$		$-.003534$
		.154151		.007550		.002425	
.70	$-\ .356675$		$-.020620$		$-.002678$		
		.133531		.004872			
.80	$-\ .223144$		$-.015748$				
		.117783					
.90	$-\ .105361$						

If to Fig. 3.1 we add connecting lines and binomial coefficients† as in Fig. 3.2, we can use this modified difference table called a *lozenge* or *Fraser diagram* to generate most of the interesting finite-difference interpolation formulas. To generate such an interpolation formula, we proceed as follows:

1. Start at an entry in the first (functional value) column and proceed along *any* path in the lozenge diagram (i.e., if a segment terminates on a difference, the path may be continued along any of the other three paths leading from the difference). End the path at any difference.

2. Then construct the formula by

   (i) writing down the functional value at which the path started and then

   (ii*a*) for every left to right segment in the path *add* a term consisting of the difference on which the segment *terminates* multiplied by the binomial coefficient directly *below* this difference, if the slope of the segment is positive, and directly *above*, if the slope of the segment is negative, and

$$\dagger\ (m + k)_n = \frac{(m + k)(m + k - 1) \cdots (m + k - n + 1)}{n!} = \binom{m + k}{n}.$$ In this section we let m be such that $x = a_0 + hm$ [cf. (3.3-2)].

(ii*b*) for every right to left segment subtract a term consisting of the difference at which the segment *originates* multiplied by the binomial coefficient directly *below* this difference, if the slope of the segment is positive (i.e., if the segment goes downward and to the left), and directly *above*, if the slope is negative.

These rules imply that, if at a given difference we change direction from right to left to left to right, this difference does not appear in the interpolation formula.   As an example of the opposite situation, the path

$$
\begin{array}{l}
\nwarrow \ (m)_1 \\
\nearrow \Delta f_0 \\
\diagup \ (m-1)_1
\end{array}
$$

gives rise to the terms

$$(m-1)_1 \, \Delta f_0 - (m)_1 \, \Delta f_0$$

For example, starting at f_0, proceeding along lines sloping downward to the right and terminating with the nth difference, we get, writing

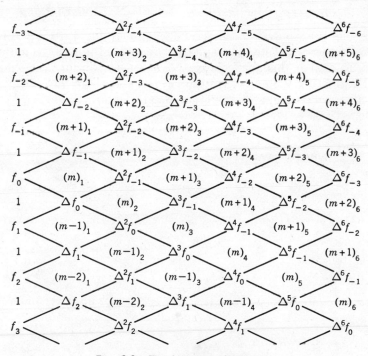

Fig. 3.2   The lozenge diagram.

$y(a_0 + hm)$ as $y(m)$,

$$y(m) = f_0 + (m)_1 \Delta f_0 + (m)_2 \Delta^2 f_0$$
$$+ \cdots + (m)_n \Delta^n f_0 = \sum_{j=0}^{n} (m)_j \Delta^j f_0 \quad (3.3\text{-}11)$$

This formula is called *Newton's forward formula* and will be discussed in more detail in Sec. 3.4.

The value of the procedure outlined above is contained in the statement that any formula derived by this procedure which terminates with an nth difference is *algebraically equivalent* to an equal-interval Lagrangian formula which uses the tabular points involved in the terminating difference. [For example, the nth difference in (3.3-11) involves the points $a_0, \ldots, a_n$; see (3.3-8).] The proof of this assertion requires that we show that

1. At least one formula has this property. In Sec. 3.4 we shall prove that Newton's forward formula has the desired property.
2. All formulas which terminate with the same difference no matter by what path they reach that difference are algebraically equivalent. We leave the proof of this to a problem {11}.

3.3-2-3 *Error propagation in difference tables.* *Table checking*

Suppose one of the entries in the second column of Fig. 3.1 is in error by ϵ. We ask the question: How will this error propagate through the difference table? To answer this question, it is sufficient to consider the auxiliary table shown in Fig. 3.3 in which all functional values are zero except for a value of ϵ corresponding to that functional value in error (why is this

f	Δ	Δ^2	Δ^3	Δ^4	Δ^5
. . . .					
0		0		0	
	0		0		ϵ
0		0		ϵ	
	0		ϵ		-5ϵ
0		ϵ		-4ϵ	
	ϵ		-3ϵ		10ϵ
ϵ		-2ϵ		6ϵ	
	$-\epsilon$		3ϵ		-10ϵ
0		ϵ		-4ϵ	
	0		$-\epsilon$		5ϵ
0		0		ϵ	
	0		0		$-\epsilon$
0		0		0	
. . . .					

Fig. 3.3 Error propagation in difference tables.

sufficient?).   Note the binomial-coefficient pattern in each column.   This error-propagation pattern is the basis of the method to be described below for using differences to check the correctness of entries in a table.

When a table of a mathematical function is compiled, it is clearly very important that every entry be correct (i.e., be correctly rounded). The rationale behind the method we are about to present is, first, that tabulated mathematical functions are locally smooth and, second, that generally some quite low order difference will be nearly zero.   The latter is equivalent to saying that the coefficients of the Taylor-series expansion of the function are all small except for the first few (why?).   We proceed as follows:

1. Difference the table.   If, at any stage of the differencing, one group of values disrupts a smooth pattern (e.g., monotonicity), this probably indicates an error.   Continue differencing until such a pattern appears or all differences are nearly zero (see remarks below on roundoff).
2. If a disrupting pattern is found and the deviation from smoothness follows the binomial-coefficient pattern of Fig. 3.3, then a single error has been detected and is easily corrected.
3. If the pattern is not binomial, then it may be that two or more errors are present and the patterns have overlapped.   In this case some ingenuity is required to untangle the patterns; see {12}.

It is important to note that roundoff errors propagating through a table can also disrupt a difference pattern.   The worst case of such propagation is shown in Fig. 3.4.   Here ϵ is the magnitude of the maximum

f	Δ	Δ^2	Δ^3	Δ^4	Δ^5
ϵ		-4ϵ		16ϵ	
	-2ϵ		8ϵ		-32ϵ
$-\epsilon$		4ϵ		-16ϵ	
	2ϵ		-8ϵ		32ϵ
ϵ		-4ϵ		16ϵ	
	-2ϵ		8ϵ		-32ϵ
$-\epsilon$		4ϵ		-16ϵ	
	2ϵ		-8ϵ		32ϵ
ϵ		-4ϵ		16ϵ	
	-2ϵ		8ϵ		-32ϵ
$-\epsilon$		4ϵ		-16ϵ	
	2ϵ		-8ϵ		32ϵ
ϵ		-4ϵ		16ϵ	

Fig. 3.4   Propagation of roundoff error.

roundoff error in the functional values. Then in the nth difference, the worst possible error is $2^n \epsilon$. In checking tables by differencing, it is important, therefore, to distinguish between irregularities in the difference pattern due to errors and those due to roundoff {13}.

Example 3.4   Find the error in the difference table

x	$f(x)$	$\Delta f(x)$	$\Delta^2 f(x)$	$\Delta^3 f(x)$
1	1			
		3		
2	4		2	
		5		0
3	9		2	
		7		−1
4	16		1	
		8		3
5	24		4	
		12		−3
6	36		1	
		13		1
7	49		2	
		15		0
8	64		2	
		17		
9	81			

A disrupting pattern is noticeable in the second difference and the binomial pattern stands out clearly in the third difference. Thus there is an error $\epsilon = -1$ in the entry for $x = 5$ which should, of course, be 25 since $f(x) = x^2$ for all the other entries.

3.4   FINITE–DIFFERENCE INTERPOLATION FORMULAS

We prove first that Eq. (3.3-11), Newton's forward formula, is algebraically equivalent to the Lagrangian interpolation formula at equal intervals for the $n + 1$ points $a_0, \ldots, a_n$. Since $(m)_n$ is a polynomial of degree n in m, it is sufficient to prove that $y(i)$ in (3.3-11) equals f_i, $i = 0, \ldots, n$ for then $y(m)$ would be the unique polynomial of degree n passing through the $n + 1$ points f_i. Using (3.3-8) in (3.3-11), we get

$$y(i) = \sum_{j=0}^{n} (i)_j \, \Delta^j f_0 = \sum_{j=0}^{n} \sum_{k=0}^{j} (-1)^{j-k} (i)_j \binom{j}{k} f_k$$

$$= \sum_{k=0}^{n} \sum_{j=k}^{n} (-1)^{j-k} (i)_j \binom{j}{k} f_k \qquad i = 0, \ldots, n \qquad (3.4-1)$$

The coefficient of f_r in $y(i)$ is then given by

$$\sum_{j=r}^{n} (-1)^{j-r}(i)_j \binom{j}{r} \qquad (3.4\text{-}2)$$

For $r > i$ this coefficient is zero since $(i)_j = 0$ if $i < j$. When $r = i$, the only nonzero term in (3.4-2) is that for $j = r$ and equals 1. When $r < i$, (3.4-2) may be written

$$\sum_{j=r}^{i} (-1)^{j-r} \binom{i}{j} \binom{j}{r} \qquad (3.4\text{-}3)$$

which, by suitable manipulation {15}, can be shown to vanish. Thus, the right-hand side of (3.4-1) is just f_i, which completes the proof.

Using the lozenge diagram, we may generate the following interpolation formulas:

1. *Newton's backward formula.* Starting at f_0 and proceeding along lines sloping upward and to the right, we get

$$y(m) = f_0 + m\,\Delta f_{-1} + (m+1)_2\,\Delta^2 f_{-2}$$
$$+ \cdots + (m+n-1)_n \Delta^n f_{-n} \qquad (3.4\text{-}4)$$

   which is equivalent to a Lagrangian formula using the points a_0, $a_{-1}, \ldots, a_{-n}$. This formula is, in fact, more conveniently expressed in terms of backward differences {16}.

2. *Gauss's forward formula.* Here we proceed in a zigzag, downward and to the right, then upward and to the right, then downward and to the right, etc. The result is

$$y(m) = f_0 + m\,\Delta f_0 + (m)_2\,\Delta^2 f_{-1}$$
$$+ (m+1)_3\,\Delta^3 f_{-1} + (m+1)_4\,\Delta^4 f_{-2} + \cdots \qquad (3.4\text{-}5)$$

   If terminated with a difference of order $2r$, (3.4-5) is equivalent to a Lagrangian formula using the points $a_0, a_{\pm 1}, \ldots, a_{\pm r}$, but if terminated with the difference of order $2r + 1$, the point a_{r+1} must be added to the above.

3. *Gauss's backward formula.* Here we proceed as in Gauss's forward formula except that the first step is upward and to the right. The formula is

$$y(m) = f_0 + m\,\Delta f_{-1} + (m+1)_2\,\Delta^2 f_{-1}$$
$$+ (m+1)_3\,\Delta^3 f_{-2} + (m+2)_4\,\Delta^4 f_{-2} \cdots \qquad (3.4\text{-}6)$$

Both Gaussian formulas are conveniently expressed in terms of central differences {16}.

Because of the result stated in Sec. 3.3-2-2, each of these formulas is algebraically equivalent to the Lagrangian formula which uses the same tabular points. The errors in these formulas are given, therefore, by (3.2-9). In the next section we shall indicate why it is useful to be able to express the same interpolation formula in a number of different forms.

If we take the mean of Gauss's forward and backward formulas as given by (3.4-5) and (3.4-6), we get *Stirling's interpolation formula*

$$y(m) = f_0 + (m/2)(\Delta f_0 + \Delta f_{-1}) + \tfrac{1}{2}[(m)_2 \Delta^2 f_{-1} + (m+1)_2 \Delta^2 f_{-\frac{1}{2}}] + \cdots \quad (3.4\text{-}7)$$

Terminated with a difference of order $2r$, this formula is also equivalent to a Lagrangian formula since both Gaussian formulas use the points a_0, $a_{\pm 1}, \ldots, a_{\pm r}$, but, if terminated with an odd difference (say, $2r + 1$), this is no longer true because one Gaussian formula uses the above points plus a_{r+1} and the other uses a_{-r-1}. In the latter case Stirling's formula uses $2r + 3$ points but has an accuracy of only order $2r + 1$. Stirling's formula can be conveniently expressed in terms of central differences {16}.

Bessel's interpolation formula is the mean of the Gaussian forward formula given by (3.4-5) and a Gaussian backward formula launched not from f_0 but from f_1. It has the form

$$y(m) = \tfrac{1}{2}(f_0 + f_1) + (m - \tfrac{1}{2}) \Delta f_0 + \tfrac{1}{2}(m)_2(\Delta^2 f_0 + \Delta^2 f_1) + \cdots$$
$$(3.4\text{-}8)$$

Note that, when (3.4-6) is modified to consider launching from f_1, m must be replaced by $m - 1$ so that the origin of m is still at a_0. Analogously to the case with Stirling's formula, Bessel's formula terminated with an *odd* difference is equivalent to a Lagrangian formula but terminated with an even difference it is not (why?). Bessel's formula is also conveniently written using central differences {16}.

Some other interpolation formulas which can be obtained by manipulating the ones derived in this section are considered in a problem {17}.

3.5   THE USE OF INTERPOLATION FORMULAS

With the exception of Stirling's formula terminated with an odd difference and Bessel's formula terminated with an even difference, all the interpolation formulas we have derived are algebraically equivalent over the same set of tabular points. For equally spaced data, the ease with which difference tables can be generated makes the finite-difference interpolation formulas more convenient than the Lagrangian formula for hand computation. To get some insight into which of the finite-difference formulas to use in a given application (why does it matter if they are all equivalent?), let us consider interpolation in a table of values.

One of the great advantages of the finite-difference interpolation formulas is the ease with which added terms of the formula may be used merely by calculating higher differences in the table of Fig. 3.1.   For example, if we add the value of ln x at 1.0 to the table of Example 3.3, we may calculate a new row of differences and thereby get a difference of order 7 in the table.   Commonly, we do not know a priori how many terms in a given interpolation formula will be sufficient to achieve the accuracy we desire.   Therefore, we generally add terms to the formula by computing higher differences until the contribution of the added terms is so small that the number of decimal places of interest to us has stabilized. [If by use of (3.2-9) we can bound the error all well and good; often, however, it will be difficult to estimate, much less bound, the derivative term in (3.2-9).]   It is desirable then to use that interpolation formula which gives the best results at every stage of the computation.

Consider the problem of estimating ln .65 using the data in the difference table of Example 3.3.   Suppose that a priori we do not know how many differences will be required to obtain the accuracy we need.†   If all the data in the table will be required to achieve the desired accuracy, then it makes no appreciable difference which finite-difference interpolation formula we use because all will be algebraically equivalent.   But if it is possible that a sufficiently accurate result can be obtained using fewer than six differences, we should choose our interpolation formula with some care.

Let us compare the use of Newton's backward formula and Gauss's forward formula.   If we may need to use all the data in the table, then the Newtonian formula must use $x_0 = .9$ (i.e., $m = -2.5$) and the Gaussian formula must use $x_0 = .6$ ($m = .5$).   But while these two formulas will be algebraically equivalent if terms through the sixth difference are used, for smaller numbers of terms, they will not be equivalent {20}.   Therefore, which should we choose?

This question is most easily answered by considering the error term (3.2-9).   The only term in the error that we can control is the $p_n(x)$ term. To minimize the magnitude of $p_n(x)$, we should choose the tabular points so that the value of x at which we wish to interpolate is as near as possible to the center of the interval spanned by the tabular points (why?). Therefore, the answer to our question is that the Gaussian formula is to be preferred in the above example because, when the number of differences used is small, it more nearly satisfies the condition above than the Newtonian formula.

From the above it follows that Newton's backward formula has its chief value when we wish to interpolate near the end of a table, for in this

† For such a simple function as this, we could, of course, estimate the error using (3.2-9).

case there would not be a sufficient number of differences available for the Gaussian formula. For example, to estimate ln .85 using the data of Example 3.3, if we used Gauss's forward formula with $x_0 = .8$, then we could only use the terms through the second difference {21}. Similarly, Newton's forward formula is chiefly valuable near the beginning of a table. But, when there are a substantial number of tabular points available on either side of the interpolation point, a Gaussian formula is more desirable than either Newtonian formula. In particular, Stirling's formula (which is just the average of two Gaussian formulas) terminated with an even difference (so that it is equivalent to a Lagrangian formula) is useful when m can be chosen near zero; similarly, Bessel's formula terminated with an odd difference is useful when m is near $\frac{1}{2}$. The justification for these conclusions is considered in {21}.

Example 3.5   Use Newton's backward formula with $x_0 = .9$ and Gauss's forward formula with $x_0 = .6$ to find an estimate of ln .65.

Using (3.4-4), (3.4-5), and the data of Example 3.3, we may construct the following table:

Number of differences used	Newton's backward formula ($m = -2.5$)	Gauss's forward formula ($m = .5$)
0	$-.105361$	$-.510826$
1	$-.399819$	$-.433751$
2	$-.429346$	$-.430229$
3	$-.430869$	$-.430701$
4	$-.430762$	$-.430821$
5	$-.430791$	$-.430792$
6	$-.430774$	$-.430775$

The true value is ln .65 $\approx -.430783$. As we expect, when the number of differences is small, the Gaussian formula is more accurate than the Newtonian formula, although both give the same value, except for roundoff, when all six differences are used. (Why is the Newtonian formula more accurate when four differences are used?) Using (3.2-9) we may verify that the error at every stage is within expected bounds {20}.

   The reader may well think that any desired degree of accuracy could be achieved merely by increasing the number of terms used in any interpolation formula (finite difference or Lagrangian).† In fact, interpolation series formed by letting the number of tabular points go to infinity are generally only asymptotically convergent; that is, as we add more points

   † We ignore here the fact that the growth of roundoff error with higher differences limits the accuracy attainable with finite-difference interpolation formulas.

the error first decreases and then at some point starts to increase and grow without bound.† One reason for this eventual divergence of interpolation series is connected with the fact that the nth derivative of all but some entire functions (functions with no singularities in the complex plane) eventually grows without bound as n increases (see Sec. 4.11). Even for entire functions, however, the interpolation series may fail to converge {22}. We note that, in practice, the desired degree of accuracy in interpolation can almost always be achieved. That is, the asymptotic convergence is generally very good indeed.

3.6   ITERATED INTERPOLATION

An important advantage of finite-difference interpolation formulas over the Lagrangian formula would seem to be the property of the former that enables a term to be added to them merely by adding one tabular point and computing an additional row of differences. As we demonstrated in Example 3.5, this enables us to generate a sequence of *interpolants* each one involving one more tabular point than the previous one. Therefore, the convergence of the interpolation procedure can be tested easily. But suppose, given the Lagrangian interpolation formula using n points, we wish to add one point to get higher accuracy. A look at (3.2-4) indicates that, even if we have saved the values of $p_n'(a_j)$, $j = 1, \ldots, n$, each $l_j(x)$, $j = 1, \ldots, n$ requires some recalculation, and we must also calculate $l_{n+1}(x)$. Our purpose in this section is to show how this seeming disadvantage of the Lagrangian formula can be overcome. We shall do this by using *iterated interpolation* in which a sequence of interpolants in the Lagrangian context is generated without the need for substantial recalculation of coefficients when going from n to $n + 1$ points.

Denote by $y_{n_1, \ldots, n_k}(x)$ the Lagrangian interpolation formula which uses the points $a_{n_1}, \ldots, a_{n_k}$ which we do not require to be equally spaced. Then in particular we may write

$$y_{1,2,\ldots,n}(x) = \frac{1}{a_n - a_{n-1}} \begin{vmatrix} y_{1,2,\ldots,n-1}(x) & a_{n-1} - x \\ y_{1,2,\ldots,n-2,n}(x) & a_n - x \end{vmatrix} \tag{3.6-1}$$

This equation can be verified by noting that the right-hand side, which is a polynomial of degree $n - 1$, takes on the values $f(a_i)$ at the points a_i, $i = 1, \ldots, n$. Equation (3.6-1) then indicates how a Lagrangian formula of order n can be generated from lower-order formulas. By use of the following table, we may generalize the result of (3.6-1) to achieve our

† The classic example of this behavior is the very well-behaved function $f(x) = 1/(1 + x^2)$ which is considered by Steffensen (1950, pp. 35–38).

object [note that $y_i(x) = f(a_i)$]:

$$
\begin{array}{llllll}
a_1 & a_1 - x & y_1(x) \\
a_2 & a_2 - x & y_2(x) & y_{1,2}(x) \\
a_3 & a_3 - x & y_3(x) & y_{1,3}(x) & y_{1,2,3}(x) \\
\cdot & \cdot & \cdot & \cdot & \cdot & \cdot \\
a_n & a_n - x & y_n(x) & y_{1,n}(x) & y_{1,2,n}(x) & \cdots & y_{1,2,3,\ldots,n}(x)
\end{array}
\tag{3.6-2}
$$

The entries in each column of the table can be generated from the entries in the previous column by analogy with (3.6-1). For example

$$
y_{1,2,n}(x) = \frac{1}{a_n - a_2} \begin{vmatrix} y_{1,2}(x) & a_2 - x \\ y_{1,n}(x) & a_n - x \end{vmatrix}
\tag{3.6-3}
$$

The entries on the diagonal in (3.6-2) are just what we were seeking. They form a sequence of Lagrangian interpolants each of which incorporates one more tabular point than the previous one. Further, since each entry in (3.6-2) is calculated using a formula analogous to (3.6-1), the process is easily mechanized. Iterated interpolation is, thus, well suited to digital-computer application and, for points not equally spaced, is also convenient for hand computation.

Example 3.6   Use iterated interpolation to calculate ln .54 using the data of Example 3.2.
   Corresponding to the table (3.6-2), we get

a_i	$a_i - x$	$y_i(x)$			
.40	$-.14$	$-.916291$			
.50	$-.04$	$-.693147$	$-.603889$		
.60	.06	$-.510826$	$-.632466$	$-.615320$	
.70	.16	$-.356675$	$-.655137$	$-.614139$	$-.616029$
.80	.26	$-.223144$	$-.673690$	$-.613196$	$-.615957$	$-.616144$

We are not bound to use the natural order of the points as above. Consider instead iterated interpolation using the ordering below

a_i	$a_i - x$	$y_i(x)$			
.50	$-.04$	$-.693147$			
.60	.06	$-.510826$	$-.620219$		
.40	$-.14$	$-.916291$	$-.603889$	$-.615320$	
.70	.16	$-.356675$	$-.625853$	$-.616839$	$-.616029$
.80	.26	$-.223144$	$-.630480$	$-.617141$	$-.615957$	$-.616144$

The difference in the two final values from the result of Example 3.2 is the result of roundoff since the same five points were used in all computations. Note, however, that the first interpolant ($-.620219$) in the second calculation is substantially more accurate than that in the first calculation ($-.603889$). This occurs because in the second computation we arranged the data so that the magnitudes in the ($a_i - x$) column would be increasing. In this way the value of $p_n(x)$ in the error term is minimized at every stage (cf. the discussion of Sec. 3.5). Therefore, if we order the tabular points so that the magnitudes in the $a_i - x$ column are increasing, then each interpolant tends to be the best possible ["tends" because the value of the derivative in the error *may* be greater when $p_n(x)$ is smaller]. In this way the convergence of the interpolation (as judged by the difference in two successive interpolants or by the stabilization of a certain number of decimal places) will tend to be most rapid.   In this example only the first interpolant is improved because only the tabular point at .40 is out of the best possible order.

3.7   INVERSE INTERPOLATION

In Chap. 8 we shall be concerned with the solution of the general non-linear equation $f(x) = 0$.   One of our basic tools in the solution of this equation will be inverse interpolation, which we shall now consider briefly.   The solution of $f(x) = 0$ is one example of the common numerical problem of finding the zero of a function.   Another case where this occurs is in the numerical integration of an ordinary differential equation (see Chap. 5) when we would like to know that value of the independent variable for which the dependent variable (i.e., the solution of the differential equation) is zero.   Inverse interpolation provides us with a straightforward and powerful way to find such zeros of functions.†

Let the function whose zero (or zeros) we wish to find be $y = f(x)$ and suppose it is tabulated at a series of points (which need not necessarily be equally spaced) so that we have

$$x: \quad x_1 \quad x_2 \quad \cdots \quad x_n$$
$$y = f(x): \quad f(x_1) \quad f(x_2) \quad \cdots \quad f(x_n) \tag{3.7-1}$$

Now let us suppose that on the interval $[x_1, x_n]$, $f(x)$ satisfies the conditions of the inverse-function theorem [i.e., in particular that $f'(x) \neq 0$] so that we may write $x = g(y)$ where g is the function inverse to f.   Therefore, finding the value of $g(0)$ is equivalent to finding a zero of $f(x)$.   To estimate $g(0)$ we first write the table (3.7-1) as

$$y: \quad f(x_1) \quad f(x_2) \quad \cdots \quad f(x_n)$$
$$x = g(y): \quad x_1 \quad x_2 \quad \cdots \quad x_n \tag{3.7-2}$$

Now in the context of interpolation let $f(x_1), \ldots, f(x_n)$ be the tabular points of the independent variable y (not equally spaced in general) and let $x_1, \ldots, x_n$ be the functional values at these points.   Then, if we use a Lagrangian interpolation formula to approximate $g(y)$ by a polynomial and then interpolate at the point $y = 0$, we get the desired approximation to $\alpha = g(0)$.

Example 3.7   Given the data

x:	.1	.2	.3	.4	5
$f(x)$:	.70010	.40160	.10810	$-.17440$	$-.43750$

find an approximate value of the zero of $f(x)$ between .3 and .4.

† We note in passing that even the Newton-Raphson method for the solution of $f(x) = 0$ can be considered to be an application of inverse interpolation; see Chap. 8.

Our approach will be to use iterated interpolation. We therefore first arrange the data in order of increasing magnitude of $f(x)$ (cf. Example 3.6) and then use the technique of the previous section to generate the table

$f(x_i)$	$f(x_i) - 0$	x_i			
.10810	.10810	.3			
−.17440	−.17440	.4	.33827		
.40160	.40160	.2	.33683	.33783	
−.43750	−.43750	.5	.33963	.33737	.33761
.70010	.70010	.1	.33652	.33792	.33771	.33765

The data for $f(x)$ are in fact values of the function $x^4 - 3x + 1$, which has a zero .33767 correctly rounded to five places.

Expressed in terms of $g(y)$ the error in inverse Lagrangian interpolation is

$$E(y) = [p_n(y)/n!]g^{(n)}(\xi) \tag{3.7-3}$$

Now derivatives of g can be expressed in terms of f, and although this relation is not simple (see {1}, Chap. 8), there is a power of $f'(x)$ in the denominator of each derivative of $g(y)$; e.g.,

$$g'(y) = 1/f'(x) \qquad g''(y) = -f''(x)/[f'(x)]^3$$

Therefore, although we can carry through the process of inverse interpolation even if $f'(x)$ vanishes in $[x_1,x_n]$, we would expect the accuracy to be very poor in this case. When $f'(x)$ vanishes near the zero we can, however, often find the zero by an iterative process involving linear inverse interpolation {30}.

3.8 HERMITE INTERPOLATION

In this section we consider the case $m = 1$ in (3.1-1). In particular, we suppose that the first derivative as well as the function is known at r of the n tabular points. In place of (3.1-5) we have then

$$f(x) = \sum_{j=1}^{n} h_j(x)f(a_j) + \sum_{j=1}^{r} \bar{h}_j(x)f'(a_j) + E(x) = y(x) + E(x)$$

$$\tag{3.8-1}$$

where now the approximation $y(x)$ is given by

$$y(x) = \sum_{j=1}^{n} h_j(x)f(a_j) + \sum_{j=1}^{r} \bar{h}_j(x)f'(a_j) \tag{3.8-2}$$

and $h_j(x)$ and $\bar{h}_j(x)$ are both polynomials. Again using the criterion of exact approximation, we require that the error term $E(x)$ be such that

$$\begin{aligned} E(a_j) &= 0 & j &= 1, \ldots, n \\ E'(a_j) &= 0 & j &= 1, \ldots, r \end{aligned} \tag{3.8-3}$$

In analogy with Eq. (3.2-1) in the Lagrangian case, this leads to the following conditions that must be satisfied by the $h_j(x)$ and $\bar{h}_j(x)$:

$$
\begin{array}{ll}
h_j(a_k) = \delta_{jk} & j, k = 1, \ldots, n \\
\bar{h}_j(a_k) = 0 & j = 1, \ldots, r; k = 1, \ldots, n \\
h'_j(a_k) = 0 & j = 1, \ldots, n; k = 1, \ldots, r \\
\bar{h}'_j(a_k) = \delta_{jk} & j, k = 1, \ldots, r
\end{array}
\tag{3.8-4}
$$

Since there are $n + r$ conditions to satisfy in (3.8-3), we expect that $y(x)$ will have to be a polynomial of degree $n + r - 1$ [i.e., we shall approximate $f(x)$ by a polynomial of degree $n + r - 1$ passing through $f(a_j)$, $j = 1,$ $\ldots, n$ and having derivatives $f'(a_j)$, $j = 1, \ldots, r$]. In deriving the $h_j(x)$ and $\bar{h}_j(x)$, we shall use the notation

$$
\begin{aligned}
p_n(x) &= (x - a_1) \cdots (x - a_n) \\
p_r(x) &= (x - a_1) \cdots (x - a_r) \\
l_{jn}(x) &= \frac{p_n(x)}{(x - a_j)p'_n(a_j)} \qquad j = 1, \ldots, n \\
l_{jr}(x) &= \frac{p_r(x)}{(x - a_j)p'_r(a_j)} \qquad j = 1, \ldots, r
\end{aligned}
\tag{3.8-5}
$$

To satisfy the conditions on $h_j(x)$, we set

$$
h_j(x) = \begin{cases} t_j(x)l_{jn}(x)l_{jr}(x) & j = 1, \ldots, r \\ l_{jn}(x)[p_r(x)/p_r(a_j)] & j = r+1, \ldots, n \end{cases}
\tag{3.8-6}
$$

where $t_j(x)$ is a linear polynomial so that $h_j(x)$ is of degree $n + r - 1$. As given by (3.8-6), $h_j(x)$ satisfies all the conditions of (3.8-4) except $h_j(a_j) = 1$, $j = 1, \ldots, r$ and $h'_j(a_j) = 0, j = 1, \ldots, r$. To satisfy these we must have

$$
\begin{array}{ll}
t_j(a_j) = 1 & j = 1, \ldots, r \\
t'_j(a_j) + l'_{jn}(a_j) + l'_{jr}(a_j) = 0 & j = 1, \ldots, r
\end{array}
\tag{3.8-7}
$$

Similarly, if we set

$$
\bar{h}_j(x) = s_j(x)l_{jr}(x)l_{jn}(x) \qquad j = 1, \ldots, r
\tag{3.8-8}
$$

with $s_j(x)$ a linear polynomial we must have

$$
\begin{array}{ll}
s_j(a_j) = 0 & j = 1, \ldots, r \\
s'_j(a_j) = 1 & j = 1, \ldots, r
\end{array}
\tag{3.8-9}
$$

in order to satisfy (3.8-4). Linear functions satisfying (3.8-7) and (3.8-9) are easily found to be {31}

$$
t_j(x) = 1 - (x - a_j)[l'_{jn}(a_j) + l'_{jr}(a_j)] \qquad s_j(x) = x - a_j
\tag{3.8-10}
$$

This completes the determination of $h_j(x)$ and $\bar{h}_j(x)$.

To find $E(x)$ we proceed in a manner similar to the Lagrangian case. Let

$$F(z) = f(z) - y(z) - [f(x) - y(x)] \frac{p_n(z)p_r(z)}{p_n(x)p_r(x)} \qquad (3.8\text{-}11)$$

with x not one of the tabular points. This function has $n + r + 1$ zeros (double zeros at $a_1, \ldots, a_r$, single zeros at $a_{r+1}, \ldots, a_n$ and x) so that by a generalization of Rolle's theorem {36}, there exists a ξ in the interval spanned by $a_1, \ldots, a_n$ and x such that

$$0 = F^{(n+r)}(\xi) = f^{(n+r)}(\xi) - [f(x) - y(x)] \frac{(n + r)!}{p_n(x)p_r(x)} \qquad (3.8\text{-}12)$$

Thus

$$E(x) = \frac{p_n(x)p_r(x)}{(n + r)!} f^{(n+r)}(\xi) \qquad (3.8\text{-}13)$$

This relation also is correct if x is one of the tabular points (why?).

The interpolation formula (3.8-1) then becomes

$$f(x) = \sum_{j=1}^{n} h_j(x)f(a_j) + \sum_{j=1}^{r} \bar{h}_j(x)f'(a_j) + \frac{p_n(x)p_r(x)}{(n + r)!} f^{(n+r)}(\xi) \quad (3.8\text{-}14)$$

with

$$h_j(x) = \begin{cases} \{1 - (x - a_j)[l'_{jn}(a_j) + l'_{jr}(a_j)]\}l_{jn}(x)l_{jr}(x) \\ \qquad\qquad\qquad\qquad\qquad\qquad j = 1, \ldots, r \quad (3.8\text{-}15) \\ l_{jn}(x)[p_r(x)/p_r(a_j)] \qquad j = r + 1, \ldots, n \end{cases}$$

$$\bar{h}_j(x) = (x - a_j)l_{jr}(x)l_{jn}(x) \qquad j = 1, \ldots, r \qquad (3.8\text{-}16)$$

and is called the *modified Hermite interpolation formula*. When $r = n$ the formula is

$$f(x) = \sum_{j=1}^{n} h_j(x)f(a_j) + \sum_{j=1}^{n} \bar{h}_j(x)f'(a_j) + \frac{p_n^2(x)}{(2n)!} f^{(2n)}(\xi) \qquad (3.8\text{-}17)$$

with

$$\begin{aligned} h_j(x) &= [1 - 2(x - a_j)l'_j(a_j)]l_j^2(x) \\ \bar{h}_j(x) &= (x - a_j)l_j^2(x) \end{aligned} \qquad j = 1, \ldots, n \qquad (3.8\text{-}18)$$

where we have replaced $l_{jn}(x)$ by $l_j(x)$. Equation (3.8-17) is the *Hermite interpolation formula,* sometimes also called the formula for osculatory interpolation.

Both the Hermite and modified Hermite formulas can be useful interpolation formulas. They also serve as useful theoretical tools in other areas of numerical analysis, as we shall see in Chaps. 4, 5, and 8.

Example 3.8   Given the table below of the natural logarithm and its derivative

x	$\ln x$	$1/x$
.40	$-.916291$	2.50
.50	$-.693147$	2.00
.70	$-.356675$	1.43
.80	$-.223144$	1.25

$n = 4$ and $\ell = 4$

estimate the value of ln .60 using the Hermite interpolation formula.
From (3.8-18) we get

$$h_1(.60) = \tfrac{11}{54} \qquad \bar{h}_1(.60) = \tfrac{1}{180}$$
$$h_2(.60) = \tfrac{8}{27} \qquad \bar{h}_2(.60) = \tfrac{2}{45}$$
$$h_3(.60) = \tfrac{8}{27} \qquad \bar{h}_3(.60) = -\tfrac{2}{45}$$
$$h_4(.60) = \tfrac{11}{54} \qquad \bar{h}_4(.60) = -\tfrac{1}{180}$$

and from (3.8-17)

$$\ln .60 \approx -.510824$$

whereas the true value is $-.510826$. Using (3.8-13) the error is bounded by

$$-.000031 \approx \frac{-1}{32768} < E(.60) < -\frac{1}{2^{23}} \approx -.0000001$$

so that the excellent agreement between the interpolated and true values is to be expected.

3.9 GENERAL POLYNOMIAL INTERPOLATION. THE DETERMINANT APPROACH

In the Lagrangian interpolation formula, $y(x)$ was required to be a polynomial of degree less than n with the property that $y(a_i) = f(a_i)$, $i = 1, \ldots, n$. This can be expressed by writing

$$y(x) = c_0 + c_1 x + \cdots + c_{n-1} x^{n-1} \tag{3.9-1}$$

and

$$f(a_i) = c_0 + c_1 a_i + \cdots + c_{n-1} a_i^{n-1} \qquad i = 1, \ldots, n \tag{3.9-2}$$

In (3.9-2) we have a system of n equations for the n c_i's. If we solve this system for each c_i using Cramer's rule and substitute the result into (3.9-1), we may write (3.9-1) in the determinantal form {33}

$$\begin{vmatrix} y(x) & 1 & x & \cdots & x^{n-1} \\ f(a_1) & 1 & a_1 & \cdots & a_1^{n-1} \\ \cdots & \cdots & \cdots & \cdots & \cdots \\ f(a_n) & 1 & a_n & \cdots & a_n^{n-1} \end{vmatrix} = 0 \tag{3.9-3}$$

The correctness of (3.9-3) is easily verified by noting that $y(x)$ is certainly a polynomial of degree $n - 1$ which vanishes at the points $a_i, i = 1, \ldots,$

n.   In a similar fashion {33}, we may show that the equation for $y(x)$ in the modified Hermite interpolation formula may be written

$$\begin{vmatrix} y(x) & 1 & x & x^2 & \cdots & x^{n+r-1} \\ f(a_1) & 1 & a_1 & \cdots\cdots\cdots & a_1^{n+r-1} \\ \cdots\cdots\cdots\cdots\cdots\cdots\cdots\cdots\cdots \\ f(a_n) & 1 & a_n & \cdots\cdots\cdots & a_n^{n+r-1} \\ f'(a_1) & 0 & 1 & 2a_1 & \cdots & (n+r-1)a_1^{n+r-2} \\ \cdots\cdots\cdots\cdots\cdots\cdots\cdots\cdots\cdots \\ f'(a_r) & 0 & 1 & 2a_r & \cdots & (n+r-1)a_r^{n+r-2} \end{vmatrix} = 0 \qquad (3.9\text{-}4)$$

Now let us consider the general problem of deriving an interpolation formula using the operator (3.1-1) with the property that at the tabular point a_i the approximation $y(x)$ and its first r_i derivatives agree with $f(x)$ and its first r_i derivatives.   The determinantal equation for $y(x)$ is then {33}

$$\begin{vmatrix} y(x) & 1 & x & \cdots & x^{r_1} & \cdots & x^{r_n} & \cdots & x^\beta \\ f(a_1) & 1 & a_1 & \cdots\cdots\cdots\cdots\cdots\cdots\cdots\cdots & a_1^\beta \\ \cdots\cdots\cdots\cdots\cdots\cdots\cdots\cdots\cdots\cdots\cdots \\ f^{(r_1)}(a_1) & 0 & \cdots\cdots & (r_1)! & \cdots\cdots\cdots\cdots & \dfrac{\beta!}{(\beta-r_1)!}a_1^{\beta-r_1} \\ \cdots\cdots\cdots\cdots\cdots\cdots\cdots\cdots\cdots\cdots\cdots \\ f(a_n) & 1 & a_n & \cdots\cdots\cdots\cdots\cdots\cdots & a_n^\beta \\ \cdots\cdots\cdots\cdots\cdots\cdots\cdots\cdots\cdots \\ f^{(r_n)}(a_n) & 0 & \cdots\cdots\cdots\cdots & (r_n)! & \cdots & \dfrac{\beta!}{(\beta-r_n)!}a_n^{\beta-r_n} \end{vmatrix} = 0$$

$$(3.9\text{-}5)$$

where $\beta = n - 1 + \sum_{i=1}^{n} r_i$.   It is easy to see that (3.9-3) and (3.9-4) are special cases of (3.9-5).   However, before we can assert that (3.9-5) defines a valid interpolation polynomial $y(x)$, we must show not only that $y(x)$ and its derivatives have the desired values at the tabular points but also that the minor of y in (3.9-5) does not vanish identically, for in this case there would be no formula.   In the case of (3.9-3) and (3.9-4) our derivations of the Lagrangian and Hermite formulas are assurance of this. Thus it should be no surprise that, in the general case (3.9-5), it can be proved that, independent of the tabular points, the minor of y does not vanish identically; we leave the proof to a problem {35}.

The interpolation polynomials [i.e., the coefficients of $f^{(r_i)}(a_i)$] for this general case may be derived by techniques similar to those used in the Lagrangian and Hermite cases, but of particular interest to us here is the form of the error term since we shall have use for this in Sec. 8.5-1.   As we would expect, (3.9-5) is exact for polynomials of degree β or less.   Therefore, by analogy with (3.2-9) and (3.8-13) the error is given by {36}

$$E(x) = \frac{f^{(\beta+1)}(\xi)}{(\beta + 1)!} \prod_{j=1}^{n} (x - a_j)^{r_j+1}$$
(3.9-6)

When all the r_j are equal, Eq. (3.9-5) is called the formula for hyperosculatory interpolation.

For the still more general case in which there may be gaps in the sequence of derivatives prescribed at a point (e.g., the function and its second derivative but not its first derivative may be specified at a point), a determinantal equation analogous to (3.9-5) may still be written down {37}, but it may now be true that for some choices of tabular points the minor of y vanishes identically {37}.

3.10   OTHER METHODS OF INTERPOLATION.   EXTRAPOLATION

In interpolation, as in all branches of numerical analysis, there will be special cases in which methods superior to the general ones derived in this chapter can be derived and used without an unreasonable expenditure of effort.   One example of this is the case of periodic functions in which methods based on Fourier-series approximations may be preferable to the polynomial approximations of this chapter; for more on this, see Sec. 6.8-1.   In fact, whenever the function to be interpolated is known to have a special functional character, an approximation based on this known functional character may be desirable {38}.   Of course, on a digital computer, if we use functions other than polynomials, these functions themselves must be evaluated using polynomial or rational approximations.

Although we are restricting ourselves in this book to functions of a single variable, interpolation of functions of two or more variables can often be effected by a sequence of interpolations using the formulas of this chapter {39}.

This chapter is entitled Interpolation, but it has been equally about extrapolation.   As their definition in Sec. 2.2-1 makes clear, interpolation and extrapolation are two aspects of the same type of procedure.   Of the two, interpolation is much more common than extrapolation.   The reason for this is straightforward and practical.   We argued in Sec. 3.5 that $p_n(x)$ is minimized when x is as nearly as possible in the center of the interval spanned by the tabular points.   Conversely, as x moves *outside* the interval spanned by the tabular points—as is the case in extrapolation—the factors $x - a_i$ in $p_n(x)$ grow, and therefore, the error tends to grow also.   Thus extrapolation is inherently a more inaccurate process than interpolation and must therefore always be used with extreme caution.

When extrapolation must be used in some form—see, for example, Chap. 5 —then the value of x should be restricted to be as near as possible to the interval spanned by the tabular points.

BIBLIOGRAPHIC NOTES

3.1–3.5   The topics covered in these sections will be found in virtually any textbook on numerical analysis.   In particular, excellent discussions of interpolation may be found in Hildebrand (1956), Kopal (1955), and Kuntzmann (1959).   The orientation in these books as well as in most other numerical analysis texts is much more toward difference and divided-difference techniques {25} than in this book.   An excellent though somewhat older reference to classical interpolation techniques is Steffensen (1950).   Hartree (1958) and Whittaker and Robinson (1948) contain a number of practical hints for special situations.

The coefficients of both the Lagrangian and finite-difference interpolation formulas have been extensively tabulated.   A bibliography of these tables may be found in Fletcher, Miller, and Rosenhead (1962).

The error term in the Lagrangian formula is discussed in a more general context in Milne (1949).   The derivation of the error term used here may also be found in Scarborough (1962).   For another approach, see Hildebrand (1956) or Kopal (1955).

Our discussion of the lozenge diagram follows closely that of Hamming (1962); see also Kopal (1955).   A thorough discussion of the use of differences in detecting errors in tables is given by Miller (1950).   The use of difference methods in the construction of mathematical tables is considered by Fox (1957b); see also Fox (1957a).

The operational techniques introduced in Prob. 10 are further considered in the problems after the next chapter.   A thorough discussion of these techniques may be found in Hildebrand (1956).

3.6   The basic references on iterated interpolation are the papers by Aitken (1932) and Neville (1934).

3.7   Inverse interpolation will be considered in much greater detail in Chap. 8; for tables of coefficients for particular cases of inverse interpolation using differences see Salzer (1943, 1944, 1945).

3.8–3.10   Hermite interpolation is discussed in many texts [e.g., Hildebrand (1956), Kopal (1955)].   The convergence of interpolation series {22} is considered by Erdos and Turan (1937).   A detailed discussion of interpolation in several variables is given by Steffensen (1950); see also Pearson (1920).

BIBLIOGRAPHY

Aitken, A. C. (1932): On Interpolation by Iteration of Proportional Parts, without the Use of Differences, *Proc. Edinburgh Math. Soc.*, vol. 3, series 2, pp. 56–76.

Erdos, P., and P. Turan (1937): On Interpolation, I, *Ann. of Math.*, vol. 38, pp. 142–155.

Fletcher, A., J. C. P. Miller, and L. Rosenhead (1962): *An Index of Mathematical Tables*, 2d ed., Addison-Wesley Publishing Company, Inc., Reading, Mass.

Fox, L. (1957a): Minimax Methods in Table Construction in *On Numerical Approximation* (R. E. Langer, ed.), The University of Wisconsin Press, Madison, Wis.

Fox, L. (1957b): *The Use and Construction of Mathematical Tables*, vol. I, National Physical Laboratory Mathematical Tables Series, London.

Hamming, R. W. (1962): *Numerical Methods for Scientists and Engineers*, McGraw-Hill Book Company, New York.

Hartree, D. R. (1958): *Numerical Analysis*, Oxford University Press, Fair Lawn, N.J.

Hildebrand, F. B. (1956): *Introduction to Numerical Analysis*, McGraw-Hill Book Company, New York.

Kopal, Z. (1955): *Numerical Analysis*, John Wiley & Sons, Inc., New York.

Kuntzmann, J. (1959): *Méthodes numériques, Interpolation—dérivées*, Dunod, Paris.

Miller, J. C. P. (1950): Checking by Differences, *MTAC*, vol. 4, pp. 3–11.

Milne, W. E. (1949): The Remainder in Linear Methods of Approximation, *J. Res. Nat. Bur. Standards*, vol. 43, pp. 501–511.

Neville, E. H. (1934): Iterative Interpolation, *J. Indian Math. Soc.*, vol. 20, pp. 87–120.

Pearson, K. (1920): *On the Construction of Tables and on Interpolation*, II, *Bivariate Interpolation*, University of London, Tracts for Computers III, Cambridge University Press, New York.

Salzer, H. E. (1943): Tables of Coefficients for Inverse Interpolation with Central Differences, *J. Math. and Phys.*, vol. 22, pp. 210–224.

Salzer, H. E. (1944): Tables of Coefficients for Inverse Interpolation with Advancing Differences, *J. Math. and Phys.*, vol. 23, pp. 75–102.

Salzer, H. E. (1945): Inverse Interpolation for Eight, Nine, Ten and Eleven Point Direct Interpolation, *J. Math. and Phys.*, vol. 24, pp. 106–108.

Scarborough, J. B. (1962): *Numerical Mathematical Analysis*, 5th ed., The Johns Hopkins Press, Baltimore.

Steffensen, J. F. (1950): *Interpolation*, Chelsea Publishing Company, New York.

Whittaker, E. T., and W. Robinson (1948): *The Calculus of Observations*, 4th ed., Blackie & Son, Ltd., Glasgow.

PROBLEMS

Section 3.2

1. (*a*) Assuming that the derivatives at x_1 can be calculated, discuss the relative accuracy of an interpolation formula based on the operator derived in Prob. 16, Chap. 2 with $N = n$ and an n-point Lagrangian interpolation formula.

(*b*) Use this interpolation formula with $n = 4$ and $x_1 = .50$ to approximate ln .60. Compare this result with that of Example 3.1. Why is ln x one of the few functions for which interpolation using a truncated Taylor series is practical?

2. (*a*) If n is the order of a Lagrangian interpolation formula, show that

$$\sum_{j=1}^{n} a_j^k l_j(x) = x^k \qquad k = 0, \ldots, n - 1$$

where the a_j are the tabular points.

(*b*) For $n = 3$ and equally spaced tabular points, compute

$$\max_{[a_1, a_3]} |l_j(x)|$$

for $j = 1, 2, 3$. Use Table 3.1 to estimate the bounds on $l_j(x)$ for $n = 5$. Use these results to make an inference on the importance of roundoff error in interpolation using equally spaced data.

Section 3.3

3. (*a*) Using equally spaced data and a three-point Lagrangian formula, find a bound on $h^3 f'''(x)$ which, on the interval spanned by the three points, assures a truncation error of less than 10^{-d} where d is an integer.

(*b*) Similarly, find a bound on $h^5 f^{\text{v}}(x)$ when using a five-point Lagrangian formula.

(*c*) Use these results to estimate the maximum value of h, for both the three- and five-point cases, that can be used to interpolate (i) sin x on $[-\pi,\pi]$, (ii) e^x on $[-4,4]$, (iii) sin $100x$ on $[-\pi,\pi]$, with a truncation error of less than 10^{-10}.

4. (*a*) Show that $y(x)$ in the Lagrangian interpolation formula is the unique polynomial of degree $n-1$ passing through the points $[a_j, f(a_j)]$.

(*b*) Use the Lagrangian interpolation formula to find the cubic passing through the points $(-3,-1)$, $(0,2)$, $(3,-2)$, $(6,10)$.

5. (*a*) Do the computation of Examples 3.1 and 3.2 with the same tabular points when $f(x) = \sin x$.

(*b*) Repeat part a using $\tan^{-1} x$.

*6. Consider the following table for the Bessel functions $J_p(x)$, $p = 0, 1, 2, 3, 4, 5$ correctly rounded to four decimal places

x	$J_0(x)$	$J_1(x)$	$J_2(x)$	$J_3(x)$	$J_4(x)$	$J_5(x)$
2.0	.2239	.5767	.3528	.1289	.0340	.0070
2.1	.1666	.5683	.3746	.1453	.0405	.0088
2.2	.1104	.5560	.3951	.1623	.0476	.0109
2.3	.0555	.5399	.4139	.1800	.0556	.0134
2.4	.0025	.5202	.4310	.1981	.0649	.0162
2.5	−.0484	.4971	.4461	.2166	.0738	.0195
2.6	−.0968	.4708	.4590	.2353	.0870	.0232
2.7	−.1424	.4416	.4696	.2540	.0950	.0274
2.8	−.1850	.4097	.4777	.2727	.1067	.0321
2.9	−.2243	.3754	.4832	.2911	.1190	.0373
3.0	−.2601	.3391	.4861	.3091	.1320	.0430

(*a*) Suppose you wished to interpolate to find values of $J_0(x)$ at $x = 2.05 + .1j$, $j = 0, \ldots, 9$. Use the relation

$$J_p'(x) = -J_{p+1}(x) + (p/x)J_p(x)$$

to find a bound on the truncation error in the worst case using (i) linear interpolation; (ii) a Lagrangian three-point formula. Which of these methods would you use if you wished to *guarantee* a *total* error in the result for every j of less than 5×10^{-4} in magnitude?

(*b*) Carry out the interpolation using this method.

(*c*) Repeat parts a and b to find values of $J_1(x)$ at $x = 2.05 + .1j, j = 1, \ldots, 9$.

(*d*) How many correctly rounded decimal places for $J_0(x)$ would have to be given in order that the use of a five-point Lagrangian formula would give significantly higher accuracy than the three-point formula?

7. Use the data of Prob. 6 and a three-point Lagrangian formula to approximate (*a*) $J_p(2.07)$, (*b*) $J_p(2.405)$, (*c*) $J_p(2.64)$, (*d*) $J_p(2.91)$, with $p = 0, 1, 2$.

8. Derive (3.3-8).

9. Show that the first difference (forward, backward, or central) of a polynomial of degree n is a polynomial of degree $n - 1$. Thus deduce that the nth difference of a polynomial of degree n is a constant and the $(n + 1)$st is zero.

10. Difference operators. Define the *shifting* operator E to be such that $Ef(x) = f(x + h)$. Using this and the definitions of Δ, ∇, and δ establish the following identities: (a) $\Delta = E - 1$; (b) $\nabla = 1 - E^{-1}$; (c) $\delta = E^{\frac{1}{2}} - E^{-\frac{1}{2}}$. Then use these relations to derive relations between Δ and ∇ and between Δ and δ.

***11.** (a) Using the rules of Sec. 3.3-2-2, show that any closed path of the form

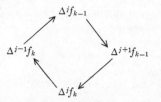

results in no contribution to any interpolation formula.

(b) Thus deduce that the path from $\Delta^{i-1}f_k$ to $\Delta^i f_{k-1}$ to $\Delta^{i+1}f_{k-1}$ results in the same contribution as the path from $\Delta^{i-1}f_k$ to $\Delta^i f_k$ to $\Delta^{i+1}f_{k-1}$. Similarly, show that the path from $\Delta^{i-1}f_k$ to $\Delta^i f_{k-1}$ to $\Delta^{i+1}f_{k-1}$ to $\Delta^i f_k$ and the path from $\Delta^{i-1}f_k$ to $\Delta^i f_k$ result in the same contribution. From these results, deduce that *any closed path* contributes nothing.

(c) Show also that the path from f_{j+1} to Δf_j to f_j contributes nothing.

(d) Use the results of parts a, b, and c to deduce that all formulas which terminate on a given difference and start anywhere in the functional-value column are algebraically equivalent.

12. (a) Suppose a table contains two errors in successive entries. Show how the difference patterns will overlap in the second difference and describe how you would determine the magnitude of each error. Do the same for the third difference. Generalize to show how you would unravel any two overlapping error patterns.

(b) The following tabulation may contain one or more misprints. By differencing the tabulation, correct these misprints. Describe the way you detect the misprints.

2001409	1634722	1267432
1949050	1582304	1215141
1896683	1529878	1162645
1844308	1477443	1110161
1791930	1424999	1057658
1739532	1372548	1005146
1687132	1320088	

[Ref.: Kopal (1955), p. 86.]

(c) Find and correct the misprints in the tabulation of $J_4(x)$ in Prob. 6.

***13.** Suppose a single entry in a table is in error by an amount ϵ in the least significant digit and let all the other entries in the table be in error by the maximum roundoff error of $\frac{1}{2}$ in the least significant digit, alternately plus and minus. Therefore, in the position of the least significant digit, the error pattern would look like . . . $-\frac{1}{2}, \frac{1}{2}, -\frac{1}{2}, \frac{1}{2}, \epsilon, \frac{1}{2}, -\frac{1}{2}, \frac{1}{2} \ldots$.

(a) In terms of ϵ, find the error in the difference of order $2k$, $k = 1, \ldots, 6$ on the line with the ϵ entry.

(b) By considering the case where $\epsilon = -\frac{1}{2}$, find ϵ_{max}, the largest error in a functional value which cannot be distinguished from roundoff in the difference of order $2k$, $k = 1, \ldots, 6$.

(c) Derive a formula for ϵ_{max} in terms of k.

[Ref.: Miller (1950).]

*14. (a) Given a table of values at an interval h, discuss how you would generate a new table ("subtabulate") at an interval ρh $(0 < \rho < 1)$ by using an appropriate interpolation formula.

(b) Show that as $n \to \infty$, the left-hand side of (3.3-11) approaches $f(a_0 + hm)$ if the series on the right-hand side converges (see Prob. 22).

(c) Let the forward-difference operator with respect to the interval ρh be represented by Δ_1. Using (3.3-8) and the result of part b, show that

$$\Delta_1^j f_0 = \sum_{i=0}^{\infty} \sum_{k=0}^{j} (-1)^{j-k} \binom{j}{k} \binom{k\rho}{i} \Delta^i f_0 \quad j = 1, 2, \ldots$$

(d) Use the results of Prob. 10 to show that in operational form

$$\Delta_1^j f_0 = [(1 + \Delta)^\rho - 1]^j f_0$$

Use this to calculate Δ_1^j, $j = 1, 2, 3, 4$ in terms of Δ^k and ρ, retaining terms through Δ^4.

(e) Use the results of part c to subtabulate the data of Prob. 6 for $J_0(x)$ with (i) $\rho = \frac{1}{2}$; (ii) $\rho = \pm\frac{1}{3}$. Compare the results for $\rho = \frac{1}{2}$ with those of Prob. 6. How could you overcome the problems that arise near the end of the tabulation?

Section 3.4

15. (a) Derive the identities

(i) $\displaystyle\sum_{k=0}^{m} (-1)^k \binom{m}{k} = 0$ (ii) $\displaystyle\binom{r}{m}\binom{m}{k} = \binom{r-k}{m-k}\binom{r}{k}.$

(b) Use these results to show that $\displaystyle\sum_{j=r}^{i} (-1)^{i-r} \binom{i}{j}\binom{j}{r}$ vanishes and thus deduce that the right-hand side of (3.4-1) is f_i.

16. (a) Use the results of Prob. 10 to express Newton's backward formula in terms of backward differences at a_0.

(b) Similarly, express Gauss's forward and backward formulas in terms of central differences at a_0.

(c) Using the notation $\mu\delta^{2m+1}f_0 = \frac{1}{2}(\delta^{2m+1}f_{\frac{1}{2}} + \delta^{2m+1}f_{-\frac{1}{2}})$ express Stirling's and Bessel's formulas in terms of central differences.

17. (a) Show that in any finite-difference interpolation formula a difference of any order can be eliminated by using the relation $\delta^m f_{k+1} - \delta^m f_k = \delta^{m+1} f_k$ or a similar relation for forward and backward differences.

(b) Use this result and the result of Prob. 16b to eliminate the odd differences from Gauss's forward formula and thus derive *Everett's interpolation formula*

$$y(m) = (1 - m)f_0 + mf_1 - \frac{m(m-1)(m-2)}{3!} \delta^2 f_0$$
$$+ \frac{(m+1)(m)(m-1)}{6} \delta^2 f_1 + \cdots$$

(This formula is useful in interpolating in tables which provide auxiliary tables of *even* central differences.)

(*c*) Similarly, eliminate the even differences in Gauss's forward formula to get *Steffensen's interpolation formula*

$$y(m) = f_0 + \frac{(m+1)m}{2!} \delta f_{\frac{1}{2}} - \frac{m(m-1)}{2} \delta f_{-\frac{1}{2}}$$
$$+ \frac{(m+2)(m+1)m(m-1)}{4!} \delta^3 f_{\frac{1}{2}} - \cdots$$

[Ref.: Hildebrand (1956), pp. 103–105, or Kopal (1955), pp. 50–54.]

*18. Throwback. (*a*) Use the result of Prob. 16*c* to show that the ratio of the coefficient B_4 of the fourth central difference in Bessel's formula to the coefficient B_2 of the second difference is $(m+1)(m-2)/12$ and that for $0 \leq m \leq 1$ this ratio varies between $-\frac{1}{6}$ and $-\frac{3}{16}$.

(*b*) Because this ratio varies very little on this interval, consider replacing B_4 by cB_2. Show that $B_4 - cB_2$ as a function of m has a maximum independent of c and two minima dependent on c on $[0,1]$. Find the two values of c which equalize the minimum and maximum values of $B_4 - cB_2$ on this interval. Show that one of these values c_1 is very nearly equal to the average value of B_4/B_2 over $[0,1]$.

(*c*) Thus rewrite Bessel's formula as $y(m) = \frac{1}{2}(f_0 + f_1) + (m - \frac{1}{2})\delta f_{\frac{1}{2}} + B_2[\delta^2 f_0 + \delta^2 f_1 + c_1(\delta^4 f_0 + \delta^4 f_1)]$. This procedure is called throwback; that is, we have "thrown back" the effect of the fourth difference onto the second difference. [Ref.: Kopal (1955), pp. 54–56.]

19. (*a*) Display the error terms for the Newtonian and Gaussian interpolation formulas terminated with the difference of order k in terms of h and m.

(*b*) Use these to derive the error terms for Stirling's and Bessel's formulas terminated with an odd or even difference.

Section 3.5

20. (*a*) What abscissas are involved in the calculation of each entry in the table in Example 3.5 for both the Gaussian and Newtonian formulas?

(*b*) Verify that the actual error using six differences is consistent with that calculated using the result of Prob. 19*a*.

21. (*a*) How many terms in Gauss's forward formula can be used if x_0 is (i) the next to last entry in a table; (ii) the fourth entry?

(*b*) Use (3.4-7) and (3.4-8) to show that, when m is near zero, Stirling's formula is a desirable one to use and that, when m is near one-half, Bessel's formula is desirable.

*22. (*a*) If h is fixed, show that in the limit as $n \to \infty$ Newton's forward formula, if it converges, becomes with $a_0 = 0$

$$f(x) = f_0 + \sum_{j=1}^{\infty} \frac{\Delta^j f_0}{j! h^j} x(x - h) \cdots [x - (j - 1)h]$$

(*b*) For $f(x) = e^{ax}$ and $a_0 = 0$, show that $\Delta^r f_0 = (e^{ah} - 1)^r$.

(*c*) By using the result of part *b* in part *a*, show that the ratio of the $k + 1$ and k terms of the series is given by

$$\frac{e^{ah} - 1}{h(k + 1)} (x - kh)$$

(*d*) By considering this ratio as $k \to \infty$, deduce that the series in part *a* converges if $e^{ah} < 2$ and diverges if $e^{ah} > 2$ unless x is a positive integral multiple of h, in which case it converges.   (A more difficult result is that for $e^{ah} = 2$ the series converges if and only if $x > -h$.)

(e) Thus deduce that Newton's forward formula is an asymptotic series for e^{ax} when $e^{ah} > 2$.   Contrast this with the convergence of the Taylor series for e^{ax} for all ax.   In practice, why would we expect Newton's formula to be asymptotic even when $e^{ah} < 2$?   [Ref.: Hildebrand (1956), pp. 114–116.]

23. Suppose you have a table of sin x at an interval $h = .1$.   How many tabular points would have to be used in interpolating in this table to assure a truncation error of less than (a) 10^{-3}; (b) 10^{-4}; (c) 10^{-5}; independent of a_0 and m?

24. Use the data of Prob. 6 and a finite-difference interpolation formula to approximate (a) $J_p(2.07)$, (b) $J_p(2.405)$, (c) $J_p(2.64)$, (d) $J_p(2.91)$, with $p = 0, 1, 2$. In each case motivate your choice of a particular interpolation formula and compare the results with those of Prob. 7.

*25. Divided differences.   The divided difference of order $k > 1$ of $f(x)$ is defined by

$$f[a_1, \ldots, a_k] = \frac{f[a_2, \ldots, a_k] - f[a_1, \ldots, a_{k-1}]}{a_k - a_1}$$

with $f[a_1] = f(a_1)$.

(a) Prove that

$$f[a_1, \ldots, a_k] = \sum_{i=1}^{k} \frac{f(a_i)}{(a_i - a_1) \cdots (a_i - a_{i-1})(a_i - a_{i+1}) \cdots (a_i - a_k)}$$

and thus deduce that the order of the arguments in a divided difference is immaterial.

(b) Use the data of Example 3.1 to generate a divided-difference table analogous to the difference table of Fig. 3.1.

(c) Show that

$$f[a_1, \ldots, a_{k-1}, x] = f[a_1, \ldots, a_k] + (x - a_k)f[a_1, \ldots, a_k, x]$$

and use this result to derive the formula

$$f(x) = f[a_1] + (x - a_1)f[a_1, a_2] + (x - a_1)(x - a_2)f[a_1, a_2, a_3]$$
$$+ \cdots + (x - a_1)(x - a_2) \cdots (x - a_{n-1})f[a_1, \ldots, a_n] + E(x)$$

where

$$E(x) = p_n(x)f[a_1, \ldots, a_n, x]$$

This formula is called *Newton's divided-difference interpolation formula*.

(d) Deduce from part c that $(x - a_k)f[a_1, \ldots, a_n, x] \to 0$ as $x \to a_k$, $k = 1$, $\ldots, n$.

(e) Use this result to show that this formula must be algebraically equivalent to the Lagrangian interpolation formula which uses the tabular points $a_1, \ldots, a_n$. Thus deduce that

$$f[a_1, \ldots, a_n, x] = \frac{1}{n!} f^{(n)}(\xi)$$

where ξ is in the interval spanned by $a_1, \ldots, a_n$ and x.

(f) Use the results of parts c and e to show that when $a_i \to a$, $i = 1, \ldots, n$ the Newton divided-difference formula and, therefore, the Lagrangian formula are both equivalent to a Taylor series with remainder.

(*g*) Use Newton's divided-difference formula and the table of part *b* to approximate ln .60.   Compare the result with Example 3.1.

(*h*) When the tabular points are equally spaced, show that

$$f[a_1, \ldots, a_k] = \frac{1}{(k-1)!h^{k-1}} \Delta^{k-1} f_1$$

and thus use part *c* to derive Newton's forward formula.

Section 3.6

26. (*a*) Show that the table of (3.6-2) can be replaced by the symmetrical arrangement

$$
\begin{array}{cccccccc}
a_1 & a_1 - x & y_1(x) \\
\cdot & \cdot & \cdot \\
 & & & y_{12}(x) \\
\cdot & \cdot & \cdot & & y_{123}(x) \\
 & & & y_{23}(x) \\
\cdot & \cdot & \cdot & \cdot & & \cdot \\
\cdot & \cdot & \cdot & & \cdot \\
\cdot & & & \cdot & & \cdot & & y_{1,2,\ldots,n}(x) \\
\cdot & \cdot & & & \cdot & & \cdot \\
\cdot & \cdot & \cdot & & \cdot \\
\cdot & \cdot & \cdot & & y_{n-2,n-1,n}(x) \\
\cdot & \cdot & \cdot & y_{n-1,n}(x) \\
a_n & a_n - x & y_n(x)
\end{array}
$$

What would the additional entries to the table be if the point a_{n+1} were used?

(*b*) Use the technique of part *a* to do the computation of Example 3.6.   [Ref.: Neville (1934).]

27. Use iterated interpolation to do the calculations of parts *a* and *b* of Prob. 7. Compare the results with those of Probs. 7 and 24.

28. *Interpolation near a singularity.*   Suppose you are given a tabulation of sine, cosine, and tangent as follows:

x	$\sin x$	$\cos x$	$\tan x$
1.566	.9999885	.0047963	208.49128
1.567	.9999928	.0037963	263.41125
1.568	.9999961	.0027963	357.61106
1.569	.9999984	.0017963	556.69098
1.570	.9999997	.0007963	1255.76559

Using these data and any interpolation formula, calculate tan (1.5695) by (*a*) using the tan *x* tabulation directly; (*b*) calculating sin (1.5695) and cos (1.5695).   Discuss the reasons for the varying errors in the two results.   [Ref.: Kopal (1955), p. 84.]

Section 3.7

29. Use the data of Prob. 6 and inverse interpolation to approximate the zero of $J_0(x)$ between 2 and 3 (cf. Prob. 7*b*).

30. *Inverse interpolation near a singularity.*   Suppose we wished to calculate that value of *x* for which sin *x* = .9999950 using the data of Prob. 28.   Why will the procedure of Sec. 3.7 not work here?   To solve this problem, do the following:

(a) Obtain an initial approximation $\bar{x}$ to x by linear inverse interpolation between $x_1 = 1.567$ and $x_2 = 1.568$.

(b) By direct interpolation, compute $\sin \bar{x}$.

If $\sin \bar{x} < .9999950$, replace x_1 by $\bar{x}$ and repeat this procedure. Otherwise, replace x_2 by $\bar{x}$. Continue until the process converges. What condition must $\sin x$ satisfy on $[x_1, x_2]$ in order for the process to converge?

Section 3.8

31. Derive Eqs. (3.8-10).

32. Use the data of Prob. 6 and Hermite interpolation to do the computation of parts a and b of Prob. 7 for $p = 0$. Compare with the previous results. Can the use of the Hermite interpolation formula be simplified for equally spaced data in a fashion analogous to that for the Lagrangian formula in Sec. 3.3-1?

Section 3.9

33. (a) Verify that, when Eqs. (3.9-3) and (3.9-4) are solved for $y(x)$, the results are, respectively, the Lagrangian and Hermite interpolation formulas.

(b) Similarly, show that $y(x)$ given by (3.9-5) is such that $y(x)$ and its first r_i derivatives agree with $f(x)$ at a_i, $i = 1, \ldots , n$.

34. (a) Show that the value of the *Vandermonde* determinant

$$\Delta(a_1, \ldots ,a_n) = \begin{vmatrix} 1 & a_1 & \cdots & a_1^{n-1} \\ 1 & a_2 & \cdots & a_2^{n-1} \\ 1 & \cdot & & \cdot \\ \cdots\cdots\cdots\cdots\cdots \\ 1 & a_n & \cdots & a_n^{n-1} \end{vmatrix}$$

contains all factors of the form $(a_j - a_i)$, $i \neq j$.

(b) By showing that there are $n(n - 1)/2$ such factors and that the determinant is a polynomial of this degree in the variables $a_1, \ldots , a_n$, deduce that

$$\Delta = \prod_{j>i=1}^{n} (a_j - a_i)$$

*35. (a) Use the result of the previous problem to derive the form of $l_j(x)$ directly from (3.9-3). Deduce that the minor of $y(x)$ in (3.9-3) does not vanish if the tabular points are distinct.

(b) Show directly that the minor of $y(x)$ in (3.9-4) does not vanish if the tabular points are distinct.

(c) Generalize this result to show that the minor of $y(x)$ in (3.9-5) does not vanish if the tabular points are distinct.

36. (a) Let $f(x)$ have zeros x_i, $i = 1, \ldots , n$ of multiplicity ν_i, $i = 1, \ldots , n$ in an interval (a,b). Let $\nu = \sum_{i=1}^{n} \nu_i$. Prove that $f^{(k)}(x)$ has at least $\nu - k$ zeros in (a,b).

(b) Use this result and a technique similar to that used to derive the Lagrangian and Hermite interpolation formula errors to derive (3.9-6).

37. (a) Write the determinantal form for an interpolation polynomial $y(x)$ which at the n tabular points is to have the same value and same second derivative as the function $f(x)$ (but not necessarily the same first derivative).

(b) Show that, for $n = 3$ and $a_1 = -1$, $a_2 = 0$, $a_3 = 1$, the minor of y in this determinant vanishes identically.   Thus deduce that there is no quintic polynomial satisfying the desired conditions.   [Ref.: Hamming (1962), p. 94.]

Section 3.10

38. Suppose it is desired to approximate $f(x)$ in the form

$$f(x) \approx \sum_{i=1}^{n} c_i e^{a_i x} = \sum_{i=1}^{n} c_i u_i^x \qquad (u_i = e^{a_i})$$

(a) If the approximation is to be exact at the n equally spaced points, 0, 1, . . . , $n - 1$, write down the n equations for the c_i's (assuming the u_i's are known).

(b) Given the data

$$x: \qquad 0 \qquad\quad 1 \qquad\quad 2$$
$$f(x): \quad 2.4400 \quad 2.0851 \quad 2.1958$$

use the results of part a to find the coefficients of an exponential approximation with $a_1 = 0$, $a_2 = -1$, $a_3 = -2$.   [Ref.: Hildebrand (1956), p. 380.]

39. Interpolation of functions of two variables.   Suppose we are given a function of two variables $f(x,y)$ tabulated at points (a_i, b_j), $i = 1, . . . , n$, $j = 1, . . . , m$.

(a) If we wish to approximate $f(x,y)$ at a nontabular point, show that we can do this by first interpolating to find $f(x,b_j)$ for a sequence of values of j and then using these values to interpolate to find $f(x,y)$ or vice versa.

(b) Given the table of values of the elliptic integral

$$E(x,y) = \int_0^y (1 - \sin^2 x \sin^2 t)^{1/2} \, dt$$

x \ y	50°	54°	58°	62°
50°	0.8134	0.8060	0.7988	0.7920
52°	0.8414	0.8332	0.8251	0.8174
54°	0.8690	0.8598	0.8508	0.8422
56°	0.8962	0.8859	0.8759	0.8663

find an approximation to $E(55.4°, 53.1°)$ by (i) interpolating horizontally to find $E(55.4°, y)$ for $y = 50°$, 52°, 54°, 56° and then interpolating vertically; (ii) interpolating vertically and then horizontally.   If the desired point lies on a diagonal [e.g., $(52°, 51°)$], how could the interpolation procedure be simplified?   [Ref.: Hildebrand (1956), p. 125.]

chapter 4

NUMERICAL DIFFERENTIATION, NUMERICAL QUADRATURE, AND SUMMATION

4.1 NUMERICAL DIFFERENTIATION FORMULAS

The form of the general numerical differentiation operator is

$$L[f(x)] = f^{(k)}(x) + \sum_{i=0}^{m} \sum_{j=1}^{n} A_{ij}(x) f^{(i)}(a_{ij}) \tag{4.1-1}$$

where at least one $A_{0j}(x) \neq 0$. In this section we shall restrict ourselves to the case $m = 0$ since this is by far the most important case in practice. Implicit in this and the following sections on numerical differentiation is the existence and, where necessary, continuity of as many derivatives of $f(x)$ as we require.

Our basic approach in deriving numerical differentiation formulas will be to differentiate the interpolation formulas of the previous chapter. If we differentiate the Lagrangian interpolation formula (3.1-5) k times, we get

$$f^{(k)}(x) = \sum_{j=1}^{n} l_j^{(k)}(x) f(a_j) + \frac{d^k}{dx^k} \left[\frac{p_n(x)}{n!} f^{(n)}(\xi) \right] = y^{(k)}(x) + \frac{d^k}{dx^k} [E(x)] \tag{4.1-2}$$

In particular, for $k = 1$ we have

$$f'(x) = \sum_{j=1}^{n} l_j'(x) f(a_j) + \frac{d}{dx} \left[\frac{p_n(x)}{n!} f^{(n)}(\xi) \right] \tag{4.1-3}$$

where the derivative of $l_j(x)$ is easily calculated using (3.2-4).   Determination of the error term in (4.1-2) or (4.1-3) presents a problem because ξ is an unknown function of x (see Sec. 3.2).   Nevertheless, we can prove the following

Theorem 4.1   Let $p_n(x)f^{(n)}(\xi)/n!$ be the error term in the Lagrangian interpolation formula with ξ in the interval spanned by $a_1, \ldots, a_n$ and x.   Then, if $f^{(nH)}(x)$ is continuous,

$$\frac{1}{n!}\frac{d}{dx}f^{(n)}(\xi) = \frac{1}{(n+1)!}f^{(n+1)}(\eta) \tag{4.1-4}$$

where η is also in the interval spanned by $a_1, \ldots, a_n$ and x.

Proof   If we take the Lagrangian interpolation formula (3.1-5) with $x \neq a_j, j = 1, \ldots, n$, divide both sides by $p_n(x)$, and differentiate, we get, using (3.2-4),

$$\frac{d}{dx}\frac{f(x)}{p_n(x)} = \sum_{j=1}^{n} \frac{f(a_j)}{-(x-a_j)^2 p_n'(a_j)} + \frac{1}{n!}\frac{d}{dx}[f^{(n)}(\xi)] \tag{4.1-5}$$

Now consider (3.1-5) with n replaced by $n+1$.   We have

$$p_{n+1}(x) = p_n(x)(x - a_{n+1})$$
$$p_{n+1}'(a_j) = \begin{cases} (a_j - a_{n+1})p_n'(a_j) & j \neq n+1 \\ p_n(a_{n+1}) & j = n+1 \end{cases} \tag{4.1-6}$$

Dividing (3.1-5) by $p_{n+1}(x)$, rearranging terms, and using (4.1-6), we may write

$$\frac{[f(x)/p_n(x)] - [f(a_{n+1})/p_n(a_{n+1})]}{x - a_{n+1}}$$
$$= \sum_{j=1}^{n} \frac{f(a_j)}{(x-a_j)(a_j - a_{n+1})p_n'(a_j)} + \frac{f^{(n+1)}(\tau)}{(n+1)!} \tag{4.1-7}$$

where τ is in the interval spanned by $a_1, \ldots, a_{n+1}$ and x.   Now take the limit of both sides of (4.1-7) as $a_{n+1} \to x$.   We get

$$\frac{d}{dx}\frac{f(x)}{p_n(x)} = \sum_{j=1}^{n} \frac{f(a_j)}{-(x-a_j)^2 p_n'(a_j)} + \frac{f^{(n+1)}(\eta)}{(n+1)!} \tag{4.1-8}$$

where η is in the interval spanned by $a_1, \ldots, a_n$ and x.   Comparing (4.1-5) and (4.1-8), the theorem is proved when $x \neq a_j$.   But using the continuity of the derivatives, (4.1-4) must be true for any x.

By an extension of this argument, we may prove that {1}

$$\frac{1}{n!} \frac{d^j}{dx^j} f^{(n)}(\xi) = \frac{j!}{(n+j)!} f^{(n+j)}(\eta_j) \tag{4.1-9}$$

with η_j in the interval spanned by $a_1, \ldots, a_n$ and x. Using the result of this theorem and Leibniz's rule, we may write the error term in (4.1-2) as

$$\frac{d^k}{dx^k} \left[\frac{p_n(x)}{n!} f^{(n)}(\xi) \right] = \sum_{i=0}^{k} \frac{k!}{i!} p_n^{(i)}(x) \frac{f^{(n+k-i)}(\eta_{k-i})}{(n+k-i)!} \tag{4.1-10}$$

and, in particular, for (4.1-3)

$$\frac{d}{dx} \left[\frac{p_n(x)}{n!} f^{(n)}(\xi) \right] = \frac{p_n(x)}{(n+1)!} f^{(n+1)}(\eta_1) + \frac{p_n'(x)}{n!} f^{(n)}(\eta_0) \tag{4.1-11}$$

From (4.1-11) we note that, if we are estimating the derivative at a tabular point, then the first term on the right-hand side is zero. This means in effect that *the derivative at a tabular point can be calculated by differentiating the Lagrangian formula while considering ξ to be a constant.* By using a technique similar to that used to derive the error in the Lagrangian formula in Sec. 3.2, we may also show that, if x is outside or at an end point of the interval spanned by $a_1, \ldots, a_n$, then the error may again be written by dropping the first term on the right-hand side of (4.1-11) {1} (and, in general, changing η_0 to some other value in the interval spanned by $a_1, \ldots, a_n$ and x).

When the tabular points are equally spaced, $y^{(k)}(x)$ in (4.1-2) becomes

$$y^{(k)}(x) = \frac{1}{h^k} \sum_{j=1}^{n} l_j^{(k)}(m) f(a_j) \qquad x = a_0 + hm \tag{4.1-12}$$

where the differentiation of $l_j(m)$ is with respect to m, and we have used the fact that

$$\frac{dy}{dx} = \frac{dy}{dm} \frac{dm}{dx} = \frac{1}{h} \frac{dy}{dm} \tag{4.1-13}$$

In a similar fashion, we may differentiate the interpolation formulas expressed in difference form. For example, if we differentiate Newton's forward formula (3.3-11), we get

$$\frac{d^k}{dx^k} y(a_0 + hm) = \frac{1}{h^k} \frac{d^k}{dm^k} y(a_0 + hm)$$

$$= \frac{1}{h^k} \sum_{j=0}^{n} \frac{d^k}{dm^k} \binom{m}{j} \Delta^j f_0 = \frac{1}{h^k} \sum_{j=k}^{n} \frac{d^k}{dm^k} \binom{m}{j} \Delta^j f_0 \tag{4.1-14}$$

Similar equations can clearly be written down for the other finite-difference interpolation formulas {2}. For the particular case $m = 0$, we may write (4.1-14) as

$$\frac{d^k}{dx^k} y(a_0) = \frac{k!}{h^k} \sum_{j=k}^n \frac{S_j^{(k)}}{j!} \Delta^j f_0 \qquad (4.1\text{-}15)$$

The $S_j^{(k)}$ are called *Stirling numbers of the first kind*. Some of their properties are considered in {4}.

More general numerical differentiation formulas can be found by differentiating the general interpolation formula (3.9-5), but as we have mentioned, it is seldom useful to have numerical differentiation formulas which depend on derivatives of the function.

4.2 COMPUTING DERIVATIVES NUMERICALLY

Superficially, there would seem to be no more difficulty to computing derivatives using the formulas of the previous section than there was in using the interpolation formulas of the previous chapter. But a closer look indicates that roundoff error, while often not significant in using interpolation formulas, is not only significant but can be disastrous in numerical differentiation. In this section we shall consider numerical differentiation using the Lagrangian interpolation formula for equally spaced data, but this discussion may easily be extended to finite-difference differentiation formulas.

The roundoff error $R(x)$ incurred in using the Lagrangian interpolation formula (3.3-3) can be bounded by

$$|R(x)| \leqq (5 \times 10^{-r-1}) \sum_{j=1}^n |l_j(m)| \qquad (4.2\text{-}1)$$

if the functional values are all correctly rounded to r decimal places. Moreover, as Table 3.1 indicates, the values of $l_j(m)$ never get much larger than 1 for reasonably small n. Thus for such values of n the roundoff error will affect only the last significant digit (i.e., the rth decimal). Contrast this, however, with Eq. (4.1-12). Computing with this formula, the roundoff error $R_k(x)$ can only be bounded by

$$|R_k(x)| \leqq \frac{5 \times 10^{-r-1}}{h^k} \sum_{j=1}^n |l_j^{(k)}(m)| \qquad (4.2\text{-}2)$$

Clearly, if h is small, the roundoff can be very large. Now for equally spaced points, each term of the truncation error contains a power of h, as can be seen using Eqs. (4.1-10) and (4.1-13). Thus, whereas in interpolation truncation error is proportional to a power of h and roundoff error *does not depend* on h, in numerical differentiation, truncation error is proportional and roundoff error is inversely proportional to a power of h. A small value of h then causes a large magnification of the roundoff error inherent in the functional values,† and a large value causes a large truncation error. This suggests the problem we now consider of finding the optimal value of h when numerically differentiating at equal intervals.

In particular, let us consider this question when the first derivative at a tabular point is desired. Then the first term on the right-hand side of (4.1-11) is zero, and we have for the truncation error

$$E_1(x) = [p'_n(x)/n!]f^{(n)}(\eta_0) \tag{4.2-3}$$

Now, using (3.3-4) and (4.1-13), we may write

$$p'_n(x) = h^{n-1}p'_n(m) \tag{4.2-4}$$

so that

$$E_1(x) = h^{n-1}[p'_n(m)/n!]f^{(n)}(\eta_0) = h^{n-1}e_1(x) \tag{4.2-5}$$

where $e_1(x)$ does not depend on h. Similarly, we may write for the roundoff error

$$R_1(x) = (1/h)r_1(x) \tag{4.2-6}$$

where $r_1(x)$ also does not depend on h. A convenient way to define the optimal value of h (see {6} for another) is to choose that value which makes the bounds on the magnitudes of $E_1(x)$ and $R_1(x)$ equal. This will lead to an accurate optimum only when the two bounds are equally good. Nevertheless, this approach is defensible since we are really only looking for a reasonable value of h.

We have

$$e_1(x) \leqq [p'_n(m)/n!]M_n \tag{4.2-7}$$

where M_n is such that

$$|f^{(n)}(\xi)| \leqq M_n \tag{4.2-8}$$

for ξ in the interval spanned by the tabular points and x. Similarly

$$|r_1(x)| \leqq \epsilon \sum_{j=1}^{n} |l'_j(m)| \tag{4.2-9}$$

where ϵ is the magnitude of the maximum roundoff error in each value of

† Because the factor $1/h^k$ causes a magnification of the roundoff error or, in engineering parlance, the "noise" in the functional values, numerical differentiation is often called a noise-magnification process.

$f(a_j)$ [$5 \times 10^{-r-1}$ in (4.2-2)]. Using (4.2-7) and (4.2-9) to equate the bounds on the roundoff and truncation errors, we get

$$h^{n-1} \frac{p_n'(m)}{n!} M_n = \frac{\epsilon}{h} \sum_{j=1}^{n} |l_j'(m)| \tag{4.2-10}$$

so that the optimal value of h is given by

$$h_{\text{opt}} = \left[\frac{\epsilon n! \sum_{j=1}^{n} |l_j'(m)|}{M_n |p_n'(m)|} \right]^{1/n} \tag{4.2-11}$$

This, of course, determines a different h_{opt} for each m, which is clearly inconvenient. Since commonly we are most interested in the derivative at the central point of an odd number of tabular points, we set

$$m = (n + 1)/2$$

in (4.2-11). But then it is convenient to renumber the tabular points as $a_{(-n+1)/2}, \ldots, a_0, \ldots, a_{(n-1)/2}$. Doing this, (4.2-11) becomes

$$h_{\text{opt}} = \left[\frac{\epsilon n! \sum_{j=-(n-1)/2}^{(n-1)/2} |l_j'(0)|}{M_n |p_n'(0)|} \right]^{1/n} \tag{4.2-12}$$

Using the definition of $l_j(m)$ and (3.3-4), we may show that {6}

$$\sum_{j=-(n-1)/2}^{(n-1)/2} |l_j'(0)| = 2|p_n'(0)| \sum_{j=1}^{(n-1)/2} \frac{1}{|p_n'(j)|j} \tag{4.2-13}$$

so that

$$h_{\text{opt}} = \left[\frac{2\epsilon n!}{M_n} \sum_{j=1}^{(n-1)/2} \frac{1}{|p_n'(j)|j} \right]^{1/n} \tag{4.2-14}$$

Example 4.1   With $n = 3$, find h_{opt} and expressions for the derivatives at the tabular points.

From (4.2-14)

$$h_{\text{opt}} = \left[\frac{12\epsilon}{M_3} \frac{1}{|p_3'(1)|} \right]^{1/3} = \left[\frac{6\epsilon}{M_3} \right]^{1/3} \tag{4.2-15}$$

Then, using (4.1-12) with the tabular points renumbered, $k = 1$, and the error term given by (4.1-11), we get

$$\begin{aligned}
f_{-1}' &= (1/2h)(-3f_{-1} + 4f_0 - f_1) + (h^2/3)f'''(\eta_{-1}) \\
f_0' &= (1/2h)(-f_{-1} + f_1) - (h^2/6)f'''(\eta_0) \\
f_1' &= (1/2h)(f_{-1} - 4f_0 + 3f_1) + (h^2/3)f'''(\eta_1)
\end{aligned} \tag{4.2-16}$$

If the h used is h_{opt}, then the truncation error in f_0' is bounded by

$$\left(\frac{6\epsilon}{M_3}\right)^{2/3}\frac{M_3}{6} = \epsilon^{2/3}\left(\frac{M_3}{6}\right)^{1/3} \tag{4.2-17}$$

and the roundoff error is bounded by

$$\frac{\epsilon}{\left(\frac{M_3}{6\epsilon}\right)^{1/3}} = \epsilon^{2/3}\left(\frac{M_3}{6}\right)^{1/3} \tag{4.2-18}$$

Thus the total error T_3 is such that

$$|T_3| \leq 2\epsilon^{2/3}\left(\frac{M_3}{6}\right)^{1/3}$$

Similar bounds could be derived for the errors in f_{-1}' and f_1'. The case $n = 5$ is considered in {8}.

In practice, we shall generally have empirical data of an unknown function and shall want to estimate the derivative at one of the tabular points. It will then be necessary to estimate M_n to get h_{opt}. Note, however, that the value of h we can use is restricted by the tabular data we are given. The following example indicates how one might calculate the derivative of a tabulated function.

Example 4.2   Given a three-place table of values of $\ln x$ at an interval of .01, find the derivative of $\ln x$ at $x = .5$ using (4.2-16).

Until we have chosen h, we do not know the range over which to estimate M_3. But suppose we estimate M_3 to be 15 in the range of interest (is this reasonable?). Since $\epsilon = 5 \times 10^{-4}$ in a three-place table, we have from (4.2-15)

$$h_{\text{opt}} = \left(\frac{6\epsilon}{M_3}\right)^{1/3} \approx 5.85 \times 10^{-2}$$

A practical value of h to choose is therefore .05. Thus we use the data

x	$\ln x$
.45	$-.799$
.55	$-.598$

and (4.2-16) to calculate

$$f_0' = \frac{1}{.1}(.799 - .598) = 2.01$$

whereas the true value is, of course, 2. The error bound (which is only approximate since we did not use h_{opt}) is

$$|T_3| \leq 2 \times (5 \times 10^{-4})^{2/3}(8/3)^{1/3} \approx 1.7 \times 10^{-2}$$

When empirical data are being differentiated even three-place accuracy may not be available. Thus the $1/2h$ factor in (4.2-16) may cause serious roundoff. If the magnitude of the derivative in the truncation error is such that h cannot be increased without making the truncation error unduly large, then determining the derivative with a reasonable degree of accuracy may be impossible.   When higher derivatives than the first are desired, the $1/h$ factor becomes a $1/h^k$ factor, where k is the order of the derivative, and the roundoff problem becomes just that much worse.

The calculation of derivatives numerically is then a hazardous operation, especially when dealing with low accuracy empirical data.   And even for high accuracy data, derivatives higher than the first are likely to have sizable errors.   A better approach to numerical differentiation than that considered here may be to first "smooth" the data and then to differentiate (cf. Chap. 6, especially Sec. 6.7).

4.3   APPROXIMATING DERIVATIVES WITH DIFFERENCES

The formulas of Sec. 4.1 enable us to express the derivatives of a function in terms of values of the function or differences of the function.   One obvious application of this is in the numerical solution of differential equations.   Consider the first-order ordinary differential equation

$$dz/dx = F(x,z) \qquad z(x_0) = z_0 \tag{4.3-1}$$

Using (4.1-14) with $k = 1$, $n = 1$, $a_0 = x_0$, and $m = 0$, we may approximate dz/dx at x_0 as

$$\left.\frac{dz}{dx}\right|_{x_0} \approx \frac{1}{h}\Delta z_0 = \frac{z_1 - z_0}{h} \tag{4.3-2}$$

Inserting (4.3-2) in (4.3-1), we get

$$z(x_1) = z(x_0) + hF(x_0,z_0) \tag{4.3-3}$$

which gives us an approximation to the solution of (4.3-1) at x_1.   Having this approximation at x_1, we could then approximate dz/dx at x_1 using (4.3-2) and then use (4.3-3) to get an approximation to the solution at x_2, etc.   By using more terms of (4.1-14), we could derive more sophisticated methods than (4.3-3).   The use of (4.1-11) would enable us to derive the errors inherent in such methods.   We shall not consider this matter further here because in Chap. 5 we shall approach the problem of the numerical solution of initial value problems of ordinary differential equations by a more general technique which subsumes all the methods derivable using difference techniques.

When dealing with partial differential equations,† however, replacing derivatives by differences lies at the heart of most methods for solving such equations.   Consider, for example, Poisson's equation

$$\partial^2 u/\partial x^2 + \partial^2 u/\partial y^2 = g(x,y) \tag{4.3-4}$$

† And with boundary value problems of ordinary differential equations.

with appropriate boundary conditions (which we shall not state) on the boundary B in Fig. 4.1. Now using (4.1-14) with $k = n = 2$ we get an approximation to the second derivative of $f(x)$ as

$$f''(a_0 + hm) \approx \frac{1}{h^2} \frac{d^2}{dm^2} \binom{m}{2} \Delta^2 f_0 = \frac{f_0 - 2f_1 + f_2}{h^2} \qquad (4.3\text{-}5)$$

This equation may also be used to approximate second partial derivatives of functions of several variables by holding all but one of the variables constant. To do this for Eq. (4.3-4), let us superimpose a square mesh on the region of Fig. 4.1. Then using (4.3-5) along the line $y = y_1$ with $a_0 = x_1$, we have

$$\left.\frac{\partial^2 u}{\partial x^2}\right|_{\substack{x = x_1 \\ y = y_1}} \approx \frac{u(x_0, y_1) - 2u(x_1, y_1) + u(x_2, y_1)}{h^2} \qquad (4.3\text{-}6)$$

Similarly, along $x = x_1$ with $a_0 = y_1$

$$\left.\frac{\partial^2 u}{\partial y^2}\right|_{\substack{x = x_1 \\ y = y_1}} \approx \frac{u(x_1, y_0) - 2u(x_1, y_1) + u(x_1, y_2)}{h^2} \qquad (4.3\text{-}7)$$

Therefore, at the point (x_1, y_1), we may approximate the partial differential

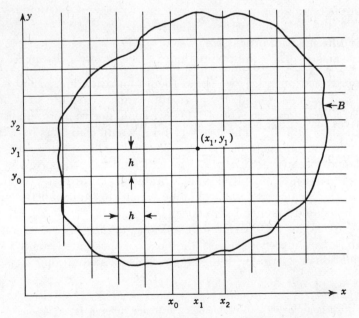

Fig. 4.1   Region in which solution of (4.3-4) is desired.

equation (4.3-4) by the equation

$$\frac{u(x_0,y_1) + u(x_2,y_1) + u(x_1,y_0) + u(x_1,y_2) - 4u(x_1,y_1)}{h^2} = g(x_1,y_1)$$

$$(4.3\text{-}8)$$

Using (4.1-10) the error in this approximation may be derived. An equation analogous to (4.3-8) may be written for every point interior to B by properly using the boundary conditions for points near B [for example, see Chap. 15 of Ralston and Wilf (1960)]. This leads to a system of *linear* equations for the unknowns $u(x_i,y_j)$ which can be solved by one of the methods of Chap. 9 to get an approximate solution to (4.3-4). Techniques very similar to this are the basis of many of the methods for the numerical solution of partial differential equations. A detailed discussion of the numerical solution of partial differential equations is beyond the scope of this book, but an understanding of the basic idea involved in approximating derivatives by differences plus a study of Chap. 9 will give the reader the necessary background for the study of this subject.

One further application of approximating derivatives by differences is in the estimation of error terms. Consider using (4.1-14) with $n = k$ to approximate the kth derivative of a function $f(x)$ at a point $a_0 + hm$. We have

$$f^{(k)}(a_0 + hm) \approx y^{(k)}(a_0 + hm) = \frac{1}{h^k}\frac{d^k}{dm^k}\binom{m}{k}\Delta^k f_0 = \frac{\Delta^k f_0}{h^k} \qquad (4.3\text{-}9)$$

Now this is certainly a very rough estimate in general, particularly if k is not small, but if the derivatives of order greater than k (and, therefore, also the differences of order greater than k) are well behaved, then (4.3-9) may give an acceptable approximation. Since the difficulty in estimating many of the error terms we have derived already and shall derive later lies in the difficulty in estimating some derivative of $f(x)$, Eq. (4.3-9) can, if used judiciously, enable estimates of error terms to be made when the derivatives of $f(x)$ are not reasonably calculable {9}.

4.4 NUMERICAL QUADRATURE—THE GENERAL PROBLEM

The form of the general numerical quadrature operator is

$$L[f(x)] = f(b) - f(a) + \sum_{j=1}^{n}\sum_{i=1}^{m} A_{ij}f^{(i)}(a_{ij}) \qquad (4.4\text{-}1)$$

If we substitute $\int_{-\infty}^{x} g(x)\,dx$ for $f(x)$ in (4.4-1), we get

$$L[f(x)] = L\left[\int_{-\infty}^{x} g(x)\,dx\right] = \int_{a}^{b} g(x)\,dx + \sum_{j=1}^{n}\sum_{i=1}^{m} A_{ij}g^{(i-1)}(a_{ij})$$

$$(4.4\text{-}2)$$

and the quadrature equation then becomes†

$$\int_a^b g(x)\ dx + \sum_{j=1}^{n} \sum_{i=1}^{m} A_{ij} g^{(i-1)}(a_{ij}) = E \qquad (4.4\text{-}3)$$

Setting $E = 0$ in (4.4-3) and solving for $\int_a^b g(x)\ dx$ then gives us an approximation to the definite integral of $g(x)$ as a linear combination of values of $g(x)$ and its derivatives. The numerical quadrature problem is to specify the A_{ij}'s and a_{ij}'s so that this approximation has desirable properties (i.e., achieves some desired accuracy).

Once again our approach will be that of exact polynomial approximation. That is, we shall attempt to choose the A_{ij}'s and a_{ij}'s so that E in (4.4-3) is zero when $g(x)$ is a polynomial of sufficiently low degree. We shall again restrict ourselves mainly to the case $m = 1$; that is, we shall try to express the integral as a linear combination of functional values alone as is done, for example, in the trapezoidal rule. This is by far the most important case both theoretically and practically. With the restriction $m = 1$, we may rewrite (4.4-3) after some obvious changes in notation as

$$\int_a^b f(x)\ dx = \sum_{j=1}^{n} H_j f(a_j) + E \qquad (4.4\text{-}4)$$

One equation of the form (4.4-4) can clearly be derived by integrating the Lagrangian interpolation formula (3.1-5). Without considering the details of this now, we can nevertheless see that, since the Lagrangian formula is exact for polynomials of degree $n - 1$ or less, then so will the formula resulting from its integration. This suggests the question: With no a priori restrictions on the "*abscissas*" a_j (such as that they be equally spaced) and the "*weights*" H_j, what is the highest-degree polynomial for which E in (4.4-4) can be made zero? We call the degree of this polynomial the *order of accuracy* of the formula. Since we have $2n$ constants at our disposal—n a_j's and n H_j's—we suspect that the answer is a polynomial of degree $2n - 1$. In the next section, we shall show that this is indeed the case.

We shall not explicitly consider the problem of evaluating the indefinite integral

$$y(x) = \int_{x_0}^{x} f(t)\ dt \qquad (4.4\text{-}5)$$

in this chapter. This problem is equivalent to solving the differential

---

† Here and in the remainder of this chapter, we shall generally denote the error by E instead of $E(x)$ because the variable x will not appear explicitly in the error term as it has previously.

equation

$$\frac{dy}{dx} = f(x) \qquad y(x_0) = 0 \tag{4.4-6}$$

and as such can be solved by the techniques of Chap. 5. For any specific value of x the methods of this chapter can, of course, be used to evaluate $y(x)$.

4.5 GAUSSIAN QUADRATURE

For now let us assume that a and b in (4.4-4) are finite. Then, if (4.4-4) is to be exact for polynomials of degree $2n - 1$ or less, we can get a set of $2n$ equations for the $2n$ unknown constants by substituting $f(x) = x^k$, $k = 0, 1, \ldots, 2n - 1$ into (4.4-4) and setting $E = 0$. We get

$$\alpha_k = \sum_{j=1}^{n} H_j a_j^k \qquad k = 0, \ldots, 2n - 1 \tag{4.5-1}$$

where

$$\alpha_k = \int_a^b x^k \, dx = \frac{b^{k+1} - a^{k+1}}{k + 1} \tag{4.5-2}$$

These nonlinear equations, if we can solve them and if the solution is real, will give us the abscissas and weights we desire. This algebraic approach to our problem is considered further in {10}, but we abandon it here in favor of an analytic approach which (1) will tell us without actually calculating the weights and abscissas whether or not they are real; (2) will enable us to determine E when $f(x)$ is not a polynomial of degree $2n - 1$ or less; (3) will enable us to show that the abscissas are in many cases the zeros of well-known polynomials. As we shall see, once the abscissas are known, the weights are easily calculable.

The starting point of our analytical approach is the Hermite interpolation formula (3.8-17)

$$f(x) = \sum_{j=1}^{n} h_j(x)f(a_j) + \sum_{j=1}^{n} \bar{h}_j(x)f'(a_j) + \frac{p_n^2(x)}{(2n)!} f^{(2n)}(\xi) \tag{4.5-3}$$

which is exact for polynomials of degree $2n - 1$ or less. Integrating (4.5-3) between a and b, we get

$$\int_a^b f(x) \, dx = \sum_{j=1}^{n} H_j f(a_j) + \sum_{j=1}^{n} \bar{H}_j f'(a_j) + E \tag{4.5-4}$$

where

$$H_j = \int_a^b h_j(x) \, dx \qquad \bar{H}_j = \int_a^b \bar{h}_j(x) \, dx \tag{4.5-5}$$

and

$$E = \int_a^b \frac{p_n^2(x)}{(2n)!} f^{(2n)}(\xi)\, dx \tag{4.5-6}$$

Since E is zero if $f(x)$ is a polynomial of degree $2n - 1$ or less, if we can choose the abscissas so that $\bar{H}_j = 0, j = 1, \ldots, n$, then (4.5-4) will have the form (4.4-4) with the desired properties. Thus $\bar{H}_j = 0, j = 1, \ldots, n$ is a sufficient condition to achieve our desired accuracy of order $2n - 1$. It is also necessary. To see this let $f(x) = h_j(x)$ in (4.4-4). If (4.4-4) is to have order $2n - 1$ then H_j in (4.4-4) must be given by H_j in (4.5-5) (why?). Therefore, since we have put no restrictions on the a_j's in (4.5-4), if we cannot find abscissas for which the $\bar{H}_j$'s are zero, then no formula of the type (4.4-4) with order of accuracy $2n - 1$ is possible.

Using (3.8-18) and (3.2-4), we have

$$\bar{H}_j = \int_a^b (x - a_j) l_j^2(x)\, dx = \int_a^b p_n(x) \frac{l_j(x)}{p_n'(a_j)}\, dx \tag{4.5-7}$$

Since $p_n(x)$ is a polynomial of degree n and $l_j(x)$ is a polynomial of degree $n - 1$, a sufficient condition for $\bar{H}_j = 0, j = 1, \ldots, n$ is for $p_n(x)$ to be *orthogonal* to all polynomials of degree $n - 1$ or less over $[a,b]$. This condition is also necessary; we leave the proof to a problem {11}. Without loss of generality, we may assume $[a,b] = [-1,1]$† in which case the orthogonal polynomial $p_n(x)$ is a multiple of $P_n(x)$, the Legendre polynomial of degree n. Since by definition $p_n(x)$ has leading coefficient 1, we have, using the standard definition of the Legendre polynomials {19},

$$p_n(x) = \frac{2^n (n!)^2}{(2n)!} P_n(x) \tag{4.5-8}$$

In the next section we shall prove that the zeros of the Legendre polynomial of any degree are real, so that this settles the question of the existence of real abscissas. The zeros of the Legendre polynomials have been tabulated for all values of n of practical interest (we shall see that large values of n are almost never desirable in practice); a short table of these zeros is given in Table 4.1.

To find the weights we again use Eqs. (3.8-18) and (3.2-4) to get

$$\begin{aligned} H_j &= \int_{-1}^1 h_j(x)\, dx = \int_{-1}^1 [1 - 2l_j'(a_j)(x - a_j)] l_j^2(x)\, dx \\ &= \int_{-1}^1 l_j^2(x)\, dx - 2l_j'(a_j) \int_{-1}^1 (x - a_j) l_j^2(x)\, dx \quad = 0 \ \ \text{for } n \leq 2 \\ &= \int_{-1}^1 l_j^2(x)\, dx \end{aligned} \tag{4.5-9}$$

† By the change of variable $y = [1/(b - a)](2x - a - b)$, the interval $[a,b]$ in x is replaced by the interval $[-1,1]$ in y.

Table 4.1   Zeros of Legendre polynomials and corresponding weights

n	Abscissas a_j	Weights H_j
2	$\pm 0.577350 = \pm \dfrac{1}{\sqrt{3}}$	1
3	0	$\tfrac{8}{9}$
	± 0.774597	$\tfrac{5}{9}$
4	± 0.339981	0.652145
	± 0.861136	0.347855
5	0	0.568889
	± 0.538469	0.478629
	± 0.906180	0.236927

since the second integral, which by definition is $\bar{H}_j$, is zero. From (4.5-9) it is obvious that the weights are all positive; see Table 4.1. A simpler expression for the weights may be found by considering (4.4-4) with $f(x) = l_k(x)$ and using the weights and abscissas found above. Since $l_k(x)$ is a polynomial of degree $n - 1$, E is zero and we have

$$\int_{-1}^{1} l_k(x)\, dx = \sum_{j=1}^{n} H_j l_k(a_j) = H_k \qquad (4.5\text{-}10)$$

since $l_k(a_j) = \delta_{kj}$. Together (4.5-9) and (4.5-10) imply

$$\int_{-1}^{1} l_j^2(x)\, dx = \int_{-1}^{1} l_j(x)\, dx \qquad (4.5\text{-}11)$$

The error term as given by (4.5-6) can be simplified using the mean-value theorem for integrals since $p_n^2(x)$ is always positive. Using $[-1,1]$ in place of $[a,b]$, we have

$$E = \frac{f^{(2n)}(\eta)}{(2n)!} \int_{-1}^{1} p_n^2(x)\, dx \qquad (4.5\text{-}12)$$

where η lies in $(-1,1)$.

Any quadrature formula whose abscissas and weights are subject to no constraints and which are determined so as to achieve a maximum order of accuracy is called a *Gaussian quadrature formula*. In particular, (4.4-4) with the abscissas given as the zeros of the Legendre polynomial of degree n and the weights by (4.5-10) is called a *Legendre-Gauss quadrature formula*.

Example 4.3   Evaluate

$$\int_1^3 \frac{dx}{x}$$

using Legendre-Gauss quadrature with $n = 3$.

With the change of variable $y = x - 2$, the integral becomes

$$\int_{-1}^1 \frac{dy}{y + 2}$$

Using Table 4.1 with $n = 3$, we have

$$\int_{-1}^1 \frac{dy}{y + 2} \approx \frac{5}{9} \frac{1}{1.225403} + \frac{8}{9} \times \frac{1}{2} + \frac{5}{9} \frac{1}{2.774597} \approx 1.098039$$

whereas the true value of the integral is $\ln 3 = 1.098612$. From Eq. (4.5-12), we have

$$E = \frac{f^{vi}(\eta)}{6!} \int_{-1}^1 p_3^2(x) \, dx$$

Using (4.5-8) and anticipating some results from Sec. 4.7 [see (4.7-10)], we have

$$\int_{-1}^1 p_3^2(x) \, dx = \frac{4}{25} \int_{-1}^1 P_3^2(x) \, dx = \frac{8}{175}$$

so that

$$E = \frac{1}{15,750} \times \frac{6!}{(\eta + 2)^7} = \frac{8}{175} \frac{1}{(\eta + 2)^7}$$

Thus

$$.000021 \approx \frac{8}{175} \times \frac{1}{(3)^7} < E < \frac{8}{175} \approx .045714$$

and the actual error is indeed within these bounds.

Gaussian quadrature formulas were seldom used in practice before the advent of digital computers. This was because the use of "simple" numbers (i.e., integers and rational numbers) is much more convenient on desk calculators than the nonsimple numbers which generally must be used in Gaussian quadrature calculations (cf. Table 4.1). For example, when using desk calculators, functions are often evaluated by table lookup, in which case simple values of the abscissas may mean that no interpolation is required. But on digital computers, functions are almost always evaluated using a rational or polynomial approximation of the type to be discussed in Chap. 7. In this case whether or not the numbers are simple generally makes no difference. On digital computers, therefore, the Gaussian quadrature formulas discussed in this section and to be discussed in the next five sections are practical for certain problems. In Sec. 4.13 we shall discuss the general problem of choosing a quadrature formula for a specific application.

4.6 WEIGHT FUNCTIONS

In this section we shall generalize the ideas of the previous section by considering in place of (4.4-4)

$$\int_a^b w(x)f(x)\,dx = \sum_{j=1}^n H_jf(a_j) + E \tag{4.6-1}$$

where $w(x)$, the *weight function*, does not appear on the right-hand side of (4.6-1). That it is not artificial to separate the integrand into two functions $w(x)$ and $f(x)$ is borne out by (1) the not uncommon need to evaluate the coefficients in an orthogonal polynomial expansion; (2) the frequency with which some functions appear in integrands, particularly when dealing with integrals over infinite intervals (see Sec. 4.8).

The advantages of the formulation (4.6-1) are also twofold: (1) Computationally it will generally be easier to evaluate $f(a_j)$ than $w(a_j)f(a_j)$. (2) It is often convenient to express the error term in terms of a derivative of $f(x)$ only, especially when the weight function or one of its derivatives is unbounded in the interval.

It is, of course, possible to treat *any* numerical quadrature problem in the form (4.6-1). That is, we can always consider splitting the integrand up into the product of two functions. But since, as we shall see below, the abscissas and weights are functions of $w(x)$, this would necessitate the evaluation of the weights and abscissas for each problem. Thus we shall consider only those weight functions which are practically or mathematically significant. Furthermore, as we shall also see below, it is important that $w(x)$ be of constant sign in $[a,b]$.

The evaluation of the weights and abscissas in the more general Gaussian quadrature formula (4.6-1) is again quite straightforward if we make use of the Hermite interpolation formula. This time we merely multiply (3.8-17) by $w(x)$ before integrating and obtain in this way

$$\int_a^b w(x)f(x)\,dx = \sum_{j=1}^n H_jf(a_j) + \sum_{j=1}^n \bar{H}_jf'(a_j) + E \tag{4.6-2}$$

where now

$$H_j = \int_a^b w(x)h_j(x)\,dx \qquad \bar{H}_j = \int_a^b w(x)\bar{h}_j(x)\,dx \tag{4.6-3}$$

Now, proceeding as in the previous section, we set $\bar{H}_j = 0, j = 1, \ldots, n$ and get as a necessary and sufficient condition on the abscissas that they be the zeros of a polynomial orthogonal with respect to $w(x)$ to all polynomials of lesser degree over $[a,b]$ {11}. That is

$$\int_a^b w(x)u_{n-1}(x)p_n(x)\ dx = 0 \tag{4.6-4}$$

where $u_{n-1}(x)$ is any polynomial of degree $n - 1$ or less. Then, corresponding to (4.5-9) and (4.5-10), we have

$$H_j = \int_a^b w(x)l_j^2(x)\ dx = \int_a^b w(x)l_j(x)\ dx \tag{4.6-5}$$

The error term becomes

$$E = \frac{1}{(2n)!} \int_a^b w(x)p_n^2(x)f^{(2n)}(\xi)\ dx \tag{4.6-6}$$

which, if $w(x)$ does not change sign in (a,b), can be written

$$E = \frac{f^{(2n)}(\eta)}{(2n)!} \int_a^b w(x)p_n^2(x)\ dx \tag{4.6-7}$$

where η lies in (a,b).

If, in fact, $w(x) \geqq 0$ in $[a,b]$, then from (4.6-5) it follows that all the weights are positive, as we found for the Legendre-Gauss quadrature formula. Assuming $w(x)$ to satisfy this condition, we may now prove

Theorem 4.2   The abscissas defined in (4.6-4) are all real and distinct and lie within the interval (a,b).

The importance of having the abscissas real is clear. The importance of their being within the interval (a,b) is also clear if one considers the error term (4.6-7) whose magnitude depends upon the magnitude of $p_n(x)$.

Proof   Let $a_1, \ldots, a_m$ be the points of (a,b) where $p_n(x)$ changes sign. Then

$$(x - a_1) \cdots (x - a_m)p_n(x)$$

does not change sign in $[a,b]$. Since $p_n(x)$ is orthogonal to all polynomials of degree less than n with respect to $w(x)$ over $[a,b]$, we have

$$\int_a^b w(x)(x - a_1) \cdots (x - a_m)p_n(x)\ dx = 0 \tag{4.6-8}$$

unless $m = n$. But the integrand does not change sign. Therefore, the integral cannot be zero and so $m = n$, which proves the zeros are real, distinct, and lie within (a,b).

Equation (4.6-1) is the general form of a Gaussian quadrature formula with the weights defined by (4.6-5), the abscissas by (4.6-4), and the error by (4.6-7).   In the next section we consider in more detail the properties of the orthogonal polynomials defined by (4.6-4).

4.7   ORTHOGONAL POLYNOMIALS AND GAUSSIAN QUADRATURE

Let $\{\phi_n(x)\}$ be a sequence of polynomials, the degree of $\phi_n(x)$ being n, orthogonal with respect to a weight function $w(x)$ over an interval $[a,b]$. Let the coefficient of x^n in $\phi_n(x)$ be A_n so that $\phi_n(x) = A_n p_n(x)$ where $p_n(x)$ is the orthogonal polynomial of the previous section.   We introduce the coefficient A_n so that the orthogonal polynomials to be considered in this and later sections may be put in their standard form, which generally has leading coefficients not equal to 1.   Note that the choice of the leading coefficient has no effect whatever on the abscissas or weights.   The details of the derivation of such sequences of orthogonal polynomials are considered in {13 to 16}.   We have

$$\int_a^b w(x)\phi_i(x)\phi_j(x)\, dx = 0 \qquad i \neq j \tag{4.7-1}$$

Let

$$\alpha_k = \frac{A_{k+1}}{A_k} \qquad \gamma_k = \int_a^b w(x)\phi_k^2(x)\, dx \tag{4.7-2}$$

The basis of the results of this section is the *Christoffel-Darboux identity*

$$\sum_{k=0}^n \frac{\phi_k(x)\phi_k(y)}{\gamma_k} = \frac{\phi_{n+1}(x)\phi_n(y) - \phi_n(x)\phi_{n+1}(y)}{\alpha_n\gamma_n(x - y)} \tag{4.7-3}$$

whose derivation we leave to a problem {17}.

If we set $y = a_j$ in (4.7-3), where a_j is a zero of $\phi_n(x)$, then we get

$$\sum_{k=0}^{n-1} \frac{\phi_k(x)\phi_k(a_j)}{\gamma_k} = -\frac{\phi_n(x)\phi_{n+1}(a_j)}{\alpha_n\gamma_n(x - a_j)} \tag{4.7-4}$$

Now, multiplying both sides of (4.7-4) by $w(x)\phi_0(x)$, integrating over $[a,b]$, and using (4.7-1), we get

$$\frac{\phi_0(a_j)}{\gamma_0}\gamma_0 = -\frac{\phi_{n+1}(a_j)}{\alpha_n\gamma_n}\int_a^b w(x)\frac{\phi_0(x)\phi_n(x)}{x - a_j}\, dx \tag{4.7-5}$$

From the definition of the Lagrangian interpolation polynomial, we have

$$l_j(x) = \frac{p_n(x)}{(x - a_j)p_n'(a_j)} = \frac{\phi_n(x)}{(x - a_j)\phi_n'(a_j)} \tag{4.7-6}$$

Using this, (4.6-5), and the fact that $\phi_0(x)$ is a constant, we may rewrite (4.7-5) as

$$
\begin{aligned}
1 &= -\frac{\phi_{n+1}(a_j)}{\alpha_r \gamma_n} \int_a^b w(x)\, \frac{\phi_n(x)}{x - a_j}\, dx \\
&= -\frac{\phi_{n+1}(a_j)\phi_n'(a_j)}{\alpha_n \gamma_n} \int_a^b w(x) l_j(x)\, dx = \frac{-\phi_{n+1}(a_j)\phi_n'(a_j)}{\alpha_n \gamma_n} H_j \quad (4.7\text{-}7)
\end{aligned}
$$

Thus

$$
H_j = \frac{-A_{n+1}\gamma_n}{A_n \phi_{n+1}(a_j)\phi_n'(a_j)} \qquad j = 1, \ldots, n \tag{4.7-8}
$$

which, given the orthogonal polynomials, is a much simpler way to calculate H_j than (4.6-5). The definition of γ_n allows an obvious simplification of (4.6-7) to give

$$
E = \frac{\gamma_n}{A_n^2 (2n)!}\, f^{(2n)}(\eta) \tag{4.7-9}
$$

These results can be used to simplify the formulas of Sec. 4.5 on Legendre-Gauss quadrature. For the Legendre polynomials $\{19\}$

$$
\gamma_n = \int_{-1}^1 P_n^2(x)\, dx = \frac{2}{2n + 1} \qquad A_n = \frac{(2n)!}{2^n (n!)^2} \tag{4.7-10}
$$

so that H_j in terms of Legendre polynomials is

$$
H_j = \frac{-2}{(n + 1)P_{n+1}(a_j)P_n'(a_j)} \tag{4.7-11}
$$

Some other similar forms of H_j are considered in $\{22\}$. For the error term we get in a corresponding manner

$$
E = \frac{2^{2n+1}(n!)^4}{(2n + 1)[(2n)!]^3}\, f^{(2n)}(\eta) \tag{4.7-12}
$$

The results of this section as well as the next two sections are summarized in Table 4.4 on page 103. In the next two sections, we shall use the results of this and the previous section to derive Gaussian quadrature formulas for particular weight functions.

4.8 GAUSSIAN QUADRATURE OVER INFINITE INTERVALS

For integrals over infinite intervals (which we shall assume are convergent), there are two possible approaches: (1) Use a knowledge of the integrand to bound the magnitude of the integral from some finite value to infinity by a positive constant $\epsilon > 0$, and then use a quadrature formula for the remaining finite interval.   (2) Use a quadrature formula especially developed for the infinite interval.   The former of these two approaches requires no further discussion.   The quadrature over the finite interval can be performed using Legendre-Gauss quadrature or one of the many methods to be presented later in this chapter.   In this section we treat the latter case.

For numerical integration over infinite and semi-infinite intervals, it is convenient to use a weight function $w(x)$ which assures the convergence of the integral of $w(x)f(x)$ when $f(x)$ is a polynomial of arbitrary degree. For the semi-infinite interval (a, ∞) (for convenience we set $a = 0$), such a weight function is $w(x) = e^{-x}$.   Therefore, the sequence of polynomials we require must be orthogonal over $(0, \infty)$ with respect to e^{-x}.   Such a sequence of polynomials is the Laguerre polynomials [see Jackson (1941) and {20}].   The polynomial of degree n, $L_n(x)$, has leading coefficient $A_n = (-1)^n$.   For the Laguerre polynomials

$$\gamma_n = \int_0^\infty e^{-x} L_n^2(x)\, dx = (n!)^2 \tag{4.8-1}$$

Then from (4.7-8) and (4.7-9)

$$H_j = \frac{(n!)^2}{L_n'(a_j) L_{n+1}(a_j)} \tag{4.8-2}$$

$$E = \frac{(n!)^2}{(2n)!} f^{(2n)}(\eta) \tag{4.8-3}$$

Table 4.2   Zeros of Laguerre polynomials and corresponding weights

n	Abscissas a_j	Weights H_j
2	0.585786	0.853553
	3.414214	0.146447
3	0.415775	0.711093
	2.294280	0.278518
	6.289945	0.010389
4	0.322548	0.603154
	1.745761	0.357419
	4.536620	0.038888
	9.395071	0.000539
5	0.263560	0.521756
	1.413403	0.398667
	3.596426	0.075942
	7.085810	0.003612
	12.640801	0.000023

The *Laguerre-Gauss* quadrature formula then has the form

$$\int_0^\infty e^{-x} f(x) \, dx = \sum_{j=1}^{n} H_j f(a_j) + E \tag{4.8-4}$$

where the a_j's are the zeros of $L_n(x)$, the H_j's are given by (4.8-2), and E by (4.8-3).   Table 4.2 is a short listing of weights and abscissas for (4.8-4).

Example 4.4   Evaluate

$$\int_0^\infty x^7 e^{-x} \, dx$$

using $n = 3$ in (4.8-4).

Using Table 4.2 we have

$$\int_0^\infty x^7 e^{-x} \, dx \approx (.711093)(.415775)^7 + (.278518)(2.294280)^7$$
$$+ (.010389)(6.289945)^7 \approx 4139.9$$

whereas the true value of the integral is $7! = 5040$.   The error given by (4.8-3) is

$$E = \frac{(3!)^2}{6!} 7! \eta = 252\eta$$

with η in $(0, \infty)$ so it cannot be bounded.   Thus the substantial error between the approximate and true values is not surprising.   This illustrates the fact that the Laguerre-Gauss quadrature formula and the Hermite-Gauss quadrature formula to be discussed below should be avoided if the derivative in the error term cannot be bounded on $(0, \infty)$.   In this case the first technique mentioned in this section will usually be preferable.   Note that in this particular example, $n = 4$ would have led to an exact result (except for roundoff) since the eighth derivative of $f(x)$ is zero.

A generalization of the weight function e^{-x} to $x^\beta e^{-\alpha x}$ is considered in {20}.

For the infinite interval $(-\infty, \infty)$ we choose, for the same reason as above, the weight function e^{-x^2}.   The sequence of polynomials we require must be orthogonal over $(-\infty, \infty)$ with respect to this weight function. This sequence is the Hermite polynomials [see Jackson (1941) and {21}]. The polynomial $H_n(x)$ of degree n has leading coefficient $A_n = 2^n$.

For these polynomials

$$\gamma_n = \int_{-\infty}^\infty e^{-x^2} H_n^2(x) \, dx = \sqrt{\pi} \, 2^n n! \tag{4.8-5}$$

Then from (4.7-8) and (4.7-9)

$$H_j = -\frac{2^{n+1} n! \sqrt{\pi}}{H_n'(a_j) H_{n+1}(a_j)} \tag{4.8-6}$$

$$E = \frac{n! \sqrt{\pi}}{2^n (2n)!} f^{(2n)}(\eta) \tag{4.8-7}$$

Table 4.3   Zeros of Hermite polynomials and corresponding weights

n	Abscissas a_j	Weights H_j
2	± 0.707107	0.886227
3	0	1.181636
	± 1.224745	0.295409
4	± 0.524648	0.804914
	± 1.650680	0.081313
5	0	0.945309
	± 0.958572	0.393619
	± 2.020183	0.019953

The *Hermite-Gauss quadrature formula* then has the form

$$\int_{-\infty}^{\infty} e^{-x^2} f(x) \, dx = \sum_{j=1}^{n} H_j f(a_j) + E \tag{4.8-8}$$

where the a_j's are the zeros of $H_n(x)$, the H_j's are given by (4.8-6), and E by (4.8-7).   Table 4.3 is a short listing of weights and abscissas for (4.8-8).

4.9 PARTICULAR GAUSSIAN QUADRATURE FORMULAS

In this section we consider Gaussian quadrature over finite intervals using weight functions of considerable theoretical and practical importance.

4.9-1 Jacobi-Gauss quadrature

We consider here the weight function $w(x) = (1 - x)^\alpha (1 + x)^\beta$, α, $\beta > -1$. The polynomials orthogonal to this weight function over $[-1,1]$ are the Jacobi polynomials $J_n(x;\alpha,\beta)$. They are generally defined so that the coefficient A_n of x^n in the polynomial of degree n is given by

$$A_n = \frac{1}{2^n n!} \frac{\Gamma(2n + \alpha + \beta + 1)}{\Gamma(n + \alpha + \beta + 1)} \tag{4.9-1}$$

and we may calculate {24}

$$\begin{aligned}
\gamma_n &= \int_{-1}^{1} (1 - x)^\alpha (1 + x)^\beta J_n^2(x;\alpha,\beta) \, dx \\
&= \frac{2^{\alpha+\beta+1}}{n!(2n + \alpha + \beta + 1)} \frac{\Gamma(n + \alpha + 1)\Gamma(n + \beta + 1)}{\Gamma(n + \alpha + \beta + 1)}
\end{aligned} \tag{4.9-2}$$

Then proceeding as in the previous section, we get the *Jacobi-Gauss quadrature formula* (sometimes called the Mehler quadrature formula)

$$\int_{-1}^{1} (1 - x)^{\alpha}(1 + x)^{\beta}f(x) \, dx = \sum_{j=1}^{n} H_j f(a_j) + E \tag{4.9-3}$$

where {24}

$$H_j = -\frac{2n + \alpha + \beta + 2}{n + \alpha + \beta + 1} \frac{\Gamma(n + \alpha + 1)\Gamma(n + \beta + 1)}{\Gamma(n + \alpha + \beta + 1)(n + 1)!}$$
$$\times \frac{2^{\alpha+\beta}}{J'_n(a_j;\alpha,\beta)J_{n+1}(a_j;\alpha,\beta)} \tag{4.9-4}$$

and

$$E = \frac{\Gamma(n + \alpha + 1)\Gamma(n + \beta + 1)\Gamma(n + \alpha + \beta + 1)}{(2n + \alpha + \beta + 1)[\Gamma(2n + \alpha + \beta + 1)]^2}$$
$$\times \frac{n!2^{2n+\alpha+\beta+1}}{(2n)!} f^{(2n)}(\eta) \tag{4.9-5}$$

The Legendre-Gauss quadrature formula of Sec. 4.5 is just a special case of the Jacobi-Gauss formula with $\alpha = \beta = 0$. In the next section, we consider another special case $\alpha = \beta = -\frac{1}{2}$ because of the importance of the weight function in this case and because it serves to introduce the Chebyshev polynomials which will play an important role in Chap. 7.

4.9-2 Chebyshev-Gauss quadrature

When $\alpha = \beta = -\frac{1}{2}$ so that $w(x) = 1/(1 - x^2)^{1/2}$ (4.9-1) yields

$$A_n = \frac{(2n - 1)!}{2^n n!(n - 1)!} \tag{4.9-6}$$

but in this case it is customary to choose

$$A_n = 2^{n-1} \tag{4.9-7}$$

Using (4.9-7) we may calculate {26}

$$\gamma_n = \pi/2 \tag{4.9-8}$$

The orthogonal polynomials $J_n(x;-\frac{1}{2},-\frac{1}{2})$ are generally denoted by $T_n(x)$ and are called Chebyshev polynomials of the first kind or, more usually, just Chebyshev polynomials. The *Chebyshev-Gauss quadrature formula* has the form

$$\int_{-1}^{1} \frac{1}{(1 - x^2)^{1/2}} f(x) \, dx = \sum_{j=1}^{n} H_j f(a_j) + E \tag{4.9-9}$$

where the a_j's are the zeros of $T_n(x)$,

$$H_j = - \frac{\pi}{T_n'(a_j) T_{n+1}(a_j)} \tag{4.9-10}$$

and

$$E = \frac{2\pi}{2^{2n}(2n)!} f^{(2n)}(\eta) \tag{4.9-11}$$

Equation (4.9-10) can be remarkably simplified by using the result {26} that

$$T_n(x) = \cos (n \cos^{-1} x) \tag{4.9-12}$$

Therefore, at a zero of $T_n(x)$ we have $\cos (n \cos^{-1} x) = 0$ and $\sin (n \cos^{-1} x) = \pm 1$. Thus

$$\begin{aligned}
T_{n+1}(a_j) &= \cos [(n + 1) \cos^{-1} a_j] \\
&= \cos (n \cos^{-1} a_j)a_j - \sin (n \cos^{-1} a_j) \sin (\cos^{-1} a_j) \\
&= \mp (1 - a_j^2)^{\frac{1}{2}}
\end{aligned} \tag{4.9-13}$$

since a_j is a zero of $T_n(x)$. Further

$$T_n'(a_j) = \sin (n \cos^{-1} a_j) \frac{n}{(1 - a_j^2)^{\frac{1}{2}}} = \frac{\pm n}{(1 - a_j^2)^{\frac{1}{2}}} \tag{4.9-14}$$

Using (4.9-13) and (4.9-14) in (4.9-10), it follows that

$$H_j = \pi/n \tag{4.9-15}$$

From (4.9-12) it also follows that

$$a_j = \cos \frac{(2j - 1)\pi}{2n} \qquad j = 1, \dots, n \tag{4.9-16}$$

Thus all the weights are equal and (4.9-9) can be written

$$\int_{-1}^{1} \frac{1}{(1 - x^2)^{\frac{1}{2}}} f(x) \, dx = \frac{\pi}{n} \sum_{j=1}^{n} f(a_j) + E \tag{4.9-17}$$

In Sec. 4.10-2 we shall consider in some generality quadrature formulas which have the property that all the weights are equal.

Example 4.5   Evaluate

$$\int_{-1}^{1} \frac{x^8 \, dx}{(1 - x^2)^{\frac{1}{2}}}$$

using $n = 3$ in (4.9-17).   The zeros of $T_3(x)$ are given by

$$a_j = \cos \frac{(2j - 1)\pi}{6} \qquad j = 1, 2, 3$$

so that in this case, we have

$$\int_{-1}^{1} \frac{x^8 \, dx}{(1 - x^2)^{1/2}} \approx \frac{\pi}{3} \left[\left(\cos \frac{\pi}{6} \right)^8 + \left(\cos \frac{\pi}{2} \right)^8 + \left(\cos \frac{5\pi}{6} \right)^8 \right] = \frac{27\pi}{128} \approx .6627$$

whereas the true value is $\int_{-\pi}^{\pi} \cos^8 \theta \, d\theta = 35\pi/128 \approx .8590$. The error is given by (4.9-11) as

$$E = \frac{2\pi}{2^6 6!} \frac{8!}{2} \eta^2 = \frac{7}{8} \pi \eta^2$$

Note that, although the error is quite large, if we had used $n = 5$, the error would have been zero.

4.9-3   Singular integrals

A common problem in numerical analysis is the need to evaluate integrals in which the integrand has a singularity. If the singularity results in an improper integral {as in the case of $1/(1 - x)^{1/2}$ on $[0,1]$}, we assume the integral is convergent. But we must also consider singularities of the form $(1 - x)^{1/2}$ on $[0,1]$. For in both cases, a Gaussian quadrature approach without weight functions would lead to trouble because of the derivative of the integrand which appears in the error.

The Chebyshev-Gauss quadrature formula is a good example of the value of the weight-function approach to singular integrals. For if $f(x)$ in (4.9-9) is analytic, the effect of making the singular term $1/(1 - x^2)^{1/2}$ the weight function is to remove this term from the summation and the error term on the right-hand side of (4.9-9). In this section we shall consider some other applications of this technique to common types of singularities. We shall restrict our discussion to integrands with singularities at the end points of the interval. However, by splitting the integral into two integrals, singularities in the interior of the interval can also be handled.

The general problem then is to find quadrature formulas of the form

$$\int_{a}^{b} s(x)f(x) \, dx = \sum_{j=1}^{n} H_j f(a_j) + E \tag{4.9-18}$$

where the weight function $s(x)$ is singular at one or both end points. Without loss of generality, we shall restrict ourselves to $[a,b] = [-1,1]$ or $[0,1]$, whichever is most convenient.

(1) $s(x) = (1 - x^2)^{1/2}$ on $[-1,1]$

This is the Jacobi weight function with $\alpha = \beta = \frac{1}{2}$. The resulting orthogonal polynomials are called Chebyshev polynomials of the second kind. Let the polynomial of degree n be $S_n(x)$. Then, analogous to

(4.9-12), we have the relation {30}

$$S_n(x) = \frac{\sin [(n + 1) \cos^{-1} x]}{\sin (\cos^{-1} x)} \qquad (4.9\text{-}19)$$

The abscissas in (4.9-18) are therefore {30}

$$a_j = \cos \frac{j\pi}{n + 1} \qquad j = 1, \ldots, n \qquad (4.9\text{-}20)$$

and, using (4.7-8), we may calculate {30}

$$H_j = \frac{\pi}{n + 1} \sin^2 \frac{j\pi}{n + 1} \qquad (4.9\text{-}21)$$

Using (4.7-9) we find {30}

$$E = \frac{\pi}{2^{2n+1}(2n)!} f^{(2n)}(\eta) \qquad (4.9\text{-}22)$$

(2) $s(x) = 1/\sqrt{x}$ on [0,1]

Here we have a singularity at one end point. By manipulation of the orthogonality integral (4.7-1), we may show that the orthogonal polynomial of degree n, $p_n(x)$ is given by {31}

$$p_n(x) = P_{2n}(\sqrt{x}) \qquad (4.9\text{-}23)$$

where $P_{2n}(x)$ is the Legendre polynomial of degree $2n$. Corresponding to each positive zero α_j of $P_{2n}(x)$, there is then an abscissa of (4.9-18) given by

$$a_j = \alpha_j^2 \qquad (4.9\text{-}24)$$

Using (4.7-8) and (4.9-23), we may also show that {31}

$$H_j = 2h_j \qquad (4.9\text{-}25)$$

where h_j is the weight corresponding to α_j in the Legendre-Gauss formula of order $2n$. For the error we get {31}

$$E = \frac{2^{4n+1}[(2n)!]^3}{(4n + 1)[(4n)!]^2} f^{(2n)}(\eta) \qquad (4.9\text{-}26)$$

Example 4.6   Evaluate

$$\int_0^1 \frac{1 + x}{\sqrt{x}} \, dx$$

using $n = 2$ in (4.9-18). From Table 4.1 and (4.9-24), we have
$a_1 = (.339981)^2 = .115587$
$a_2 = (.861136)^2 = .741555$

and

$H_1 = 1.304290$
$H_2 = .695710$

Therefore, our approximation to the integral is

$$\int_0^1 \frac{1 + x}{\sqrt{x}}\, dx \approx (1.304290)(1.115587) + (.695710)(1.741555) \approx 2.666666$$

whereas the true value is $\frac{8}{3}$. Since $f(x) = 1 + x$, the derivative in (4.9-26) is zero and so, except for roundoff, the result is exact as it should be.

(3) $s(x) = \sqrt{x}$ on $[0,1]$

Again the singularity is at one end point, but this time the singularity is in the derivatives of the function. In a manner similar to the previous case, we may show that {31}

$$p_n(x) = (1/\sqrt{x})P_{2n+1}(\sqrt{x}) \tag{4.9-27}$$

Therefore, if α_j is a positive zero of $P_{2n+1}(x)$, the abscissa in (4.9-18) is given by

$$a_j = \alpha_j^2 \tag{4.9-28}$$

Again using (4.7-8) we find that the corresponding weight is given by {31}

$$H_j = 2h_j\alpha_j^2 \tag{4.9-29}$$

where h_j is the weight corresponding to α_j in the Legendre-Gauss formula of order $2n + 1$. Finally, for the error we get {31}

$$E = \frac{2^{4n+3}[(2n + 1)!]^4}{(4n + 3)[(4n + 2)!]^2(2n)!} f^{(2n)}(\eta) \tag{4.9-30}$$

(4) $s(x) = [x/(1 - x)]^{1/2}$ on $[0,1]$

This time the weight function has a singularity at one end and its derivatives have a singularity at the other end point. In this case we get {32}

$$p_n(x) = (1/\sqrt{x})T_{2n+1}(\sqrt{x}) \tag{4.9-31}$$

where $T_{2n+1}(x)$ is the Chebyshev polynomial of degree $2n + 1$. From this it follows that

$$a_j = \cos^2\frac{(2j - 1)\pi}{4n + 2} \tag{4.9-32}$$

From (4.7-8) we get {32}

$$H_j = \frac{2\pi}{2n + 1} a_j \tag{4.9-33}$$

and from (4.7-9)

$$E = \frac{\pi}{2^{4n+1}(2n)!} f^{(2n)}(\eta) \tag{4.9-34}$$

Table 4.4   Summary of Gaussian quadrature formulas of the form

$$\int_a^b w(x)f(x)\,dx \approx \sum_{j=1}^{n} H_j f(a_j)$$

Weight function $w(x)$	Interval $[a,b]$	Abscissas a_j are zeros of	Weights H_j given by Eq.	Error given by Eq.
1	$[-1,1]$	$P_n(x)$	(4.7-11)	(4.7-12)
e^{-x}	$(0,\infty)$	$L_n(x)$	(4.8-2)	(4.8-3)
e^{-x^2}	$(-\infty,\infty)$	$H_n(x)$	(4.8-6)	(4.8-7)
$(1-x)^\alpha(1+x)^\beta$	$[-1,1]$	$J_n(x;\alpha,\beta)$	(4.9-4)	(4.9-5)
$1/(1-x^2)^{1/2}$	$[-1,1]$	$T_n(x)$	(4.9-15)	(4.9-11)
$(1-x^2)^{1/2}$	$[-1,1]$	$S_n(x)$	(4.9-21)	(4.9-22)
$1/\sqrt{x}$	$[0,1]$	$P_{2n}(\sqrt{x})$	(4.9-25)	(4.9-26)
$\sqrt{x}$	$[0,1]$	$\dfrac{1}{\sqrt{x}}P_{2n+1}(\sqrt{x})$	(4.9-29)	(4.9-30)
$\left(\dfrac{x}{1-x}\right)^{1/2}$	$[0,1]$	$\dfrac{1}{\sqrt{x}}T_{2n+1}(\sqrt{x})$	(4.9-33)	(4.9-34)

4.10 QUADRATURE FORMULAS WITH CONSTRAINTS

Thus far all the quadrature formulas we have considered have been Gaussian; that is, we have determined the abscissas and weights to achieve a maximum order of accuracy, and we have put no conditions whatever on the abscissas and weights.   Some reasons why we might wish to put constraints on the weights or the abscissas are the following:

1. If the behavior of the function $f(x)$ near the end points of the interval is particularly significant, we might prescribe that the n abscissas include one or both end points.
2. The expected roundoff error in a quadrature formula is reduced the more nearly all the weights are equal.   Thus, if roundoff is significant in comparison with truncation error, it may be desirable to prescribe—as in fact it turned out in Chebyshev-Gauss quadrature for a particular weight function—that all the weights be equal.
3. For integrating functions given in tabular form (i.e., at equal intervals), it is clearly desirable to require the abscissas to be equally spaced.

In this section we shall consider quadrature formulas satisfying the first two of the three types of constraints considered above.   In Sec. 4.12 we shall consider the third type of constraint.

4.10-1   Assigned abscissas.   Radau and Lobatto quadrature

Suppose $n - r$ of the n abscissas are assigned.   Then we are left with n weights and r abscissas to assign so that we expect to make the quadrature formula exact for polynomials of degree $n + r - 1$ or less.   To derive the general form of such a formula, we shall use the modified Hermite interpolation formula (3.8-14) in a precisely analogous fashion to the way in which we used the Hermite interpolation formula in the previous sections. The modified Hermite formula is

$$f(x) = \sum_{j=1}^{n} h_j(x)f(a_j) + \sum_{j=1}^{r} \bar{h}_j(x)f'(a_j) + E(x) \tag{4.10-1}$$

with $h_j(x)$ and $\bar{h}_j(x)$ given by (3.8-15) and (3.8-16) and $E(x)$ by (3.8-13). We let the assigned abscissas be $a_{r+1}, \ldots, a_n$.   Using a weight function $w(x)$, we multiply (4.10-1) by $w(x)$ and integrate over $[a,b]$ obtaining

$$\int_a^b w(x)f(x)\,dx = \sum_{j=1}^{n} H_j f(a_j) + \sum_{j=1}^{r} \bar{H}_j f'(a_j) + E \tag{4.10-2}$$

where

$$
\begin{aligned}
H_j &= \int_a^b w(x)h_j(x)\,dx \qquad j = 1, \ldots, n \\
\bar{H}_j &= \int_a^b w(x)\bar{h}_j(x)\,dx \qquad j = 1, \ldots, r \\
E &= \frac{1}{(n+r)!}\int_a^b w(x)p_n(x)p_r(x)f^{(n+r)}(\xi)\,dx
\end{aligned}
\tag{4.10-3}
$$

If we can choose $a_1, \ldots, a_r$ so that $\bar{H}_j = 0, j = 1, \ldots, r$, we shall have achieved the desired result.   From (3.8-16)

$$
\begin{aligned}
\bar{H}_j &= \int_a^b w(x)\bar{h}_j(x)\,dx = \int_a^b w(x)(x - a_j)l_{jr}(x)l_{jn}(x)\,dx \\
&= \frac{1}{p_n'(a_j)p_r'(a_j)}\int_a^b w(x)v(x)p_r(x)\frac{p_r(x)}{x - a_j}\,dx
\end{aligned}
\tag{4.10-4}
$$

where

$$v(x) = \frac{p_n(x)}{p_r(x)} = (x - a_{r+1}) \cdots (x - a_n) \tag{4.10-5}$$

A sufficient condition for $\bar{H}_j = 0$ is that $p_r(x)$ be orthogonal to all polynomials of degree less than r with respect to the weight function $w(x)v(x)$ over the interval $[a,b]$.   This condition may also be shown to be necessary {36}.

The error term may be written

$$E = \frac{1}{(n+r)!}\int_a^b w(x)v(x)p_r^2(x)f^{(n+r)}(\xi)\,dx \tag{4.10-6}$$

and, if $w(x)v(x)$ does not change sign in $[a,b]$

$$E = \frac{f^{(n+r)}(\eta)}{(n+r)!} \int_a^b w(x)v(x)p_r^2(x) \, dx \tag{4.10-7}$$

We may simplify H_j as given by (4.10-3) by using (3.8-15), but a somewhat simpler approach is to consider the function

$$f(x) = (x - a_1) \cdots (x - a_{k-1})(x - a_{k+1}) \cdots (x - a_n) \tag{4.10-8}$$

for which (4.10-2) becomes (with $\bar{H}_j = 0$)

$$\int_a^b w(x)f(x) \, dx = \sum_{j=1}^n H_j f(a_j)$$
$$\stackrel{\cdot}{=} H_k(a_k - a_1) \cdots (a_k - a_{k-1})(a_k - a_{k+1})$$
$$\cdots (a_k - a_n) \tag{4.10-9}$$

Now suppose we consider the Lagrangian interpolation formula (3.1-5) applied to the function of (4.10-8). Since this function is a polynomial of degree $n - 1$, the Lagrangian formula will be exact. If we multiply both sides of (3.1-5) by $w(x)$ and integrate, we get

$$\int_a^b w(x)f(x) \, dx = \sum_{j=1}^n H_j' f(a_j)$$
$$= H_k'(a_k - a_1) \cdots (a_k - a_{k-1})(a_k - a_{k+1})$$
$$\cdots (a_k - a_n) \tag{4.10-10}$$

where

$$H_j' = \int_a^b w(x)l_j(x) \, dx \qquad j = 1, \ldots, n \tag{4.10-11}$$

Comparing (4.10-10) with (4.10-9), we see that the weights must be the same. Therefore, the weights in (4.10-2) are given by (4.10-11), which we rewrite as

$$H_j = \int_a^b w(x)l_{jn}(x) \, dx \qquad j = 1, \ldots, n \tag{4.10-12}$$

to make the notation of this section consistent.

By noting that

$$l_{jn}(x) = \frac{v(x)p_r(x)}{(x - a_j)[v(x)p_r(x)]_{x=a_j}'} \tag{4.10-13}$$

we may write

$$H_j = \frac{1}{[v(x)p_r(x)]_{x=a_j}'} \int_a^b w(x)v(x) \frac{p_r(x)}{x - a_j} \, dx$$
$$j = 1, \ldots, n \tag{4.10-14}$$

For $j = 1, \ldots, r$, a_j is a zero of $p_r(x)$; so (4.10-14) may be written

$$H_j = \frac{1}{v(a_j) p_r'(a_j)} \int_a^b w(x) v(x) \frac{p_r(x)}{x - a_j} \, dx \qquad j = 1, \ldots, r \quad (4.10\text{-}15)$$

If we replace $p_r(x)$ by $(1/A_r) \phi_r(x)$ and use the Christoffel-Darboux identity then, by an argument precisely similar to that in Sec. 4.7, we get

$$H_j = - \frac{A_{r+1} \gamma_r}{A_r v(a_j) \phi_r'(a_j) \phi_{r+1}(a_j)} \qquad j = 1, \ldots, r \qquad (4.10\text{-}16)$$

where

$$\gamma_r = \int_a^b w(x) v(x) \dot\phi_r^2(x) \, dx \qquad (4.10\text{-}17)$$

The weights corresponding to the assigned abscissas are given by (4.10-14) which, in terms of $\phi_r(x)$, is

$$H_j = \frac{1}{[v(x) \phi_r(x)]_{x=a_j}'} \int_a^b w(x) v(x) \frac{\phi_r(x)}{x - a_j} \, dx$$
$$j = r + 1, \ldots, n \quad (4.10\text{-}18)$$

If $w(x) v(x)$ does not change sign in $[a,b]$, we can prove, as in Sec. 4.6, that the unassigned abscissas $x_1, \ldots, x_r$ are real, distinct, and lie in the interval $[a,b]$ {36}.

As we have said, the cases of chief interest are those where the assigned abscissas are one or both end points of the interval. In the remainder of this section, we let $[a,b] = [-1,1]$ and let $w(x) = 1$. Consider first assigning one abscissa $a_n = -1$. Then $v(x) = x + 1$ and the orthogonal polynomials $\phi_{n-1}(x)$, $n = 1, 2, \ldots$ can be shown to be {37}

$$\phi_{n-1}(x) = \frac{P_{n-1}(x) + P_n(x)}{x + 1} \qquad (4.10\text{-}19)$$

where $P_{n-1}(x)$ and $P_n(x)$ are Legendre polynomials. Therefore, we may calculate

$$\gamma_{n-1} = \frac{2}{n} \qquad A_{n-1} = \frac{(2n - 1)!}{2^{n-1} n [(n - 1)!]^2} \qquad (4.10\text{-}20)$$

From (4.10-16) and (4.10-18) we get

$$H_j = \frac{1 - a_j}{n^2 [P_{n-1}(a_j)]^2} \qquad j = 1, \ldots, n - 1$$
$$\qquad (4.10\text{-}21)$$
$$H_n = \frac{2}{n^2}$$

and the error is given by

$$E = \frac{2^{2n-1} n [(n - 1)!]^4}{[(2n - 1)!]^3} f^{(2n-1)}(\eta) \qquad (4.10\text{-}22)$$

Table 4.5   Abscissas and weights for the Radau and Lobatto quadrature formulas

n	Abscissas a_j	Weights H_j
Radau		
2	-1	$\frac{1}{2}$
	$\frac{1}{3}$	$\frac{3}{2}$
3	-1	0.222222
	-0.289898	1.024972
	0.689898	0.752806
4	-1	0.125000
	-0.575319	0.657689
	0.181066	0.776387
	0.822824	0.440925
5	-1	0.080000
	-0.720480	0.446207
	-0.167181	0.623653
	0.446314	0.562712
	0.885792	0.287427
Lobatto		
3	0	$\frac{4}{3}$
	± 1	$\frac{1}{3}$
4	± 0.447214	$\frac{5}{6}$
	± 1	$\frac{1}{6}$
5	0	$3\frac{2}{45}$
	± 0.654654	$49\frac{9}{90}$
	± 1	$\frac{1}{10}$

The quadrature formula

$$\int_{-1}^{1} f(x)\, dx = \frac{2}{n^2} f(-1) + \sum_{j=1}^{n-1} H_j f(a_j) + E \qquad (4.10\text{-}23)$$

with the a_j's the roots of $\phi_{n-1}(x)$, the H_j's given by (4.10-21), and E by (4.10-22) is called the *Radau quadrature formula*. Table 4.5 gives a short listing of the weights and abscissas for this formula.

If we now assign both end points so that $a_{n-1} = -1$, $a_n = 1$, and $v(x) = x^2 - 1$, the corresponding results are {38}

$$\phi_{n-2}(x) = P'_{n-1}(x) \qquad (4.10\text{-}24)$$

$$\gamma_{n-2} = -\frac{2n(n-1)}{2n-1} \qquad A_{n-2} = \frac{(2n-2)!}{2^{n-1}(n-1)!(n-2)!} \qquad (4.10\text{-}25)$$

$$H_j = \frac{2}{n(n-1)[P_{n-1}(a_j)]^2} \qquad j = 1, \ldots, n-2$$

$$H_{n-1} = H_n = \frac{2}{n(n-1)}$$

(4.10-26)

$$E = -\frac{n(n-1)^3 2^{2n-1}[(n-2)!]^4}{(2n-1)[(2n-2)!]^3} f^{(2n-2)}(\eta)$$

(4.10-27)

The quadrature formula

$$\int_{-1}^{1} f(x)\, dx = \frac{2}{n(n-1)} [f(-1) + f(1)] + \sum_{j=1}^{n-2} H_j f(a_j) + E$$

(4.10-28)

is called the *Lobatto quadrature formula*. Table 4.5 gives a short listing of the weights and abscissas for this formula.

Example 4.7   Evaluate

$$\int_1^3 \frac{dx}{x}$$

using first the Radau and then the Lobatto quadrature formulas, both with $n = 3$. Changing variable as in Example 4.3 we get, using Table 4.5,

$$\int_{-1}^{1} \frac{dy}{y+2} \approx (.222222) + (1.024972)\frac{1}{1.710102} + (.752806)\frac{1}{2.689898} \approx 1.101449$$

from the Radau formula and, from the Lobatto formula,

$$\int_{-1}^{1} \frac{dy}{y+2} = \frac{1}{3} \times 1 + \frac{4}{3} \times \frac{1}{2} + \frac{1}{3} \times \frac{1}{3} = \frac{10}{9} \approx 1.111111$$

Note that the errors, which can be estimated using (4.10-22) and (4.10-27), are both larger than the error in Example 4.3 and that the Lobatto error is greater than the Radau error. This is to be expected since the order of accuracy of the Radau and Lobatto formulas is 4 and 2, respectively, compared with 6 in Example 4.3. There is, of course, no reason to wish to emphasize the region near the ends of this integral which we have used only for illustrative purposes.

4.10-2   Chebyshev quadrature

A Chebyshev quadrature formula is one in which all the weights are equal. We encountered one example of this in Sec. 4.9-2 in the Chebyshev-Gauss quadrature formula where $w(x) = 1/(1 - x^2)^{1/2}$. In this section we shall consider three other weight functions

$$w(x) = e^{-x} \text{ on } (0, \infty) \qquad w(x) = e^{-x^2} \text{ on } (-\infty, \infty) \qquad w(x) = 1 \text{ on } [-1,1]$$

The general *Chebyshev quadrature formula* has the form

$$\int_a^b w(x)f(x)\, dx = H \sum_{j=1}^{n} f(a_j) + E$$

(4.10-29)

With $n + 1$ parameters at our disposal—n a_j's and H—we would hope to make (4.10-29) exact for polynomials of degree n or less, but we shall see that this hope will be frustrated in many cases by our inability to find real values for the abscissas. The weight H is quickly determined from the condition that (4.10-29) be exact for $f(x) = 1$. Thus

$$H = \frac{1}{n} \int_a^b w(x)\, dx \tag{4.10-30}$$

To determine the abscissas and, particularly, to determine if they are real, we go back to the algebraic approach of Sec. 4.5, which becomes feasible when the weights are all equal. If (4.10-29) is to be exact for polynomials of degree n or less, then, for $f(x) = x^k$, $k = 1, \ldots, n$, we must have

$$\int_a^b w(x)x^k\, dx = H \sum_{j=1}^n a_j^k \qquad k = 1, \ldots, n \tag{4.10-31}$$

with H given by (4.10-30).

When $w(x) = e^{-x}$ and $(a,b) = (0, \infty)$, we have

$$\int_0^\infty e^{-x}x^k\, dx = k!$$

so that $H = 1/n$, and (4.10-31) becomes

$$\sum_{j=1}^n a_j^k = nk! \qquad k = 1, \ldots, n \tag{4.10-32}$$

We shall show that for $n > 2$ no solution to Eqs. (4.10-32) exists with all the a_j's real. To do this we shall use *Jensen's inequality* [see Hardy, Littlewood, and Polya (1952), p. 28], which states that, if $a_1, \ldots, a_n$ are nonnegative, then

$$\left(\sum_{j=1}^n a_j^r \right)^{1/r} \geq \left(\sum_{j=1}^n a_j^s \right)^{1/s} \qquad \text{if } r < s \tag{4.10-33}$$

In order to consider the case $w(x) = e^{-x}$, it is convenient to restate this slightly to say that, if $a_1, \ldots, a_n$ are real and r is even, then (4.10-33) holds {41}. Now for n odd, consider (4.10-32) for $k = n - 1$ and n. If all the a_j's are to be real, then from (4.10-33)

$$[n(n - 1)!]^{1/(n-1)} \geq [nn!]^{1/n} \tag{4.10-34}$$

which can be simplified to {42}

$$n! \geq n^{n-1} \tag{4.10-35}$$

which is true only for $n = 1$ when n is odd.   When n is even, we consider (4.10-32) for $k = n - 2$ and $n - 1$ and after suitable manipulation get, in place of (4.10-35), {42}

$$n(n - 2)! \geqq (n - 1)^{n-2} \tag{4.10-36}$$

which is true only for $n = 2$ when n is even.   Thus we have the result that, when $w(x) = e^{-x}$, the Chebyshev quadrature formula (4.10-29) cannot exist (i.e., has some nonreal abscissas) for all $n \geqq 3$.   For $n = 1$, (4.10-32) has the trivial solution $a_1 = 1$, and for $n = 2$, $a_1 = 0$, $a_2 = 2$ is a solution.   Thus, for $n = 1$ and 2, the Chebyshev quadrature formula does exist.

When $w(x) = e^{-x^2}$ and $(a,b) = (-\infty, \infty)$, we have $H = \sqrt{\pi}/n$ and, corresponding to (4.10-32), we have {42}

$$\sum_{j=1}^{n} a_j^k = n \frac{(k - 1)!}{2^{k-1}(k/2 - 1)!} \qquad k = 2, 4, \ldots \begin{cases} n & n \text{ even} \\ n - 1 & n \text{ odd} \end{cases} \tag{4.10-37}$$

which may be written

$$\sum_{j=1}^{n} (a_j^2)^r = n \frac{(2r - 1)!}{2^{2r-1}(r - 1)!} \qquad r = 1, \ldots \begin{cases} \dfrac{n}{2} & n \text{ even} \\ \dfrac{n - 1}{2} & n \text{ odd} \end{cases} \tag{4.10-38}$$

We consider (4.10-38) for the two highest values of r.   Since a_j^2 is positive, we may use Jensen's inequality directly.   We get, after suitable manipulation {42},

$$\begin{aligned} (n - 3)(n - 5) \cdots 1 &\geqq (1/n)(n - 1)^{(n-2)/2} & n \text{ even } (n > 2) \\ (n - 4)(n - 6) \cdots 1 &\geqq (1/n)(n - 2)^{(n-3)/2} & n \text{ odd } (n > 3) \end{aligned} \tag{4.10-39}$$

Note that the cases $n = 1, 2$, and 3 are trivial (why?).   These inequalities hold only for $n = 4$ and 5 {42}.   Thus the Chebyshev quadrature formula with $w(x) = e^{-x^2}$ cannot exist for $n \geqq 6$.   For $n = 1$, $a_1 = 0$; for $n = 2$, using symmetry, $-a_1 = a_2 = 1/\sqrt{2}$; for $n = 3$, $-a_1 = a_3 = \sqrt{3}/2$, $a_2 = 0$; and for $n = 4$ and 5, it can be shown that (4.10-37) has no solution with all real a_j's {42}.   Thus, with $w(x) = e^{-x^2}$, the Chebyshev quadrature formula exists only for $n = 1, 2, 3$.

For the case $w(x) = 1$, the approach using Jensen's inequality does not work {43}, but an ingenious analysis due to Bernstein (1937) gives the result that *only* for $n = 1, 2, 3, 4, 5, 6, 7, 9$ does the Chebyshev quadrature formula over $[-1,1]$ exist.   The gap at $n = 8$, which appears particularly remarkable at first glance, occurs in fact because the system of equations (4.10-31) must be really considered as forming two systems, one for n even and one for n odd {43}.

For the case $w(x) = 1$, the sequence of values of n for which Chebyshev quadrature exists is sufficient to make it useful because, as we shall point out in the next section, we generally shall use quadrature formulas of low order.

A method due to Chebyshev for deriving the polynomial whose zeros are the abscissas in (4.10-29) is considered in {44}. The error term in (4.10-29) is not derivable by the methods we have used thus far [except when $w(x) = 1/(1 - x^2)^{1/2}$], but the error can be derived by a method to be discussed in Sec. 5.3. Note that, when n is even and $w(x) = 1$, the Chebyshev quadrature formula is, for reasons of symmetry, exact for polynomials of degree $n + 1$.

4.11 COMPOSITE QUADRATURE FORMULAS

We must face the same problem in choosing n, the number of abscissas in a quadrature formula, that we faced in choosing the number of points in an interpolation formula. As n gets larger, the constant in the error term decreases but the order of the derivative increases. One problem in using large values of n is the difficulty of estimating high-order derivatives. Another is the fact that we mentioned in Sec. 3.5 that, ultimately, the derivatives of all but certain entire functions increase without bound. This result is most easily derived by showing that any function $f(z)$ of a complex variable with bounded derivatives of all orders at a point z_0 must be entire. The Taylor-series expansion of $f(z)$ about z_0 is given by

$$f(z) = \sum_{j=0}^{\infty} A_j(z - z_0)^j \qquad A_j = f^{(j)}(z_0)/j! \tag{4.11-1}$$

If all the derivatives of $f(z)$ at z_0 are bounded so that $|f^{(j)}(z_0)| < M$ for some M and all j, then from (4.11-1)

$$|f(z)| \leqq \sum_{j=0}^{\infty} |A_j| \, |z - z_0|^j < M \sum_{j=0}^{\infty} \frac{|z - z_0|^j}{j!} = Me^{|z-z_0|} \tag{4.11-2}$$

Since this implies the Taylor series converges for all finite z, $f(z)$ is entire.

When $f(z)$ is not entire, we may estimate the rate of growth of the derivatives by writing the coefficients in (4.11-1) in the form

$$A_j = \frac{1}{2\pi i} \oint_C \frac{f(z)}{(z - z_0)^{j+1}} \, dz \tag{4.11-3}$$

where C is any circle centered at z_0 of radius less than the radius of convergence R of the Taylor series.   If L is a bound on the magnitude of $f(z)$ in the circle $|z - z_0| < R$, then it follows from (4.11-3) that

$$|f^{(j)}(z_0)| = j!|A_j| \leq Lj!/R^j$$

Therefore, the derivatives may grow eventually as fast as $j!/R^j$.   Since in fact rapid growth of derivatives may start for quite low derivatives (e.g., see Example 4.5) and because of the difficulty in estimating high derivatives, high-order quadrature formulas are seldom used.   But low-order ones may not be sufficiently accurate.   Consider, for example, the error term in the Legendre-Gauss quadrature formula (4.7-12).   Suppose $f(x)$ is such that we can estimate its derivatives only up to order 4 but that, for $n = 1$ and 2, the bound on E does not assure us of the accuracy we desire.   To avoid this predicament, we may proceed as follows: (1) Break up the interval $[a,b]$ into a number, say m, of subintervals. (2) On each subinterval apply a quadrature formula and sum the results.

The effectiveness of this technique depends upon the fact—which may have been obscured by our use of the interval $[-1,1]$—that the error in all the finite-interval quadrature formulas we have developed is proportional to some power of the length of the interval.   To see this, consider the problem of evaluating

$$\int_a^b f(x)\, dx \tag{4.11-4}$$

by Legendre-Gauss quadrature.   We first make the change of variable

$$y = \frac{1}{b-a}(2x - a - b) \qquad x = \tfrac{1}{2}[(b-a)y + a + b] \tag{4.11-5}$$

which changes (4.11-4) to

$$\int_a^b f(x)\, dx = \frac{b-a}{2} \int_{-1}^1 g(y)\, dy \tag{4.11-6}$$

with

$$g(y) = f[\tfrac{1}{2}(b-a)y + \tfrac{1}{2}(a+b)]$$

Using Legendre-Gauss quadrature, the error in $\int_{-1}^1 g(y)\, dy$ is given by (4.7-12) as

$$E = \frac{2^{2n+1}(n!)^4}{(2n+1)[(2n)!]^3} g^{(2n)}(\bar{\eta}) \qquad \bar{\eta}\, \varepsilon\, (-1,1) \tag{4.11-7}$$

where the derivative is with respect to y.   But using (4.11-5)

$$\frac{d}{dy} g(y) = \frac{dx}{dy}\frac{d}{dx} f(x) = \frac{b-a}{2} f'(x) \tag{4.11-8}$$

Thus the error incurred in $\int_a^b f(x)\,dx$ is

$$E = \left(\frac{b-a}{2}\right)^{2n+1} \frac{2^{2n+1}(n!)^4}{(2n+1)[(2n)!]^3} f^{(2n)}(\eta) \qquad \eta \;\varepsilon\; (a,b) \qquad (4.11\text{-}9)$$

If now we write

$$\int_a^b f(x)\,dx = \int_a^{(a+b)/2} f(x)\,dx + \int_{(a+b)/2}^b f(x)\,dx \qquad (4.11\text{-}10)$$

and apply to each of the integrals on the right-hand side of (4.11-10) a Legendre-Gauss formula with n points, then it follows as above that the error is

$$E = \frac{1}{2^{2n+1}}\left(\frac{b-a}{2}\right)^{2n+1} \frac{2^{2n+1}(n!)^4}{(2n+1)[(2n)!]^3} [f^{(2n)}(\eta_1) + f^{(2n)}(\eta_2)]$$

$$\eta_1 \;\varepsilon\; \left(a, \frac{a+b}{2}\right) \qquad \eta_2 \;\varepsilon\; \left(\frac{a+b}{2}, b\right) \qquad (4.11\text{-}11)$$

which, assuming continuity of the $2n$th derivative of $f(x)$, may be written

$$E = \frac{1}{2^{2n}}\left(\frac{b-a}{2}\right)^{2n+1} \frac{2^{2n+1}(n!)^4}{(2n+1)[(2n)!]^3} f^{(2n)}(\eta_3) \qquad \eta_3 \;\varepsilon\; (a,b)$$

$$(4.11\text{-}12)$$

Thus dividing the interval in two and using an n-point formula in both intervals has brought an extra factor of $1/2^{2n}$ into the error term, leaving everything else the same [except that the $2n$th derivative is evaluated at different points in (4.11-9) and (4.11-12)]. If, instead of two intervals, we had divided $[a,b]$ into m intervals, the added factor would have been $1/m^{2n}$ {46}. Thus the procedure outlined above is indeed an effective way of performing numerical quadrature more accurately by adding abscissas to the interval $[a,b]$ but without increasing the order of the quadrature formula used.

Performing the integral over $[a,b]$ of $f(x)$ by the method outlined here is familiar to all users of the trapezoidal and parabolic rules which we shall consider in Sec. 4.12-1. As an example in the Gaussian context let us consider evaluating (4.11-4) by dividing $[a,b]$ into $m/2$ intervals (m even) and using a Legendre-Gauss quadrature formula with $n = 2$ over each interval. Using Table 4.1, the integral is approximated as

$$\int_a^b f(x)\,dx \approx h \sum_{j=0}^{(m/2)-1} f\{a + h[(1 + 1/\sqrt{3}) + 2j]\}$$

$$+ f\{a + h[(1 - 1/\sqrt{3}) + 2j]\} \qquad (4.11\text{-}13)$$

where $h = (b-a)/m$. The error in (4.11-13) is given, using (4.11-12) with 2^{2n} replaced by $(m/2)^{2n}$, by

$$E = \frac{(b-a)^5}{270m^4} f^{iv}(\eta) = \frac{mh^5}{270} f^{iv}(\eta) \tag{4.11-14}$$

A quadrature formula of the type (4.11-13), which is the sum of a number of quadrature formulas over subintervals, is called a *composite quadrature formula* or *composite rule*. From (4.11-14) we see that, if $f^{iv}(\eta)$ is bounded in $[a,b]$, we may, by increasing the number of subintervals, make the error arbitrarily small [which is the same as saying that the $1/2^{2n}$ factor in (4.11-12) can be made arbitrarily small]. In general, if the derivative in the error term is bounded on the interval of integration, then, in the limit as the number of subintervals $m \to \infty$, the approximation must converge to the true value of the integral. For this reason composite quadrature formulas are used in a large majority of all numerical quadrature work.

A further advantage of composite formulas will be indicated in Secs. 4.12-1 and 4.12-2, where we shall develop a method to get a more accurate result than that given by two or more composite quadratures, each using a different number of subintervals.

Example 4.8   Evaluate the integral of Example 4.3 using (4.11-13) with $m = 4$. We have $h = \frac{1}{2}$; therefore,

$$\int_1^3 \frac{dx}{x} \approx \frac{1}{2} \sum_{j=0}^1 \left\{ \frac{1}{1 + \frac{1}{2}\left[\left(1 + \frac{1}{\sqrt{3}}\right) + 2j\right]} + \frac{1}{1 + \frac{1}{2}\left[\left(1 - \frac{1}{\sqrt{3}}\right) + 2j\right]} \right\}$$

$$\approx 1.097713$$

Using (4.11-14), the error is bounded by

$$.000046 \approx \frac{1}{90}\frac{1}{(3)^5} < E < \frac{1}{90} \approx .011111$$

and, in fact, we have achieved a substantially more accurate result than in Example 4.3 at the cost of using four abscissas instead of three.

4.12   NEWTON–COTES QUADRATURE FORMULAS

We noted in Sec. 4.5 the advantage of having abscissas and weights which are "simple" numbers when using a desk calculator. To the reasons for this that we adduced previously we might add that simplicity of numbers also serves to reduce blunders. In this section we shall develop a class of quadrature formulas that are ideal in this sense for desk-calculator work. Most readers are undoubtedly familiar with the most common members of this class—the trapezoidal formula and Simpson's rule. It should not be thought, however, that this class of formulas is applicable mainly for hand rather than automatic computation. As we shall see in Sec. 4.13, more often than not a member of this class is the best method to use on a digital computer.

A quadrature formula in which the abscissas are constrained to be equally spaced is called a *Newton-Cotes quadrature formula*. They are thus, in particular, ideally suited for the numerical quadrature of tabulated functions. Newton-Cotes formulas of practical value fall into one of two classes: (1) closed formulas where the end points of the interval are abscissas and (2) open formulas where the end points are not abscissas and the other abscissas are symmetrically placed with respect to the end points. Other types, such as half-open and half-closed formulas, are possible but are seldom of use in practice.

Closed Newton-Cotes quadrature formulas have the form

$$\int_a^b w(x)f(x)\,dx = \sum_{j=0}^n H_j f(a + hj) + E \tag{4.12-1}$$

where $h = (b - a)/n$ and $w(x)$ is a weight function. Thus (4.12-1) involves $n + 1$ abscissas; we have summed from 0 to n (in contrast to our previous notation) for notational simplicity in what follows in this section. Also for convenience of notation let $a_j = a + hj$ so that $a = a_0$ and $b = a_n$. Then (4.12-1) becomes

$$\int_{a_0}^{a_n} w(x)f(x)\,dx = \sum_{j=0}^n H_j f(a_j) + E \tag{4.12-2}$$

We have the $n + 1$ weights H_j at our disposal so that we expect to be able to make (4.12-2) exact for polynomials of degree n or less. In fact we shall see that, when n is even, we get exactness for polynomials of degree $n + 1$ also {48}.

To determine the weights, we use the Lagrangian interpolation formula with the abscissas chosen as above, multiply both sides by $w(x)$, and integrate between a_0 and a_n:

$$\int_{a_0}^{a_n} w(x)f(x)\,dx = \sum_{j=0}^n H_j f(a_j) + \frac{1}{(n+1)!} \int_{a_0}^{a_n} w(x) p_{n+1}(x) f^{(n+1)}(\xi)\,dx \tag{4.12-3}$$

where

$$H_j = \int_{a_0}^{a_n} w(x) l_j(x)\,dx \tag{4.12-4}$$

and $p_{n+1}(x) = (x - a_0) \cdots (x - a_n)$. Because of the $(n + 1)$st derivative in the error term, the H_j's given by (4.12-4) make (4.12-2) exact for polynomials of degree n or less. These H_j's are called *Cotes numbers*.

The simplification of the error term in (4.12-3) is considerably more difficult than before because, even if $w(x)$ does not change sign in $[a_0, a_n]$, $p_{n+1}(x)$ does. Thus the second law of the mean cannot be applied. In order to simplify the error, we assume that $w(x)$ is an even function with respect to the center of the interval {i.e., $w[x - (a_0 + a_n)/2] = w[(a_0 + a_n)/2 - x]$} and consider first the case where n is even. Integrating by parts

$$E = \frac{1}{(n+1)!} \int_{a_0}^{a_n} w(x) p_{n+1}(x) f^{(n+1)}(\xi)\, dx$$

$$= -\frac{1}{(n+1)!} \int_{a_0}^{a_n} q(x) \frac{d}{dx} [f^{(n+1)}(\xi)]\, dx \quad (4.12\text{-}5)$$

where

$$q(x) = \int_{a_0}^{x} w(t) p_{n+1}(t)\, dt \quad (4.12\text{-}6)$$

The part integrated out in (4.12-5) is zero because $q(a_0) = 0$ and $q(a_n)$ is also zero. The latter follows because $p_{n+1}(x)$ is an odd function of $x - (a_0 + a_n)/2$ (why?), and we have assumed $w(x)$ is an even function of the same argument.

In the remainder of this section we shall consider the particular case $w(x) = 1$. We leave to a problem {49} the result that in this case $q(x)$ is of constant sign in $[a_0, a_n]$. Then using Theorem 4.1 in (4.12-5), we get the result that

$$E = -\frac{f^{(n+2)}(\eta)}{(n+2)!} \int_{a_0}^{a_n} q(x)\, dx = \frac{f^{(n+2)}(\eta)}{(n+2)!} \int_{a_0}^{a_n} x p_{n+1}(x)\, dx \quad (4.12\text{-}7)$$

the latter result following from an integration by parts {49}. Therefore, with n even the Newton-Cotes closed formula with $w(x) = 1$ is exact for polynomials of degree $n + 1$ or less. When n is odd the derivation is

Table 4.6   Weights and error term coefficients for Newton-Cotes closed formulas

n	A	W_0	W_1	W_2	W_3	W_4	Error coefficient
1	$\frac{1}{2}$	1	1				$-\frac{1}{12}$
2	$\frac{1}{3}$	1	4	1			$-\frac{1}{90}$
3	$\frac{3}{8}$	1	3	3	1		$-\frac{3}{80}$
4	$\frac{2}{45}$	7	32	12	32	7	$-\frac{8}{945}$
5	$\frac{5}{288}$	19	75	50	50	75	$-\frac{275}{12,096}$
6	$\frac{1}{140}$	41	216	27	272	27	$-\frac{9}{1400}$
7	$\frac{7}{17,280}$	751	3577	1323	2989	2989	$-\frac{8183}{518,400}$
8	$\frac{4}{14,175}$	989	5888	-928	10,496	-4540	$-\frac{2368}{467,775}$

Table 4.7   Weights and error term coefficients for Newton-Cotes open formulas

n	A	W_1	W_2	W_3	Error coefficient
2	2	1			$\frac{1}{3}$
3	$\frac{3}{2}$	1	1		$\frac{3}{4}$
4	$\frac{4}{3}$	2	-1	2	$\frac{14}{45}$
5	$\frac{5}{24}$	11	1	1	$\frac{95}{144}$
6	$\frac{3}{10}$	11	-14	26	$\frac{41}{140}$

[handwritten annotation: $= \frac{1}{(n+1)!} \int_{a_0}^{a_n} p_{n+1}(x)\, dx$, "open"]

somewhat more difficult {50}; the result is that

[handwritten: n odd]

$$E = \frac{f^{(n+1)}(\eta)}{(n+1)!} \int_{a_0}^{a_n} p_{n+1}(x)\, dx \quad = \left(\text{Error Coeff}\right) h^{k+1} f^{(k)}(\eta) \tag{4.12-8}$$

which is the result that would be obtained if the second law of the mean could, in fact, be applied to the error term in (4.12-3).

For the case $w(x) = 1$ the weights are given in Table 4.6 for values of n from 1 to 8 (where $n + 1$ is the number of abscissas). The value of H_j in (4.12-2) is given by hAW_j where h is the spacing of the abscissas. Also given are the coefficients of $h^{k+1}f^{(k)}(\eta)$ in the error term where $k = n + 1$ if n is odd and $n + 2$ if n is even. Because of the symmetry of the weights, only a portion of the complete table need be given. The case $n = 1$ is the trapezoidal formula and $n = 2$ is Simpson's rule.

For the same reasons discussed in the previous section, high-order Newton-Cotes formulas are seldom used. Note that some of the weights for $n = 8$ are negative. In fact, it can be shown {51} that only for $n \leq 7$ and $n = 9$ are all the weights positive. Since the sum of the weights is always the length of the interval (why?), if some of the weights are negative, this adversely affects roundoff error [cf. (1.4-7)].

Open Newton-Cotes formulas have the form

$$\int_{a_0}^{a_n} w(x)f(x)\, dx = \sum_{j=1}^{n-1} H_j f(a_j) + E \tag{4.12-9}$$

In this case we have $n - 1$ weights. For n odd (4.12-9) is exact for polynomials of degree $n - 2$ or less, but for n even, as in the case of the closed formulas, we get a bonus in that (4.12-9) is exact for polynomials of degree $n - 1$ or less {52}. The derivation of the error term is similar to that for the closed formulas {52}.

Table 4.7 is the analog of Table 4.6 for open formulas. The error coefficients are the coefficients of $h^{k+1} f^{(k)}(\eta)$ where $k = n$ for n even and $n - 1$ for n odd.

There is seldom any advantage in using a Newton-Cotes open-type formula in preference to the closed formula using the same number of abscissas (see Sec. 4.13), but as we shall see in Chap. 5, open-type formulas do have application to the numerical integration of ordinary differential equations. The weights in the open-type formulas are all positive only for $n = 3$ and 5.

Newton-Cotes formulas with weight functions other than $w(x) = 1$ are sometimes of use also, particularly for singular integrands of the type considered in Sec. 4.9-3. We shall not consider such weight functions here but refer the reader to the references in the bibliographic notes.

4.12-1   Composite   Newton-Cotes   formulas.   Richardson   extrapolation

The same reasons for wishing to use Gaussian quadrature formulas in composite rules apply to Newton-Cotes formulas. Moreover, there is one further advantage to composite rules involving closed Newton-Cotes formulas. Since the end points of each subinterval (except for the end points of the whole interval) are abscissas for two subintervals, the total number of abscissas used is not equal to the number m of subintervals times the number $n + 1$ of points in each subinterval but is $m - 1$ less than this number. This can be best illustrated using $n = 1$ in Table 4.6. Suppose the interval $[a,b]$ is divided into m subintervals of length h and we use (4.12-2) with $n = 1$ used on each subinterval. Then our approximation is

$$\int_a^b f(x)\, dx \approx h(\tfrac{1}{2} f_0 + f_1 + f_2 + \cdots + f_{m-2} + f_{m-1} + \tfrac{1}{2} f_m)$$

$$(4.12\text{-}10)$$

where $f_j = f(a + hj)$ and $h = (b - a)/m$. Although there are m subintervals and each application of (4.12-2) uses two abscissas, there are only $m + 1$ abscissas in (4.12-10). Equation (4.12-10) is, of course, the trapezoidal rule. The error is given by

$$E = -\frac{(b-a)^3}{12m^2} f''(\eta) = -\frac{mh^3}{12} f''(\eta) = -\frac{(b-a)h^2}{12} f''(\eta)$$

$$(4.12\text{-}11)$$

where η is in (a,b). As in the case of (4.11-13), the error can be made arbitrarily small by making m sufficiently large [assuming $f''(\eta)$ is bounded in (a,b)†].

† In fact, since the trapezoidal rule is a Riemann sum, it converges as $m \to \infty$ for any function $f(x)$ continuous on $[a,b]$.

As another example, we divide the interval $[a,b]$ into $m/2$ intervals of length $2h$ (m even) and use (4.12-2) with $n = 2$ over each subinterval. Then we get

$$\int_a^b f(x)\, dx \approx \frac{h}{3}\, (f_0 + 4f_1 + 2f_2 + 4f_3$$
$$+ \cdots + 4f_{m-3} + 2f_{m-2} + 4f_{m-1} + f_m) \quad (4.12\text{-}12)$$

with $h = (b - a)/m$. The error is given by

$$E = -\frac{(b-a)^5}{180m^4}\, f^{\mathrm{iv}}(\eta) = -\frac{mh^5}{180}\, f^{\mathrm{iv}}(\eta) = -\frac{(b-a)h^4}{180}\, f^{\mathrm{iv}}(\eta)$$

$$(4.12\text{-}13)$$

Equation (4.12-12) is the parabolic rule.

Similar composite rules could be derived using other Newton-Cotes closed formulas or using Newton-Cotes open formulas, although in the latter case, because the end points are not abscissas, we do not get a reduction in the total number of abscissas. One advantage of the low-order composite rules, particularly the trapezoidal rule, is the lack of fluctuation in the coefficients which results in good roundoff properties [cf. (1.4-7)]. When an integral is approximated using a large value of m in a composite rule, roundoff error may become a significant factor. Since the expected roundoff error will be minimized when the coefficients are most nearly equal, the trapezoidal rule has almost ideal roundoff properties. Higher-order Newton-Cotes formulas in which some of the weights may even be negative have quite bad roundoff properties. Note that the Gaussian composite rule (4.11-13) has ideal roundoff properties.

Suppose we use (4.12-10) to estimate the $\int_a^b f(x)\, dx$ for two separate values of m, m_1 and m_2. Let I be the true value of the integral and I_1 and I_2 the respective approximations. Then, using (4.12-11),

$$I = I_1 - \frac{(b-a)^3}{12m_1^2}\, f''(\eta_1) \qquad I = I_2 - \frac{(b-a)^3}{12m_2^2}\, f''(\eta_2) \qquad (4.12\text{-}14)$$

where η_1 and η_2 are both in (a,b). Now suppose we assume that the two second derivatives are equal and eliminate these derivatives from (4.12-14), obtaining

$$I \approx \frac{m_2^2 I_2 - m_1^2 I_1}{m_2^2 - m_1^2} = I_2 + \frac{m_1^2}{m_2^2 - m_1^2}\, (I_2 - I_1) \qquad (4.12\text{-}15)$$

The value of this approximation is clearly dependent on how good the assumption is that the two second derivatives are equal. Suppose that we have a sequence of approximations to I, corresponding to an increasing number of subintervals, which appear to be converging monotonically.

Then this assumption is probably good since the differences in the errors are probably being caused mainly by the m^2 term in the denominator of (4.12-11). A procedure of this type in which two approximate results are used to get a third and, hopefully, better one is called a *Richardson-type extrapolation*, or Richardson's deferred approach to the limit.

From a computational point of view, it is desirable to choose $m_2 = 2m_1$, for in this case all the abscissas used in the computation with m_1 subintervals are also abscissas for the m_2 subintervals calculation (why?), thus reducing the number of evaluations of $f(x)$. This consideration will be important in the next section.

Example 4.9   Evaluate the integral of Example 4.3 using (4.12-10) with $m = 2$ and 4 and then use (4.12-15) to obtain a third approximation.

When $m = 2$, we have $h = 1$

$$\int_1^3 \frac{dx}{x} \approx 1(\tfrac{1}{2} \times \tfrac{1}{1} + \tfrac{1}{2} + \tfrac{1}{2} \times \tfrac{1}{3}) = \tfrac{7}{6} = 1.166667$$

When $m = 4$

$$\int_1^3 \frac{dx}{x} \approx \tfrac{1}{2}(\tfrac{1}{2} + \tfrac{2}{3} + \tfrac{1}{2} + \tfrac{2}{5} + \tfrac{1}{2} \times \tfrac{1}{3}) = \tfrac{67}{60} = 1.116667$$

Then from (4.12-15) $I \approx I_2 + \dfrac{m_1^2}{m_2^2 - m_1^2}\left(I_2 - I_1\right)$

$$\int_1^3 \frac{dx}{x} \approx \tfrac{67}{60} + \frac{4}{16 - 4}(-.05) = \tfrac{11}{10}$$

with the true result $\ln 3 = 1.098612$. Note that the Richardson extrapolation gives an improved value, but even this value is not so good as that using (4.11-13) where the error term has the fourth power of the number of subintervals in the denominator.

The Richardson extrapolation we have illustrated here is a special case of the more general case in which the error in a numerical computation based on an interval h can be expressed in the asymptotic form

$$E = \sum_{j=K}^{\infty} a_j h^j \qquad a_K \neq 0 \qquad (h \to 0) \tag{4.12-16}$$

where the a_j's are constants which may depend on $f(x)$ but do not depend on h. If the computation is carried out for two different values of h, h_1 and h_2, resulting in two answers, ϕ_1 and ϕ_2, then the true value ϕ is given by

$$\phi = \phi_1 + \sum_{j=K}^{\infty} a_j h_1^j \tag{4.12-17}$$

or

$$\phi = \phi_2 + \sum_{j=K}^{\infty} a_j h_2^j \tag{4.12-18}$$

Multiplying (4.12-17) by h_2^K and (4.12-18) by h_1^K, subtracting, and then solving for ϕ, we get

$$\phi = \frac{1}{h_1^K - h_2^K} (h_1^K \phi_2 - h_2^K \phi_1) + \sum_{j=K+1}^{\infty} a_j \frac{h_1^K h_2^j - h_2^K h_1^j}{h_1^K - h_2^K} \qquad (4.12\text{-}19)$$

and, in particular, when $h_1 = 2h_2$

$$\phi = \frac{1}{2^K - 1} (2^K \phi_2 - \phi_1) + \sum_{j=K+1}^{\infty} \frac{2^K - 2^j}{2^K - 1} a_j h^j \qquad (4.12\text{-}20)$$

where we have written h for h_2. Thus the effect of the Richardson extrapolation is to increase the power of the smallest power of h in the error. Of course, in general, we could have chosen a method initially with an error of the order of h^{K+1}. But the point here is that, when a method has been chosen initially for some reason, a Richardson extrapolation may always be used to improve the result when convergence is near.

4.12-2 Romberg integration

Any computation based on a fixed spacing h is then a candidate for Richardson extrapolation. To extend the procedure outlined here, we may consider performing M computations each using a different value of h (i.e., a different number of subintervals in the quadrature context) and then eliminate the first $M - 1$ terms in (4.12-16). An intuitive objection to carrying this procedure too far would be that, because of our discussion of high-order derivatives in Sec. 4.11, we would expect the higher powers of h in the error term to be accompanied by increasingly large coefficients. Therefore, we should not be surprised if this procedure did not converge. However, in the case of the trapezoidal rule, it does converge and leads to the following elegant and useful method of Romberg.

It is perhaps not obvious that the error in the trapezoidal rule can be expressed in the form (4.12-16). But, as we shall derive in Sec. 4.15-1 [cf. (4.15-17)], the trapezoidal rule may indeed be written as

$$\int_a^b f(x)\,dx = h(\tfrac{1}{2}f_0 + f_1 + f_2 + \cdots + f_{m-1} + \tfrac{1}{2}f_m) + \sum_{j=1}^{\infty} a_j h^{2j}$$

$$(4.12\text{-}21)$$

with $h = (b - a)/m$, and where the a_j's depend only on a, b, and $f(x)$ [cf. (4.12-11)]. Now let

$$J = \int_a^b f(x)\,dx \qquad (4.12\text{-}22)$$

and let

$$T_{0,k} = \frac{b-a}{2^k} \left(\tfrac{1}{2}f_0 + f_1 + f_2 + \cdots + f_{2^k-1} + \tfrac{1}{2}f_{2^k} \right) \qquad (4.12\text{-}23)$$

be the trapezoidal rule approximation for 2^k subintervals.   Then

$$T_{0,k} = J - \sum_{j=1}^{\infty} a_j \left(\frac{b-a}{2^k} \right)^{2j} \qquad (4.12\text{-}24)$$

We define

$$T_{1,k} = \tfrac{1}{3}(4T_{0,k+1} - T_{0,k}) \qquad k = 0, 1, \ldots \qquad (4.12\text{-}25)$$

Using (4.12-24) we have

$$T_{1,k} = J - \sum_{j=1}^{\infty} \frac{1}{3} \left(\frac{4}{2^{2j}} - 1 \right) a_j \left(\frac{b-a}{2^k} \right)^{2j}$$

$$= J - \sum_{j=2}^{\infty} \frac{1}{3} \left(\frac{4}{2^{2j}} - 1 \right) a_j \left(\frac{b-a}{2^k} \right)^{2j} \qquad k = 0, 1, \ldots$$

$$(4.12\text{-}26)$$

Equation (4.12-26) states that, if we perform the trapezoidal rule to approximate J using a spacing $h_1 = (b-a)/2^{k+1}$ and $h_2 = (b-a)/2^k$, then the resulting approximation has a leading term in the error of the order of h_2^4.   This equation is therefore directly analogous to (4.12-15). The approximation $T_{1,k}$ is, in fact, precisely the parabolic rule for 2^k subintervals {57}.

Now, in general, we define

$$T_{m,k} = \frac{1}{4^m - 1} (4^m T_{m-1,k+1} - T_{m-1,k}) \qquad \begin{matrix} k = 0, 1, \cdots \\ m = 1, 2, \cdots \end{matrix} \qquad (4.12\text{-}27)$$

The approximation $T_{2,k}$ is the composite rule found using the Newton-Cotes closed formula with $n = 4$ and 2^k subintervals, but for $m > 2$, there is no direct relation between $T_{m,k}$ and a Newton-Cotes composite rule {57}.

Using (4.12-27) it follows that

$$T_{m,k} = \sum_{j=0}^{m} c_{m,m-j} T_{0,k+j} \qquad (4.12\text{-}28)$$

That is, each $T_{m,k}$ is a linear combination of trapezoidal rules using 2^k, $2^{k+1}, \ldots, 2^{k+m}$ subintervals.   Moreover, analogously to (4.12-26), we may show that the leading term in the error of $T_{m,k}$ as an approximation to J is of the order of $[(b-a)/2^k]^{2(m+1)}$ {57}.   We would arrange the calculations as indicated in the following table:

$$
\begin{array}{llll}
T_{0,0} & & & \\
T_{0,1} & T_{1,0} & & \\
T_{0,2} & T_{1,1} & T_{2,0} & \\
\cdot & \cdot & & \cdot \\
\cdot & \cdot & & \cdot \\
\cdot & \cdot & & \cdot \\
T_{0,m} & T_{1,m-1} & \cdots\cdots\cdots & T_{m,0}
\end{array}
\tag{4.12-29}
$$

That is, using the $m + 1$ evaluations of the trapezoidal rule in the first column, we may then, using (4.12-27), calculate all the remaining entries in (4.12-29). We know that, if the second derivative of $f(x)$ is bounded in $[a,b]$, then as $m \to \infty$, $T_{0,m}$ converges to J. But here we are interested in proving that, as $m \to \infty$, $T_{m,0}$ converges to J. Note that, since $T_{m,0}$ has a leading term in its error of the order of $[(b - a)/2^k]^{2(m+1)}$, while that of $T_{0,m}$ is $[(b - a)/2^k]^2$, we would hope that, if $T_{m,0}$ converges, it would converge much more rapidly than $T_{0,m}$.

Using (4.12-28) we may write

$$
\begin{bmatrix}
T_{0,0} \\
T_{1,0} \\
\cdot \\
\cdot \\
\cdot \\
T_{m,0}
\end{bmatrix}
=
\begin{bmatrix}
c_{00} & 0 & \cdots\cdots\cdots & 0 \\
c_{11} & c_{10} & 0 & \cdots & 0 \\
\cdot & & \cdot & & \cdot \\
\cdot & & & \cdot & \cdot \\
\cdot & & & & 0 \\
c_{mm} & \cdots\cdots\cdots & & c_{m0}
\end{bmatrix}
\begin{bmatrix}
T_{0,0} \\
\cdot \\
\cdot \\
\cdot \\
\cdot \\
T_{0,m}
\end{bmatrix}
\tag{4.12-30}
$$

We need first a means for generating the coefficients c_{mj}. We leave to a problem {58} the proof of the result that the c_{mj} are the coefficients of

$$
t_m(z) = \sum_{j=0}^{m} c_{mj} z^j = \frac{(4 - z)(4^2 - z) \cdots (4^m - z)}{(4 - 1)(4^2 - 1) \cdots (4^m - 1)}
\tag{4.12-31}
$$

In particular

$$
\sum_{j=0}^{m} |c_{mj}| = t_m(-1) = \prod_{j=1}^{m} \frac{4^j + 1}{4^j - 1} < \prod_{j=1}^{\infty} \frac{4^j + 1}{4^j - 1}
\tag{4.12-32}
$$

Since this infinite product converges {58}, the sum of magnitudes of the elements in any row of (4.12-30) is bounded. It also follows from (4.12-31) that $c_{m,m-j} \to 0$ as $m \to \infty$ {58}; that is, each column in (4.12-30) converges to zero. Finally, $\sum_{j=0}^{m} c_{mj} = t_m(1) = 1$. The coefficient matrix in (4.12-30) therefore satisfies the conditions for Toeplitz convergence [see Zygmund (1952)], which means that, since $T_{0,m}$ converges to J, so does

$T_{m,0}$. In Example 4.10 in the next section, we shall consider a problem in which $T_{m,0}$ not only converges but converges much more rapidly than $T_{0,m}$.

Equation (4.12-28) may also be written in terms of ordinates as

$$T_{m,k} = h \sum_{j=0}^{2^{m+k}} d_{jm} f(a + jh) \qquad h = \frac{b-a}{2^{m+k}} \tag{4.12-33}$$

We leave to a problem {59} the proof of the result that d_{jm} is positive for all j and m. Therefore, in contrast to the higher-order Newton-Cotes formulas, the coefficients in Romberg integration do not change sign.

We shall not derive the error term in Romberg integration here, but it can be shown [see Bauer, Rutishauser, and Stiefel (1963)] that this error may be expressed in the standard form of a constant times h^{2m+2} times a $2m + 2$ derivative of $f(x)$ with h as in (4.12-33). The convergence of the sequence $\{T_{m,0}\}$ implies that this constant becomes small very rapidly (why?).

4.13 CHOOSING A QUADRATURE FORMULA

Our purpose here is not to give hard-and-fast rules for choosing a quadrature formula—there are none—but rather to point out the factors affecting the choice in various situations. Usually, we choose first the type of quadrature formula we are going to use (e.g., Newton-Cotes, Legendre-Gauss, Radau). Then we decide whether or not to use a composite formula and what order of accuracy we wish to use, whether composite or not.

Consider first the problem of tabulating the integral of a tabulated function. Because the data are available at equal intervals, we would almost certainly choose a Newton-Cotes formula in order to avoid interpolation. If derivatives of the tabulated function can be evaluated or at least bounded, and if the derivatives do not grow too rapidly, then we may choose n, the order of the Newton-Cotes formula, so that the error bound assures us of the accuracy we desire.

We can, of course, use open or closed Newton-Cotes formulas. Tables 4.6 and 4.7 might lead us to believe that, for the same number of abscissas, the closed-type formula is clearly superior. Consider the case where the number of abscissas is three. Using $n = 2$ in Table 4.6, the error is $-\frac{1}{90}h^5 f^{\mathrm{iv}}(\eta)$ and using $n = 4$ in Table 4.7, the error is $\frac{14}{45}h^5 f^{\mathrm{iv}}(\eta)$. But note that h is $(b - a)/2$ in the first case and h is $(b - a)/4$ in the second. So, in fact, the errors are, respectively, $-[(b - a)^5/2880]f^{\mathrm{iv}}(\eta)$ and $[7(b - a)^5/23{,}040]f^{\mathrm{iv}}(\eta)$ and the open formula is slightly better. In Table 4.8 the coefficients of the corresponding error terms, with h replaced by $(b - a)/n$, are given for n equals 2 to 5. For 2 and 3, the open formula

Table 4.8   Error term coefficients in Newton-
Cotes closed and open formulas

Number of abscissas	Error coefficient	
	Closed	Open
2	$-\frac{1}{12}$	$\frac{1}{36}$
3	$-\frac{1}{2880}$	$\frac{7}{23,040}$
4	$-\frac{1}{6480}$	$\frac{19}{90,000}$
5	$-\frac{1}{1,935,360}$	$\frac{41}{39,191,040}$

is slightly better, but for 4 and 5 the closed formula is better; for $n > 5$ the advantage of the closed formula becomes more marked.

If we cannot bound the derivatives, then no matter what order Newton-Cotes formula we use, we have no assurance that we shall achieve the desired accuracy. Here the safest technique is to use a composite formula and increase the number of subintervals until the number of decimal places of accuracy that we desire has stabilized (i.e., remains unchanged) in two successive approximations.

Example 4.10   Use the trapezoidal rule to evaluate the integral of Example 4.3 with an error of less than $\frac{1}{2}$ in the fourth decimal place.

In Example 4.9 we used the trapezoidal rule with $m = 2$ and 4 and got the results

$m = 2$:   1.166667
$m = 4$:   1.116667

In order to use those abscissas at which $f(x)$ has already been calculated, we continue to double the number of subintervals. The results are

$m = 8$:   1.103211
$m = 16$:   1.099768
$m = 32$:   1.098902
$m = 64$:   1.098685
$m = 128$:   1.098630

At this point the third decimal place has surely stabilized and the fourth appears to be in error by no more than $\frac{1}{2}$ unit. Applying (4.12-15) to the results for $m = 64$ and $m = 128$, we get $I \approx 1.098612$ which is, in fact, accurate to six decimal places. Applying Romberg integration to this problem, we get for the table (4.12-29)

```
1.333333
1.166667   1.111111
1.116667   1.100000   1.099259
1.103211   1.098726   1.098641   1.098631
1.099768   1.098620   1.098613   1.098613
1.098902   1.098613   1.098613   1.098613
1.098685   1.098613   1.098613   1.098613
1.098630   1.098612   1.098612   1.098612
```

so that, except for roundoff error, convergence is achieved after the use of only 16 sub-intervals (fifth line of table).

Of course, higher-order composite rules than the trapezoidal rule may also be used. The parabolic rule, for example, ultimately converges more rapidly than the trapezoidal rule because of the $1/m^4$ term in (4.12-13) in contrast to the $1/m^2$ term in (4.12-11). Because of the high-order derivative in the error term, higher-order composite rules (i.e., composite rules derived from higher-order Newton-Cotes formulas) are seldom used. Indeed our general conclusion is that the simplicity and rapid convergence of Romberg integration make the trapezoidal rule the best Newton-Cotes formula to use for most problems.

It is important to realize that, because of the results of our discussion in Sec. 4.11 on the growth of higher-order derivatives, it is not true in general that any desired degree of accuracy can be achieved by an arbitrarily high-order formula. To illustrate this let us, following Hildebrand (1956), consider $\int_{-4}^{4} \frac{dx}{1 + x^2} = 2 \tan^{-1} 4 \approx 2.6516353$. In Table 4.9 the results of evaluating this integral using varying numbers of abscissas and various closed Newton-Cotes formulas are shown. It is reasonably clear that the Newton-Cotes formulas of high order are not converging. In contrast, the parabolic rule is oscillating about the true solution with decreasing amplitude and the trapezoidal rule is converging monotonically to the true result. Both the parabolic and trapezoidal rules must converge to the true solution with increasing n, and eventually, the parabolic rule must, as it does, give better results than the trapezoidal rule (why?). For purposes of comparison, Table 4.9 also contains the results using

Table 4.9   Evaluation of $\int_{-4}^{4} \frac{dx}{1 + x^2}$ by Newton-Cotes techniques

Number of abscissas n	Newton-Cotes formula of order n	Parabolic rule	Trapezoidal rule	Romberg integration
3	5.490	5.490	4.235	5.490
5	2.278	2.478	2.918	2.278
7	3.329	2.908	2.701	
9	1.941	2.573	2.659	2.584
11	3.596	2.695	2.6511	
17		2.6477	2.6505	2.6542
33		2.651627	2.65135	2.65186
65		2.6516353	2.65156	2.651631
129		2.6516353	2.651617	2.6516353

Table 4.10   Comparison of accuracy of Gaussian and Newton-Cotes (closed) formulas

Order of accuracy n	Legendre-Gauss formula		Newton-Cotes formula	
	Number of abscissas	Error coefficient	Number of abscissas	Error coefficient
3	2	$\frac{1}{135}$	3	$-\frac{1}{90}$
5	3	$\frac{1}{15,750}$	5	$-\frac{1}{15,120}$
7	4	$\frac{1}{3,472,875}$	7	$-\frac{1}{3,061,800}$
9	5	8.08×10^{-10}	9	-1.21×10^{-9}

Romberg integration. For 17 or more abscissas, Romberg gives better results than the trapezoidal rule, and for 129 or more abscissas, it would give better results than the parabolic rule except for roundoff.

The singularity of the integrand at $x = \pm i$, which limits the radius of convergence of the Taylor-series expansion, is the cause of the difficulty with the higher-order Newton-Cotes formulas. But the reader will agree that the example chosen is not so contrived that we would expect the occurrence of this phenomenon to be rare.

If the function whose integral we wish to calculate is not tabulated but rather is given analytically, then we must consider the use of Gaussian as well as Newton-Cotes formulas for use on an automatic computer. If a single quadrature formula—perhaps of high order—is to be used, then the case for using some Gaussian formula (or one of the formulas of Sec. 4.10) is very good. The reason for this is that the Gaussian formulas achieve higher accuracy with the use of fewer abscissas than Newton-Cotes methods. This is illustrated in Table 4.10 for the Legendre-Gauss formula. The integral in all cases is considered to be over the interval $[-1,1]$. The order of accuracy n is the highest-degree polynomial integrated exactly by the method and the error coefficient is the coefficient of $f^{(n+1)}(\eta)$ in the error term. Thus not only do the Gaussian formulas require calculation of fewer values of $f(x)$ but also they have slightly more favorable error terms. In this case then, the general superiority of the Gaussian formulas is clear.

Furthermore, in contrast to the Newton-Cotes case, if $f(x)$ is continuous and $w(x)$ is any integrable, nonnegative weight function, then any desired degree of accuracy is obtainable by using a sufficiently high order Gaussian quadrature formula. To see this let $\epsilon > 0$ be given and let $p(x)$ be a polynomial, say of degree N, such that $|f(x) - p(x)| < \epsilon$ on $[a,b]$. The existence of such a polynomial is guaranteed by the Weierstrass approximation theorem (p. 28).   Now, using the notation of (4.6-1),

$$|E| = \left| \int_a^b w(x)f(x)\,dx - \sum_{j=1}^n H_j f(a_j) \right| \leq \left| \int_a^b w(x)[f(x) - p(x)]\,dx \right|$$

$$+ \left| \int_a^b w(x)p(x)\,dx - \sum_{j=1}^n H_j p(a_j) \right|$$

$$+ \left| \sum_{j=1}^n H_j[p(a_j) - f(a_j)] \right| \quad (4.13\text{-}1)$$

If $2n - 1 \geq N$, the second term on the right is zero (why?).   Then, since the sum of the weights in any Gaussian quadrature formula is the integral of the weight function over the interval [to see this let $f(x) = 1$ in (4.6-1)] and since all the Gaussian weights are positive, we have

$$|E| \leq \epsilon \int_a^b w(x)\,dx + \epsilon \int_a^b w(x)\,dx = 2\epsilon \int_a^b w(x)\,dx \quad (4.13\text{-}2)$$

which proves the assertion that the error can be made arbitrarily small. Therefore, using a sequence of Gaussian formulas with increasing n will lead to a convergent sequence of approximations.   However, because it is inconvenient to have to store a sequence of Gaussian weights and abscissas in a computer, because it is difficult to estimate the magnitude of the error term for all but quite small n, and because of the efficiency of using composite rules, this approach is seldom used in practice.   Note that this proof of convergence is valid for any sequence of quadrature formulas of increasing order provided only that the weights are all positive, a condition which is not satisfied by Newton-Cotes formulas.   But this condition is satisfied by Romberg integration [cf. (4.12-33)], and therefore the above argument also provides a proof of the convergence of the Romberg technique.

   When a composite rule for a sequence of 2, 4, 8, 16 $\cdots$ subintervals is to be used to approximate the integral of an analytically given function, the comparison of Gaussian and Newton-Cotes formulas no longer favors the Gaussian approach.   The error-term comparison remains the same. But because the abscissas in the Newton-Cotes formula with m subintervals are also abscissas for the $2^k m$ ($k = 1, 2, \ldots$) subinterval cases and because this is never the case for Gaussian formulas (when more than one abscissa per subinterval is used), the computational advantage is on the Newton-Cotes side [since most of the computational time in evaluating an integral numerically is in the evaluation of $f(x)$].   In fact, we can state the following result leaving its derivation to {64}: If a composite rule is used with n abscissas per subinterval and with 1, 2, 4, $\ldots$, 2^m

Table 4.11   Number of abscissas in various composite rules

n	m	Newton-Cotes closed	Newton-Cotes open	Gaussian
2	3	9	16	30
4	3	25	32	60
5	3	33	47	75
6	5	161	192	378

subintervals, the total number of different abscissas is

$$n + (n - 1)(2^m - 1) \qquad \text{Newton-Cotes closed formulas}$$

$$\left.\begin{array}{ll} n \times 2^m & n \text{ even} \\ n + (n + 1)(2^m - 1) & n \text{ odd} \end{array}\right\} \quad \text{Newton-Cotes open formulas}$$

$$n(2^{m+1} - 1) \qquad \text{Gaussian formulas}$$

Table 4.11 tabulates these numbers for some sample values of m and n and clearly indicates the advantage of the Newton-Cotes closed formulas. In most cases this computational advantage will override the accuracy advantage of the Gaussian formulas.   In particular, our conclusion again is that, because of the advantages of Romberg integration, the trapezoidal rule is the most generally useful of all composite rules.

4.14 NUMERICAL EVALUATION OF MULTIPLE INTEGRALS

With the availability of digital computers, the numerical evaluation of multiple integrals of any complexity has become feasible for the first time. The result has been a *relatively* greater advance in techniques for evaluating multiple integrals numerically than in techniques for single integrals. There is now a large literature on this subject.   Most of it is, however, beyond the scope of this book, and we shall content ourselves here with a brief introduction to the subject.

For convenience, we shall consider only double integrals in what follows.   First, suppose that the limits of integration are constants so that we wish to evaluate an integral of the form

$$\int_a^b \int_c^d f(x,y) \, dy \, dx \tag{4.14-1}$$

Using any of the quadrature formulas we have developed previously in this chapter, we have

$$F(x) = \int_c^d f(x,y) \, dy = \sum_{j=1}^n H_j f(x,a_j) + E[f(x,y)] \tag{4.14-2}$$

where $E[f(x,y)]$ is expressed in terms of partial derivatives with respect to y. Then using the same or another quadrature formula, we may write

$$\int_a^b F(x)\, dx = \sum_{k=1}^m \bar{H}_k F(\bar{a}_k) + \bar{E}[F(x)] \qquad (4.14\text{-}3)$$

where the bars denote that the weights, abscissas, and error term in (4.14-3) may be different from those in (4.14-2). Combining (4.14-2) and (4.14-3), we have

$$\int_a^b \int_c^d f(x,y)\, dy\, dx = \sum_{k=1}^m \sum_{j=1}^n \bar{H}_k H_j f(\bar{a}_k, a_j) + E \qquad (4.14\text{-}4)$$

where E combines the error terms of (4.14-2) and (4.14-3); the detailed form of the error term will be left to a problem {65}.

In the more common case where the region of integration R is not rectangular so that the limits are not all constants, we may generalize (4.4-4) as

$$\int \int_R f(x,y)\, dy\, dx = \sum_{k=1}^m \sum_{j=1}^n H_{kj} f(b_k, a_j) + E \qquad (4.14\text{-}5)$$

For triple or higher-order integrals, the extension of (4.14-5) is clear. There are now mn weights and $m + n$ abscissas. One approach would be to try to determine these weights and abscissas so as to make (4.14-5) exact when $f(x,y)$ has a certain polynomial form. Even in the case of constant limits, this approach of determining the weights and abscissas directly for the double integral may be more advantageous than use of two single-integral quadrature formulas. Thus, whereas with single integrals we fit a polynomial to the integrand, with double integrals we fit a surface, and so forth for higher-order integrals. We shall not pursue this further here except to point out some of the difficulties involved in the numerical evaluation of double integrals in contrast to single integrals:

1. In deriving methods for single integrals, we regularly normalized the interval $[a,b]$ to $[-1,1]$. This enabled us to determine weights and abscissas once and for all and then, by a simple change of variable, to use these results on any interval. For rectangular regions in n space, the same technique is possible using the unit n cube, but for general regions—even in 2 space—this cannot be done. Thus each region tends to require a separate derivation of the weights and abscissas, although other classes of regions (e.g., circular or "star-shaped" regions) can be normalized.

2. No satisfactory theory of orthogonal polynomials in more than one variable exists which can be used as we have used orthogonal polynomials in the one-variable case.
3. For Gaussian-type formulas where the abscissas must also be determined, we have in general no assurance that real abscissas can be found to satisfy the conditions we wish to impose.

Although a number of particular cases of multiple-quadrature formulas have been derived, there is a great deal of work to be done before the quality of the theory of multiple quadrature is equal to that for single integrals.

4.15 SUMMATION

Our interest in this section is in approximating the sum

$$\sum_{j=0}^{n} f(x_0 + jh) \tag{4.15-1}$$

where n may be infinite.   As a by-product of the development of methods to do this, we shall arrive at another and useful technique for numerical quadrature.

4.15-1   The Euler-Maclaurin sum formula

We begin by introducing the *Bernoulli polynomials* $B_k(x)$ which are defined to be the polynomials of degree k which are the coefficients of $t^k/k!$ in the expansion

$$\frac{t(e^{xt} - 1)}{e^t - 1} = \sum_{k=0}^{\infty} B_k(x) \frac{t^k}{k!} \tag{4.15-2}$$

from which it follows that

$$\begin{align} B_k(0) &= 0 \qquad k \geq 0 \\ B_k(1) &= 0 \qquad k \neq 1 \end{align} \tag{4.15-3}$$

By expanding the left-hand side of (4.15-2) in a power series, we may compute the first few Bernoulli polynomials as

$$\begin{align} B_0(x) &= 0 \qquad B_1(x) = x \\ B_2(x) &= x^2 - x \qquad B_3(x) = x^3 - 3x^2/2 + \tfrac{1}{2}x \end{align} \tag{4.15-4}$$

The expansion of the left-hand side of (4.15-2) with the $e^{xt} - 1$ term deleted may be written

$$\frac{t}{e^t - 1} = \sum_{k=0}^{\infty} B_k \frac{t^k}{k!} \tag{4.15-5}$$

where the constants B_k are the *Bernoulli numbers*.† Of the many identities involving Bernoulli polynomials and numbers, the following three are of particular interest to us:

$$B_{2k+1} = 0 \qquad\qquad\qquad\qquad\qquad k > 0 \tag{4.15-6}$$
$$B'_{2k}(x) = 2kB_{2k-1}(x) \qquad\qquad\qquad k > 1 \tag{4.15-7}$$
$$B'_{2k+1}(x) = (2k+1)[B_{2k}(x) + B_{2k}] \qquad k \geqq 0 \tag{4.15-8}$$

We leave the derivations to a problem {66}. The first few nonzero Bernoulli numbers are $B_0 = 1$, $B_1 = -\frac{1}{2}$, $B_2 = \frac{1}{6}$, $B_4 = -\frac{1}{30}$, $B_6 = \frac{1}{42}$, $B_8 = -\frac{1}{30}$, $B_{10} = \frac{5}{66}$, $B_{12} = -\frac{691}{2730}$, $B_{14} = \frac{7}{6}$, $B_{16} = -\frac{3617}{510}$, $B_{18} = \frac{43,867}{798}$, $B_{20} = -\frac{174,611}{330}$. Now we define

$$X_k = \frac{1}{(2k)!} \int_0^h B_{2k}\left(\frac{y}{h}\right) f^{(2k)}(x + y)\, dy \tag{4.15-9}$$

where $f(x)$ is the function of (4.15-1). Integrating by parts twice and using (4.15-3), (4.15-7), and (4.15-8), we get

$$h^2 X_k - X_{k-1} = \frac{B_{2k-2}}{(2k-2)!}\left[f^{(2k-3)}(x+h) - f^{(2k-3)}(x)\right] \qquad k > 1 \tag{4.15-10}$$

When $k = 1$ we have, also by integration by parts,

$$\begin{aligned}
X_1 &= \frac{1}{2} \int_0^h B_2\left(\frac{y}{h}\right) f''(x + y)\, dy \\
&= \frac{1}{2} \int_0^h \left(\frac{y^2}{h^2} - \frac{y}{h}\right) f''(x + y)\, dy \\
&= -\int_0^h \left(\frac{y}{h^2} - \frac{1}{2h}\right) f'(x + y)\, dy \\
&= -\frac{1}{2h}[f(x + h) + f(x)] + \frac{1}{h^2} \int_0^h f(x + y)\, dy \\
&= -\frac{1}{2h}[f(x + h) + f(x)] + \frac{1}{h^2} \int_x^{x+h} f(y)\, dy \tag{4.15-11}
\end{aligned}$$

---

† The Bernoulli polynomials and numbers are defined somewhat differently by different authors. Our notation follows generally that of Bromwich (1947). See Steffensen (1950) for a somewhat different notation. These polynomials should not be confused with the Bernstein polynomials (p. 28).

Using (4.15-10) and (4.15-11) we have

$$\frac{1}{2}[f(x + h) + f(x)] = \frac{1}{h} \int_x^{x+h} f(y)\, dy - hX_1$$

$$= \frac{1}{h} \int_x^{x+h} f(y)\, dy + \frac{hB_2}{2!} [f'(x + h) - f'(x)] - h^3X_2$$

$$= \frac{1}{h} \int_x^{x+h} f(y)\, dy + \frac{hB_2}{2!} [f'(x + h) - f'(x)]$$

$$+ \frac{h^3B_4}{4!} [f'''(x + h) - f'''(x)] - h^5X_3 = \cdots$$

$$= \frac{1}{h} \int_x^{x+h} f(y)\, dy + \sum_{k=1}^m \frac{B_{2k}}{(2k)!} h^{2k-1}[f^{(2k-1)}(x + h) - f^{(2k-1)}(x)]$$

$$- h^{2m+1}X_{m+1} \quad (4.15\text{-}12)$$

We define

$$\bar{B}_k(x) = \begin{cases} B_k(x) & 0 \leq x < 1 \\ \bar{B}_k(x - 1) & \text{otherwise} \end{cases} \quad (4.15\text{-}13)$$

Now consider (4.15-9) with the limits going from jh to $(j + 1)h$ and with $B_{2k}(y/h)$ replaced by $\bar{B}_{2k}(y/h)$. We may repeat the derivation of (4.15-12) for $j = 1, \ldots, n - 1$. Then summing the results, replacing x by x_0, and noting that the series on the right-hand side of (4.15-12) telescopes, we get

$$\sum_{j=0}^n f(x_0 + jh) = \frac{1}{h} \int_{x_0}^{x_0+nh} f(y)\, dy + \frac{1}{2}[f(x_0 + nh) + f(x_0)]$$

$$+ \sum_{k=1}^m \frac{B_{2k}}{(2k)!} h^{2k-1}[f^{(2k-1)}(x_0 + nh) - f^{(2k-1)}(x_0)] + E_m \quad (4.15\text{-}14)$$

where, using (4.15-9),

$$E_m = -\frac{h^{2m+1}}{(2m + 2)!} \int_0^{nh} \bar{B}_{2m+2}\left(\frac{y}{h}\right) f^{(2m+2)}(x_0 + y)\, dy \quad (4.15\text{-}15)$$

Using the properties of the Bernoulli polynomials {68} (4.15-15) can be simplified to

$$E_m = \frac{nh^{2m+2}B_{2m+2}}{(2m + 2)!} f^{(2m+2)}(\xi) \quad (4.15\text{-}16)$$

where $x_0 < \xi < x_0 + nh$. Equation (4.15-14) is the *Euler-Maclaurin sum formula*. It is useful even when the upper limit in the summation is infinite, although in this case the error can no longer be expressed in the form (4.15-16). A useful error estimate in the infinite case (and when n is finite) is that the error is less than the magnitude of the first neglected term in the summation on the right-hand side of (4.15-14) if $f^{(2m+2)}(x)$ and $f^{(2m+4)}(x)$ do not change sign and are of the same sign for $x_0 < x < x_0 + nh$ {69}. If just $f^{(2m+2)}(x)$ does not change sign in the interval, then the error is less than twice the first neglected term {70}.

Example 4.11   Use (4.15-14) to approximate the

$$\sum_{j=0}^{\infty} \frac{1}{(1+j)^2}$$

·We use $f(x) = 1/x^2$ with $x_0 = h = 1$. The true sum is $\pi^2/6 \approx 1.644934067$. Using (4.15-14) our approximation for the sum is

$$\sum_{j=0}^{\infty} \frac{1}{(1+j)^2} \approx \int_1^{\infty} \frac{1}{x^2}\, dx + \frac{1}{2} + \sum_{k=1}^{m} B_{2k} = \frac{3}{2} + \sum_{k=1}^{m} B_{2k}$$

The following table indicates the error between the true result and the approximation as a function of m:

m:	0	1	2	3	4	5
Error:	.145	$-.022$	.012	$-.012$	.021	$-.055$
m:	6	7	8	9	10	
Error:	.198	$-.968$	6.124	-48.847	480.277	

The approximations, after initially converging, are clearly diverging. Suppose now we try to approximate

$$\sum_{j=0}^{\infty} \frac{1}{(10+j)^2}$$

Then we have from (4.15-14), now with $x_0 = 10$

$$\sum_{j=0}^{\infty} \frac{1}{(10+j)^2} \approx \frac{1}{10} + \frac{1}{2} \times \frac{1}{10^2} + \sum_{k=1}^{m} \frac{B_{2k}}{10^{2k+1}}$$

With $m = 2$ we get

$$\tfrac{1}{10} + \tfrac{1}{200} + \tfrac{1}{6} \times 1/(10)^3 - \tfrac{1}{30} \times 1/(10)^5 \approx .1051663333$$

which, when added to the directly calculated sum $\sum_{j=1}^{9} 1/j^2 \approx 1.5397677311$, gives

1.6449340644, which is correct to almost nine decimals, a remarkable change from the previous case.   To account for this, we note that all derivatives of $f(x)$ are of constant sign in $(0, \infty)$ so that the error is less than the first neglected term.   In the first case this is B_{2m+2} and in the second it is $B_{2m+2}/10^{2m+3}$.   Now it is known [see Steffensen (1950)] that ultimately the Bernoulli numbers B_{2i} grow as $(2i)!$ so that $B_{2m+2}/x_0^{2m+3} \rightarrow \infty$ as $m \rightarrow \infty$ for any x_0.   Thus the Euler-Maclaurin sum formula diverges for $f(x) = 1/(x_0 + x)^2$ for all x_0.   In particular, it diverges for both the above cases. But the series on the right-hand side of (4.15-14), although divergent when $f(x) = 1/(x_0 + x)^2$, is asymptotically convergent; that is, it converges for a while before it starts to diverge.   When $x_0 = 1$, the convergence never gets very far, but for $x_0 = 10$, when $m = 2$, $B_{2m+2}/10^{2m+3} = B_6/10^7 \approx 2.4 \times 10^{-9}$ so that the asymptotic convergence is very good.   To get similar accuracy by direct summation of the series, we would need to sum over 10^9 terms!

This example illustrates the power of the Euler-Maclaurin formula if used judiciously.   It is worth remarking that judiciousness is necessary in dealing with most asymptotic series.   One exception to this rule is the case of interpolation series (see Prob. 22, Chap. 3) which are in fact asymptotic series.   In practical application of interpolation formulas, we are virtually always in the region of convergence of the interpolation series.

By rearranging terms, (4.15-14) becomes a quadrature formula

$$\int_{x_0}^{x_0+nh} f(y)\,dy = h \sum_{j=0}^{n} f(x_0 + jh) - \frac{h}{2}[f(x_0 + nh) + f(x_0)]$$

$$- \sum_{k=1}^{m} \frac{B_{2k}}{(2k)!}\, h^{2k}[f^{(2k-1)}(x_0 + nh) - f^{(2k-1)}(x_0)] - hE_m \quad (4.15\text{-}17)$$

The first two terms on the right-hand side of (4.15-17) are just the trapezoidal-rule approximation to the integral.   Equation (4.15-17) may then be looked at as the trapezoidal rule with correction terms.   If we use Eq. (4.1-14) to approximate the derivatives in (4.15-17), the result is *Gregory's formula*

$$\int_{x_0}^{x_0+nh} f(y)\,dy = h(\tfrac{1}{2}f_0 + f_1 + \cdots + f_{n-1} + \tfrac{1}{2}f_n)$$

$$+ \frac{h}{12}(\Delta f_0 - \Delta f_{n-1}) - \frac{h}{24}(\Delta^2 f_0 + \Delta^2 f_{n-2})$$

$$+ \frac{19h}{720}(\Delta^3 f_0 - \Delta^3 f_{n-3}) - \frac{3h}{160}(\Delta^4 f_0 + \Delta^4 f_{n-4}) + \cdots \quad (4.15\text{-}18)$$

where we have written f_j for $f(x_0 + jh)$.   This formula is one of the few examples where it is convenient to use differences on a digital computer. For, if we use (4.15-17), we must program the computer to calculate not only $f(x)$, but also m derivatives.   Moreover, we may not know how large m need be a priori.   But we can add terms to (4.15-18) merely by computing higher differences, and these differences will generally be much easier to compute than the derivatives.

Example 4.12   Use (4.15-18) to improve the result of Example 4.10 for 16 subintervals.

Using a difference table for $1/x$, we may calculate with $a_0 = 1$ and $h = \frac{1}{8}$

$$\Delta f_0 = -\tfrac{1}{9} \qquad \Delta f_{15} = -\tfrac{1}{69}$$

and the first difference correction term in (4.15-18) is

$$\tfrac{1}{96}(\tfrac{1}{69} - \tfrac{1}{9}) = -.001006$$

which, added to 1.099768, the result for 16 subintervals, gives 1.098762.   Similarly, we calculate

$$\Delta^2 f_0 = \tfrac{1}{45} \qquad \Delta^2 f_{14} = \tfrac{1}{759}$$

so that the second difference correction term is

$$-\tfrac{1}{192}\left(\tfrac{1}{45} + \tfrac{1}{759}\right) = -.000123$$

which, added to the above result, gives 1.098639.   These corrections give successively better results than the trapezoidal rule.   Care must be taken not to carry the correction process too far because Gregory's formula is also only asymptotically convergent in general.   Moreover, of course, roundoff becomes a factor with higher differences. In {72} a direct connection between Gregory's formula and higher-order Newton-Cotes formulas is considered.

4.15-2   Summation of rational functions.   Factorial functions

In this section we confine ourselves to the case where $f(x)$ in (4.15-1) is a rational function.   In Example 4.11 we applied the Euler-Maclaurin sum formula to such a function.   Our technique there—as it will be with all slowly convergent series whose sum cannot be expressed in closed form— was to replace the sum of the slowly convergent series by the sum of a rapidly convergent series.   In this section, we first consider a class of rational functions whose sum can be expressed in closed form, and then use this class to convert other slowly convergent series of rational functions to more rapidly convergent ones.

Our basic tool here will be the sequence of *factorial functions* denoted by $x^{(n)}$ and defined by

$$x^{(n)} = x(x - 1)(x - 2) \cdots (x - n + 1)$$
$$\qquad\qquad\qquad\qquad\qquad n \text{ a positive integer} \qquad (4.15\text{-}19)$$
$$x^{(0)} = 1$$

so that $n^{(n)} = n!$.

Consider first the forward difference of $x^{(n)}$ with unit spacing:

$$\Delta x^{(n)} = (x + 1)^{(n)} - x^{(n)} = x(x - 1)$$
$$\cdots (x - n + 2)[(x + 1) - (x - n + 1)] = nx^{(n-1)} \qquad (4.15\text{-}20)$$

Therefore, the factorial functions play the same role with respect to differences that the powers of x do with respect to differentiation.   Thus we have

$$\sum_{x=M}^{N-1} x^{(n)} = \frac{1}{n + 1} \sum_{x=M}^{N-1} \Delta x^{(n+1)} = \frac{N^{(n+1)} - M^{(n+1)}}{n + 1} \qquad (4.15\text{-}21)$$

since

$$\sum_{x=M}^{N-1} \Delta f(x) = f(N) - f(M) \tag{4.15-22}$$

for any $f(x)$. When n is negative, we define $x^{(n)}$ by

$$x^{(n)} = \frac{1}{(x-n)^{(-n)}} \qquad n \text{ a negative integer} \tag{4.15-23}$$

For this case too, we can show that (4.15-20) holds and, when $n \neq -1$, that (4.15-21) also holds. Note, in particular, that $0^{(n)} \neq 0$ when n is a negative integer (why?).

We shall now use (4.15-21) to convert slowly convergent infinite series of rational functions to more rapidly convergent ones. Note that in such infinite series the degree of the denominator must exceed that of the numerator by 2 or more (why?). The basic idea of this method, which is known as *Kummer's method*, bears an analogy to the comparison test used to determine convergence or divergence of infinite series. Suppose the series we wish to sum is

$$S = \sum_{x=M}^{\infty} R(x) \tag{4.15-24}$$

where $R(x)$ is a rational function. If there is a series

$$\bar{S} = \sum_{x=M}^{\infty} \bar{R}(x) \tag{4.15-25}$$

whose sum we know and such that $\bar{R}(x)$ and $R(x)$ have the same difference in degree d between numerator and denominator, then we can use $\bar{S}$ to convert S to a more rapidly convergent series. This technique is most easily illustrated by an example.

Example 4.13   Evaluate

$$S = \sum_{x=2}^{\infty} \frac{x}{x^4 + 1}$$

Let $\bar{R} = \dfrac{1}{(x-1)(x)(x+1)} = \dfrac{1}{(x+1)^{(3)}} = (x-2)^{(-3)}$. Then from (4.15-21),

$\bar{S} = \frac{1}{4}$ {77}. Now

$$S = \bar{S} + (S - \bar{S}) = \frac{1}{4} - \sum_{2}^{\infty} \frac{x^9 + 1}{(x^4 + 1)x(x^2 - 1)}$$

which converges as $1/x^5$ and, therefore, much more rapidly than (4.15-24).   We could

also have used $\bar{R} = \dfrac{1}{x(x+1)(x+2)} = (x-1)^{(-3)}$.   In this case $\bar{S} = \frac{1}{12}$ and

$$S = \frac{1}{12} - \sum_{2}^{\infty} \frac{1 - 2x^2 - 3x^3}{x(x+1)(x+2)(x^4+1)}$$

which converges as $1/x^4$.

The general result is that, if $R(x)$ and $\bar{R}(x)$ both have a denominator degree which exceeds the numerator degree by d and if

$$\lim_{x \to \infty} x^d R(x) = \lim_{x \to \infty} x^d \bar{R}(x) \tag{4.15-26}$$

then $R(x) - \bar{R}(x)$ has a difference in degree between numerator and denominator of *at least $d+1$* {78}.   In the above example, we saw how a judicious choice of $\bar{R}(x)$ made the resulting difference $d+2$.   The procedure used in the above example can be applied again and again to make the summation even more rapidly convergent, but the algebra usually becomes tedious quite rapidly.

We have at best touched the surface of the existing mine of methods to sum series.   References to others will be found in the bibliographic notes that follow.

BIBLIOGRAPHIC NOTES

4.1–4.3   Numerical differentiation is discussed in most of the standard numerical analysis texts.   In particular, Kopal (1955) and Hildebrand (1956) have extensive discussions.   In these two books as well as in Steffensen (1950), the error term is derived using divided differences.   Theorem 4.1 is proved by Ralston (1963). Coefficients for the Lagrangian differentiation formulas based on differences have been extensively tabulated.   Some tables and references to others are given by Kopal (1955).

The literature on the use of differences in the numerical solution of partial differential equations is extensive.   A good reference text is Forsythe and Wasow (1960); some examples of their use may be found in Chaps. 12, 13, and 16 of Ralston and Wilf (1960).

4.4–4.13   Krylov (1962), which is an excellent book and the only one available devoted entirely to numerical quadrature, has discussions of much of the material of this chapter.   For the insight provided by other points of view and for some topics not covered here, see Kopal (1955), Hartree (1958), and Mineur (1952), as well as Krylov.   Stroud (1961) gives an extensive bibliography on quadrature methods.

4.5–4.9   More complete accounts of the properties of the Gaussian weights and abscissas may be found in Winston (1934).   The most complete reference available on orthogonal polynomials is Szegö (1939), but most of the results we have used here are available in a more accessible form in Jackson (1941).   Much of the material in Sec. 4.9-3 is from Mineur (1952).

4.10   Chebyshev (1874) gave the derivation of the Chebyshev quadrature formula which we consider in Prob. 44.   The results for infinite intervals are due to Wilf (1961).   Greenwood and Danford (1949) consider the Chebyshev problem for the weight function x.   Salzer (1955) considers the interesting problem of how high an order of accuracy can be achieved with real abscissas for a given n.

4.11–4.13   The error term in the Newton-Cotes quadrature formulas has been considered by a number of authors; see Steffensen (1950), Barrett (1952), and Sard (1948).   Following the original paper by Richardson and Gaunt (1927), many authors have discussed Richardson extrapolation; see, for example, Kopal (1955). Davis (1959) gives an interesting comparison of the trapezoidal rule and Gaussian formulas.   A good discussion of Romberg's method may be found in the paper by Bauer, Rutishauser, and Stiefel (1963).   Newton-Cotes formulas with weights other than $w(x) = 1$ have been considered by Kaplan (1952) and Luke (1952).   An interesting treatment of the weight function $\sin kx$ is given by Filon (1928).   A quadrature formula which is particularly efficient in composite rules is considered by Ralston (1959); see also Prob. 63.   The proof that arbitrarily high accuracy can be obtained with Gaussian quadrature formulas is from chap. 3 of Todd (1962).

4.14   An excellent recent survey of the field is given by Hammer (1959). The case of rectangular regions is treated by Miller (1960).

4.15   Steffensen (1950) discusses the Bernoulli polynomials and numbers in detail, but his notation is different from ours.   Hamming (1962) considers a number of miscellaneous methods of summation; see also Cherry (1950), Rosser (1951), Shanks (1955), and Szasz (1949).

BIBLIOGRAPHY

Barrett, W. (1952): On the Remainders of Numerical Formulae with Special Reference to Differentiation, *J. London Math. Soc.*, vol. 27, pp. 456–464.

Bauer, F. L., H. Rutishauser, and E. Stiefel (1963): New Aspects in Numerical Quadrature in *Experimental Arithmetic, High Speed Computing and Mathematics*, vol. 15, *Proceedings of Symposia in Applied Mathematics*, American Mathematical Society, Providence, R.I.

Bernstein, S. (1937): Sur les formules de quadrature de Cotes et de Tchebycheff, *C. R. de l'Academie des Sciences de l'URSS*, vol. 14, pp. 323–326.

Bromwich, T. J. (1947): *An Introduction to the Theory of Infinite Series*, 2d ed., The Macmillan Company, New York.

Chebyshev, P. L. (1874): Sur les Quadratures, *J. Math. Pures Appl.*, vol. 19, pp. 19–34.

Cherry, T. M. (1950): Summation of Slowly Convergent Series, *Proc. Cambridge Philos. Soc.*, vol. 46, pp. 436–449.

Davis, P. (1959): On the Numerical Integration of Analytic Functions in *On Numerical Approximation* (R. E. Langer, ed.), The University of Wisconsin Press, Madison, Wis.

Filon, L. N. G. (1928): On a Quadrature Formula for Trigonometric Integrals, *Proc. Roy. Soc. Edinburgh*, vol. 49, pp. 38–47.

Forsythe, G. E., and W. Wasow (1960): *Finite Difference Methods for Partial Differential Equations*, John Wiley & Sons, Inc., New York.

Greenwood, R. E., and B. B. Danford (1949): Numerical Integration with a Weight Function x, *J. Math. and Phys.*, vol. 28, pp. 99–106.

Hammer, P. C. (1959): Numerical Evaluation of Multiple Integrals in *On Numerical*

Approximation (R. E. Langer, ed.), The University of Wisconsin Press, Madison, Wis.

Hamming, R. W. (1962): *Numerical Methods for Scientists and Engineers*, McGraw-Hill Book Company, New York.

Hardy, G. H., J. E. Littlewood, and G. Polya (1952): *Inequalities*, 2d ed., Cambridge University Press, New York.

Hartree, D. R. (1958): *Numerical Analysis*, 2d ed., Oxford University Press, Fair Lawn, N.J.

Hildebrand, F. B. (1956): *Introduction to Numerical Analysis*, McGraw-Hill Book Company, New York.

Jackson, D. (1941): *Fourier Series and Orthogonal Polynomials*, Carus Mathematical Monographs, Mathematical Association of America, Oberlin, Ohio.

Kaplan, E. L. (1952): Numerical Integration Near a Singularity, *J. Math. and Phys.*, vol. 31, pp. 1–28.

Kopal, Z. (1955): *Numerical Analysis*, John Wiley & Sons, Inc., New York.

Krylov, V. I. (1962): *Approximate Calculation of Integrals* (translated by A. H. Stroud), The Macmillan Company, New York.

Luke, Y. L. (1952): Mechanical Quadrature Near a Singularity, *MTAC*, vol. 6, pp. 215–219.

Miller, J. C. P. (1960): Numerical Quadrature Near a Rectangular Domain in Two or More Dimensions, *MTAC*, vol. 14, pp. 13–20, 130–138, 240–248.

Mineur, H. (1952): *Techniques de calcul numerique*, Librarie Polytechnique, Paris.

Ralston, A. (1959): A Family of Quadrature Formulas Which Achieve High Accuracy in Composite Rules, *J. Assoc. Comput. Mach.*, vol. 6, pp. 384–394.

Ralston, A. (1963): On Differentiating Error Terms, *Amer. Math. Monthly*, vol. 70, pp. 187–188.

Ralston, A., and H. S. Wilf (eds.) (1960): *Mathematical Methods for Digital Computers*, John Wiley & Sons, Inc., New York.

Richardson, L. F., and J. A. Gaunt (1927): The Deferred Approach to the Limit, *Trans. Roy. Soc. London*, vol. 226A, pp. 299–361.

Rosser, J. B. (1951): Transformations to Speed the Convergence of Series, *J. Res. Nat. Bur. Standards*, vol. 46, pp. 56–64.

Salzer, H. E. (1955): Equally Weighted Quadrature Formulas over Semi-infinite and Infinite Intervals, *J. Math. and Phys.*, vol. 34, pp. 54–63.

Sard, A. (1948): Integral Representation of Remainders, *Duke Math. J.*, vol. 15, pp. 333–345.

Shanks, D. (1955): Nonlinear Transformations of Divergent and Slowly Convergent Sequences, *J. Math. and Phys.*, vol. 34, pp. 1–42.

Steffensen, J. F. (1950): *Interpolation*, 2d ed., Chelsea Publishing Company, New York.

Stroud, A. H. (1961): A Bibliography on Approximate Integration, *Math. Comput.*, vol. 15, pp. 52–80.

Szasz, O. (1949): Summation of Slowly Convergent Series, *J. Math. and Phys.*, vol. 28, pp. 272–279.

Szegö, G. (1939): *Orthogonal Polynomials*, vol. 23, American Mathematical Society Colloquium Publications, New York.

Todd, J. (ed.) (1962): *Survey of Numerical Analysis*, McGraw-Hill Book Company, New York.

Wilf, H. S. (1961): The Possibility of Tschebycheff Quadrature on Infinite Intervals, *Proc. Nat. Acad. Sci. U.S.A.*, vol. 47, pp. 209–213.

Winston, C. (1934): On Mechanical Quadrature Involving the Classical Orthogonal Polynomials, *Ann. of Math.*, vol. 35, pp. 658–677.

Zygmund, A. (1952): *Trigonometric Series*, 2d ed., Chelsea Publishing Company, New York.

PROBLEMS

Section 4.1

*1. (a) Use Leibniz's rule to show that

$$\frac{d^k}{dx^k} \frac{\frac{1}{k!}\frac{f(x)}{p_n(x)} - \frac{f(a_{n+1})}{p_n(a_{n+1})}}{x - a_{n+1}} = \frac{1}{k!}\frac{d^k}{dx^k}\frac{f(x)}{p_n(x)} - k\frac{d^{k-1}}{dx^{k-1}}\frac{\frac{1}{k!}\frac{f(x)}{p_n(x)} - \frac{f(a_{n+1})}{p_n(a_{n+1})}}{x - a_{n+1}}$$

(b) Use this result and the technique of the proof of Theorem 4.1, based now on an $n + m$ point Lagrangian interpolation formula, to show that

$$\frac{1}{m!}\frac{d^m}{dx^m}\frac{f(x)}{p_n(x)} = \sum_{j=1}^{n}\frac{(-1)^m f(a_j)}{(x - a_j)^{m+1}p_n'(a_j)} + \frac{f^{(n+m)}(\eta)}{(n + m)!}$$

where η lies in the interval spanned by $a_1, \ldots, a_n$ and x.

(c) Use this result to deduce (4.1-9).

(d) Use the technique of Sec. 3.2 to show that, when x is *not* in the interior of the interval spanned by $a_1, \ldots, a_n$, the error in (4.1-2) is given by

$$\frac{f^{(n)}(\eta)}{n!}p_n^{(k)}(x)$$

where η is in the interval spanned by $a_1, \ldots, a_n$ and x. Why doesn't this procedure work when x is in the interval spanned by $a_1, \ldots, a_n$?

2. (a) With $n = 5$ use (4.1-14) to generate approximations to the first four derivatives of $f(x)$ at $x = a_0$.

(b) Use the results of Prob. 16, Chap. 3 to do the same thing in terms of backward and central differences, retaining differences through order 5.

3. (a) Using the notation of Prob. 10, Chap. 3, show that the Taylor-series expansion of $f(x)$ may be written $Ef(x) = e^{hD}f(x)$ where D is the operator with the property $Df(x) = f'(x)$.

(b) From this deduce the relations $hD = \ln E = \ln (1 + \Delta) = -\ln (1 - \nabla)$.

4. Stirling numbers:

(a) Use the results of the previous problem and the limiting version of (4.1-15) as $n \to \infty$ to show that

$$[\ln (1 + \Delta)]^k = k! \sum_{j=k}^{\infty}\frac{S_j^{(k)}}{j!}\Delta^j$$

(b) Deduce that $S_j^{(0)} = 0, j > 0$ and, using the Maclaurin expansion of $\ln (1 + \Delta)$, that $S_k^{(k)} = 1$. (See also Prob. 75.)

Section 4.2

5. Use a numerical differentiation formula with differences through order four to find the coefficients of the differential equation $y'' + ay' + by = x$ satisfied by the function $f(x)$ in the tabulation below; then determine $f(x)$ itself.

x:	.6	.7	.8	.9	1.0	1.1
$f(x)$:	1.164642	1.344218	1.517356	1.683327	1.841471	1.991207

6. (a) Use (4.2-5) and (4.2-6) to show that, if the optimum value of h in numerical differentiation is to be chosen to make $E_1^2(x) + R_1^2(x)$ a minimum, then

$$h_{\text{opt}} = \left[\frac{1}{n-1} \frac{r_1^2(x)}{e_1^2(x)} \right]^{1/(2n+2)}$$

(b) Derive (4.2-13).

7. (a) Find the first derivative of $f(x) = 1/(1 + x)$ at $x = .005$ by using a Lagrangian formula with $n = 3$. Use equally spaced intervals with the middle point at $x = .005$ and $h = 1.0, .1, .01$, respectively. Round all values of $f(x)$ to four decimal places.

(b) What is the determining factor in choosing a value of h for the problem of part a? Why can't (4.2-14) be used to choose the best value of h?

(c) Repeat the calculations of part a with $h = .01$ using (4.1-14) and retaining terms through the second difference. Compare these results with those of part a.

8. (a) For $n = 5$ derive the formulas analogous to (4.2-16).

(b) Suppose you are given a nine-place table of $\ln x$ at an interval of .01. As in Example 4.2 choose a value of h near h_{opt} and approximate the derivative of $\ln x$ at $x = .5$ using the results of part a. Check that the error is within expected bounds.

Section 4.3

9. Instead of numerically differentiating the tabulation of Prob. 5, approximate the first and second derivatives at .6 and .7 using the formula (4.3-9). How do these compare with the derivatives calculated in Prob. 5? Show how the error in the approximation (4.3-9) may be estimated using the $(k + 1)st$ difference.

Sections 4.4, 4.5, 4.6

10. (a) Let $c_0, \ldots, c_{n-1}$ be a solution of the system of linear equations

$$\alpha_{i+n} + \sum_{k=0}^{n-1} c_k \alpha_{i+k} = 0 \quad i = 0, \ldots, n-1$$

with α_k given by (4.5-2) By writing (4.5-1) in the form

$$\alpha_{i+k} = \sum_{j=1}^{n} H_j a_j^{i+k} \quad i = 0, \ldots, n-1; k = 0, \ldots, n$$

and substituting into the above linear system show that the zeros of the polynomial

$$x^n + \sum_{k=0}^{n-1} c_k x^k$$

may be used as the a_j's. Then deduce that the weights can be found by solving the linear system consisting of the first n equations of (4.5-1).

(b) Apply this technique to try to find the abscissa and weight of the quadrature formula

$$\int_{-1}^{1} xf(x)\, dx \approx H_1 f(a_1)$$

which is to be exact for 1 and x. Here $\alpha_k = \int_{-1}^{1} x^{k+1}\, dx$. How do you explain the result? Use the result to state an assumption which is implicit in the statement of part a.

11. By making use of the function $f(x) = p_n(x)u_{n-1}(x)$, where $u_{n-1}(x)$ is an arbitrary polynomial of degree $n - 1$ or less, prove that it is necessary for $p_n(x)$ in (4.5-7) to be orthogonal to all polynomials of lesser degree if the Gaussian quadrature formula is to be exact for polynomials of degree $2n - 1$ or less. Does this argument have to be modified when there is a weight function?

12. (a) Use Legendre-Gauss quadrature with $n = 2, 3, 4, 5$ to approximate the integral

$$\int_{-4}^{4} \frac{dx}{1 + x^2}$$

and compare the results with the true value (see also Sec. 4.13).

(b) Repeat part a for $\int_{0}^{1} e^{-10x} \sin x\, dx$

(c) Repeat part a for $\int_{0}^{5} xe^{-3x^2}\, dx$

(d) Repeat part a for $\int_{-1}^{1} (1 - x^2)^{3/2} \cos x\, dx = 3\pi J_2(1) \approx 1.08294$

(e) Repeat part a for $\int_{-1}^{1} \frac{\cos x}{(1 - x^2)^{1/2}}\, dx = \pi J_0(1) \approx 2.40394$

Section 4.7

13. Orthogonal polynomials: Let $\{\phi_r(x)\}$ be a sequence of polynomials such that $\phi_r(x)$ is of degree r and is orthogonal to all polynomials of lesser degree over the interval $[a,b]$ with respect to the weight function $w(x)$. In this and the following problems, we assume that $w(x)$ is of constant sign in $[a,b]$.

(a) By letting

$$w(x)\phi_r(x) = \frac{d^r U_r(x)}{dx^r}$$

show that $U_r(x)$ must satisfy the equation

$$[U_r^{(r-1)}q_{r-1} - U_r^{(r-2)}q_{r-1}' + U_r^{(r-3)}q_{r-1}'' + \cdots + (-1)^{r-1}U_r q_{r-1}^{(r-1)}]_a^b = 0$$

where $q_{r-1}(x)$ is any polynomial of degree $r - 1$ or less, superscripts denote differentiation, and the notation $\bigg]_a^b$ means that the value of the expression in brackets at $x = a$ is to be subtracted from that at $x = b$.

(b) Show that the boundary conditions

$$U_r(a) = U_r'(a) = U_r''(a) = \cdots = U_r^{(r-1)}(a) = 0$$
$$U_r(b) = U_r'(b) = U_r''(b) = \cdots = U_r^{(r-1)}(b) = 0$$

satisfy the requirements of part a and serve to determine $\phi_r(x)$ uniquely.

(c) Finally deduce that

$$\phi_r(x) = \frac{1}{w(x)} \frac{d^r U_r(x)}{dx^r}$$

where $U_r(x)$ satisfies the differential equation

$$\frac{d^{r+1}}{dx^{r+1}} \left[\frac{1}{w(x)} \frac{d^r U_r(x)}{dx^r} \right] = 0$$

subject to the boundary conditions of part b.

14. (a) By writing

$$\phi_r(x) = A_r x^r + q_{r-1}(x)$$

show that

$$\gamma_r = \int_a^b w(x) \phi_r^2(x) \, dx = A_r \int_a^b x^r w(x) \phi_r(x) \, dx$$

(b) With $U_r(x)$ defined as in Prob. 13a, use the results of Prob. 13b to show that

$$\gamma_r = (-1)^r r! A_r \int_a^b U_r(x) \, dx$$

15. Prove that, if $w(x)$ does not change sign in $[a,b]$, the zeros of $\phi_r(x)$ are real, distinct, and lie within $[a,b]$.

16. Recurrence relations:

(a) Show that

$$\phi_{r+1}(x) - \alpha_r x \phi_r(x) = b_r \phi_r(x) + b_{r-1} \phi_{r-1}(x) + \cdots + b_0 \phi_0(x)$$

where $\alpha_r = A_{r+1}/A_r$ and the b_i's are constants.

(b) Use the orthogonality property of the polynomials to show that $b_i = 0$, $i = 0, \ldots, r - 2$ and thus deduce that the polynomials satisfy the recurrence relation

$$\phi_{r+1}(x) = (\alpha_r x + b_r) \phi_r(x) + b_{r-1} \phi_{r-1}(x)$$

(c) Show that

$$b_r = \alpha_r (B_{r+1}/A_{r+1} - B_r/A_r)$$

where B_r is the coefficient of x^{r-1} in $\phi_r(x)$.

(d) Show that

$$b_{r-1} = -\frac{A_{r+1} A_{r-1}}{A_r^2} \frac{\gamma_r}{\gamma_{r-1}}$$

by multiplying the recurrence relation in part b first by $w(x)\phi_{r+1}(x)$ and then by $w(x)\phi_{r-1}(x)$, integrating each equation over $[a,b]$, and solving for b_{r-1} in the resulting set of equations.

*(e) Use the recurrence relation to show that, if $r_1 < r_2 < \cdots < r_n$ are the zeros of $\phi_n(x)$ and $s_1 < s_2 < \cdots < s_{n+1}$ are the zeros of $\phi_{n+1}(x)$, then $a < s_1 < r_1 < s_2 < r_2 < s_3 < \cdots < s_n < r_n < s_{n+1} < b$. (*Hint:* Assume that $A_r > 0$ for all r.)

17. The Christoffel-Darboux identity:

(a) Divide the recurrence relation of part b of the previous problem by $\alpha_r \gamma_r$, multiply the result by $\phi_r(y)$, subtract from this the same equation with x and y interchanged, and use part d of the previous problem to obtain

$$(x - y)\frac{\phi_r(x)\phi_r(y)}{\gamma_r} = \frac{\phi_{r+1}(x)\phi_r(y) - \phi_r(x)\phi_{r+1}(y)}{\alpha_r \gamma_r} - \frac{\phi_r(x)\phi_{r-1}(y) - \phi_{r-1}(x)\phi_r(y)}{\alpha_{r-1}\gamma_{r-1}}$$

(b) Sum this result from $r = 0$ to $r = n$ to obtain the Christoffel-Darboux identity (4.7-3).

18. (a) When $[a,b] = [0,1]$ and $w(x) = x^k$ with k a positive integer, derive $U_r(x)$ and from this an expression for $\phi_r(x)$ under the condition $\phi_r(0) = 1$.

(b) Use this result to calculate γ_r and A_r.

(c) Thus derive the form of the weights and error in the corresponding Gaussian quadrature formula as given by (4.7-8) and (4.7-9).

19. Legendre polynomials:

(a) When $w(x) = 1$ and $[a,b] = [-1,1]$, use the results of Prob. 13 to show that

$$U_r = C_r(x^2 - 1)^r$$

where C_r is an arbitrary constant.

(b) With $C_r = 1/2^r r!$, show that

$$A_r = (2r)!/2^r(r!)^2 \qquad \text{and} \qquad \gamma_r = 2/(2r + 1)$$

(c) Show that the Legendre polynomials, denoted by $P_r(x)$, satisfy the recurrence relation

$$P_{r+1}(x) = \frac{2r + 1}{r + 1}xP_r(x) - \frac{r}{r + 1}P_{r-1}(x)$$

(d) Show that $P_0(x) = 1$, $P_1(x) = x$ and use part c to generate the next six Legendre polynomials.

Section 4.8

20. Laguerre polynomials:

(a) When $w(x) = x^\beta e^{-\alpha x}(\alpha > 0, \beta > -1)$ and $(a,b) = (0, \infty)$, show that

$$U_r(x) = C_r e^{-\alpha x}x^{\beta+r}$$

(b) With $C_r = 1$, show that

$$A_r = (-1)^r \alpha^r \qquad \text{and} \qquad \gamma_r = r!\Gamma(r + \beta + 1)/\alpha^{1+\beta}$$

(c) When $\alpha = 1$, $\beta = 0$ these polynomials are called Laguerre polynomials and are denoted by $L_r(x)$. Show that they satisfy the recurrence relation

$$L_{r+1}(x) = (1 + 2r - x)L_r(x) - r^2 L_{r-1}(x)$$

(d) Show that $L_0(x) = 1$, $L_1(x) = 1 - x$, and use part c to generate the next six Laguerre polynomials.

21. Hermite polynomials:

(a) When $w(x) = e^{-\alpha^2 x^2}$ and $(a,b) = (-\infty, \infty)$, show that

$$U_r(x) = C_r e^{-\alpha^2 x^2}$$

(b) With $C_r = (-\alpha)^{-r}$, show that

$$A_r = (2\alpha)^r \quad \text{and} \quad \gamma_r = (2^r r!/\alpha) \sqrt{\pi}$$

(c) When $\alpha = 1$ these polynomials are called Hermite polynomials and are denoted by $H_r(x)$. Show that they satisfy the recurrence relation

$$H_{r+1}(x) = 2xH_r(x) - 2rH_{r-1}(x)$$

(d) Show that $H_0(x) = 1$, $H_1(x) = 2x$, and use part c to generate the next six Hermite polynomials.

22. (a) Use the recurrence relation of part b of Prob. 16 to show that (4.7-8) may be written

$$H_j = \frac{A_n \gamma_{n-1}}{A_{n-1} \phi'_n(a_j) \phi_{n-1}(a_j)}$$

(b) Apply this result to get new expressions for the weights in the Legendre-Gauss, Laguerre-Gauss, and Hermite-Gauss quadrature formulas.

(c) Use the following relations from Szegö (1939):

$$(1 - x^2)P'_n(x) = (n + 1)xP_n(x) - (n + 1)P_{n+1}(x)$$
$$xL'_n(x) = (x - n - 1)L_n(x) + L_{n+1}(x)$$
$$H'_n(x) = 2xH_n(x) - H_{n+1}(x)$$

to express the weights in terms of the polynomials of degree $n + 1$ only.

23. (a) Use Laguerre-Gauss quadrature to approximate the integral

$$\int_0^\infty e^{-10x} \sin x \, dx$$

using $n = 2, 3, 4, 5$, and compare the results with the true value.

(b) Approximate the integral of part a by using the result of part b of Prob. 12 and finding a bound on the integral from 1 to ∞. Compare the two results.

(c) Repeat part a for $\int_0^\infty \dfrac{e^{-x}}{1 + e^{-2x}} \, dx$.

(d) Use Hermite-Gauss quadrature to approximate the integral $\int_{-\infty}^\infty |x| e^{-3x^2} \, dx$, with $n = 2, 3, 4, 5$, and compare the results with the true value.

(e) Approximate the integral of part d by using the result of part c of Prob. 12 and finding a bound on the integral outside of $[-5,5]$. Compare the two results.

(f) Repeat part d for $\int_{-\infty}^\infty e^{-x^2} \cos x \, dx$.

Section 4.9

24. Jacobi polynomials:
(a) When $w(x) = (1 - x)^\alpha (1 + x)^\beta$, $\alpha, \beta > -1$ and $[a,b] = [-1,1]$, show that

$$U_r(x) = C_r(1 - x)^{\alpha+r}(1 + x)^{\beta+r}$$

(b) With $C_r = (-1)^r/(2^r r!)$, derive the relations (4.9-1) and (4.9-2). [For a recurrence relation for the Jacobi polynomials, see Jackson (1941), p. 173.]

(c) Thus verify (4.9-4) and (4.9-5).

(d) When $\alpha = \beta = 0$, verify that Jacobi-Gauss quadrature is identical to Legendre-Gauss quadrature.

*25. (*a*) When $\alpha = \beta = 1$, show that

$$J_n(x;1,1) = \frac{2}{n+2} P'_{n+1}(x) + p_{n-1}(x)$$

where $P_{n+1}(x)$ is the Legendre polynomial of degree $n + 1$ and $p_{n-1}(x)$ is some polynomial of degree $n - 1$.

(*b*) Use the relationship given in Prob. 22c and pertinent orthogonality relationships to deduce that $p_{n-1}(x)$ must be identically zero.

(*c*) Thus derive expressions for the weights and error term in the quadrature formula

$$\int_{-1}^{1} (1 - x^2)f(x) \, dx = \sum_{j=1}^{n} H_j f(a_j) + E$$

What are the abscissas?

26. Chebyshev polynomials:

(*a*) With $\alpha = \beta = -\frac{1}{2}$ in Prob. 24 and using $C_r = (-2)^r r!/(2r)!$, use (4.9-1) and (4.9-2) to show that

$$A_r = 2^{r-1} \quad \text{and} \quad \gamma_r = \pi/2$$

(*b*) Use these results to derive (4.9-10) and (4.9-11).

(*c*) By making the substitution $x = \cos \theta$ in the integral expressing the orthogonality of $T_r(x)$ to polynomials of lesser degree, show that this integral implies that

$$\int_0^{\pi} T_r(\cos \theta) \cos k\theta \, d\theta = 0 \quad k = 1, \ldots, r - 1$$

(*d*) Thus deduce that

$$T_r(\cos \theta) = c_r \cos r\theta$$

(*e*) Use part *a* to deduce that $c_r = 1$ and thus deduce (4.9-12).

(*f*) Show that the Chebyshev polynomials $T_r(x)$ satisfy the recurrence relation

$$T_{r+1}(x) = 2xT_r(x) - T_{r-1}(x)$$

27. (*a*) Verify (4.9-13) and (4.9-14).   (*b*) Thus verify (4.9-15).

28. Let $F(\theta)$ be an even, periodic function of θ of period 2π. Show how the Fourier series for this function can be converted into a series of Chebyshev polynomials (cf. Sec. 7.6).

29. (*a*) Use Chebyshev-Gauss quadrature with $n = 2, 3, 4, 5$ to approximate the integral $\int_{-1}^{1} \frac{\cos x}{(1 - x^2)^{1/2}} \, dx$ and compare the results with the true value and the results of part *e* of Prob. 12.

(*b*) Repeat part *a* for $\int_{-1}^{1} \frac{|x| \, dx}{(1 - x^4)^{1/2}}$.

*30. (*a*) Derive (4.9-19) by integrating by parts the orthogonality integral for $T_{r+1}(x)$ and requiring that $A_r = 2^{r-1}$.

(*b*) Use (4.9-19) to calculate γ_n and then derive (4.9-20) to (4.9-22).

*31. (*a*) Use the change of variable $y = \sqrt{x}$ in (4.7-1) to derive (4.9-23).

(*b*) Then use (4.7-10) and the recurrence relation in Prob. 19c to derive (4.9-25) and (4.9-26).

(*c*) Similarly, derive (4.9-27), (4.9-29), and (4.9-30).

*32. (a) Use the change of variable $y = \sqrt{x}$ to derive (4.9-31).

(b) Then use Sec. 4.9-2 and the recurrence relation in Prob. 26f to derive (4.9-32) to (4.9-34).

33. (a) Approximate the integral $\int_0^1 \sqrt{x} \cos x \, dx$ using (4.9-18) with $n = 2$. Find a bound on the error in your approximation.

(b) Approximate the integral $\int_0^1 \left(\frac{x}{1 - x} \right)^{\frac{1}{2}} e^x \, dx$ using (4.9-18) with $n = 2$. Again find a bound on the error.

34. (a) Remove the singularity in $\int_1^a \frac{e^{-\alpha x}}{(x^2 - 1)^{\frac{1}{2}}} \, dx$ by making a change of variable.

(b) Consider the integral $\int_0^a x^p f(x) \, dx$ for $p > -1$ and not an integer where $f(x)$ is regular at $x = 0$ so that the integral has a singularity at 0. By writing

$$\int_0^t x^p f(x) \, dx = \frac{1}{p + 1} t^{p+1} h(t)$$

and differentiating, derive a differential equation for $h(t)$. [This differential equation may be integrated numerically by one of the methods of the next chapter to find $h(a)$, which in turn gives the value of the integral.] At $t = 0$ find initial conditions for $h(t)$ and its first two derivatives. [Ref.: Hartree (1958), pp. 110–111.]

35. Consider the problem of calculating

$$g(y) = \frac{d}{dy} \int_0^y \frac{f(x)}{(y - x)^{\frac{1}{2}}} \, dx \qquad 0 \le y \le 1$$

(a) Why can't we differentiate under the integral sign?

(b) Suppose $f(x)$ is given at $x = 0, h, 2h, \ldots, 1$. Show how numerical quadrature and numerical differentiation can be combined to find an approximation for $g(y)$.

(c) By making the change of variable $x = y \sin^2 \theta$ and using Lagrangian interpolation to get a polynomial approximation for $f(x)$, derive another method for approximating $g(y)$. [Ref.: Hamming (1962), pp. 21–22.]

Section 4.10

36. (a) Use the technique of Prob. 11 to prove that a necessary condition on $p_r(x)$ in Sec. 4.10 is that it be orthogonal to all polynomials of lesser degree over $[a,b]$ with respect to $v(x)w(x)$.

(b) If $v(x)w(x)$ does not change sign in $[a,b]$, prove that the unassigned abscissas are real, distinct, and lie within $[a,b]$.

*37. (a) In Radau quadrature, show that the abscissas are zeros of

$$\phi_{n-1}(x) = \frac{1}{x + 1} \frac{d^{n-1}}{dx^{n-1}} U_{n-1}(x)$$

where

$$U_{n-1}(x) = C_{n-1}(x + 1)(x^2 - 1)^{n-1}$$

(b) With $C_{n-1} = \frac{1}{2^{n-1}(n - 1)!}$ and using the result of Prob. 25, show that

$$\phi_{n-1}(x) = P_{n-1}(x) + \frac{x - 1}{n} P'_{n-1}(x)$$

Then use the results of Prob. 19 and the recurrence relation of Prob. 22c to derive (4.10-19) to (4.10-23).

*38. Similarly verify (4.10-24) to (4.10-28).

39. Show that the Lobatto quadrature formula with $n = 3$ is equivalent to Simpson's rule. Why would you expect a priori that this would be true? Would you expect that any other Lobatto quadrature formula would be equivalent to a Newton-Cotes formula? Why?

40. (a) Use Radau quadrature to approximate the integral $\int_{-1}^{1} e^{-5x} \sin x \, dx$ for $n = 2, 3, 4, 5$. Compare these results with the true value and the results obtained using Legendre-Gauss quadrature.

(b) Use Lobatto quadrature to approximate the integral $\int_{-1}^{1} \cosh x \cos x \, dx$ for $n = 3, 4, 5$. Compare these results with the true value and the results obtained using Legendre-Gauss quadrature.

41. Show that, if r is even, the restriction that the a_i's be nonnegative in Jensen's inequality (4.10-33) is unnecessary.

*42. (a) Derive (4.10-32), (4.10-35), and (4.10-36), and from these equations derive the result on the existence of Chebyshev quadrature when $w(x) = e^{-x}$. For $n = 1, 2$ derive the weights and abscissas.

(b) Similarly, derive (4.10-37) to (4.10-39) and the results on existence when $w(x) = e^{-x^2}$. For $n = 1, 2, 3$ derive the weights and abscissas.

*43. (a) Try to use Jensen's inequality for the case $w(x) = 1$ and show why this approach fails.

(b) When $w(x)$ is an even function with respect to the center of the interval $[a,b]$, show that the systems of equations to be satisfied by the abscissas in Chebyshev quadrature form two separate sequences, one for n even and one for n odd.

*44. (a) If a Chebyshev quadrature formula over $[-1,1]$ with respect to the weight function $w(x)$ is applied to the function

$$f(x) = \frac{1}{u - x} \qquad u > 1$$

show that the quadrature formula becomes

$$\int_{-1}^{1} \frac{w(x)\, dx}{u - x} = \frac{\lambda}{n} \frac{d}{du} \ln p_n(u) + E\left[\frac{1}{u - x}\right]$$

where $\lambda = \int_{-1}^{1} w(x)\, dx$ and $p_n(x) = (x - a_1) \cdots (x - a_n)$.

(b) Thus deduce that

$$p_n(u) = C_n u^n \exp\left[\frac{n}{\lambda} \int_{-1}^{1} w(x) \ln\left(1 - \frac{x}{u}\right) dx\right] \exp\left[\frac{n}{\lambda} Q(u)\right]$$

where C_n is an arbitrary constant and

$$Q(u) = \int_{u}^{\infty} E\left[\frac{1}{u - x}\right] du$$

(c) Show that the argument of the first exponential above may be replaced by

$$-\frac{n}{\lambda} \sum_{j=1}^{\infty} \frac{c_j}{ju^j}$$

where $c_j = \int_{-1}^{1} x^j w(x) \, dx$.

(d) Assuming that the argument of the second exponential term in part b can be written

$$\sum_{j=1}^{\infty} \frac{d_j}{u^{n+k}}$$

(see Prob. 9, Chap. 5) show that

$$p_n(x) = x^n \exp\left[-\frac{n}{\lambda} \sum \frac{c_j}{jx^j}\right]$$

where the expansion of the exponential is to be terminated with the term in $1/x^n$. [Ref.: Hildebrand (1956), pp. 346–348.]

45. (a) Use the result of the previous problem to find the abscissas of the Chebyshev quadrature formula with $w(x) = 1$ for $n = 2, 3$.

(b) Use these results to approximate the integral $\int_{-1}^{1} x^2 e^{-x^2} \, dx$ and compare the approximations with the value found using a table of the error function.

Section 4.11

46. (a) Show that, if in a Legendre-Gauss composite formula m instead of two subintervals are used, the only change in (4.11-12) is to replace the $1/2^{2n}$ factor by $1/m^{2n}$.

(b) Derive the equations corresponding to (4.11-13) and (4.11-14) when $n = 3$ and $m/3$ subintervals are used.

47. (a) Use a Legendre-Gauss composite formula with $n = 1$ and $m = 2, 4, 8$ to approximate the integral of part a of Prob. 12. Compare the results with those obtained in Prob. 12.

(b) Repeat part a for $n = 2$ and $m = 2, 4, 8$ [i.e., use (4.11-13)].

(c) Repeat parts a and b for the integral of part e of Prob. 12. Compare results with those obtained in Probs. 12 and 29.

Section 4.12

48. Use an argument based on symmetry to prove that, when $w(x) = 1$, the closed Newton-Cotes quadrature formula when n is even is exact for polynomials of degree $n + 1$.

*49. In order to derive (4.12-7), consider the integral

$$I_j = \int_{a_j}^{a_{j+1}} p_{n+1}(x) \, dx \qquad n \text{ even}$$

(a) Show that $I_j = -I_{n-1-j}$.

(b) Use the mean-value theorem for integrals to show that

$$I_{j-1} = \frac{\xi - a_n - h}{\xi - a_0} I_j \qquad a_j < \xi < a_{j+1} \qquad j < \frac{n}{2}$$

(c) Thus, deduce that $|I_{j-1}| \geq |I_j|$, $j < n/2$ and from this deduce that $q(x)$ is of constant sign in $[a_0, a_n]$.

(d) Finally, derive both forms of the error in (4.12-7). [Ref.: Steffensen (1950), pp. 155–157.]

*50. When n is odd, the error has the form

$$E = \frac{1}{(n+1)!} \int_{a_0}^{a_n} p_{n+1}(x) f^{(n+1)}(\xi)\, dx$$

(a) Write this integral as the sum of two integrals, one from a_0 to a_{n-1} and the other from a_{n-1} to a_n, and apply the mean-value theorem for integrals to express the latter integral in the form (4.12-8).

(b) Show that

$$\frac{1}{(n+1)!}(x - a_n) f^{(n+1)}(\xi) = \frac{1}{n!} f^{(n)}(\eta) + c$$

where c is a constant and η lies in the interval spanned by $a_0, \ldots, a_{n-1}$ and x. (*Hint:* Use a technique similar to that in Theorem 4.1.)

(c) Use this result to write the former of the two integrals in part a in the form

$$\frac{1}{n!} \int_{a_0}^{a_{n-1}} p_n(x) f^{(n)}(\eta)\, dx$$

where $p_n(x) = (x - a_0) \cdots (x - a_{n-1})$.

(d) Finally, use the result of the previous problem to derive (4.12-8). [Ref.: Steffensen (1950), pp. 162–165.]

*51. (a) Let the quadrature formula

$$\int_{-1}^{1} f(x)\, dx \approx H_0 f(-1) + \sum_{j=1}^{n} H_i f(a_i)$$

be exact for polynomials of degree $2m - 1$ or less ($m < n$). Prove that, if all the weights are positive and all the a_j's are in $[-1,1]$, then there exists at least one a_j in the interval $[-1, \beta_1]$ where β_1 is the smallest of the zeros of $P'_m(x)$, the derivative of the Legendre polynomial of degree m. {*Hint:* Use the Lobatto quadrature formula (4.10-28) with $n = m + 1$ and consider the function $f(x) = \dfrac{[P'_m(x)]^2(1 - x^2)}{x - \beta_1}$.}

(b) Thus deduce that in the quadrature formula (4.12-1) with $[a,b] = [-1,1]$

$$\frac{2 - n}{n} < \beta_1$$

if (4.12-1) is to be exact for polynomials of degree $2m - 1$ and all the weights are positive.

(c) It can be shown that

$$\beta_1 < \frac{8}{(m-1)(m+3)} - 1$$

for $m > 1$. Use this and the fact that Newton-Cotes closed formulas are exact for polynomials of degree $n + 1$ when n is even and n when n is odd to prove that the weights of such formulas are positive only when $n \leq 7$ and $n = 9$. [Ref.: Bernstein (1937).]

52. (a) Show that the Newton-Cotes open formulas with n even are exact for polynomials of degree $n - 1$.

(b) When $w(x) = 1$ derive the error terms for the open formulas by using the techniques of Probs. 49 and 50.

*53. (a) Show that the Newton-Cotes quadrature formulas without the error term are equivalent to (3.9-3) with $y(x)$ replaced by $\int_a^b f(x)\,dx$, x^k by $\int_a^b x^k\,dx$, and with a row added corresponding to a_0.

(b) Using an equation analogous to (4.5-1), deduce that the Cotes numbers may be calculated using the inverse of the matrix

$$A_n = \begin{bmatrix} 1 & 1 & \cdots & \cdots & \cdots & 1 \\ a_0 & a_1 & \cdots & \cdots & \cdots & a_n \\ a_0^2 & \cdots & \cdots & \cdots & \cdots & a_n^2 \\ \cdots & \cdots & \cdots & \cdots & \cdots & \cdots \\ a_0^n & \cdots & \cdots & \cdots & \cdots & a_n^n \end{bmatrix}$$

(c) Let

$$\pi_i(x) = (x - a_0)(x - a_1) \cdots (x - a_{i-1})(x - a_{i+1}) \cdots (x - a_n)$$

$$= \sum_{k=0}^{n} C_{ik}x^k \qquad i = 0, \ldots, n$$

Show that the element in the mth row and kth column of $S_n = A_n^{-1}$ is

$$\frac{C_{m-1,k-1}}{\pi_{m-1}(a_{m-1})}$$

(d) Derive $S_1(-\tfrac{1}{2},\tfrac{1}{2})$ and $S_2(-1,0,1)$ where the values in parentheses are the abscissas.

(e) Show how the matrix $S_2(-1,0,1)$ can be used to generate any quadrature formula of the form

$$\int_a^b w(x)f(x)\,dx \approx H_0 f(-1) + H_1 f(0) + H_2 f(1)$$

Apply this to the cases (i), $w(x) = x$ and $[a,b] = [0,1]$, and (ii), $w(x) = x^2$ and $[a,b] = [-1,1]$. [Ref.: Hamming (1962), Chap. 10.]

*54. (a) Use the Lagrangian interpolation formula to prove that

$$\sum_{j=-k}^{k} (-1)^j \binom{2k}{k+j} f(x + jh) = (-1)^k h^{2k} f^{(2k)}(\xi) \qquad x - kh < \xi < x + kh$$

(b) Use this result with $k = 2$ and the Newton-Cotes closed-type five-point formula ($n = 4$) to derive the formula

$$\int_{x-2h}^{x+2h} f(x)\,dx = \frac{2h}{9}\,[f(x - 2h) + 8f(x - h) + 8f(x + h) + f(x + 2h)]$$

$$+ \frac{4h^5}{945}\,[21f^{\mathrm{iv}}(\eta_1) - 2h^2 f^{\mathrm{vi}}(\eta_2)]$$

(c) Similarly, using the Newton-Cotes closed-type seven-point formula, derive *Weddle's rule*

$$\int_{x-3h}^{x+3h} f(x)\,dx = \frac{3h}{10}\,[f(x-3h) + 5f(x-2h) + f(x-h) + 6f(x) + f(x+h)$$

$$+ 5f(x+2h) + f(x+3h)] - \frac{h^7}{1400}\,[10f^{vi}(\eta_1) + 9h^2 f^{viii}(\eta_2)]$$

(d) Using the same seven-point formula, derive *Hardy's rule*

$$\int_{x-3h}^{x+3h} f(x)\,dx = \frac{h}{100}\,[28f(x-3h) + 162f(x-2h) + 220f(x) + 162f(x+2h)$$

$$+ 28f(x+3h)] + \frac{9h^7}{1400}\,[2f^{vi}(\eta_1) - h^2 f^{viii}(\eta_2)]$$

55. (a) Derive the equation analogous to (4.12-15) for the parabolic rule.

(b) Use the parabolic rule with $m = 4$ and 8 to approximate the integral of Example 4.3.

(c) Use the result of part a to get a third approximation. Compare the results with those of part b and Example 4.3.

56. By considering the significance of the derivative term in quadrature formula errors, discuss why the efficiency of Richardson extrapolation is dependent on the monotonic convergence of successive approximations using an increasing number of subintervals.

*57. (a) Show that $T_{1,k}$ in Romberg integration is the parabolic rule for 2^k subintervals.

(b) Similarly, show that $T_{2,k}$ is the composite rule formed using the Newton-Cotes closed formula with $n = 4$ (5 points) and 2^k subintervals.

(c) Show that the leading term in the error of $T_{m,k}$ is of the order of $[(b-a)/2^k]^{2(m+1)}$.

(d) Use this and the number of abscissas that $T_{m,k}$ uses in each subinterval to show that $T_{m,k}$ corresponds to no Newton-Cotes composite rule for $m \geq 3$.

*58. (a) Use induction, (4.12-27), and (4.12-28) to derive (4.12-31).

(b) Use (4.12-32) to show that $\displaystyle\sum_{j=0}^{m} |c_{mj}|$ is bounded and, in fact, less than $e^{8/9}$. [The true value of the infinite product in (4.12-32) is approximately 1.969.]

(c) Use (4.12-31) and the boundedness of the c_{mj} to show that $c_{m,m-j} \to \infty$ as $m \to \infty$ for any j.

*59. (a) Show that d_{jm} in (4.12-33) is given by

$$d_{jm} = c_{m0} + 2c_{m1} + 4c_{m2} + \cdots + 2^p c_{mp} \qquad j = 1, \ldots, 2^{m+k} - 1$$

where $p < m$ and 2^p is the greatest power of 2 which divides j. For $j = 0$ and 2^{m+k}, show that d_{jm} is given by one-half the above.

(b) Use (4.12-31) to show that

$$|c_{mj}| > 3|c_{m,j+1}|$$

(c) Deduce then that $d_{jm} > 0$ for all j and m and that

$$\tfrac{4}{9} < d_{jm} < \alpha$$

where $\alpha = \lim_{m \to \infty} t_m(0) \approx 1.452$.

60. Let $\phi(x)$ be a function such that

$$\phi(1/4^m) = T_{0,m}$$

Use (4.12-27) to show that Romberg's method is equivalent to using Neville's method of iterated interpolation (see Prob. 26, Chap. 3) to approximate $\phi(0)$.

61. (a) Use Romberg integration to approximate the integral of part a of Prob. 12. In particular, calculate $T_{m,0}$, $m = 1, \ldots, 6$. Compare this result with the results of Probs. 12 and 47 and Table 4.9.

(b) Repeat part a for the integrals of parts b, c, and d of Prob. 12.

62. (a) For $n = 1, 2$ derive the weights for the closed Newton-Cotes quadrature formula

$$\int_0^1 \sqrt{x}\, f(x)\, dx \approx \sum_{j=0}^n H_j f(a + j/n)$$

so that the formula will be exact for polynomials of degree n or less.

(b) Repeat part a with $\sqrt{x}$ replaced by $1/\sqrt{x}$.

(c) Use the results of parts a and b to find approximate values of the integrals of part a of Prob. 33 and Example 4.6, respectively, and compare the corresponding results.

*63. Consider the quadrature formula

$$\int_a^b f(x)\, dx \approx H_0[f(b) - f(a)] + \sum_{j=1}^n H_j f(a_j)$$

(a) Show that

$$p_n(x) = \frac{C}{(x - a)(x - b)} \frac{d^{n-1}}{dx^{n-1}} [(x - a)^n (x - b)^n (x - \alpha)]$$

is orthogonal over $[a,b]$ to all polynomials of degree $n - 2$ or less with respect to the weight function $(x - a)(x - b)$ where C and α are arbitrary constants.

(b) Let the abscissas be the zeros of $p_n(x)$. Derive two simultaneous equations for H_0 and α by requiring the quadrature formula to be exact when $f(x) = p_n(x)$ and $xp_n(x)$.

(c) Find an expression for the H_j's by requiring the formula to be exact when

$$f(x) = l_j(x) = \frac{p_n(x)}{(x - a_j)p_n'(a_j)}$$

(d) By using the expression $x^k = \sum_{j=1}^n l_j(x)a_j^k$, $k = 0, 1, \ldots, n - 1$, show that the quadrature formula is exact for polynomials of degree $n - 1$ or less. Then use this result, the result of part b, and an inductive argument to show that the quadrature formula is exact for polynomials of degree $2n$ or less. [*Hint:* Write a general polynomial of degree $2n$ as $\sum_{j=0}^n c_j x^j p_n(x) + q_{n-1}(x)$ where $q_{n-1}(x)$ is a polynomial of degree $n - 1$.]

(e) Prove that the zeros of $p_n(x)$ are real and distinct. (They can also be shown to lie within the interval $[a,b]$.) For $n = 1$ and $[a,b] = [0,h]$, determine H_0, H_1, α, and a_1. What advantage does this quadrature formula have in composite rules? [Ref.: Ralston (1959).]

Section 4.13

64. Derive the formulas for the number of abscissas required in a sequence of uses of various composite rules as given in Sec. 4.13.

Section 4.14

65. Let the quadrature formula used in (4.14-2) have an error term of the form $c_1 h^{k_1+1} f^{(k_1)}(\eta)$ when applied to functions of one variable. Let the corresponding error in (4.14-3) be $c_2 h^{k_2+1} f^{(k_2)}(\bar{\eta})$. Show that, if the weights are positive, the error term in (4.14-4) has the form

$$E = C_1 h^{k_1+1} \frac{\partial^{k_1}}{\partial y^{k_1}} f(\bar{\eta}_2,\eta_1) + C_2 h^{k_2+1} \frac{\partial^{k_2}}{\partial x^{k_2}} f(\bar{\eta}_1,\eta_2) + C_3 h^{k_1+k_2+2} \frac{\partial^{k_1+k_2}}{\partial x^{k_2}\partial y^{k_1}} f(\bar{\eta}_1,\eta_2)$$

where C_1, C_2, C_3 are constants, $a < \eta_i < b$, $c < \bar{\eta}_i < d$, $i = 1, 2.$ ⌉

Section 4.15

66. (a) Use the definitions of the Bernoulli polynomials and numbers and (4.15-6) to derive (4.15-7) and (4.15-8).
  (b) Use these identities to derive (4.15-10).
  (c) Use (4.15-2) to generate $B_k(x)$, $k = 0, 1, 2, 3$.
****67.** (a) Show that

$$\frac{t}{e^t - 1} + \frac{t}{2} = \frac{t}{2} \coth \frac{t}{2}$$

and from this deduce the result (4.15-6).
  (b) Similarly, show that

$$\frac{t}{e^{t/2} + 1} - \frac{t}{2} = -\frac{t}{2} \tanh (\tfrac{1}{4}t)$$

and from this deduce that $B_{2k+1}(\tfrac{1}{2}) = 0$, $k > 0$.
  (c) Use (4.15-2) to show that

$$B_k(1 - x) + B_k = (-1)^k [B_k(x) + B_k]$$

and thus deduce that for $k \geq 1$, $B_{2k}(x - \tfrac{1}{2})$ is an even function and $B_{2k+1}(x - \tfrac{1}{2})$ is an odd function.
  (d) Use parts b and c, (4.15-7), and (4.15-8) to deduce that, if $B_{2k+1}(x)$ vanishes anywhere in [0,1] other than at 0, $\tfrac{1}{2}$, and 1, then $B_{2k+1}(x)$ has at least five zeros on [0,1] and $B_{2k}(x) + B_{2k}$ has at least four zeros. Thus show that $B_{2k-1}(x)$ must also have five zeros. By continuing this argument, find a contradiction and thus deduce that $B_{2k}(x)$ can vanish only at the end points of [0,1] and that $B_{2k}(x)$ takes on its extreme value in [0,1] at $x = \tfrac{1}{2}$.

68. (a) Use part d of the previous problem to deduce that (4.15-15) may be written

$$E_m = - \frac{n h^{2m+1} f^{(2m+2)}(\eta)}{(2m + 2)!} \int_0^h B_{2m+2}\left(\frac{y}{h}\right) dy$$

when $x_0 < \eta < x_0 + nh$.
  (b) Use (4.15-8) and the previous problem to show that

$$\int_0^1 B_{2m+2}(t)\, dt = -B_{2m+2}$$

  (c) Use this result to deduce (4.15-16).

*69. (a) Use (4.15-7) and (4.15-8) to show that

$$B''_{2k+2}(x) = (2k + 1)(2k + 2)[B_{2k}(x) + B_{2k}]$$

(b) Use (4.15-3), part b of the previous problem, and part a to deduce that $B''_{2k+2}(0)$ has a sign different from that of $B_{2k}(x)$ on [0,1].

(c) Deduce from this that $B_{2k}(x)$ and $B_{2k+2}(x)$ have opposite signs on [0,1] and, therefore, that B_{2k} and B_{2k+2} have opposite signs.

(d) Use this result and (4.15-16) to deduce that, if $f^{(2m+2)}(x)$ and $f^{(2m+4)}(x)$ do not change sign and have the same sign on $[x_0, x_0 + nh]$, then the error in the Euler-Maclaurin sum formula is less than the magnitude of the first neglected term.

*70. (a) Use (4.15-2) and (4.15-5) to show that

$$\frac{t}{e^{t/2} - e^{-t/2}} = \sum_{k=0}^{\infty} [B_k(\tfrac{1}{2}) + B_k] \frac{t^k}{k!}$$

(b) Use (4.15-5) to show that

$$\frac{t}{e^{t/2} - e^{-t/2}} = \sum_{k=0}^{\infty} (2^{-k+1} - 1)B_k \frac{t^k}{k!}$$

(c) Deduce then that

$$B_k(\tfrac{1}{2}) = 2(2^{-k} - 1)B_k$$

(d) Use this result, Eq. (4.15-15), and part d of Prob. 67 to show that, if $f^{(2m+2)}(x)$ does not change sign on $[x_0, x_0 + nh]$, then the error in the Euler-Maclaurin sum formula is less than twice the first neglected term.

71. If we sum the ordinates halfway between the successive ordinates in (4.15-14), we may derive the *second Euler-Maclaurin sum formula* [see Steffensen (1950), pp. 134–135]:

$$\sum_{j=0}^{n-1} f[x_0 + (j + \tfrac{1}{2})h] = \frac{1}{h} \int_{x_0}^{x_0+nh} f(y)\,dy) - \sum_{k=1}^{m} \frac{(1 - 2^{1-2k})B_{2k}h^{2k-1}}{(2k)!}$$
$$\times [f^{(2k-1)}(x_0 + nh) - f^{(2k-1)}(x_0)] + E_m$$

where

$$E_m = -n \frac{(1 - 2^{-1-2m})B_{2m+2}h^{2m+2}}{(2m + 2)!} f^{(2m+2)}(\xi)$$

where $x_0 < \xi < x_0 + nh$. Show that, when this formula is used as a quadrature formula, it corresponds to a composite rule based on the Newton-Cotes open-type one-point formula with correction terms. From this formula, derive an analog of Gregory's formula.

72. (a) Show that, if Gregory's formula (4.15-18) is written to include differences through order n, it is exact for polynomials of degree n. Thus deduce that Gregory's formula with differences through order n is equivalent to a Newton-Cotes closed formula with $n + 1$ points.

(b) Write the equivalent to Gregory's formula using central differences. This formula is called *Gauss's formula*. (Use the notation of Prob. 16c, Chap. 3.) [Ref.: Hamming (1962), p. 157.]

73. Euler's constant γ is defined as

$$\gamma = \lim_{n \to \infty} \left(\sum_{i=1}^{n} \frac{1}{i} - \ln n \right) \approx .57721566$$

(a) Use the Euler-Maclaurin sum formula with $x_0 = 1$ to try to approximate γ to eight decimal places. Explain your results.

(b) Repeat part a with $x_0 = 10$ and again explain your results.

74. (a) Use Gregory's formula with $n = 16$ and retaining differences through the second to approximate the integral of part a of Prob. 12. (Use the results of Prob. 61a to get the trapezoidal-rule approximation.) Compare the results with those of Probs. 12, 47, and 61 and Table 4.9.

(b) Repeat part a with $n = 8$. How do you explain the result?

75. (a) Show that

$$x^{(n)} = n!(x)_n$$

(b) Write

$$x^{(n)} = \sum_{k=0}^{n} \alpha_{nk} x^k$$

and use part a to show that

$$\frac{d^j}{dx^j} (x)_n = \frac{1}{n!} \sum_{k=j}^{n} \frac{k!}{(k-j)!} \alpha_{nk} x^{k-i} \qquad j \leqq n$$

(c) By setting $x = 0$ in part b and using (4.1-15) and (4.15-20), show that

$$\alpha_{nk} = S_n^{(k)}$$

(d) Use this result to derive the recurrence relation

$$S_{n+1}^{(k)} = S_n^{(k-1)} - nS_n^{(k)} \qquad k = 1, 2, \ldots, n$$

Use this relation and the results of Prob. 4 to tabulate the Stirling numbers for $n = 1$, 2, 3, 4, 5.

76. (a) Show that x^n may be written as a linear combination of the $x^{(k)}$, $k = 0$, 1, . . . , n. The coefficients $s_n^{(k)}$ in this linear combination are called Stirling numbers of the second kind.

(b) How would you use part a to evaluate

$$\sum_{x=M}^{N-1} p(x)$$

where $p(x)$ is any polynomial.

(c) Show that $s_n^{(n)} = 1$ for any n and $s_n^{(0)} = 0$ for $n > 0$.

(d) Derive the recurrence relation

$$s_{n+1}^{(k)} = s_n^{(k-1)} + ks_n^{(k)}$$

and with this tabulate the Stirling numbers of the second kind for $n = 1, 2, 3, 4, 5$.

77. (*a*) Verify that $\tilde{S}$ in Example 4.13 equals $\frac{1}{4}$.

(*b*) Use the technique of Sec. 4.15-2 to convert the problem of summing

$$S = \sum_{x=1}^{\infty} \frac{x}{(x^2 + 1)^2}$$

to one of summing a more rapidly convergent series.

(*c*) Repeat part *b* for

$$S = \sum_{k=1}^{\infty} \frac{1}{x^4}$$

By summing a few terms of S and the more rapidly convergent series, compare the convergence of both to the true result $\pi^4/90$.   [Ref.: Hamming (1962), p. 49.]

78. Prove that, if (4.15-26) is satisfied when $R(x)$ and $\bar{R}(x)$ both have denominator degrees which exceed the numerator degrees by d, then $R(x) - \bar{R}(x)$ has a difference in degree between numerator and denominator of at least $d + 1$.

chapter 5

THE NUMERICAL SOLUTION
OF ORDINARY DIFFERENTIAL
EQUATIONS

5.1 STATEMENT OF THE PROBLEM

Our concern in this chapter is the solution of the first-order differential equation

$$dy/dx = f(x,y) \qquad y(x_0) = y_0 \tag{5.1-1}$$

We assume that

1. $f(x,y)$ is defined and continuous in the strip $x_0 \leqq x \leqq b$, $-\infty < y < \infty$ with x_0 and b finite.
2. There exists a constant L such that for any x in $[x_0,b]$ and any two numbers y and y^*

$$|f(x,y) - f(x,y^*)| \leqq L|y - y^*|$$

These conditions are sufficient to prove that there exists on $[x_0,b]$ a unique continuous, differentiable function $y(x)$ satisfying (5.1-1).† The Lipschitz condition (2) is weaker than the assumption that $\partial f/\partial y$ is continuous and bounded (why?).

More generally, we may consider (5.1-1) to be a system of N first-order differential equations in which y, y_0, and f are vectors with N com-

---

† If the reader has not recently looked at the basic existence theory for the solution of (5.1-1), he would be well advised to do so now; see, for example, Henrici (1962a, pp. 15–26).

ponents.   Much of what we shall develop in this chapter will be equally true for single equations and for systems.   However, some of our results, particularly those on stability, will be developed for single equations only, because with systems the algebraic problems become intractable.   Considered as a system, the formulation (5.1-1) is quite general in the sense that any higher-order equation or system of higher-order equations can be reduced to (5.1-1) if (and only if) the system can be rewritten with the highest-order derivative in each dependent variable appearing as the left-hand side of one equation and appearing nowhere else {1}.   For example, the equation

$$d^2y/dx^2 = f(x,y,y') \tag{5.1-2}$$

may be written

$$dz/dx = f(x,y,z) \qquad dy/dx = z \tag{5.1-3}$$

For single differential equations of order 3 or more, there is seldom any drawback to converting the equation to the form (5.1-1).   However, second-order differential equations are sufficiently common and important for there to exist a number of special methods directly designed for the solution of such equations.   We shall consider some of these in Sec. 5.8-1.

Our object in solving (5.1-1) will be to find y at a sequence of values of x, $\{x_i\}$.   We distinguish here between two types of methods for effecting this solution:

1. Those in which $f(x,y)$ will be evaluated only at the points (x_i,y_i) where y_i is the computed value of y at $x = x_i$.   Such methods are special cases of the general operator of Sec. 2.2 (why?), and will be called *numerical integration methods*.
2. Those in which $f(x,y)$ will be evaluated at points other than (x_i,y_i). Such methods are not special cases of the general operator and will be called *Runge-Kutta type methods*.

For reasons which will become clear later in the chapter, our emphasis will be on numerical integration methods, although Runge-Kutta methods have an important role to play, as we discuss in Sec. 5.6-3.

In deriving methods for the numerical solution of differential equations, the following considerations will be important:

1. How much error is incurred at each step of the computation (truncation and roundoff error) and how this error affects the results in subsequent steps.   This is the first instance in which we have had to consider the *propagation* of error incurred at one stage of a calculation into later stages.   This extremely important phenomenon, which occurs in many areas of numerical analysis (see, in

particular, Chap. 9), is generally discussed under the heading of stability, a stable method being one in which errors incurred at one step do not tend to be magnified in later steps (we shall formalize this intuitive notion in Sec. 5.4).†

2. Related to the problem of errors and error propagation is the problem of being able to estimate the error at a given stage of the computation as a function of computed results.

3. How the solution can be started. Equation (5.1-1) contains an initial condition at $x = x_0$. But many numerical integration methods require values of y at more than one point to compute another point. Thus auxiliary means of starting the computation will often be required. Closely related to this problem is that of changing the interval between successive x_i's during the course of the computation.

4. The speed of the method. In the solution of large systems of equations ($N > 10$), the time required for the computation—even on the fastest of computers—can be considerable. Since no reasonable discussion of problems in numerical analysis can avoid such a practical consideration, speed of computation will affect our evaluation of the methods to be derived here.

5.2 NUMERICAL INTEGRATION METHODS

First we introduce some notation. Let $Y(x)$ be the true solution of (5.1-1) and $y(x)$ the calculated solution. Further, let

$$
\begin{aligned}
Y_i &= Y(x_i) & y_i &= y(x_i) \\
Y_i' &= \left. \frac{dY}{dx} \right|_{x = x_i} = f(x_i, Y_i) & y_i' &= f(x_i, y_i) \\
h &= x_{i+1} - x_i
\end{aligned}
\tag{5.2-1}
$$

Note that, since Y is the true solution, $f(x_i, Y_i)$ is equal to $\left. \dfrac{dY}{dx} \right|_{x = x_i}$. However, the function $y(x)$ "exists" only at the points x_i, $i = 1, 2, 3 \ldots$. Thus, when we replace $f(x_i, y_i)$ by y_i', this is a notational convenience.

† This phenomenon should not be confused with inherent instability in the differential equations themselves. For example, the system $y_1' = y_2$, $y_2' = y_1$, which has the general solution $y_1 = a_1 e^x + a_2 e^{-x}$, $y_2 = a_1 e^x - a_2 e^{-x}$, is inherently unstable with respect to the initial conditions $y_1(0) = -y_2(0) = 1$. In this case $a_1 = 0$, $a_2 = 1$, but any perturbation of the initial conditions results in a nonzero a_1 and, therefore, in a solution in which the e^x term eventually is dominant. Since the per step error introduced by *any* numerical method results in a numerical solution at each point x_i which satisfies the differential equations with perturbed initial conditions (why?), it is not possible to obtain an accurate numerical solution of this system with the initial conditions given above.

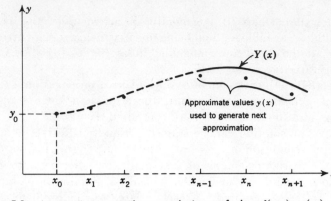

Fig. 5.1   Approximate and true solutions of $y' = f(x,y)$, $y(x_0) = y_0$.

The reader should, however, have an intuitive feeling that, if $y(x)$ is a good approximation to the true solution, then $f(x_i,y_i)$ will be a good approximation to Y_i'.   It is important that the reader realize that these seemingly tiresome (and perhaps obvious) distinctions between true and calculated solutions need to be made here because the approximation to the solution of (5.1-1) at each point x_i will be calculated using *approximate* values of the solution at previous points (cf. Fig. 5.1).   By contrast in interpolation, we used *true* functional values at a set of points to calculate an approximate value at another point.†

The interval h between steps will generally remain constant over a number of steps but can be changed when error considerations make this desirable; see Sec. 5.6-4.

Using the notation of Sec. 2.2, the general numerical integration equation can be written

$$\sum_{j=1}^{n} \sum_{i=0}^{m} A_{ij} Y^{(i)}(x_{ij}) = T \tag{5.2-2}$$

where we use T instead of E for the error in order to emphasize that this is truncation error.   The equation we calculate with is then

$$\sum_{j=1}^{n} \sum_{i=0}^{m} A_{ij} y^{(i)}(x_{ij}) = 0 \tag{5.2-3}$$

with at least two A_{0j}'s required to be nonzero so that each calculated value depends upon at least one previous value of y.   Also at least one $A_{1j} \neq 0$ so that (5.2-3) indeed depends on the differential equation.   By analogy

† Of course, because of roundoff the functional values were approximate also, but the point here is that the approximate values at one stage of the computation are the results of a sequence of roundoff and truncation errors at previous steps.

with (5.2-1), we may calculate higher derivatives of y than the first.   For example,

$$y''(x_i) = \frac{d}{dx} f(x,y) \Big|_{(x_i,y_i)} \tag{5.2-4}$$

But, because this tends to be quite tedious if $f(x,y)$ is at all complicated and because the analysis of methods using higher derivatives can become very difficult, we shall restrict ourselves mainly to the case $m = 1$.   In Sec. 5.8, we shall consider briefly methods with $m > 1$.

In line with our assumption that in numerical integration methods $f(x,y)$ is to be evaluated only at points (x_i,y_i), we restrict each x_{1j} to be equal to some x_{0k}.   Thus, when $m = 1$, we may write (5.2-3) as

$$y_{n+1} = \sum_{i=0}^{p} a_i y_{n-i} + h \sum_{i=-1}^{p} b_i y'_{n-i} \tag{5.2-5}$$

where we have further changed the notation to let the last value of x at which y was calculated be x_n and to let the number of past values used to compute y_{n+1} be $p + 1$.   The interval h has been introduced for later notational convenience.

The following points about (5.2-5) should be noted:

1. In any particular specialization of (5.2-5), any of the a_i's or b_i's may be zero, but we assume that either a_{n-p} or b_{n-p} is not zero.
2. If $b_{-1} = 0$, then y_{n+1} is expressed as a linear combination of (computationally) known past values of y_n and is thus easily computed. Formulas with $b_{-1} = 0$ are called explicit or *forward-integration formulas*.
3. If $b_{-1} \neq 0$, (5.2-5) is only an implicit equation for y_{n+1} since $y'_{n+1} = f(x_{n+1},y_{n+1})$ and will generally be solvable only by an iterative procedure.   It will probably be no surprise to the reader that the greater difficulty of using formulas with $b_{-1} \neq 0$ is made up by their more desirable properties (otherwise they would hardly be worth a mention!).   Formulas with $b_{-1} \neq 0$ are called implicit or *iterative formulas*.   Note, however, that, if the differential equation (5.1-1) is linear, then (5.2-5) may be solved explicitly for y_{n+1} {3}.

When $b_{-1} = 0$, then (5.2-5) is an extrapolation equation in the sense of Chap. 2.   When $b_{-1} \neq 0$, (5.2-5) still defines y_{n+1} as some function of $y_n, \ldots, y_{n-p}, y'_n, \ldots, y'_{n-p}$ and is thus also an extrapolation equation although not in the sense of Chap. 2.   Thus we may say that the numerical solution of ordinary differential equations is essentially a process of successive extrapolations.

5.2-1   The method of undetermined coefficients

We are ready now to consider specifying the coefficients in (5.2-5). As in the previous two chapters, we shall do this so as to make (5.2-5) exact if $Y(x)$ is a polynomial of some specified degree. By "exact" here we mean that, if $Y(x)$ is a polynomial of the specified degree and if the values on the right-hand side of (5.2-5) are true values of the solution then, except for roundoff, y_{n+1} will also be a true value. In contrast to the previous two chapters, however, we shall often not specify the coefficients so as to achieve the highest possible order of accuracy. If, for example, we have five coefficients and determine them so that (5.2-5) is exact for polynomials of degree 3 or less only, then in general we shall have one free parameter which we may use to do one or more of the following:

1. Make the coefficient in the error term small.
2. Make the error-propagation properties of the formula as desirable as possible.
3. Give the formula certain other desirable computational properties such as zero coefficients.

Let us suppose that we wish to make (5.2-5) exact for polynomials of degree r. As in the previous chapter, we shall say that such a formula has an accuracy of order r or is of order r. Then the method of undetermined coefficients consists in considering the $r + 1$ equations derived by letting $y_i = x_i^j, j = 0, \ldots, r$ in (5.2-5). Before actually doing this, we note that (1) There is no loss of generality in setting $h = 1$ because putting $y_i = x_i^j$ in (5.2-5) results in the cancellation of h (why?). (2) There is no loss of generality in letting $x_n = 0$ since the coefficients will be independent of the origin of the coordinate (why?).

With $h = 1$ and $x_n = 0$, we have

$$1 = \sum_{i=0}^{p} a_i \qquad\qquad\qquad\qquad j = 0$$

$$1 = -\sum_{i=0}^{p} ia_i + \sum_{i=-1}^{p} b_i \qquad\qquad j = 1 \qquad\qquad (5.2\text{-}6)$$

$$1 = \sum_{i=0}^{p} (-i)^j a_i + j \sum_{i=-1}^{p} (-i)^{j-1} b_i \qquad j = 2, \ldots, r$$

These are $r + 1$ equations for the $2p + 3$ or fewer coefficients in (5.2-5) [some of the coefficients (e.g., b_{-1}) may be postulated equal to zero]. If the number of coefficients is $r + 1$, then, generally, (5.2-6) may be solved for the a_i's and b_i's. If the number of coefficients is greater than $r + 1$, we shall have free parameters in general, and if the number is less than $r + 1$, there will in general be no solution.

If the first two equations of (5.2-6) are satisfied, we say that the associated numerical integration method is *consistent*. Consistency is thus equivalent to (5.2-5) being exact for linear polynomials. All the numerical integration procedures that we shall consider will be consistent.

Example 5.1   Determine the coefficients in

$$y_{n+1} = a_0 y_n + h(b_{-1} y'_{n+1} + b_0 y'_n) \tag{5.2-7}$$

if the formula is to be exact for polynomials of degree 2 (i.e., $r = 2$, $p = 0$).
The equations (5.2-6) are

$$1 = a_0 \qquad 1 = b_{-1} + b_0 \qquad 1 = 2b_{-1} \tag{5.2-8}$$

so that the equation is

$$y_{n+1} = y_n + (h/2)(y'_{n+1} + y'_n) \tag{5.2-9}$$

If, instead of polynomials of degree 2, we had required exactness only for polynomials of degree 1, then only the first two equations of (5.2-8) would have to be satisfied and (5.2-7) would then be

$$y_{n+1} = y_n + h[(1 - b_0)y'_{n+1} + b_0 y'_n]$$

with b_0 a free parameter.

Equation (5.2-9) is precisely the trapezoidal rule, as is easily seen by replacing $f(x)$ by $y'(x)$ in (4.12-10). Since it is the trapezoidal rule, we know that the truncation error incurred at each step is $-h^3 Y'''(\eta)/12$, $x_n < \eta < x_{n+1}$. This truncation error needs to be properly interpreted. It would be the difference between y_n and the true solution (exclusive of roundoff) if the values on the right-hand side of (5.2-9) were *true values*. It is also worth noting at this point that the truncation error in formulas of the form (5.2-5) will not always be simply determinable as in this case; see the next section.

Example 5.1 is a special case of the general result that any Newton-Cotes quadrature formula becomes a numerical integration formula if $f(x)$ is replaced by $y'(x)$. More generally, if we replace $f(x)$ by $y'(x)$ in the Lagrangian interpolation formula at equal intervals for the points x_n, $x_{n-1}, \ldots, x_{n-p}$ and then integrate between x_{n-j} and x_{n+1} for any j, the result is a formula of the form (5.2-5) {5}. We shall not consider this way of generating numerical integration formulas any further because the method of undetermined coefficients enables us to derive all numerical integration methods, including many of interest which are not derivable from Newton-Cotes formulas.

5.3   TRUNCATION ERROR IN NUMERICAL INTEGRATION METHODS

As we noticed in the previous section, when a numerical integration method is equivalent to one of the numerical quadrature methods of Chap.

4, then the truncation-error term can be easily written down.   In general, however, numerical integration methods of the form (5.2-2) are not equivalent to numerical quadrature methods.   Our object here is to determine the truncation error T in (5.2-2) for formulas of the specific type (5.2-5), although the method we present is also applicable to the general case (5.2-2).   If the numerical integration method is of the form (5.2-5), then the true solution satisfies the equation

$$Y_{n+1} = \sum_{i=0}^{p} a_i Y_{n-i} + h \sum_{i=-1}^{p} b_i Y'_{n-i} + T_n \qquad (5.3\text{-}1)$$

where the notation T_n denotes the truncation error at the step from x_n to x_{n+1}.

In order to find an expression for T_n, it is tempting to assume that

$$T_n = ch^{r+1}Y^{(r+1)}(\eta) \qquad (5.3\text{-}2)$$

where c is a constant and r is the order of accuracy of (5.3-1), in analogy with the trapezoidal-rule error and the general form of the error in numerical quadrature methods.   If T_n has the form (5.3-2), then c may be found by letting $Y(x)$ be x^{r+1} and substituting this into (5.3-1) (why?).   In fact, most numerical integration as well as most quadrature formulas of interest do have errors of the form (5.3-2).   However, as the following derivation will indicate, the truncation error cannot always be written in the form (5.3-2).

Our approach is to expand each Y_i and Y'_i in (5.3-1) in a Taylor series about some value of x which, for the sake of computational convenience, we choose to be x_n.   We have

$$Y_{n-i} = Y_n - ihY'_n + \frac{i^2 h^2}{2!} Y''_n + \cdots$$

$$+ \frac{(-1)^r i^r h^r}{r!} Y_n^{(r)} + \frac{1}{r!} \int_{x_n}^{x_{n-i}} (x_{n-i} - s)^r Y^{(r+1)}(s)\, ds \qquad (5.3\text{-}3)$$

and

$$Y'_{n-i} = Y'_n - ihY''_n + \cdots + \frac{(-1)^{r-1} i^{r-1} h^{r-1}}{(r-1)!} Y_n^{(r)}$$

$$+ \frac{1}{(r-1)!} \int_{x_n}^{x_{n-i}} (x_{n-i} - s)^{r-1} Y^{(r+1)}(s)\, ds \qquad (5.3\text{-}4)$$

where r is the order of accuracy of (5.3-1).   Substituting (5.3-3) and (5.3-4) into (5.3-1), solving for T_n, and remembering that (5.3-1) is exact when $Y(x)$ is a polynomial of degree r or less, we get

$$T_n = \frac{1}{r!}\left[\int_{x_n}^{x_{n+1}} (x_{n+1} - s)^r Y^{(r+1)}(s)\, ds\right.$$

$$- \sum_{i=0}^{p} a_i \int_{x_n}^{x_{n-i}} (x_{n-i} - s)^r Y^{(r+1)}(s)\, ds$$

$$\left.- rh \sum_{i=-1}^{p} b_i \int_{x_n}^{x_{n-i}} (x_{n-i} - s)^{r-1} Y^{(r+1)}(s)\, ds\right] \quad (5.3\text{-}5)$$

which we rewrite as

$$T_n = \frac{1}{r!}\int_{x_{n-p}}^{x_{n+1}} \left\{\overline{(x_{n+1} - s)}^r - rhb_{-1}\overline{(x_{n+1} - s)}^{r-1}\right.$$

$$+ \sum_{i=1}^{p} [a_i\overline{(x_{n-i} - s)}^r + rhb_i\overline{(x_{n-i} - s)}^{r-1}]\Big\} Y^{(r+1)}(s)\, ds$$

$$= \frac{1}{r!}\int_{x_{n-p}}^{x_{n+1}} G(s) Y^{(r+1)}(s)\, ds \quad (5.3\text{-}6)$$

where

$$\overline{(x_{n-i} - s)} = \begin{cases} x_{n-i} - s & \begin{cases} x_{n-i} \leqq s \leqq x_n & i \neq -1 \\ x_n \leqq s & i = -1 \end{cases} \\ 0 & \text{otherwise} \end{cases} \quad (5.3\text{-}7)$$

The function $G(s)$ is called the *influence function*. If $G(s)$ is of constant sign in $[x_{n-p}, x_{n+1}]$, then we may apply the second law of the mean to get

$$T_n = \frac{Y^{(r+1)}(\eta)}{r!} \int_{x_{n-p}}^{x_{n+1}} G(s)\, ds \quad (5.3\text{-}8)$$

where $x_{n-p} < \eta < x_{n+1}$. Equation (5.3-8) is indeed of the form (5.3-2) (why?). But if $G(s)$ does change sign in $[x_{n-p}, x_{n+1}]$, then the error cannot be expressed in the form (5.3-2) {6}, although we may still bound the error as

$$|T_n| < \frac{|Y^{(r+1)}(\eta)|}{r!} \int_{x_{n-p}}^{x_{n+1}} |G(s)|\, ds \quad (5.3\text{-}9)$$

Some examples of the use of the influence function to find errors are considered in the problems {8 to 11}.

Example 5.2   Consider the numerical integration method

$$y_{n+1} = (1 - a)y_n + ay_{n-1} + (h/12)[(5 - a)y'_{n+1} + (8 + 8a)y'_n + (5a - 1)y'_{n-1}] \quad (5.3\text{-}10)$$

where the parameter a is to be specified. It can be easily verified that (5.3-10) is exact for polynomials of degree 3 or less for all a (and for polynomials of degree 4 when $a = 1$). Using $r = 3$ in (5.3-6), we get for the influence function

$$G(s) = \begin{cases} (x_{n+1} - s)^3 - (h/4)(5 - a)(x_{n+1} - s)^2 & x_n \leqq s \leqq x_{n+1} \\ a(x_{n-1} - s)^3 + (h/4)(5a - 1)(x_{n-1} - s)^2 & x_{n-1} \leqq s \leqq x_n \end{cases} \quad (5.3\text{-}11)$$

from which it is verifiable that for $a \leqq \frac{1}{5}$ $G(s) \leqq 0$ in $[x_{n-1}, x_{n+1}]$ and for $a \geqq 5$ $G(s) \geqq 0$ in this interval but that for any other value of a, $G(s)$ changes sign in the interval. For $a \leqq \frac{1}{5}$ and $a \geqq 5$, we may use (5.3-8) to express the error as

$$T_n = \frac{-(1 - a)h^4}{24} Y^{iv}(\eta) \quad (5.3\text{-}12)$$

(The case $a = 1$ will be considered in Example 5.5.)

The method we have used here to find the error in numerical integration methods can also be fruitfully applied to finding the error in numerical quadrature methods. For consider the general quadrature formula (4.6-1). If the accuracy of this formula is r, then expanding $f(x)$ and each $f(a_j)$ about $x = a$ leads to the following expression for the error {7}:

$$E = \int_a^b \frac{w(x)}{r!} \int_a^x (x - s)^r f^{(r+1)}(s) \, ds \, dx$$

$$- \sum_{j=1}^n H_j \frac{1}{r!} \int_a^{a_j} (a_j - s)^r f^{(r+1)}(s) \, ds = \frac{1}{r!} \int_a^b G(s) f^{(r+1)}(s) \, ds \quad (5.3\text{-}13)$$

where

$$G(s) = \left[\int_a^b w(x)(\overline{x - s})^r \, dx - \sum_{j=1}^n H_j (\overline{a_j - s})^r \right] \quad (5.3\text{-}14)$$

with

$$(\overline{x - s}) = \begin{cases} x - s & \text{if } x > s \\ 0 & \text{if } x \leqq s \end{cases} \quad (5.3\text{-}15)$$

We could have used this technique to calculate all the error terms in Chap. 4. In particular, the error in Chebyshev quadrature (see Sec. 4.10-2), which we did not calculate in Chap. 4, can be derived using this technique {9}.

5.4   STABILITY OF NUMERICAL INTEGRATION METHODS

In this section we shall be interested, firstly, in considering how well the solution of the difference equation (5.2-5) approximates that of the differential equation and, secondly, how we can derive bounds for the accumulated error at any stage. We shall limit ourselves to the case $N = 1$ (i.e., a single first-order ordinary differential equation). Some of the results we shall obtain are directly applicable to systems of equations.

For others, the extension to systems leads to generally intractable algebraic problems {12}.

To get an intuitive feeling for this problem, it is instructive to consider the differential equation

$$y' = -Ky \qquad y(x_0) = y_0 \tag{5.4-1}$$

whose solution is

$$Y = y_0 e^{-K(x-x_0)} \tag{5.4-2}$$

For this differential equation, (5.2-5) becomes

$$y_{n+1}(1 + hKb_{-1}) = \sum_{i=0}^{p} (a_i - hKb_i)y_{n-i} \tag{5.4-3}$$

This is a linear difference equation with constant coefficients and has the solution

$$y_n = \sum_{i=0}^{p} c_i r_i^n \tag{5.4-4}$$

where the c_i's are constants and the r_i's are the roots of

$$(1 + hKb_{-1})r^{p+1} = \sum_{i=0}^{p} (a_i - hKb_i)r^{p-i} \tag{5.4-5}$$

We have assumed in (5.4-4) that the roots in (5.4-5) are distinct. If the roots are not distinct, then terms of the form $c_i n^\alpha r_i^n$ will appear in (5.4-4) (where α is less than the multiplicity of the root). Such multiple roots will affect the details but not the substance of the development that follows.

The first thing we wish to show is that one of the roots of (5.4-5), say r_0, has the form†

$$r_0 = 1 - Kh + O(h^2) \tag{5.4-6}$$

Since we are assuming that (5.2-5) is a consistent method, we get from the first equation of (5.2-6) that, when $h = 0$, (5.4-5) has a root $r_0 = 1$. For $h \neq 0$, suppose we write this root as

$$r_0 = 1 + \sum_{i=1}^{\infty} \beta_i h^i \tag{5.4-7}$$

Substituting this into (5.4-5) and using the second equation of (5.2-6), we

† If $f(x) = O[g(x)]$ as $x \to x_0$, then there exists a positive constant c such that $|f(x)| \leq c|g(x)|$ for x sufficiently close to x_0. Except where specified otherwise, we shall always have $x_0 = 0$.

can show $\{13\}$ that $\beta_1 = -K$, which establishes (5.4-6).† Now since

$$1 - Kh = e^{-Kh} + O(h^2) \tag{5.4-8}$$

we may write

$$r_0^k = [1 - Kh + O(h^2)]^k = e^{-Khk} + O(h^2) = e^{-K(x_k-x_0)} + O(h^2) \tag{5.4-9}$$

The constants c_i are determined by the $p + 1$ initial conditions required to solve (5.4-3). We have noted previously that in general numerical integration methods require starting values that are not available from the statement of the problem and, in Sec. 5.6, we shall consider how to obtain these values. Here we are interested in calculating c_0, the coefficient of r_0^n. Let $y_0, \ldots, y_p$ be the initial values of y, with y_0 the given initial condition of the differential equation. Then (5.4-4) is a system of $p + 1$ equations for the c_i's. Using Cramer's rule, we have

$$c_0 = \frac{\begin{vmatrix} y_0 & 1 & \cdots & 1 \\ y_1 & r_1 & \cdots & r_p \\ \cdot & \cdot & \cdots & \cdot \\ y_p & r_1^p & \cdots & r_p^p \end{vmatrix}}{\begin{vmatrix} 1 & \cdots & \cdots & 1 \\ r_0 & \cdots & \cdots & r_p \\ r_0^2 & \cdots & \cdots & r_p^2 \\ \cdot & \cdots & \cdots & \cdot \\ r_0^p & \cdots & \cdots & r_p^p \end{vmatrix}} \tag{5.4-10}$$

The initial conditions $y_1, \ldots, y_p$ will generally all have errors in them, but it is reasonable to assume that as $h \to 0$, these values approach true values. This is equivalent to saying that, whatever process we use to get the initial values, the error will be the order of some power of h; see Sec. 5.6. Thus the first column of the numerator approaches y_0 times the first column of the denominator as $h \to 0$, which in turn means that $c_0 \to y_0$ as $h \to 0$. This, together with our result on r_0, means that the first term of (5.4-4) approximates the true solution of the differential equation and, in fact, approaches it as $h \to 0$.

What then of the remaining terms in (5.4-4), the so-called *parasitic solution*? Note that the parasitic solution arises because the order of the difference equation $(p + 1)$ is greater than the order of the differential equation (1). The same argument used to estimate c_0 above can be used to show that, as $h \to 0$, all the other c_i approach zero $\{13\}$. Thus, for small h, we expect the coefficients $c_1, \ldots, c_p$ to be small. If the solution

† In fact, the $O(h^2)$ term is actually $O(h^{r+1})$ where r is the order of the numerical integration method (why?).

of the difference equation is to be a useful approximation to the solution of the differential equation, then each of the terms $c_i r_i^n$ in (5.4-4) must remain small with respect to $c_0 r_0^n$. This requires that

$$|r_i| \leq |r_0| \qquad i = 1, \ldots, p \tag{5.4-11}$$

The roots r_i, $i = 0, \ldots, p$ are functions of h. As $h \to 0$, we know that $r_0 \to 1$. Thus, for (5.4-11) to hold as $h \to 0$, it is necessary *that all roots of (5.4-5) lie on or within the unit circle.* If r_i, $i > 0$ lies on the unit circle when $h = 0$, then (5.4-11) may not hold for any positive h, but if all r_i, $i > 0$ lie within the unit circle, then for some range of positive h (5.4-11) will hold (why?). Our first conclusion then is that, if the solution of (5.4-3) is to be a good approximation to the solution of (5.4-1), then (5.4-11) must hold.

Now let us consider the general case when the differential equation has the form (5.1-1). Because of the derivative terms, we cannot solve (5.2-5) explicitly. But as $h \to 0$, the solution of (5.2-5) must approach that of (5.4-3). Thus, for sufficiently small h, we would expect to get results analogous to those above. We are now ready then to formalize the notion of stability as it applies to a general equation of the form (5.1-1).

5.4-1 Convergence and stability

Definition 5.1   Let the initial conditions $y_k = y_k(h)$, $k = 0, \ldots, p$ used in solving the difference equation (5.2-5) be such that

$$\lim_{h \to 0} y_k(h) = y_0 \qquad k = 0, \ldots, p \tag{5.4-12}$$

where y_0 is the given initial condition in the differential equation (5.1-1). Then the numerical integration method (5.2-5) is said to be *convergent* if, for any initial-value problem (5.1-1) such that $f(x,y)$ satisfies the conditions of Sec. 5.1, the solution of (5.2-5) is such that

$$\lim_{\substack{h \to 0 \\ (n \to \infty)}} y_n = Y(x) \qquad hn = x - x_0 \tag{5.4-13}$$

for all $x \, \varepsilon \, [x_0, b]$.

The condition (5.4-12) is, of course, required because the initial conditions used in (5.2-5) will generally not be true solutions of (5.1-1). Our discussion of Eq. (5.4-1) then implies

Theorem 5.1   A necessary condition for a numerical integration method to be convergent is that no root of

$$r^{p+1} = \sum_{i=0}^{p} a_i r^{p-i} \tag{5.4-14}$$

[i.e., (5.4-5) with $h = 0$] lies outside the unit circle and that roots of magnitude 1 are simple.

Proof   Consider the equation $y' = 0$, $y(0) = 0$ whose exact solution is $Y(x) = 0$. Let the roots of (5.4-14) be $r_0, r_1, \ldots, r_p$ and suppose that they are real and simple. Then for this equation $y_k = \sum_{i=0}^{p} hr_i^k$ is a solution of (5.2-5) for $k = p + 1,\ p + 2,\ \ldots$ (why?). Moreover, for $k = 0, \ldots, p$, y_k satisfies (5.4-12) (why?). In order for y_n to satisfy (5.4-13), it is clear that the magnitude of each r_i must be less than or equal to 1. This proves the theorem in this case. In the case of complex or multiple roots, some more proof is required; we leave this to a problem {14}.

For the equation $y' = 0$, $y(0) = 0$, the sufficiency of the condition in Theorem 5.1 is not hard to prove {14}. In fact, for consistent methods the condition is sufficient in general, but the proof of this is beyond the scope of this book; see Henrici (1962a, pp. 244–246).

From the first equation of (5.2-6) it follows that $r = 1$ is always a root of (5.4-14). Our discussion of stability later in this section will indicate that it is in fact desirable to have the other roots of (5.4-14) as small as possible in magnitude.

Example 5.3   Determine for what values of a the method of Example 5.2 is convergent.

Equation (5.4-14) is, since $p = 1$

$$r^2 = (1 - a)r + a$$

whose solutions are

$$r = 1 \quad \text{and} \quad r = -a$$

Thus, for convergence $-1 < a \le 1$. Note, a must be greater than -1 to avoid a double root at 1.

Another necessary condition for convergence is given by the following

Theorem 5.2   A necessary condition for the convergence of a numerical integration method is that the first two equations of (5.2-6) must be satisfied (i.e., consistency is necessary for convergence).

Proof   Consider the equation $y' = 0$, $y(0) = 1$ whose exact solution is $Y(x) = 1$. For this equation, the numerical integration method (5.2-5) becomes

$$y_{n+1} = \sum_{i=0}^{p} a_i y_{n-i} \tag{5.4-15}$$

Let the starting values $y_0, \ldots, y_p$ be exact (i.e., equal to 1). Now letting $h \to 0$ and $n \to \infty$ $(nh = x)$ means that all values of y in (5.4-15) must approach 1 if the method is convergent. This proves that the first equation of (5.2-6) must be satisfied. Now consider $y' = 1$, $y(0) = 0$ whose solution is $Y(x) = x$. The difference equation now is

$$y_{n+1} = \sum_{i=0}^{p} a_i y_{n-i} + h \sum_{i=-1}^{p} b_i \qquad (5.4\text{-}16)$$

Now consider the sequence defined by

$$y_n = nhA \qquad n = 0, 1, \ldots \qquad (5.4\text{-}17)$$

where

$$A = \frac{\displaystyle\sum_{i=-1}^{p} b_i}{1 + \displaystyle\sum_{i=0}^{p} i a_i} \qquad (5.4\text{-}18)$$

This sequence satisfies the restrictions (5.4-12) on the initial conditions and also satisfies the difference equation (5.4-16) {15}. Since the solution of (5.4-16) must approach the true solution as $h \to 0$, $n \to \infty$ $(nh = x)$, we conclude from (5.4-17) that $A = 1$. Then (5.4-18) is the second equation of (5.2-6), which completes the proof.

We have defined convergence in the limit as $h \to 0$. But in practice, we are interested in what happens for finite values of h. First, we should like to know when the parasitic solutions of (5.2-5) are small in relation to the solution which approximates the solution of the differential equation, and when this is so, we should like to be able to estimate or bound the error in the computed solution. In order to discuss these matters, it is convenient to introduce the *accumulated* error after n steps, which is the difference between the true solution and the computed solution. We define

$$\epsilon_n = Y_n - y_n \qquad (5.4\text{-}19)$$

Before we derive an equation for ϵ_n, we correct (5.2-5) by introducing the roundoff error R_n at each step

$$y_{n+1} = \sum_{i=0}^{p} a_i y_{n-i} + h \sum_{i=-1}^{p} b_i y'_{n-i} + R_n \qquad (5.4\text{-}20)$$

We note that, if y_{n-i} and y'_{n-i} are both correctly rounded to d decimals, then, neglecting inaccuracies in the a_i's, b_i's, and h

$$|R_n| < 5 \times 10^{-(d+1)} \left(\sum_{i=0}^{p} |a_i| + h \sum_{i=-1}^{p} |b_i| \right) \qquad (5.4\text{-}21)$$

In most solutions of ordinary differential equations on digital computers, truncation error is far larger than roundoff error. However, in certain applications, particularly in the case of real-time† computations, roundoff error may be significant.

Subtracting (5.4-20) from (5.3-1), we get

$$\epsilon_{n+1} = \sum_{i=0}^{p} a_i \epsilon_{n-i} + h \sum_{i=-1}^{p} b_i \epsilon'_{n-i} + E_n \tag{5.4-22}$$

where $E_n = T_n - R_n$ is the error *introduced* at the step from x_n to x_{n+1} (in contrast to ϵ_n, which is the total error that has *accumulated* after the n steps). Using the mean-value theorem, we write

$$\begin{aligned}
\epsilon'_{n-i} = Y'_{n-i} - y'_{n-i} &= f(x_{n-i}, Y_{n-i}) - f(x_{n-i}, y_{n-i}) \\
&= (Y_{n-i} - y_{n-i}) f_y(x_{n-i}, \eta_{n-i}) = \epsilon_{n-i} f_y(x_{n-i}, \eta_{n-i})
\end{aligned} \tag{5.4-23}$$

where the subscript y denotes partial differentiation and η_{n-i} lies between y_{n-i} and Y_{n-i}. Substituting (5.4-23) into (5.4-22), we get

$$\epsilon_{n+1}[1 - hb_{-1} f_y(x_{n+1}, \eta_{n+1})] = \sum_{i=0}^{p} [a_i + hb_i f_y(x_{n-i}, \eta_{n-i})]\epsilon_{n-i} + E_n \tag{5.4-24}$$

When the differential equation is (5.4-1), this difference equation becomes, using the simplifying assumption that the per step error E_n is a constant E,

$$\epsilon_{n+1}(1 + hb_{-1}K) = \sum_{i=0}^{p} (a_i - hb_i K)\epsilon_{n-i} + E \tag{5.4-25}$$

which has the same form as (5.4-3) except for the inhomogeneous term E. If no roots are multiple, the solution of (5.4-25) is

$$\epsilon_n = \sum_{i=0}^{p} d_i r_i^n + \frac{E}{hK \displaystyle\sum_{i=-1}^{p} b_i} \tag{5.4-26}$$

where we have used the first equation of (5.2-6) in getting the particular solution. The r_i's are the same as those in (5.4-4), but the d_i's depend on the initial conditions on the error for $n = 0, 1, \ldots, p$. For example, d_0 is given by an equation analogous to (5.4-10) with the first column in the numerator replaced by the initial errors. We assume that the initial errors

---

† Real-time applications are those in which the computer is intimately tied to an operative physical system, e.g., missile tracking, on-line control of a chemical plant. In such cases, the number of digits used in the computation may, because of inherent physical inaccuracies, be small and thus the roundoff may be large.

are such that $|d_0| \ll |c_0|$, for otherwise the computed solution will be of no use quite aside from the errors caused by the parasitic solution.

We note that, if $|r_0| > 1$ for small h, which corresponds to $-K > 0$ [cf. (5.4-6)], the solution is an increasing exponential. Since we cannot expect to keep the error bounded when the solution is unbounded, it is not surprising that the $d_0 r_0^n$ term in (5.4-26) is also unbounded in this case. What we can hope to do is to keep the error *small relative to the true solution*, in which case we shall say the method of solution is stable. Since $|d_0| \ll |c_0|$, this will be true if the terms in (5.4-26) for $i = 1, \ldots, p$, which correspond to the parasitic solution, remain small relative to the r_0 term. This is equivalent to saying that an error introduced in the initial conditions or at a later stage of the computation will not propagate with a magnitude which increases relative to the magnitude of the true solution. This brings us back to the condition (5.4-11). But before we give a formal definition of stability, let us consider again the general case of Eq. (5.4-24).

This equation is not tractable as it stands, so that some simplifying assumptions are necessary. The most natural way of modifying (5.4-24) is to replace each f_y by some constant value $-K$ and E_n by E and thus get an equation of the form (5.4-25). Let us consider two ways of choosing the constants K and E:

1. Suppose K and E are such that

$$|f_y(x,y)| < -K \qquad |E_n| < E \tag{5.4-27}$$

for all n and for all points which occur in the solution of (5.4-24). Consider a new equation formed from (5.4-24) by replacing f_y by $-K$, E_n by E, b_i by $|b_i|$, and a_i by $|a_i|$. Suppose also that the initial conditions used in the solution of this new equation are all greater than or equal to the magnitudes of the corresponding initial conditions in (5.4-24). We leave to a problem {16} the proof of the result that, if $|hb_{-1}K| < 1$, the solution of the new equation is greater than or equal to the magnitude of the solution of (5.4-24) *for all n*. This approach leads to a bound on ϵ_n which tends to be very conservative.

In order to elucidate how the error propagates from one step to the next, which is the essence of stability and which is a *local* behavior, we use a different approach.

2. Consider (5.4-24) for any value of n. For this n let $-K$ be a *characteristic* or average value of f_y for points in the neighborhood of those in (5.4-24). Similarly, let E be a characteristic value of E_n. Then, since in practice both f_y and E_n change slowly with n, we expect that locally the solution of (5.4-25) will behave like that of (5.4-24).

In what follows we shall use the latter approach. The stability of a numerical integration method will be defined in terms of the solution of the characteristic equation (5.4-5) of the difference equation (5.4-25). In (5.4-5), therefore, $-K$ is to be taken as a characteristic value of $f_y(x,y)$. Thus, whether or not a method is stable will depend upon the particular equation (5.1-1) to which it is being applied.

Definition 5.2   Let (5.2-5) be a consistent numerical integration method. Let r_i, $i = 0, \ldots, p$ be the roots of (5.4-5) with r_0 the root which corresponds to the term in (5.4-4) which approximates the solution of the differential equation. Then this method is said to be *stable* on an interval $[\alpha,\beta]$, which must include zero if, for all hK in this interval,

$$\left| \frac{r_i}{r_0} \right| \leqq 1 \qquad i = 1, \ldots, p \tag{5.4-28}$$

and if, when $|r_i| = |r_0|$, r_i is a simple root.

Remarks

1. With $[\alpha,\beta]$ required to include zero, we are assured that for any K we can make the solution stable by choosing h sufficiently small. Since (5.4-28) must hold for $h = 0$, a necessary condition for stability is that, when $h = 0$, no r_i, $i = 1, \ldots, p$ lie outside the unit circle and that those roots on the unit circle must be simple. Thus, from Theorem 5.1, we conclude that *convergence is necessary for stability*.

2. We allow roots of magnitude equal to r_0 because, if the errors in the initial conditions are small, then we shall have $|d_i| \ll |d_0|$, $i = 1, \ldots, p$. Thus, if $|r_i| = |r_0|$, although the parasitic solution will not decrease in magnitude relative to the r_0 term, it will remain small relative to the r_0 term. The requirement of no multiple roots of magnitude $|r_0|$ is necessary because of the factor $n^\alpha r_i^n$ introduced into (5.4-26) by a multiple root. Definition 5.2 in fact requires that r_0 be real. This is reasonable because we cannot expect the term in (5.4-4) in r_0 to be a good approximation to the solution of a real differential equation when r_0 is complex.

3. A more common definition of stability than that given in Definition 5.2 requires only that $|r_i| \leqq 1$, $i = 1, \ldots, p$ when $hK > 0$. This definition is equivalent to requiring that, when the solution of (5.1-1) is decreasing in magnitude, all the parasitic solutions also decrease in magnitude (why?). This definition makes the determination of those values of hK for which a method is stable easier than our definition {17, 18}, but it does not really give the desired

information about a method {20}. Our definition might be called a definition of *relative stability* in contrast to the one considered in this paragraph. In Sec. 8.10-1, we shall consider a computational procedure for determining the range $[\alpha, \beta]$ of relative stability.

4. In order that a numerical integration method may be stable for as large a class of differential equations as possible, it is desirable that $[\alpha, \beta]$ be as large as possible. It follows then that it is desirable to have all the roots of the convergence equation (5.4-14), except the one at $r = 1$, as small as possible. Since the roots of (5.4-3) are continuous functions of the coefficients, the range of Kh for which (5.4-28) is satisfied will tend to be larger the smaller the roots $r_i, i = 1, \ldots, p$. In particular, it is desirable to have that r_i, $i = 1, \ldots, p$ of greatest magnitude as small as possible.

Example 5.4   Determine for what values of hK the consistent method of Example 5.1 [i.e., (5.2-9)] is stable.

Since $p = 0$, Eq. (5.4-5) becomes

$$(1 + \tfrac{1}{2}hK)r = (1 - \tfrac{1}{2}hK)$$

Thus there is only one root

$$r = \frac{1 - \tfrac{1}{2}hK}{1 + \tfrac{1}{2}hK}$$

When $h = 0$, $r = 1$ so that by Theorem 5.1 the method is convergent. Since there is just one root, Definition 5.2 is trivially satisfied and so this method is stable on the interval $(-\infty, \infty)$.

Example 5.5   For $a = 1$, determine the values of hK for which the consistent method of Example 5.2 is stable.

The equation for the roots is

$$(1 + \tfrac{1}{3}hK)r^2 = -(\tfrac{4}{3}hK)r + (1 - \tfrac{1}{3}hK) \tag{5.4-29}$$

and its solution is

$$r = \frac{1}{2(1 + \tfrac{1}{3}hK)} \{-\tfrac{4}{3}hK \pm [4 + \tfrac{4}{3}(hK)^2]^{1/2}\}$$

The plus sign corresponds to r_0 since this root approaches 1 as $h \to 0$. As $h \to 0$, $r_1 \to -1$ so that the method is convergent. The magnitude of the ratio of the roots is

$$\left|\frac{r_1}{r_0}\right| = \left|\frac{-\tfrac{4}{3}hK - [4 + \tfrac{4}{3}(hK)^2]^{1/2}}{-\tfrac{4}{3}hK + [4 + \tfrac{4}{3}(hK)^2]^{1/2}}\right|$$

For $hK < 0$ this magnitude is always less than 1, but for $hK > 0$, it is always greater than 1. When $hK = 0$, $r_0 = 1$ and $r_1 = -1$. Therefore, this method is stable only on intervals of the form $[\alpha, 0]$ where α is any negative number. Whenever f_y is negative (i.e., $hK > 0$), r_1 has magnitude greater than r_0, and we would expect this method to exhibit bad error behavior; that this is so we shall indicate in Sec. 5.7.

Since generally any differential equation or system of differential equations is such that f_y takes on both positive and negative values, this method should be avoided.

Because convergence is necessary for stability, it is an obvious first step in testing the stability of a numerical integration method to test to see if the roots of (5.4-12) lie on or within the unit circle when $h = 0$. Two ways of doing this which do not require calculating the roots of (5.4-5) are considered in {17, 18}. If this necessary condition is satisfied, then we may proceed to determine the range of values of hK for which the method is stable; see Sec. 5.5-4.

5.4-2   Propagated-error bounds and estimates

If a stable method is used to compute the solution of (5.4-1), then the main contribution to the accumulated or *propagated* error in the summation in (5.4-26) is given by the r_0 term. To estimate d_0, we use Cramer's rule and get, analogously to (5.4-10),

$$d_0 = \frac{\begin{vmatrix} e + \gamma & 1 & \cdots & 1 \\ e + \gamma & r_1 & \cdots & r_p \\ \cdots\cdots\cdots\cdots\cdots \\ e + \gamma & r_1^p & \cdots & r_p^p \end{vmatrix}}{\begin{vmatrix} 1 & 1 & \cdots & 1 \\ r_0 & r_1 & \cdots & r_p \\ \cdots\cdots\cdots\cdots\cdots \\ r_0^p & r_1^p & \cdots & r_p^p \end{vmatrix}} \tag{5.4-30}$$

where $\gamma = (-E)/hK \sum\limits_{i=-1}^{p} b_i$, and we have assumed for simplicity that the errors in the initial conditions $y_0, \ldots, y_p$ are all equal to e.† The root r_0, we have seen, is close to 1; so, making the further simplifying assumption that it is 1, we get

$$d_0 \approx e + \gamma \tag{5.4-31}$$

An estimate of the propagated error is then given by the first term in the summation (5.4-26) plus the particular solution

$$\epsilon_n \approx d_0 r_0^n + \frac{E}{hK \sum\limits_{i=1}^{p} b_i} \approx \left(e - \frac{E}{hK \sum\limits_{i=-1}^{p} b_i} \right) e^{-Khn} + \frac{E}{hK \sum\limits_{i=-1}^{p} b_i} \tag{5.4-32}$$

† The error in y_0 is caused by the necessity of rounding the given initial condition when inserting it in the computer. The other y_i's also are in error because of the truncation error in the method used to calculate them; see Sec. 5.6.

where we have replaced r_0 by its approximate value e^{-Kh}. [Note the different approximations for r_0 which led to (5.4-31) and (5.4-32); why are they both reasonable?] To get an estimate of the propagated error in the general case of Eq. (5.1-1), we replace f_y by $-K$ as in the previous section. If E and K are such that the conditions (5.4-27) are satisfied, then (5.4-32) will usually be a bound on the error and a quite conservative one [cf. {16}].

To use (5.4-32) we need estimates of e, E, and K, and the latter, at least, is often very difficult to get. As we shall see in the next section, there is an effective way of estimating the error at each step, and for a stable method, this may be used to control the overall error in the computation. However, (5.4-32) does indicate what quantities affect the error and how they affect it.

The definition and discussion of convergence in this section did not depend on the fact that only one equation was being considered. Definition 5.1 and Theorems 5.1 and 5.2 are all valid if the relevant quantities are vectors. The discussion of stability, however, does require some modifications in the case of systems of equations. By careful application of the mean-value theorem in (5.4-23), we arrive at a system of equations (5.4-25). For nonzero values of h, this system is cross-coupled; that is, errors corresponding to different dependent variables appear in the same equation. The resultant system of polynomial equations corresponding to (5.4-5) is generally somewhat intractable {12}.

5.5 PREDICTOR–CORRECTOR METHODS

Consider the two numerical integration methods

$$y_{n+1} = y_n + (h/2)(y'_{n+1} + y'_n) \tag{5.5-1}$$
$$y_{n+1} = y_{n-2} + (3h/2)(y'_n + y'_{n-1}) \tag{5.5-2}$$

Both these equations are of order 2 [see Example 5.1 for (5.5-1)], and their truncation errors are immediately determinable since they are equivalent to a Newton-Cotes closed and open formula, respectively. These truncation errors are, respectively, $-(h^3/12)\,Y'''(\eta_1)$ and $(3h^3/4)\,Y'''(\eta_2)$. Equation (5.5-1), which is an iterative formula, is substantially more accurate—by a factor of 9 in general—than (5.5-2), which is a forward-integration formula. This is an illustration of the general rule that, for formulas of corresponding order, iterative formulas are substantially more accurate than forward formulas. Thus, despite their added difficulty in use, it is worthwhile to use them. In this section, we consider methods by which this can be most efficiently done. Again for convenience we let the number of equations be one, but the extension to systems is straightforward.

5.5-1   Convergence of the iterations

In order to solve (5.2-5) for y_{n+1} when $b_{-1} \neq 0$, it will be necessary in general to use an iterative procedure. That is, we guess or somehow estimate an initial value of y_{n+1}, call it $y_{n+1}^{(0)}$, calculate $f[x_{n+1}, y_{n+1}^{(0)}]$, insert this on the right-hand side of (5.2-5) to get $y_{n+1}^{(1)}$, and continue this process until convergence to some desired degree of accuracy is obtained. But first we must be sure that the process will converge. To derive the condition for convergence, we rewrite (5.2-5) as

$$y_{n+1}^{(j+1)} = \sum_{i=0}^{p} (a_i y_{n-i} + h b_i y_{n-i}') + h b_{-1} [y_{n+1}^{(j)}]' \tag{5.5-3}$$

where $y_{n+1}^{(j)}$ is the jth approximation to y_{n+1}. The correct value,[†] y_{n+1}, satisfies (5.2-5), which we rewrite for convenience as

$$y_{n+1} = \sum_{i=0}^{p} (a_i y_{n-i} + h b_i y_{n-i}') + h b_{-1} y_{n+1}' \tag{5.5-4}$$

Subtracting (5.5-3) from (5.5-4), we get

$$y_{n+1} - y_{n+1}^{(j+1)} = h b_{-1} \{y_{n+1}' - [y_{n+1}^{(j)}]'\} \tag{5.5-5}$$

which, using the mean-value theorem, becomes

$$y_{n+1} - y_{n+1}^{(j+1)} = h b_{-1} f_y[x_{n+1}, \eta^{(j)}][y_{n+1} - y_{n+1}^{(j)}] \tag{5.5-6}$$

where $\eta^{(j)}$ lies between y_{n+1} and $y_{n+1}^{(j)}$. If, in a neighborhood of (x_{n+1}, y_{n+1}) which includes all points $(x_{n+1}, y_{n+1}^{(j)})$,

$$|f_y(x,y)| < K \tag{5.5-7}$$

then[‡]

$$|y_{n+1} - y_{n+1}^{(j+1)}| < h b_{-1} K |y_{n+1} - y_{n+1}^{(j)}| \tag{5.5-8}$$

and, by induction,

$$|y_{n+1} - y_{n+1}^{(j+1)}| < (h b_{-1} K)^{j+1} |y_{n+1} - y_{n+1}^{(0)}| \tag{5.5-9}$$

Thus, if

$$h b_{-1} K < 1 \tag{5.5-10}$$

then, as $j \to \infty$, $y_{n+1}^{(j+1)} \to y_{n+1}$ and the iteration converges. Moreover, the difference $|y_{n+1} - y_{n+1}^{(j)}|$ is monotonically decreasing for all n. In all

---

† That is, the true solution of (5.2-5), not the true solution of the differential equation.

‡ In what follows, we assume that b_{-1} is positive as, in all practical cases, it is.

that follows, we shall assume that h has been chosen so that (5.5-10) is satisfied.   The magnitude of $hb_{-1}K$ determines the rate at which the iteration converges so that for rapid convergence we should have $hb_{-1}K \ll 1$ {21}.

5.5-2   Predictors and correctors

Suppose we are going to use an iterative method to solve the differential equation (5.1-1).   The only term in (5.5-3) that changes from one iteration to the next is the last term on the right-hand side.   Thus the major calculation in each iteration is the value of $[y_{n+1}^{(j)}]' = f[x_{n+1},y_{n+1}^{(j)}]$.   In practice, the evaluation of $f(x,y)$ will generally be much more time-consuming than evaluation of the whole right-hand side of (5.5-3).   Thus, in comparing the computational efficiency of various methods, we shall be interested particularly in how many evaluations of $f(x,y)$ are necessary at each step.

In practice, we shall perform the iteration of the previous section until two successive iterates differ by less than some tolerance.   We shall then accept the final iterate as y_{n+1}.   The number of iterations required [each of which requires one evaluation of $f(x,y)$] will depend upon

1. The accuracy of the initial guess or estimation.   Clearly, the nearer $y_{n+1}^{(0)}$ is to the y_{n+1}, the faster the iteration will converge.
2. The accuracy desired in the final value of y_{n+1}.   For example, if the error E_n at each step is of the order 10^{-5}, there is no reason to require y_{n+1} to be correct to 10 decimals.   This question is considered in more detail in Sec. 5.7.

Our first object here is to consider ways of *predicting* $y_{n+1}^{(0)}$ as accurately as possible consistent with other properties that are desirable in such *predictors*.   Using the predicted value, we shall then use an iterative formula to *correct* the prediction, hence the name *predictor-corrector methods*.

The best way to predict $y_{n+1}^{(0)}$ is to use a forward-integration formula since such a formula expresses y_{n+1} in terms of known past values of y and y'.   Thus, for example, (5.5-2) could be used as a predictor for (5.5-1).   The predictor-corrector system would then be

Predictor: $\quad y_{n+1}^{(0)} = y_{n-2} + (3h/2)(y_n' + y_{n-1}')$

$\qquad\qquad\quad [y_{n+1}^{(0)}]' = f[x_{n+1},y_{n+1}^{(0)}]$ (5.5-11)

Corrector: $\quad y_{n+1}^{(j+1)} = y_n + (h/2)\{[y_{n+1}^{(j)}]' + y_n'\}$ $j = 0, 1, \ldots$

where the corrector is iterated until the desired degree of convergence is achieved.   We noted previously that the truncation error of both predictor and corrector involves a third derivative.   As we shall see in Sec. 5.5-3, it is important that both predictor and corrector have error terms with the same order derivative.

Equation (5.5-11) is a second-order predictor-corrector system. A fourth-order system using corresponding open and closed Newton-Cotes integration formulas is

Predictor: $y_{n+1}^{(0)} = y_{n-3} + (4h/3)(2y_n' - y_{n-1}' + 2y_{n-2}')$

$[y_{n+1}^{(0)}]' = f[x_{n+1}, y_{n+1}^{(0)}]$ (5.5-12)

Corrector: $y_{n+1}^{(j+1)} = y_{n-1} + (h/3)\{[y_{n+1}^{(j)}]' + 4y_n' + y_{n-1}'\}$

where the truncation-error terms of predictor and corrector are, respectively, $\frac{14}{45}h^5 Y^{\mathrm{v}}(\eta_1)$ and $-\frac{1}{90}h^5 Y^{\mathrm{v}}(\eta_2)$. The corrector is, of course, just Simpson's rule. This predictor-corrector method is known as *Milne's method*. In Example 5.5 we showed that the corrector in (5.5-12) is not stable for any positive value of hK (i.e., $\partial f/\partial y$ negative). For this reason,

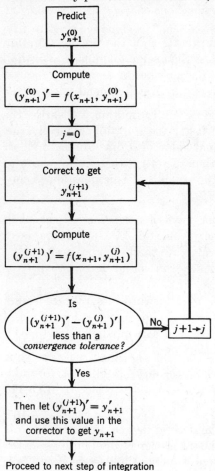

Fig. 5.2   The use of predictor-corrector methods.

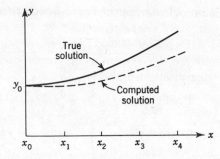

Fig. 5.3   The point-slope method.

the use of (5.5-12) is not advisable unless the number of steps of the integration to be carried out is too small to allow the parasitic solution to achieve a substantial magnitude or unless it is known that $\partial f/\partial y$ is positive.   In Sec. 5.5-4, we shall consider a modification of (5.5-12) which is stable for sufficiently small values of hK.

In Fig. 5.2, we have indicated the sequence of steps required to use either (5.5-11) or (5.5-12) in proceeding from x_n to x_{n+1}.   The use of convergence tolerances and other computational matters alluded to in Fig. 5.2 will be discussed in some detail in Sec. 5.7.

We are, of course, not restricted to using a Newton-Cotes open formula as predictor or a closed formula as corrector.   In one common type of predictor, we set, using the notation of (5.2-5), $a_0 = 1$ and $a_i = 0$, $i \neq 0$.   The b_i's may then be chosen so that the formula attains an order of $p + 1$ {22}.   For example, we have

$$p = 0: \qquad y_{n+1} = y_n + hy_n' \tag{5.5-13}$$
$$p = 1: \qquad y_{n+1} = y_n + (h/2)(3y_n' - y_{n-1}') \tag{5.5-14}$$
$$p = 2: \qquad y_{n+1} = y_n + (h/12)(23y_n' - 16y_{n-1}' + 5y_{n-2}') \tag{5.5-15}$$

Predictors of this type are called *Adams-Bashforth predictors*.   The case $p = 0$ is called *Euler's method* or the *point-slope method*.   Adams-Bashforth predictors can all be generated by integrating Newton's backward interpolation formula, and thus the truncation-error terms in (5.5-13) to (5.5-15) are easily found {22}.

If the point-slope method is used to integrate (5.4-1), the error for the case $K < 0$ is indicated graphically in Fig. 5.3.   We see that the calculated solution always lags behind the true solution.   Clearly, this will be the case for any exponentially increasing solution.   A formula that attempts to avoid this difficulty is the *midpoint method*

$$y_{n+1} = y_{n-1} + 2hy_n' \tag{5.5-16}$$

where the derivative used is at the midpoint between the two abscissas. The midpoint method is a special case of a method known as *Nystrom's method* {24}.

Table 5.1   Fourth-order predictors

	P_1 (Adams)	P_2 (Milne)	P_3	P_4	P_5	P_6
a_0	1	0	0	0	$\frac{1}{3}$	-9
a_1	0	0	0	1	$\frac{1}{3}$	9
a_2	0	0	1	0	$\frac{1}{3}$	1
a_3	0	1	0	0	0	0
b_0	$\frac{55}{24}$	$\frac{8}{3}$	$\frac{21}{8}$	$\frac{8}{3}$	$\frac{91}{36}$	6
b_1	$-\frac{59}{24}$	$-\frac{4}{3}$	$-\frac{9}{8}$	$-\frac{5}{3}$	$-\frac{63}{36}$	6
b_2	$\frac{37}{24}$	$\frac{8}{3}$	$\frac{15}{8}$	$\frac{4}{3}$	$\frac{57}{36}$	0
b_3	$-\frac{9}{24}$	0	$-\frac{3}{8}$	$-\frac{1}{3}$	$-\frac{13}{36}$	0
Error coeff.	$\frac{251}{720}$	$\frac{224}{720}$	$\frac{243}{720}$	$\frac{232}{720}$	$\frac{242}{720}$	$\frac{72}{720}$

Another class of predictors can be derived from the Hermite or modified Hermite interpolation formulas by letting $x = x_{n+1}$ and replacing $f(x)$ by $y(x)$. A fifth-order example of such a formula derived from (3.8-17) with $n = 3$ is

$$y_{n+1} = -18y_n + 9y_{n-1} + 10y_{n-2} + h(9y'_n + 18y'_{n-1} + 3y'_{n-2})$$
$$(5.5\text{-}17)$$

Note that the fluctuation in coefficients means that this formula has bad roundoff properties. Other formulas of this type are considered in {25}; see also P_6 in Table 5.1.

On a digital computer it is most common to use fourth-order predictor-corrector methods since methods of this order provide sufficient accuracy for most problems, and they are reasonably straightforward to derive and use. In Table 5.1 we have listed a number of fourth-order predictors. The error coefficient is the coefficient of $h^5 Y^v(\eta)$ in the error term. The choice of a predictor is not nearly so critical as the choice of a corrector. By far the most important factor is low truncation error in order to assure as good a prediction as possible. Other factors of some importance are: (1) Ease of computation; for example, zero coefficients make the evaluation of the predictor easier. (2) Roundoff properties; note that the extremely bad roundoff properties of P_6 lower its value despite its extremely good truncation error.

The choice of a corrector depends importantly on stability. For this reason we defer discussion of the choice of a corrector until Sec. 5.5-4, in which corrector stability is considered.

5.5-3 Error estimation

At each step in the use of predictor-corrector methods, we get two estimates of the solution at x_{n+1}, the predicted value and the corrected value. This enables us to obtain an *estimate* of the error incurred *at each step*. This estimation—which gives us an idea of the order of magnitude of the error—enables us to judge whether to (1) decrease the interval size h if the error is too large or (2) increase the interval size and thereby speed up the computation if the error is smaller than needed for the accuracy we desire or (3) leave the interval unchanged. Implicit in the above is an assumption to be used throughout this section; namely, that truncation error is the dominant source of error.

We shall use the method (5.5-12) to illustrate error estimation. Using (5.3-1) and the definition of ϵ_n in (5.4-19), the predictor in (5.5-12) may be written

$$
\begin{aligned}
y_{n+1}^{(0)} = {}& Y_{n-3} + (4h/3)(2Y_n' - Y_{n-1}' + 2Y_{n-2}') - \epsilon_{n-3} \\
& - (4h/3)(2\epsilon_n' - \epsilon_{n-1}' + 2\epsilon_{n-2}') = Y_{n+1} - \epsilon_{n-3} \\
& - (4h/3)(2\epsilon_n' - \epsilon_{n-1}' + 2\epsilon_{n-2}') - \tfrac{14}{45}h^5 Y^v(\eta_1) \quad (5.5\text{-}18)
\end{aligned}
$$

Similarly, removing the superscripts, the corrector may be written

$$
y_{n+1} = Y_{n+1} - \epsilon_{n-1} - (h/3)(\epsilon_{n+1}' + 4\epsilon_n' + \epsilon_{n-1}') + \tfrac{1}{90}h^5 Y^v(\eta_2) \quad (5.5\text{-}19)
$$

where y_{n+1} is the value that would be obtained if the corrector were iterated to convergence. Subtracting (5.5-18) from (5.5-19), we get

$$
\begin{aligned}
y_{n+1} - y_{n+1}^{(0)} = {}& \tfrac{1}{90}h^5 Y^v(\eta_2) + \tfrac{14}{45}h^5 Y^v(\eta_1) \\
& - (h/3)(\epsilon_{n+1}' - 4\epsilon_n' + 5\epsilon_{n-1}' - 8\epsilon_{n-2}') + \epsilon_{n-3} - \epsilon_{n-1} \quad (5.5\text{-}20)
\end{aligned}
$$

If we assume (1) that ϵ_i changes slowly from step to step and (2) that $(h/3)\epsilon_i'$ is small compared with the truncation error, then we may drop the ϵ_i and ϵ_i' terms from (5.5-20). Then, if we further assume that $Y^v(x)$ does not change greatly between η_1 and η_2, we may write

$$
y_{n+1} - y_{n+1}^{(0)} \approx \tfrac{29}{90}h^5 Y^v(\eta) \quad (5.5\text{-}21)
$$

Thus an estimate of $h^5 Y^v(\eta)$ is given by

$$
h^5 Y^v(\eta) \approx \tfrac{90}{29}[y_{n+1} - y_{n+1}^{(0)}] \quad (5.5\text{-}22)
$$

The truncation error incurred at each step T_n can then be estimated as

$$
T_n = -\tfrac{1}{90}h^5 Y^v(\eta) \approx -\tfrac{1}{29}[y_{n+1} - y_{n+1}^{(0)}] \quad (5.5\text{-}23)
$$

Therefore, we can use the difference in the predicted and corrected values to estimate how much error is being made at each step.

The truncation error in the predictor can be estimated as

$$
T_n^{(0)} = \tfrac{14}{45}h^5 Y^v(\eta) \approx \tfrac{28}{29}[y_{n+1} - y_{n+1}^{(0)}] \quad (5.5\text{-}24)
$$

This not only enables us to estimate how good our predictions are but also lets us improve the prediction. For, assuming that the difference between the predicted and corrected values at each step changes slowly, we can estimate $T_n^{(0)}$ as

$$T_n^{(0)} \approx {}^{28}\!/_{29}[y_n - y_n^{(0)}] \tag{5.5-25}$$

Therefore,

$$\bar{y}_{n+1}^{(0)} = y_{n+1}^{(0)} + {}^{28}\!/_{29}[y_n - y_n^{(0)}] \tag{5.5-26}$$

will, in general, be an improved value of the prediction. The complete predictor-corrector method (5.5-12) then is

$$
\begin{aligned}
\text{Predictor:}\quad & y_{n+1}^{(0)} = y_{n-3} + (4h/3)(2y_n' - y_{n-1}' + 2y_{n-2}') \\
\text{Modifier:}\quad & \bar{y}_{n+1}^{(0)} = y_{n+1}^{(0)} + {}^{28}\!/_{29}[y_n - y_n^{(0)}] \\
& [\bar{y}_{n+1}^{(0)}]' = f[x_{n+1}, \bar{y}_{n+1}^{(0)}] \\
\text{Corrector:}\quad & y_{n+1}^{(j+1)} = y_{n-1} + (h/3)\{[y_{n+1}^{(j)}]' + 4y_n' + y_{n-1}'\}
\end{aligned}
\tag{5.5-27}
$$

with $[\bar{y}_{n+1}^{(0)}]'$ being used in the corrector initially.†

This procedure that we have illustrated for (5.5-12) can clearly be used for any predictor-corrector method as long as the *order of predictor and corrector are the same*. The corresponding case for (5.5-11) is considered in {26}.

A reasonable question to ask at this point is why we do not use the estimate of the corrector truncation error (5.5-23) to improve the corrected value. In fact this can be done, but as shown in {27} doing this is equivalent to using a system of one higher order (in this case, 5). Moreover, correcting the corrector affects the stability properties of the corrector. Therefore, rather than correcting the corrector, it is probably a better idea to use a higher-order system in the first place.

5.5-4 Stability

Two basic factors determine the value of a given corrector formula in comparison with others of the same order: (1) the coefficient in the error term and (2) its stability properties. That these two properties tend to work against each other will probably not surprise the reader. Other factors of subsidiary importance are (3) the roundoff properties and (4) the ease with which it may be computed (zero coefficients, "simple" coefficients, etc.). Our aim here is to develop a fourth-order corrector with as desirable properties as possible. To do this, we consider a corrector of the form

$$y_{n+1} = a_0 y_n + a_1 y_{n-1} + a_2 y_{n-2} + h(b_{-1} y_{n+1}' + b_0 y_n' + b_1 y_{n-1}') \tag{5.5-28}$$

---

† At the first predictor-corrector step (i.e., after starting values have been computed; see Sec. 5.6), there will be no previous value of $y_n^{(0)}$ to use in the modifier which, therefore, should be omitted at this step.

which uses data at only the last three points and contains six coefficients, one more than is necessary to achieve an order of 4. We shall use this extra degree of freedom to give the corrector desirable stability properties. We could also include a term $b_2 y'_{n-2}$ in (5.5-28) and thus achieve another degree of freedom, still using data at only three past points. This other degree of freedom could, for example, be used to achieve good roundoff properties. This is considered in {28}.

The requirement that (5.5-28) be exact for $y(x) = x^j, j = 0, \ldots, 4$ leads to the equations {5}

$$
\begin{aligned}
a_0 &= \tfrac{1}{8}(9 - 9a_1) & b_{-1} &= \tfrac{1}{24}(9 - a_1) \\
a_1 &= a_1 & b_0 &= \tfrac{1}{12}(9 + 7a_1) \\
a_2 &= -\tfrac{1}{8}(1 - a_1) & b_1 &= \tfrac{1}{24}(-9 + 17a_1)
\end{aligned} \tag{5.5-29}
$$

where a_1 is the free parameter. The influence function in the truncation error is given by

$$
\begin{aligned}
G(s) = \overline{(x_{n+1} - s)^4} + a_1\overline{(x_{n-1} - s)^4} + a_2\overline{(x_{n-2} - s)^4} \\
+ 4h[-b_{-1}\overline{(x_{n+1} - s)^3} + b_1\overline{(x_{n-1} - s)^3}] \tag{5.5-30}
\end{aligned}
$$

It is naturally of interest to determine when $G(s)$ is of constant sign in $[x_{n-2}, x_{n+1}]$ as a function of a_1. We leave determination of this to a problem {11}, but note here that, for a_1 in $[-.6, 1.0]$, $G(s)$ is indeed of constant sign.

The stability equation for (5.5-28) [i.e., the equation corresponding to (5.4-5)] is

$$
(1 + hKb_{-1})r^3 = (a_0 - hKb_0)r^2 + (a_1 - hKb_1)r + a_2 \tag{5.5-31}
$$

To determine the values of hK for which (5.4-28) holds as a function of

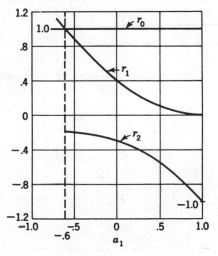

Fig. 5.4   Roots of (5.5-31) with $h = 0$.

a_1 is quite difficult for this cubic. We start by considering the case $h = 0$. As a function of a_1, the three roots are shown in Fig. 5.4. We conclude that only in the interval $-.6 \leq a_1 \leq 1.0$ can there be stability. Because the roots of (5.5-31) are continuous functions of hK, for any value of a_1 interior to $[-.6, 1.0]$, there will be some range of hK for which the method is stable. In order to get some insight into the best value of a_1 to choose, consider the data in Table 5.2. The error coefficient is the coefficient of $h^5 Y^v(\eta)$ in the error term. We see that the error coefficient steadily decreases from 1.0 to $-.6$ [note that $a_1 = 1$ is Milne's corrector in (5.5-12)]. Also the roundoff properties, judged by the sum of the squares of a_0, a_1, and a_2, become steadily worse in this direction from $9/17$ on down. A reasonable choice would seem to be $a_1 = 0$ since it is near the center of the interval [and thus is likely to be stable for a greater range of hK than values near the ends of the interval (why?)], has one zero coefficient, a reasonable error-term coefficient, and reasonable roundoff properties. In Fig. 5.5 we have plotted the roots of (5.5-31) for $a_1 = 0$. For $hK \leq +.69$ and all negative hK of importance, the stability condition (5.4-28) is always satisfied.

When $a_1 = 0$ the condition (5.5-10) for convergence of the iterations is that $|hK|$ be less than $8/3$ since $b_{-1} = 3/8$. In fact, in order to get rapid convergence of the corrector, we would want $|hK| \ll 8/3$. Thus the requirement $hK \leq +.69$ is not restrictive in practice.

Our conclusion then is that the corrector (5.5-28) with $a_1 = 0$

$$y_{n+1} = \tfrac{1}{8}(9y_n - y_{n-2}) + (3h/8)(y'_{n+1} + 2y'_n - y'_{n-1}) \qquad (5.5\text{-}32)$$

is a desirable fourth-order corrector to use in place of Milne's corrector in (5.5-12). Using this corrector and Milne's predictor, we obtain

Table 5.2   Correctors for sample values of a_1

a_1	1	$9/17$	$1/9$	0	$-1/7$	$-9/31$	$-3/5$
a_0	0	$9/17$	1	$9/8$	$9/7$	$45/31$	$9/5$
a_1	1	$9/17$	$1/9$	0	$-1/7$	$-9/31$	$-3/5$
a_2	0	$-1/17$	$-1/9$	$-1/8$	$-1/7$	$-5/31$	$-1/5$
b_{-1}	$1/3$	$6/17$	$10/27$	$3/8$	$8/21$	$12/31$	$2/5$
b_0	$4/3$	$18/17$	$22/27$	$3/4$	$2/3$	$18/31$	$2/5$
b_1	$1/3$	0	$-8/27$	$-3/8$	$-10/21$	$18/31$	$-4/5$
Error coeff.	$-1/90$	$-3/170$	$-19/810$	$-1/40$	$-17/630$	$-9/310$	$-1/30$

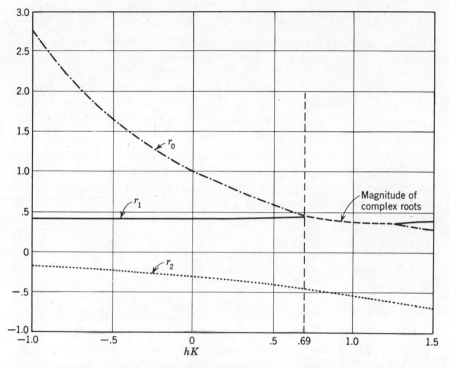

Fig. 5.5 Roots of (5.5-31) for $a_1 = 0$.

Hamming's method {30}

Predictor: $y_{n+1}^{(0)} = y_{n-3} + (4h/3)(2y_n' - y_{n-1}' + 2y_{n-2}')$
Modifier: $\bar{y}_{n+1}^{(0)} = y_{n+1}^{(0)} + {}^{112}\!/_{121}[y_n - y_n^{(0)}]$
            $[\bar{y}_{n+1}^{(0)}]' = f[x_{n+1}, \bar{y}_{n+1}^{(0)}]$ (5.5-33)
Corrector: $y_{n+1}^{(j+1)} = \frac{1}{8}(9y_n - y_{n-2})$
            $\qquad\qquad + (3h/8)\{[y_{n+1}^{(j)}]' + 2y_n' - y_{n-1}'\}$

Using Table 5.2 we get, analogously to (5.5-23),

$$T_n = -\tfrac{1}{40}h^5 Y^{\mathrm{v}}(\eta) \approx {}^9\!/_{121}[y_{n+1} - y_{n+1}^{(0)}]   \qquad (5.5\text{-}34)$$

In Sec. 5.7 we shall give some numerical examples comparing this method with (5,5-27). An analysis similar to that in this section is possible for methods of any order {30}.

5.6   STARTING THE SOLUTION AND CHANGING THE INTERVAL

We come now to two problems we have thus far put off:

1. How do we obtain the starting values (initial conditions) for (5.2-5) that are required besides the initial condition of the differential equation?
2. How do we change the interval h during the computation if our error estimate indicates that this is desirable?

There are, of course, some *self-starting methods*—Eq. (5.5-13) is an example—which require no starting values other than that provided by the differential equation. But these methods are of low order and therefore not sufficiently accurate for most problems.

5.6-1   Analytic methods

1. Taylor series. The Taylor-series expansion of $y(x)$ about x_0 may be written

$$y(x_0 + hs) = y_0 + hsy_0' + (h^2s^2/2)y_0'' + \cdots \tag{5.6-1}$$

Using the given initial condition y_0, we may, using (5.1-1), calculate y_0'. Then by differentiating the differential equation, higher derivatives of y at x_0 can be calculated. Thus (5.6-1) may be used to approximate $y(x_0 + hs)$ for any s for which the series converges.

Example 5.6   Use (5.6-1) to calculate initial values at x_1, x_2, and x_3 for the differential equation $y' = y^2$, $y(0) = 1$ with $h = .01$.
We calculate as follows:

$$y'(0) = 1 \qquad y'' = 2yy' \qquad y''(0) = 2$$
$$y''' = 2(y')^2 + 2yy'' \qquad y'''(0) = 2 + 4 = 6 \qquad \text{etc.}$$

Then

$$y(hs) = 1 + .01s + 10^{-4}s^2 + 10^{-6}s^3 + \cdots$$

which may be used with $s = 1, 2, 3$ to approximate y_1, y_2, y_3 {36}.

If the Taylor series converges for the requisite values of x, this process can be used to get initial values of any desired accuracy. Customarily, one would desire the accuracy of the initial values to be at least as great as that of the numerical integration procedure to be used. An alternative approach to the above is considered in {35}.

2. The method of successive approximations (*Picard's method*). Equation (5.1-1) may be written

$$y(x) = y_0 + \int_{x_0}^{x} f(x, y)\, dx \tag{5.6-2}$$

Assuming an initial approximation $y(x) = y_0(x)$ and inserting this on the right-hand side of (5.6-2), we generate an approximation $y_1(x)$. This process may be iterated, and, if $f(x,y)$ satisfies the conditions on page 159 [see Ince (1926)], the process will converge in a neighborhood of x_0. Thus we can obtain approximations to $Y(x)$ at the desired values of x. This technique is of great importance in the theory of the existence of solutions of (5.1-1), but the difficulty of evaluating the integral in (5.6-2) makes it impractical for numerical computations.

Both these methods involve *analytic* operations and therefore are not suitable for a mechanized solution on a digital computer. Thus we turn now to *numerical* methods for the calculation of starting values.

5.6-2   A numerical method

Suppose, as in Example 5.6, three values of y besides y_0 are needed. Let us approximate $y'(x)$ by a Lagrangian interpolation formula using the four equally spaced abscissas x_0, x_1, x_2, and x_3. Then we insert the result of this on the right-hand side of (5.6-2) and integrate from x_0 to, respectively, x_1, x_2, and x_3. So doing, we get {37}

$$y_1 = y_0 + (h/24)(9y_0' + 19y_1' - 5y_2' + y_3')$$
$$y_2 = y_0 + (h/3)(y_0' + 4y_1' + y_2')$$
$$y_3 = y_0 + (h/8)(3y_0' + 9y_1' + 9y_2' + 3y_3') \qquad (5.6\text{-}3)$$

where the error term in all three equations can be shown to be $O(h^5)$ {37}. To use (5.6-3), we make an initial estimate of y_1, y_2, and y_3, use (5.1-1) to calculate y_1', y_2', and y_3', and then use (5.6-3) to get new values of y_1, y_2, and y_3. This process may be iterated and, if it converges, will give the four required starting values. Note, for example, that the method (5.5-33) requires precisely four starting values.

Two disadvantages of this method are its possible lack of convergence and, in any case, the tedious computation involved. It can, of course, be mechanized but has no advantage in this respect over the Runge-Kutta methods to be discussed below which are preeminently the most desirable methods to use in generating starting values.

5.6-3   Runge-Kutta methods

These methods can be used to generate not only starting values but, in fact, the whole solution. They are self-starting and easy to program for a digital computer, but these advantages do not overcome their disadvantages in error-estimation ability and speed relative to predictor-corrector methods. Their value in starting the solution, however, is great.

The basis of all Runge-Kutta methods is to express the difference between the values of y at x_{n+1} and x_n as

$$y_{n+1} - y_n = \sum_{i=1}^{m} w_i k_i \tag{5.6-4}$$

where the w_i's are constants and

$$k_i = h_n f\left(x_n + \alpha_i h_n,\ y_n + \sum_{j=1}^{i-1} \beta_{ij} k_j\right) \tag{5.6-5}$$

with $h_n = x_{n+1} - x_n$ and $\alpha_1 = 0$. We use h_n instead of h since it is possible, although seldom desirable, to vary the interval at each stage of the use of a Runge-Kutta method. Clearly, given the w_i's, α_i's, and β_{ij}'s, (5.6-4) is a self-starting method for the solution of (5.1-1).

Equation (5.6-4) is *not* a special case of the general operator of Sec. 2.2 because the arguments of f in (5.6-5) need not correspond to points $[x, y(x)]$ on the calculated solution curve of (5.1-1). In this section we shall again consider a single equation, but the extension to N equations is straightforward {46}.

Our object is to determine the w_i's, α_i's, and β_{ij}'s so that (5.6-4) has the properties we desire. In particular, our object is to make the coefficients of h_n^r in the Taylor-series expansion of both sides of (5.6-4) about (x_n, y_n) identical for $r = 1, 2, \ldots, M$. As we shall see, we can do no better than $M = m$. The resulting formula will be called a *Runge-Kutta method of order M*. For convenience, we shall, throughout this section, not distinguish notationally between the true and calculated solutions. In particular, we shall differentiate y as if it were the true solution.

The expansion of the left-hand side of (5.6-4) is

$$y_{n+1} - y_n = \sum_{t=1}^{\infty} h_n^t y_n^{(t)}/t! \tag{5.6-6}$$

From (5.1-1)

$$y_n^{(t)} = \frac{d^{t-1}}{dx^{t-1}} f(x_n, y_n) = \left(\frac{\partial}{\partial x} + \frac{dy}{dx}\frac{\partial}{\partial y}\right)^{t-1} f(x_n, y_n)$$
$$= \left(\frac{\partial}{\partial x} + f\frac{\partial}{\partial y}\right)^{t-1} f(x_n, y_n) \tag{5.6-7}$$

where $f = f(x, y)$. Using this, (5.6-6) becomes

$$y_{n+1} - y_n = \sum_{t=0}^{\infty} \frac{h_n^{t+1}}{(t+1)!}\left(\frac{\partial}{\partial x} + f\frac{\partial}{\partial y}\right)^t f(x_n, y_n) \tag{5.6-8}$$

We define

$$D = \partial/\partial x + f_n(\partial/\partial y) \qquad f_n = f(x_n, y_n) \tag{5.6-9}$$

and so can write, for example,

$$[\partial/\partial x + f(\partial/\partial y)]^2 f(x_n, y_n) = D^2 f + f_y Df \Big|_n \tag{5.6-10}$$

where the notation $\Big|_n$ means that all quantities should be evaluated at (x_n, y_n) (and h should be replaced by h_n).

Using (5.6-10), the first few terms of (5.6-8) are

$$\begin{aligned}
y_{n+1} - y_n = [hf &+ (h^2/2!)Df + (h^3/3!)(D^2 f + f_y Df) \\
&+ (h^4/4!)(D^3 f + f_y D^2 f + f_y^2 Df + 3Df Df_y) + (h^5/5!)(D^4 f \\
&+ 6Df D^2 f_y + 4D^2 f Df_y + D^2 f f_y^2 + Df f_y^3 + 3(Df)^2 f_{yy} + D^3 f f_y \\
&\qquad\qquad\qquad\qquad + 7f_y Df Df_y)] \Big|_n + O(h_n^6) \quad (5.6\text{-}11)
\end{aligned}$$

To get the expansion of the right-hand side of (5.6-4), we first use the Taylor-series expansion for two variables to write

$$f\left[x_n + \alpha_i h_n, y_n + \left(\sum_{j=1}^{i-1} \beta_{ij} \right) h_n f_n \right] = \sum_{t=0}^{\infty} h_n^t D_i^t f(x_n, y_n)/t! \tag{5.6-12}$$

where

$$D_i = \alpha_i \frac{\partial}{\partial x} + \left(\sum_{j=1}^{i-1} \beta_{ij} \right) f_n \frac{\partial}{\partial y} \tag{5.6-13}$$

Using (5.6-12) and (5.6-13), we can get expansions for each k_i on the right-hand side of (5.6-4).

Since $\alpha_1 = 0$

$$k_1 = h_n f_n \tag{5.6-14}$$

For k_2 we have

$$\begin{aligned}
k_2 = h_n f(x_n + \alpha_2 h_n, y_n + \beta_{21} k_1) &= h_n f(x_n + \alpha_2 h_n, y_n + \beta_{21} h_n f_n) \\
&= h_n \sum_{t=0}^{\infty} h_n^t D_2^t f(x_n, y_n)/t! \quad (5.6\text{-}15)
\end{aligned}$$

where D_2 is given by (5.6-13). For k_3 we proceed as follows using (5.6-14) and (5.6-15):

$$\begin{aligned}
k_3 &= h_n f(x_n + \alpha_3 h_n, y_n + \beta_{31} k_1 + \beta_{32} k_2) \\
&= h_n f[x_n + \alpha_3 h_n, y_n + (\beta_{31} + \beta_{32}) h_n f_n + \beta_{32}(k_2 - h_n f_n)] \\
&= h_n \sum_{t=0}^{\infty} [h_n D_3 + \beta_{32}(k_2 - h_n f_n)(\partial/\partial y)]^t f(x_n, y_n)/t! \quad (5.6\text{-}16)
\end{aligned}$$

By using (5.6-15) in (5.6-16), we may consider (5.6-16) to be an expansion in powers of h_n. The procedure for k_3 suggests the general procedure for k_i. We write

$$k_i = h_n f\left(x_n + \alpha_i h_n,\ y_n + \sum_{j=1}^{i-1} \beta_{ij} k_j\right)$$

$$= h_n f\left\{x_n + \alpha_i h_n,\ y_n + \sum_{j=1}^{i-1} [\beta_{ij} h_n f_n + \beta_{ij}(k_j - h_n f_n)]\right\}$$

$$= h_n \sum_{t=0}^{\infty} \left[h_n D_i + \sum_{j=2}^{i-1} \beta_{ij}(k_j - h_n f_n)\frac{\partial}{\partial y}\right]^t f(x_n,y_n)/t! \quad (5.6\text{-}17)$$

and then use the results for $k_j,\ j < i$ to write k_i as an expansion in powers of h_n. Leaving the algebra to a problem {38}, we give the results for $i = 1,\ 2,\ 3,\ 4$, retaining terms through h_n^5:

$$k_1 = hf\Big|_n \qquad (5.6\text{-}18)$$

$$k_2 = hf + h^2 D_2 f + (h^3/2!)D_2^2 f + (h^4/3!)D_2^3 f + (h^5/4!)D_2^4 f\Big|_n + O(h_n^6) \qquad (5.6\text{-}19)$$

$$k_3 = hf + h^2 D_3 f + h^3(\tfrac{1}{2}D_3^2 f + \beta_{32} f_y D_2 f) + h^4[\tfrac{1}{6}D_3^3 f$$
$$+ (\beta_{32}/2)f_y D_2^2 f + \beta_{32} D_2 f D_3 f_y] + h^5[\tfrac{1}{24}D_3^4 f + (\beta_{32}/6)f_y D_2^3 f$$
$$+ (\beta_{32}/2)D_2^2 f D_3 f_y + (\beta_{32}^2/2)f_{yy}(D_2 f)^2 + (\beta_{32}/2)D_2 f D_3^2 f_y]\Big|_n$$
$$+ O(h_n^6) \quad (5.6\text{-}20)$$

$$k_4 = hf + h^2 D_4 f + h^3(\tfrac{1}{2}D_4^2 f + \beta_{42} f_y D_2 f + \beta_{43} f_y D_3 f)$$
$$+ h^4[\tfrac{1}{6}D_4^3 f + \tfrac{1}{2}\beta_{42} f_y D_2^2 f + \beta_{32}\beta_{43}(f_y)^2 D_2 f + \tfrac{1}{2}\beta_{43} f_y D_3^2 f$$
$$+ \beta_{42} D_2 f D_4 f_y + \beta_{43} D_3 f D_4 f_y] + h^5[\tfrac{1}{24}D_4^4 f + \tfrac{1}{6}\beta_{42} f_y D_2^3 f$$
$$+ \tfrac{1}{2}\beta_{32}\beta_{43}(f_y)^2 D_2^2 f + \beta_{32}\beta_{43} f_y D_2 f D_3 f_y + \tfrac{1}{6}\beta_{43} f_y D_3^3 f$$
$$+ \tfrac{1}{2}\beta_{42} D_4 f_y D_2^2 f + \tfrac{1}{2}\beta_{43} D_4 f_y D_3^2 f + \tfrac{1}{2}\beta_{42}^2 f_{yy} D_2^2 f$$
$$+ \beta_{42}\beta_{43} f_{yy} D_2 f D_3 f + \tfrac{1}{2}\beta_{43}^2 f_{yy} D_3^2 f + \tfrac{1}{2}\beta_{42} D_2 f D_4^2 f_y$$
$$+ \tfrac{1}{2}\beta_{43} D_3 f D_4^2 f_y + \beta_{43}\beta_{32} f_y D_2 f D_4 f_y]\Big|_n + O(h_n^6) \quad (5.6\text{-}21)$$

Equations (5.6-18) to (5.6-21) will enable us to develop all Runge-Kutta methods through order 4 (this order being sufficient for almost all applications; see Sec. 5.5-2) and the terms in h_n^5 will facilitate discussion of the error term.

Substituting (5.6-18) to (5.6-21) and (5.6-11) into (5.6-4) and matching powers of h_n through h_n^4, we get

$$h_n: \qquad w_1 + w_2 + w_3 + w_4 = 1 \qquad (5.6\text{-}22)$$

$$h_n^2: \qquad w_2 D_2 f + w_3 D_3 f + w_4 D_4 f = (1/2!)Df \qquad (5.6\text{-}23)$$

$$h_n^3: \qquad \tfrac{1}{2}[w_2 D_2^2 f + w_3 D_3^2 f + w_4 D_4^2 f] + f_y[w_3\beta_{32} D_2 f$$
$$+ w_4(\beta_{42} D_2 f + \beta_{43} D_3 f)] = (1/3!)(D^2 f + f_y Df) \quad (5.6\text{-}24)$$

h_n^4: $\frac{1}{6}[w_2 D_2^3 f + w_3 D_3^3 f + w_4 D_4^3 f] + \frac{1}{2} f_y [w_3 \beta_{32} D_2^2 f$

$+ w_4(\beta_{42} D_2^2 f + \beta_{43} D_3^2 f)] + [w_3 \beta_{32} D_2 f D_3 f_y + w_4(\beta_{42} D_2 f D_4 f_y$

$+ \beta_{43} D_3 f D_4 f_y)] + [w_4 \beta_{32} \beta_{43} (f_y)^2 D_2 f] = (1/4!)[D^3 f + f_y D^2 f$

$$+ 3 D f D f_y + f_y^2 D f] \qquad (5.6\text{-}25)$$

These are in reality not four but eight equations since, if the values of the w_i's, α_i's, and β_{ij}'s are to be independent of $f(x,y)$, as they must be to be useful, then the expressions in square brackets on the left-hand sides of (5.6-24) and (5.6-25), which are homogeneous in the operators, must equal the corresponding terms on the right-hand sides {38}. Moreover, if the resulting eight equations are to be independent of $f(x,y)$, then the ratios

$$D_j f / D f \qquad j = 2, 3, 4 \qquad \text{and} \qquad D_j f_y / D f_y \qquad j = 3, 4 \qquad (5.6\text{-}26)$$

must be constant. This will be true if

$$\alpha_i = \sum_{j=1}^{i-1} \beta_{ij} \qquad i = 2, 3, 4 \tag{5.6-27}$$

for then

$$D_i = \alpha_i D \tag{5.6-28}$$

Finally, then the eight equations are

$$
\begin{aligned}
&w_1 + w_2 + w_3 + w_4 = 1 \\
&w_2 \alpha_2 + w_3 \alpha_3 + w_4 \alpha_4 = \tfrac{1}{2} \\
&w_2 \alpha_2^2 + w_3 \alpha_3^2 + w_4 \alpha_4^2 = \tfrac{1}{3} \\
&w_3 \alpha_2 \beta_{32} + w_4(\alpha_2 \beta_{42} + \alpha_3 \beta_{43}) = \tfrac{1}{6} \\
&w_2 \alpha_2^3 + w_3 \alpha_3^3 + w_4 \alpha_4^3 = \tfrac{1}{4} \\
&w_3 \alpha_2^2 \beta_{32} + w_4(\alpha_2^2 \beta_{42} + \alpha_3^2 \beta_{43}) = \tfrac{1}{12} \\
&w_3 \alpha_2 \alpha_3 \beta_{32} + w_4(\alpha_2 \beta_{42} + \alpha_3 \beta_{43})\alpha_4 = \tfrac{1}{8} \\
&w_4 \alpha_2 \beta_{32} \beta_{43} = \tfrac{1}{24}
\end{aligned}
\tag{5.6-29}
$$

where the first equation corresponds to (5.6-22), the second to (5.6-23), the next two to (5.6-24), and the last four to (5.6-25). The system (5.6-27) and (5.6-29) has 11 equations and 13 unknowns, which will generally be sufficient to determine the parameters with two degrees of freedom. We note that, because of the last equation, it is *necessary* to include the k_4 term in order to achieve accuracy through h_n^4 (why?), thus verifying that m must be at least M. For the cases $M = 2$ and 3, we may also show that $m = M$. The general result that $m \geq M$ is not hard to prove {39}. Since we shall be considering in detail only the cases $M = 2, 3, 4$ we may hereafter use m in place of M. Before considering these cases, however, it will be convenient to consider the errors in Runge-Kutta methods.

5.6-3-1   *Errors in Runge-Kutta methods*

Here alone in our discussion of Runge-Kutta methods is it important to consider a single differential equation. For systems of equations, the algebra becomes intractable.

1. *Truncation error.* Equation (5.6-4) is to be exact for powers of h_n through h_n^m. Therefore, the truncation error T_m may be written

$$T_m = \gamma_m h_n^{m+1} + O(h_n^{m+2}) \tag{5.6-30}$$

where, of course, both γ_m and T_m really depend on $f(x,y)$. To estimate T_m, we are forced to consider only γ_m because consideration of the higher-order terms is algebraically intractable. The bounds on γ_m that we shall obtain will be very conservative (i.e., the true magnitude of γ_m will generally be much less than the bound). Thus, if the $O(h_n^{m+2})$ term is small compared with $\gamma_m h_n^{m+1}$, as we expect it will be if h_n is small, then the bound on $\gamma_m h_n^{m+1}$ will usually be a bound on the error as a whole.

Using (5.6-11), (5.6-18) to (5.6-21), and (5.6-28), we calculate

$$\gamma_2 = (\tfrac{1}{6} - \alpha_2^2 w_2/2)D^2 f + \tfrac{1}{6} f_y D f \tag{5.6-31}$$

$$\gamma_3 = \left[\frac{1}{4!} - \frac{1}{3!}(\alpha_2^3 w_2 + \alpha_3^3 w_3)\right] D^3 f + \left(\frac{1}{4!} - \frac{1}{2!}\alpha_2^2 \beta_{32} w_3\right) f_y D^2 f$$

$$+ \left(\frac{3}{4!} - \alpha_2 \alpha_3 \beta_{32} w_3\right) D f D f_y + \frac{1}{4!} f_y^2 D f \tag{5.6-32}$$

$$\gamma_4 = \left(\frac{1}{120} - \frac{w_2 \alpha_2^4 + w_3 \alpha_3^4 + w_4 \alpha_4^4}{24}\right) D^4 f$$

$$+ \left[\frac{1}{20} - \frac{w_3 \alpha_2 \alpha_3^2 \beta_{32} + w_4 \alpha_4^2(\alpha_2 \beta_{42} + \alpha_3 \beta_{43})}{2}\right] D^2 f_y D f$$

$$+ \left[\frac{1}{30} - \frac{w_3 \beta_{32} \alpha_2^2 \alpha_3 + w_4 \alpha_4(\beta_{42} \alpha_2^2 + \beta_{43} \alpha_3^2)}{2}\right] D f_y D^2 f$$

$$+ \left(\frac{1}{120} - \frac{w_4 \beta_{43} \beta_{32} \alpha_2^2}{2}\right) f_y^2 D^2 f$$

$$+ \left[\frac{1}{40} - \frac{w_3 \beta_{32}^2 \alpha_2^2 + w_4(\beta_{43}\alpha_3 + \beta_{42}\alpha_2)^2}{2}\right] f_{yy} D^2 f$$

$$+ \left[\frac{1}{120} - \frac{w_3 \beta_{32} \alpha_2^3 + w_4(\beta_{43}\alpha_3^3 + \beta_{42}\alpha_2^3)}{6}\right] f_y D^3 f$$

$$+ \left[\frac{7}{120} - w_4 \beta_{43} \beta_{32} \alpha_2(\alpha_3 + \alpha_4)\right] f_y D f_y D f + \frac{1}{120} f_y^3 D f \tag{5.6-33}$$

In order to bound γ_m, we assume the following bounds for $f(x,y)$ and its derivatives in a region R about (x_n, y_n) containing all points in (5.6-5):

$$|f(x,y)| < M \qquad \left|\frac{\partial^{i+j} f}{\partial x^i \, \partial y^j}\right| < \frac{L^{i+j}}{M^{j-1}} \qquad i + j \leqq m \tag{5.6-34}$$

the latter being chosen because it leads to the convenient forms below. Using these bounds and (5.6-9), we can, for example, bound D^2f as

$$|D^2f| = \left| \frac{\partial^2 f}{\partial x^2} + 2f_n \frac{\partial^2 f}{\partial x\, \partial y} + f_n^2 \frac{\partial^2 f}{\partial y^2} \right| < 4ML^2$$

Bounding the other derivative terms in (5.6-31) and (5.6-32) similarly, we get {40}

$$|\gamma_2| < \left(4 \left| \frac{1}{6} - \frac{\alpha_2^2 w_2}{2} \right| + \frac{1}{3} \right) ML^2 \tag{5.6-35}$$

$$|\gamma_3| < [8|\tfrac{1}{24} - \tfrac{1}{6}(\alpha_2^3 w_2 + \alpha_3^3 w_3)| + 4|\tfrac{1}{24} - \tfrac{1}{2}\alpha_2^2\beta_{32}w_3| \\ + 4|\tfrac{1}{8} - \alpha_2\alpha_3\beta_{32}w_3| + \tfrac{1}{12}]ML^3 \tag{5.6-36}$$

$$|\gamma_4| < (16|b_1| + 4|b_2| + |b_2 + 3b_3| + |2b_2 + 3b_3| + |b_2 + b_3| \\ + |b_3| + 8|b_4| + |b_5| + |2b_5 + b_7| + |b_5 + b_6 + b_7| + |b_6| \\ + |2b_6 + b_7| + |b_7| + 2|b_8|)ML^4 \tag{5.6-37}$$

where

$$\begin{aligned}
b_1 &= \tfrac{1}{120} - \tfrac{1}{24}(\alpha_2^4 w_2 + \alpha_3^4 w_3 + w_4) \\
b_2 &= \tfrac{1}{20} - \tfrac{1}{2}[\alpha_2\alpha_3^2\beta_{32}w_3 + (\alpha_2\beta_{42} + \alpha_3\beta_{43})w_4] \\
b_3 &= \tfrac{1}{120} - \tfrac{1}{6}[\alpha_3^2\beta_{32}w_3 + (\alpha_3^3\beta_{42} + \alpha_3^3\beta_{43})w_4] \\
b_4 &= \tfrac{1}{80} - \tfrac{1}{2}[\alpha_2^2\alpha_3\beta_{32}w_3 + (\alpha_2^2\beta_{42} + \alpha_3^2\beta_{43})w_4] \\
b_5 &= \tfrac{1}{120} - \tfrac{1}{2}\alpha_2^2\beta_{32}^2\beta_{43}w_4 \\
b_6 &= \tfrac{1}{40} - \tfrac{1}{2}[\alpha_2^2\beta_{32}w_3 + (\alpha_2\beta_{42} + \alpha_3\beta_{43})^2 w_4] \\
b_7 &= \tfrac{7}{120} - \alpha_2(1 + \alpha_3)\beta_{32}\beta_{43}w_4 \\
b_8 &= \tfrac{1}{120}
\end{aligned} \tag{5.6-38}$$

We have noted that, for $m = 4$, the system (5.6-29) is underdetermined. As we shall see, the corresponding systems for $m = 2$ and 3 are also underdetermined. In all three cases the extra parameters can be used to minimize the above bound on γ_m, as we shall indicate in Secs. 5.6-3-2 to 5.6-3-4.

2. *Propagated error bounds.* If Runge-Kutta methods are used for the complete solution of (5.1-1), then bounds on the propagated error will also be important. Since Runge-Kutta methods should usually be used only to start the solution, we shall content ourselves here with stating without proof [see Galler and Rozenberg (1960)] the following theorem on propagated error bounds which covers many of the specific Runge-Kutta methods we shall consider [but cf. (5.6-49)].

Theorem 5.3   If $w_i > 0$, $\alpha_i > 0$, $\beta_{ij} > 0$ ($i = 1, \ldots, 4, j = 1, \ldots, 3, ij \neq 42$), $\beta_{42} < 0$, if $\partial f/\partial y$ is continuous, negative, and bounded from above and below in a region D in the xy plane:

$$-M_2 < \partial f/\partial y < -M_1 < 0$$

if the maximum error (truncation and roundoff) committed in any step is less than E in magnitude and if the solution remains in a region D^*, approaching no closer to the boundary of D than $Qh + |\epsilon_i|$ where $Q = \max\limits_{(x,y)\, \varepsilon\, D} f(x,y)$, then the total error at the ith step ϵ_i satisfies the inequality

$$|\epsilon_i| < 2E/hM_1$$

where h is constant for all steps and must be such that

$$h < \min\,[4M_1^3/M_2^4, M_1/(M_2^2 - 2w_4\beta_{42}M_2^2 - 2w_4\beta_{42}\alpha_2 M_1 M_2)]$$

This theorem indicates the difficulty of obtaining definitive results about Runge-Kutta methods. The bound obtained may be expected to be very conservative.

3. *Roundoff error.* We could choose the free parameters to minimize the roundoff in (5.6-4) (i.e., to make the w_i as nearly equal as possible). But, as with numerical integration methods, roundoff is generally not significant compared with truncation, and so we shall ignore it when choosing the free parameters.

5.6-3-2   *Second-order methods*

For the case $m = 2$ the system (5.6-29) retains only the equations pertaining to h_n^2. These together with (5.6-27) for $i = 2$ are

$$w_1 + w_2 = 1 \qquad \alpha_2 w_2 = \tfrac{1}{2} \qquad \beta_{21} = \alpha_2 \qquad\qquad (5.6\text{-}39)$$

Three second-order methods of interest correspond to $\alpha_2 = \tfrac{1}{2},\ \tfrac{2}{3},\ 1$ for which (5.6-4) becomes, respectively,

$$y_{n+1} - y_n = h_n f(x_n + \tfrac{1}{2}h_n, y_n + \tfrac{1}{2}h_n f_n) \qquad\qquad (5.6\text{-}40)$$
$$y_{n+1} - y_n = \tfrac{1}{4}h_n[f(x_n,y_n) + 3f(x_n + \tfrac{2}{3}h_n, y_n + \tfrac{2}{3}h_n f_n)] \qquad (5.6\text{-}41)$$
$$y_{n+1} - y_n = \tfrac{1}{2}h_n[f(x_n,y_n) + f(x_n + h_n, y_n + h_n f_n)] \qquad\quad (5.6\text{-}42)$$

The method (5.6-40) in which $w_1 = 0$ corresponds to the Newton-Cotes open-type formula with one point when $f(x,y)$ is a function of x only (why?). Similarly, when $f(x,y)$ is a function of x only, (5.6-42) is the trapezoidal rule. Equation (5.6-41) is that for which the bound on γ_2 in (5.6-35) is minimized {42}. The bounds for (5.6-40) to (5.6-42) are, respectively, $\tfrac{1}{2}ML^2$, $\tfrac{1}{3}ML^2$, and $\tfrac{2}{3}ML^2$.

5.6-3-3   *Third-order methods*

The equations are

$$w_1 + w_2 + w_3 = 1 \qquad \alpha_2 w_2 + \alpha_3 w_3 = \tfrac{1}{2} \qquad \alpha_2^2 w_2 + \alpha_3^2 w_3 = \tfrac{1}{3}$$
$$\qquad\qquad\qquad\qquad\qquad\qquad\qquad\qquad\qquad\qquad (5.6\text{-}43)$$
$$\alpha_2\beta_{32}w_3 = \tfrac{1}{6} \qquad \alpha_2 = \beta_{21} \qquad \alpha_3 = \beta_{31} + \beta_{32}$$

which is a two-parameter family and may be written

$$w_1 = 1 + \frac{2 - 3(\alpha_2 + \alpha_3)}{6\alpha_2\alpha_3}$$

$$w_2 = \frac{3\alpha_3 - 2}{6\alpha_2(\alpha_3 - \alpha_2)}$$

$$w_3 = \frac{2 - 3\alpha_2}{6\alpha_3(\alpha_3 - \alpha_2)}$$

$$\beta_{21} = \alpha_2$$

$$\beta_{31} = \frac{3\alpha_2\alpha_3(1 - \alpha_2) - \alpha_3^2}{\alpha_2(2 - 3\alpha_2)}$$

$$\beta_{32} = \frac{\alpha_3(\alpha_3 - \alpha_2)}{\alpha_2(2 - 3\alpha_2)}$$

$$\begin{aligned} &\alpha_2 \neq \alpha_3 \\ &\alpha_2,\ \alpha_3 \neq 0 \\ \\ &\alpha_2 \neq 2/3 \end{aligned} \qquad (5.6\text{-}44)$$

The cases $\alpha_2 = \alpha_3$ and α_2 or $\alpha_3 = 0$ we leave to a problem {41}. Two third-order methods of interest are

$$\begin{aligned} y_{n+1} - y_n &= \tfrac{2}{9}k_1 + \tfrac{1}{3}k_2 + \tfrac{4}{9}k_3 \\ k_1 &= h_n f(x_n, y_n) \\ k_2 &= h_n f(x_n + \tfrac{1}{2}h_n, y_n + \tfrac{1}{2}k_1) \\ k_3 &= h_n f(x_n + \tfrac{3}{4}h_n, y_n + \tfrac{3}{4}k_2) \end{aligned} \qquad (5.6\text{-}45)$$

$$\begin{aligned} y_{n+1} - y_n &= \tfrac{1}{6}(k_1 + 4k_2 + k_3) \\ k_1 &= h_n f(x_n, y_n) \\ k_2 &= h_n f(x_n + \tfrac{1}{2}h_n, y_n + \tfrac{1}{2}k_1) \\ k_3 &= h_n f(x_n + h_n, y_n - k_1 + 2k_2) \end{aligned} \qquad (5.6\text{-}46)$$

When $f(x,y)$ is a function of x only, (5.6-46) is Simpson's rule. The method (5.6-45) is that for which the bound on γ_3 is minimized {42}. For the methods (5.6-45) and (5.6-46), the bounds are, respectively, $\tfrac{1}{9}ML^3$ and $\tfrac{13}{36}ML^3$.

5.6-3-4 Fourth-order methods

The two-parameter system (5.6-29) may be solved to give

$$w_1 = \frac{1}{2} + \frac{1 - 2(\alpha_2 + \alpha_3)}{12\alpha_2\alpha_3} \qquad w_2 = \frac{2\alpha_3 - 1}{12\alpha_2(\alpha_3 - \alpha_2)(1 - \alpha_2)}$$

$$w_3 = \frac{1 - 2\alpha_2}{12\alpha_3(\alpha_3 - \alpha_2)(1 - \alpha_3)} \qquad w_4 = \frac{1}{2} + \frac{2(\alpha_2 + \alpha_3) - 3}{12(1 - \alpha_2)(1 - \alpha_3)}$$

$$\beta_{32} = \frac{\alpha_3(\alpha_3 - \alpha_2)}{2\alpha_2(1 - 2\alpha_2)} \qquad \alpha_4 = 1 \qquad (5.6\text{-}47)$$

$$\beta_{42} = \frac{(1 - \alpha_2)[\alpha_2 + \alpha_3 - 1 - (2\alpha_3 - 1)^2]}{2\alpha_2(\alpha_3 - \alpha_2)[6\alpha_2\alpha_3 - 4(\alpha_2 + \alpha_3) + 3]}$$

$$\beta_{43} = \frac{(1 - 2\alpha_2)(1 - \alpha_2)(1 - \alpha_3)}{\alpha_3(\alpha_3 - \alpha_2)[6\alpha_2\alpha_3 - 4(\alpha_2 + \alpha_3) + 3]}$$

except when α_2, $\alpha_3 = 0$, α_2, $\alpha_3 = 1$, $\alpha_2 = \alpha_3$ or the denominators of β_{32}, β_{42}, or β_{43} vanish. These special cases are considered in {43} and {44}. The most commonly used fourth-order Runge-Kutta method is one in which $\alpha_2 = \alpha_3 = \frac{1}{2}$, and its equations are

$$y_{n+1} - y_n = \frac{1}{6}(k_1 + 2k_2 + 2k_3 + k_4)$$
$$k_1 = h_n f(x_n, y_n)$$
$$k_2 = h_n f(x_n + \frac{1}{2}h_n, y_n + \frac{1}{2}k_1)$$
$$k_3 = h_n f(x_n + \frac{1}{2}h_n, y_n + \frac{1}{2}k_2) \qquad (5.6\text{-}48)$$
$$k_4 = h_n f(x_n + h_n, y_n + k_3)$$

The method for which the error bound on γ_4 is minimized corresponds to $\alpha_2 = .4$, $\alpha_3 = \frac{7}{8} - \frac{3}{16}\sqrt{5}$ and has the equations

$$y_{n+1} - y_n = .17476028k_1 - .55148066k_2 + 1.20553560k_3$$
$$+ .17118478k_4$$

$$k_1 = h_n f(x_n, y_n)$$
$$k_2 = h_n f(x_n + .4h_n, y_n + .4k_1) \qquad (5.6\text{-}49)$$
$$k_3 = h_n f(x_n + .45573725h_n, y_n + .29697761k_1 + .15875964k_2)$$
$$k_4 = h_n f(x_n + h_n, y_n + .21810040k_1 - 3.05096516k_2$$
$$+ 3.83286476k_3)$$

The error bounds on the methods (5.6-48) and (5.6-49) are, respectively, $\frac{73}{720}ML^4$ and $5.4627 \times 10^{-2}ML^4$.

In order to compare Runge-Kutta methods with corresponding order predictor-corrector methods, we note the following points:

1. Runge-Kutta methods are self-starting, the interval between steps may be changed at will, and in general, they are particularly straightforward to apply on a digital computer.
2. They are comparable in accuracy—often more accurate—than corresponding order predictor-corrector methods {45}. But because of the difficulty of estimating the per-step error, the step size h must generally be chosen conservatively (i.e., smaller than is actually necessary to achieve the desired accuracy).
3. Further, they require a number of evaluations of $f(x,y)$ at each step equal to the order of the method. As we shall see in the next section, predictor-corrector methods of fourth order generally require only two evaluations per step. Since evaluation of $f(x,y)$ is usually the most time-consuming part of solving (5.1-1), this means that fourth-order predictor-corrector methods are generally nearly twice as fast as fourth-order Runge-Kutta methods.

On a digital computer reasons 2 and 3 are much more compelling than 1, and thus predictor-corrector methods are the indicated methods to use.

On desk calculators, the argument in favor of predictor-corrector methods is perhaps still more compelling, since in this case their ease of use is comparable with that of Runge-Kutta methods.

The self-starting characteristic of Runge-Kutta methods makes them an ideal adjunct to predictor-corrector methods for starting the solution. Since they will be used for only a few steps of the computation, truncation error and not stability is the key consideration. Therefore, for this purpose, the minimum error bound Runge-Kutta methods should be used. The methods we have derived may be used for systems of equations {46}, although the error bounds were derived for single equations. It is reasonable to assume, however, that methods which are best in this sense for single equations will be at least nearly best for systems.

5.6-4   Changing the interval

Usually the solution of (5.1-1) is desired for some final value of x, say x_F, and at this value of x it is desired that the value of y should be in error by no more than some predetermined tolerance. Normally the initial value of h will be chosen so that, if the a priori estimate of the per step error is correct, the solution will have the desired accuracy. However, as the computation proceeds, the error-estimation procedure of Sec. 5.5-3 may indicate that (1) the per step error is larger at each step than is allowable if the final value of y is to have the desired accuracy, or (2) the error is significantly smaller than is necessary. Assuming, as we shall here, that truncation error is the dominant error, the indicated action in the first case above is to decrease the step size h since truncation error depends on a power of h. Conversely, in the second case, we increase the step size so that the computation will proceed more rapidly. Since predictor-corrector methods require a constant step size, whenever the interval is changed, more "starting" values must be generated. For example, suppose the second-order method (5.5-11) is being used and, after y_n has been computed, it is desired to halve the value of h. Then in calculating $y(x_n + \frac{1}{2}h)$ the predictor requires values of y at x_n, $x_n - \frac{1}{2}h$, and x_{n-1}. Thus, in order to proceed with the computation, we need the value of y at $x_n - \frac{1}{2}h$. An effective method for doing this would be to use a second-order Runge-Kutta method [because (5.5-11) is a second-order method] starting from x_{n-1} with a step size $h/2$. An alternative procedure would be to use the second-order Runge-Kutta method starting from x_n to generate values of y at $x_n + \frac{1}{2}h$ and $x_n + h$ and then switch back to the use of the predictor-corrector method. The use of Runge-Kutta methods to change the interval h is particularly simple on a digital computer when the Runge-Kutta method has been used to calculate starting values and is therefore already part of the computer program. Runge-Kutta methods are, in fact, easily used when the interval h is to be increased or decreased by any factor whatsoever.

Another approach to changing the interval is to use one of the interpolation formulas of Chap. 3 and previously computed values of $y(x)$ to interpolate or extrapolate to get those values of y [such as $y(x_n - \frac{1}{2}h)$] which are required to continue the computation at the new interval. A particular example of this is considered in {48}. With such interpolation or extrapolation procedures, it is convenient to halve the interval when decreasing it and to double it when increasing it. But when the interval is to be doubled, it is possible to avoid the use of Runge-Kutta methods or interpolation methods entirely {48}. In the next section, we shall give an example of changing the interval in practice.

5.7 USING PREDICTOR–CORRECTOR METHODS

One computational problem that we have deferred thus far is the determination of when to stop iterating the corrector. Let us assume that, because of the final accuracy that we desire in our solution, we have determined a bound on the per step error or the per step relative error which, if not exceeded during the computation, will enable us to achieve the desired accuracy. It is reasonable then to require that any error made by not iterating the corrector to convergence be small compared with the allowable error, or to put it another way, this error should be small compared with truncation and roundoff errors.

Before we consider how to estimate the error incurred by not iterating the corrector to convergence, it is necessary to realize that in actual computational practice we compute one more value of y than of y' (cf. Fig. 5.2). This is because the cost of computing one extra ordinate is small compared with the cost of computing y'.

Let y be the value that would be obtained if the corrector were iterated to convergence, and let $y^{(i)}$ be the value of the ith iterate [with $y^{(0)}$ the predicted value] where, for convenience, we have dropped the subscript n. As in Sec. 5.5-1 we assume that b_{-1} is positive. Then, since only the b_{-1} term in the numerical integration method (5.2-5) changes from one iteration to the next,

$$y^{(i+1)} - y^{(i)} = hb_{-1}\{[y^{(i)}]' - [y^{(i-1)}]'\} \tag{5.7-1}$$

Let $|[y^{(i)}]' - [y^{(i-1)}]'| = \delta_i$. Then

$$|y^{(i+1)} - y^{(i)}| = hb_{-1}\delta_i \tag{5.7-2}$$

Using the mean-value theorem,

$$\delta_{i+1} = |[y^{(i+1)}]' - [y^{(i)}]'| = |f[x,y^{(i+1)}] - f[x,y^{(i)}]|$$
$$\leqq |y^{(i+1)} - y^{(i)}|K < hb_{-1}\delta_i K \tag{5.7-3}$$

if $|\partial f/\partial y| < K$ in the region of interest.   Then from (5.7-2)

$$|y^{(i+2)} - y^{(i+1)}| \leqq (hb_{-1})^2 \delta_i K \tag{5.7-4}$$

and in this way the differences of successive iterates can be bounded. Now

$$|y - y^{(i+1)}| \leqq |y^{(i+2)} - y^{(i+1)}| + |y^{(i+3)} - y^{(i+2)}| + \cdots$$

and using the above results, we get

$$|y - y^{(i+1)}| \leqq h^2 b_{-1}^2 \delta_i K (1 + hb_{-1}K + h^2 b_{-1}^2 K^2 + \cdots)$$
$$= h^2 b_{-1}^2 \delta_i K / (1 - hb_{-1}K) \tag{5.7-5}$$

if $|hb_{-1}K| < 1$ which, in fact, it must be for convergence of the corrector iterations.   Indeed, in order to get rapid convergence of the corrector, we have noted that we should have $|hb_{-1}K| \ll 1$.   Thus we have the result that $h^2 b_{-1}^2 \delta_i K$ should be a good approximation to the right-hand side of (5.7-5).   In fact, since we have considered only the maximum values of quantities in this derivation, we expect that $h^2 b_{-1}^2 \delta_i K$ will be a quite conservative bound on the error incurred by stopping the iteration after the computation of $[y^{(i)}]'$ and $y^{(i+1)}$.   This suggests the following procedure: After each corrector iteration, compute δ_i and compare it with a *convergence factor* chosen so that, if δ_i is less than the convergence factor, then terminating the iteration with $[y^{(i)}]'$ and $y^{(i+1)}$ will result in a value of $h^2 b_{-1}^2 \delta_i K$ which is small compared with the allowable per step error.   We would compare δ_i with the product of the convergence factor and $y^{(i)}$ if we were interested in controlling the relative error.   In either case the test requires some estimate of K, the bound on $|\partial f/\partial y|$.   Since

$$\left| \frac{\partial f}{\partial y} \right| \approx \left| \frac{[y^{(i)}]' - [y^{(i-1)}]'}{y^{(i)} - y^{(i-1)}} \right| = \frac{\delta_i}{|y^{(i)} - y^{(i-1)}|} \tag{5.7-6}$$

and since, as we have noted, $h^2 b_{-1}^2 \delta_i K$ is a conservative bound on the error incurred by terminating the iteration, equation (5.7-6) may be used as the estimate of K.

Generally in the numerical solution of differential equations, the test described above will be satisfied after the *first* application of the corrector (i.e., $i = 1$) because the modified predicted value itself will usually be quite accurate.   Thus generally only *two* evaluations of $f(x,y)$ are required at each step, one after computing the modified predicted value and one after computing the first corrected value.   This is why fourth-order predictor-corrector methods are generally substantially faster than fourth-order Runge-Kutta methods which require four evaluations of $f(x,y)$ per step.

Our main object in this section is to compare the use of two predictor-corrector methods, that of Milne (5.5-27) and that of Hamming (5.5-33), in the solution of some differential equations in order to illustrate a number of the points made in this chapter.   The first equation we consider is

$$dy/dx = -y \qquad y(0) = 1 \tag{5.7-7}$$

whose solution is $Y = e^{-x}$. Using a value of $h = .1$, the results of this computation for various values of x are shown in Table 5.3. All the computation was carried out on a digital computer using floating-point arithmetic with $d = 10$, $m = 8$ (cf. Sec. 1.5-2). For both predictor-corrector methods, the fourth-order Runge-Kutta method (5.6-49) was used to calculate the values through $x = .4$.† The truncation errors for the two methods are

$$\begin{aligned}
\text{Hamming:} \qquad & T_n = -\tfrac{1}{40}h^5 Y^v(\eta) = 2.5 \times 10^{-7}e^{-\eta} \\
\text{Milne:} \qquad & T_n = -\tfrac{1}{90}h^5 Y^v(\eta) \approx 1.1 \times 10^{-7}e^{-\eta}
\end{aligned} \tag{5.7-8}$$

Since the solution of (5.7-7) is rapidly decreasing, we used a relative-error criterion in determining when to terminate the corrector iteration.   The convergence factor used was 1.0×10^{-5}.   For, if δ_i is less than this convergence factor, then, with $K = 1$,

$$h^2 b_{-1}^2 \delta_i K < \begin{cases} \tfrac{9}{64} \times 10^{-7} & \text{Hamming} \\ \tfrac{1}{9} \times 10^{-7} & \text{Milne} \end{cases} \tag{5.7-9}$$

Since we are using relative error, these must be compared with the coefficients of $e^{-\eta}$ in (5.7-8).   For Hamming's and Milne's method, the bounds in (5.7-9) are, respectively, about $\tfrac{1}{18}$ and $\tfrac{1}{10}$ the coefficients in (5.7-8). Therefore, we conclude that, if δ_i is less than 1.0×10^{-5}, the error incurred by not iterating the corrector to convergence will not be serious.

During the early stages of the computation until $x = 4.0$, the smaller truncation error of Milne's method results in smaller errors using this method.   From $x = 4.0$ on, however, the superiority of Hamming's method becomes manifest.   At $x = 15.0$ there is a relative error of 10^{-5} in Hamming's method.   Correspondingly, the relative error in Milne's method at $x = 15.0$ is about -25.   The reason why the early good behavior of Milne's method is not continued is, of course, the instability of Milne's method for all positive K that we discussed in Sec. 5.5-4. (Here $\partial f/\partial y = -1$ so that $K = 1$.)   In the early stages of the computation, the coefficient of r_1 in (5.4-26) is small because of the accuracy of the initial conditions generated using (5.6-49).   During this part of the computation, the per step truncation error determines the error, and thus Milne's method gives more accurate results than Hamming's.   But sooner or later the term in r_1^n must predominate in the error in Milne's method, thereby producing the instability which is evident later in the computation.   In fact, late in the computation the sign of y alternates from one step to the

---

† Actually, only values through $x = .3$ are required to start Milne's or Hamming's methods.

Table 5.3   Results of numerical solution of $y' = -y$, $y(0) = 1$

x	e^{-x}	Hamming's method y	Hamming's method Error	Milne's method y	Milne's method Error	Hermite method y	Hermite method Error
.1	.90483742	.90483753	-1.1×10^{-7}	.90483753	-1.1×10^{-7}	.90483753	-1.1×10^{-7}
.2	.81873075	.81873093	-1.8×10^{-7}	.81873093	-1.8×10^{-7}	.81873093	-1.8×10^{-7}
.3	.74081822	.74081846	-2.4×10^{-7}	.74081846	-2.4×10^{-7}	.74081846	-2.4×10^{-7}
.4	.67032005	.67032033	-2.8×10^{-7}	.67032033	-2.8×10^{-7}	.67032033	-2.8×10^{-7}
.5	.60653066	.60653078	-1.2×10^{-7}	.60653078	-1.2×10^{-7}	.60653092	-2.6×10^{-7}
.6	.54881164	.54881160	4.0×10^{-8}	.54881183	-1.9×10^{-7}	.54881188	-2.4×10^{-7}
.7	.49658530	.49658511	1.9×10^{-7}	.49658534	-4.0×10^{-8}	.49658553	-2.4×10^{-7}
.8	.44932896	.44932865	3.1×10^{-7}	.44932910	-1.4×10^{-7}	.44932918	-2.3×10^{-7}
.9	.40656966	.40656924	4.2×10^{-7}	.40656964	-2.0×10^{-8}	.40656986	-2.2×10^{-7}
1.0	.36787944	.36787894	5.0×10^{-7}	.36787953	-9.0×10^{-8}	.36787963	-2.0×10^{-7}
2.0	.13533528	.13533469	5.9×10^{-7}	.13533534	-6.0×10^{-8}	.13533536	-1.9×10^{-7}
3.0	4.9787068×10^{-2}	4.9786674×10^{-2}	3.9×10^{-7}	4.9787174×10^{-2}	-1.1×10^{-7}	4.9787110×10^{-2}	-4.2×10^{-8}
4.0	1.8315639×10^{-2}	1.8315434×10^{-2}	2.1×10^{-7}	1.8315820×10^{-2}	-1.8×10^{-7}	1.8315655×10^{-2}	-1.6×10^{-8}
5.0	6.7379470×10^{-3}	6.7378495×10^{-3}	9.8×10^{-8}	6.7382209×10^{-3}	-2.7×10^{-7}	6.7379539×10^{-3}	-6.9×10^{-9}
6.0	2.4787522×10^{-3}	2.4787080×10^{-3}	4.4×10^{-8}	2.4791447×10^{-3}	-3.9×10^{-7}	2.4787550×10^{-3}	-2.8×10^{-9}
7.0	9.1188197×10^{-4}	9.1186306×10^{-4}	1.9×10^{-8}	9.1243460×10^{-4}	-5.5×10^{-7}	9.1188321×10^{-4}	-1.2×10^{-9}
8.0	3.3546263×10^{-4}	3.3545448×10^{-4}	8.2×10^{-9}	3.3623582×10^{-4}	-7.7×10^{-7}	3.3546314×10^{-4}	-5.1×10^{-10}
9.0	1.2340980×10^{-4}	1.2340648×10^{-4}	3.3×10^{-9}	1.2448957×10^{-4}	-1.1×10^{-6}	1.2341002×10^{-4}	-2.2×10^{-10}
10.0	4.5399930×10^{-5}	4.5398555×10^{-5}	1.4×10^{-9}	4.6906894×10^{-5}	-1.5×10^{-6}	4.5400018×10^{-5}	-8.8×10^{-11}
11.0	1.6701701×10^{-5}	1.6701140×10^{-5}	5.6×10^{-10}	1.8804490×10^{-5}	-2.1×10^{-6}	1.6701734×10^{-5}	-3.3×10^{-11}
12.0	6.1442124×10^{-6}	6.1439854×10^{-6}	2.3×10^{-10}	9.0782370×10^{-6}	-2.9×10^{-6}	6.1442251×10^{-6}	-1.3×10^{-11}
13.0	2.2603294×10^{-6}	2.2602384×10^{-6}	9.1×10^{-11}	6.3541098×10^{-6}	-4.1×10^{-6}	2.2603344×10^{-6}	-5.0×10^{-12}
13.5	1.3709591×10^{-6}			$-3.4646962 \times 10^{-6}$	4.8×10^{-6}		
14.0	8.3152872×10^{-7}	8.3149279×10^{-7}	3.6×10^{-11}	6.5434628×10^{-6}	-5.7×10^{-6}	8.3153061×10^{-7}	-1.9×10^{-12}
14.5	5.0434766×10^{-7}			$-6.2426818 \times 10^{-6}$	6.7×10^{-6}		
15.0	3.0590232×10^{-7}	3.0588805×10^{-7}	1.4×10^{-12}	8.2755880×10^{-6}	-8.0×10^{-6}	3.0590305×10^{-7}	-7.3×10^{-13}

next (e.g., note the entries for $x = 13.5$ and 14.5). The stability of Hamming's method is best illustrated by noticing the quite slow growth in the relative error as the computation proceeds. This example is a good illustration of the necessity of using a stable method for any solution of a differential equation that is going to proceed over more than just a few steps in h.

For each of the 146 steps of the computation using (5.5-33), the test of the convergence factor was satisfied after one application of the corrector so that just two evaluations of $f(x,y)$ were needed at each step. The instability of Milne's method, however, necessitated an average of three corrector iterations per step, one near the beginning but five toward the end. Finally, we note that in this example the truncation error is substantially greater than roundoff; for a contrast, see the third example of this section.

As a second example, we consider the equation

$$dy/dx = y \qquad y(0) = 1 \tag{5.7-10}$$

whose solution is $Y = e^x$. In Table 5.4, we have the results of this computation tabulated. Again an interval of $h = .1$ was used, the first four steps were calculated using (5.6-49), and floating-point arithmetic was used throughout with a convergence factor of 1.0×10^{-5} and a relative-error criterion. This time the superior per step error of Milne's method causes the solution with that method to be more accurate throughout the computation. For with $\partial f/\partial y = 1$ the magnitude of r_1 is less than that of r_0 (see Example 5.5). The smaller error in Hamming's method for $x = .5$ to $x = .9$ is a result of the errors in the values calculated using (5.6-49). These errors are positive, as we see from Table 5.4, but the truncation errors of both Milne's and Hamming's method are negative (why?) so that the *larger* negative error in Hamming's method overcomes the positive error in the initial values more rapidly than the error in Milne's method. For both methods only one application of the corrector was needed at each step.

The growth of the error as x increases makes this example a good one with which to illustrate change of interval. The quantity $y_n - y_n^{(0)}$ grows from 3.9×10^{-6} at $x = .5$ to 7.9×10^{-2} at $x = 10.0$ using Hamming's method and from 4.0×10^{-6} to 5.9×10^{-2} using Milne's method. For illustrative purposes in Table 5.5, we give the results of changing the interval to $h = .05$ at $x = 10.0$. The values of y at $x = 10.05$, 10.1, 10.15, 10.2 were calculated using (5.6-49). The percentage improvement in the error is substantially greater for Milne's than for Hamming's method. The reason for this is that the propagated error terms in the solution are not negligible at $x = 10.0$ in Hamming's method, and the reduction in h and, therefore, in the truncation error does not prevent

Table 5.4 **Results of numerical solution of** $y' = y$, $y(0) = 1$

x	e^x	Hamming's method		Milne's method		Hermite method	
		y	Error	y	Error	y	Error
.1	1.1051709	1.1051708	1.0×10^{-7}	1.1051708	1.0×10^{-7}	1.1051708	1.0×10^{-7}
.2	1.2214028	1.2214024	4.0×10^{-7}	1.2214024	4.0×10^{-7}	1.2214024	4.0×10^{-7}
.3	1.3498588	1.3498582	6.0×10^{-7}	1.3498582	6.0×10^{-7}	1.3498582	6.0×10^{-7}
.4	1.4918247	1.4918238	9.0×10^{-7}	1.4918238	9.0×10^{-7}	1.4918238	9.0×10^{-7}
.5	1.6487213	1.6487205	8.0×10^{-7}	1.6487206	7.0×10^{-7}	1.6487203	1.0×10^{-6}
.6	1.8221188	1.8221184	4.0×10^{-7}	1.8221179	9.0×10^{-7}	1.8221178	1.0×10^{-6}
.7	2.0137527	2.0137529	-2.0×10^{-7}	2.0137520	7.0×10^{-7}	2.0137516	1.1×10^{-6}
.8	2.2255409	2.2255418	-9.0×10^{-7}	2.2255400	9.0×10^{-7}	2.2255397	1.2×10^{-6}
.9	2.4596031	2.4596048	-1.7×10^{-6}	2.4596024	7.0×10^{-7}	2.4596017	1.4×10^{-6}
1.0	2.7182818	2.7182845	-2.7×10^{-6}	2.7182810	8.0×10^{-7}	2.7182803	1.5×10^{-6}
2.0	7.3890561	7.3890860	-3.0×10^{-5}	7.3890573	-1.2×10^{-6}	7.3890511	5.0×10^{-6}
3.0	20.085537	20.085675	-1.4×10^{-4}	20.085548	-1.1×10^{-5}	20.085520	1.7×10^{-5}
4.0	54.598150	54.598685	-5.4×10^{-4}	54.598204	-5.4×10^{-5}	54.598097	5.3×10^{-5}
5.0	148.41316	148.41509	-1.9×10^{-3}	148.41337	-2.1×10^{-4}	148.41301	1.5×10^{-4}
6.0	403.42879	403.43529	-6.5×10^{-3}	403.42952	-7.3×10^{-4}	403.42837	4.2×10^{-4}
7.0	1096.6332	1096.6542	-2.1×10^{-2}	1096.6357	-2.5×10^{-3}	1096.6319	1.3×10^{-3}
8.0	2980.9580	2981.0243	-6.6×10^{-2}	2980.9661	-8.1×10^{-3}	2980.9541	3.9×10^{-3}
9.0	8103.0839	8103.2885	$-.20$	8103.1094	-2.6×10^{-2}	8103.0722	1.2×10^{-2}
10.0	22026.466	22027.089	$.62$	22026.544	-7.8×10^{-2}	22026.432	3.4×10^{-2}
11.0	59874.142	59876.025	-1.9	59874.381	$-.24$	59874.046	$.096$
12.0	162754.79	162760.39	-5.6	162755.51	$-.72$	162754.51	$.28$
13.0	442413.39	442429.93	-16.5	442415.51	-2.1	442412.57	$.82$
14.0	1202604.3	1202652.9	-48.6	1202610.6	-6.3	1202602.0	2.3
15.0	3269017.4	3269159.6	-142.2	3269035.8	-18.4	3269011.1	6.3

Table 5.5   Change of interval in the solution of $y' = y$, $y(0) = 1$

		Hamming's method		Milne's method		Hermite method	
x	e^x	y	Error	y	Error	y	Error
11.0	59874.142	59875.835	−1.7	59874.339	− .20	59874.043	.099
12.0	162754.79	162759.51	−4.7	162755.29	− .50	162754.53	.26
13.0	442413.39	442426.39	−13.0	442414.63	−1.2	442412.69	.70
14.0	1202604.3	1202640.2	−35.9	1202607.5	−3.2	1202602.3	2.0
15.0	3269017.4	3269117.1	−99.7	3269025.2	−7.8	3269012.1	5.3

the continuation of this error propagation.   In Milne's method the error-propagation terms are very small when $x = 10.0$, and thus the reduction in truncation error has more effect on the overall error.

This second example illustrates the general rule, that between two *stable* methods, the one with the smaller truncation error should usually be chosen.   It is well to emphasize at this point that a priori, in most numerical solutions of differential equations, we do not know much about the behavior of $\partial f / \partial y$ and, moreover, that in most cases $\partial f / \partial y$ will take on both positive and negative values during the computation (with systems the behavior will be even more complex).   Thus we must generally choose a method such as Hamming's, which is stable for both positive and negative $\partial f / \partial y$, rather than Milne's.

We did not explicitly use the error-estimation ability of Sec. 5.5-3 in either of these examples.   In fact, the change of interval discussed above could have been done automatically using error estimation {50}.

As a third and final example, we consider the equation

$$y' = 1/(1 + \tan^2 y) \qquad y(0) = 0 \tag{5.7-11}$$

whose solution is $Y = \tan^{-1} x$.   Again with $h = .1$, using (5.6-49) for the first four values and using floating-point arithmetic, some values for the computation are shown in Table 5.6.   Since the magnitude of the solution does not change greatly, we used an absolute-error criterion with a convergence factor of 5.0×10^{-5}.   In both cases, only one application of the corrector per step was needed.   As in the second example, $\partial f / \partial y$ is always positive so that again Milne's method does not lead to instability. Thus, again the smaller truncation error in Milne's method causes that method to give higher accuracy until late in the computation when the errors in the two computations become almost equal in magnitude although opposite in sign.   This is because, early in the computation, the roundoff error becomes a significant part of the total error and late in the computation the roundoff dominates.   This occurs because $\tan^2 y$ gets very large

Table 5.6 Results of numerical solution of $y' = 1/(1 + \tan^2 y)$, $y(0) = 0$

x	$\tan^{-1} x$	Hamming's method y	Error	Milne's method y	Error	Hermite method y	Error
.1	9.9668652×10^{-2}	9.9668686×10^{-2}	-3.4×10^{-8}	9.9668686×10^{-2}	-3.4×10^{-8}	9.9668686×10^{-2}	-3.4×10^{-8}
.2	.19739556	.19739560	-4.0×10^{-8}	.19739560	-4.0×10^{-8}	.19739560	-4.0×10^{-8}
.3	.29145679	.29145683	-4.0×10^{-8}	.29145683	-4.0×10^{-8}	.29145683	-4.0×10^{-8}
.4	.38050638	.38050639	-1.0×10^{-8}	.38050639	-1.0×10^{-8}	.38050639	-1.0×10^{-8}
.5	.46364761	.46364675	8.6×10^{-7}	.46364707	5.4×10^{-7}	.46364772	-1.1×10^{-7}
.6	.54041950	.54041660	2.9×10^{-6}	.54041858	9.2×10^{-7}	.54041974	-2.4×10^{-7}
.7	.61072596	.61072066	5.3×10^{-6}	.61072458	1.4×10^{-6}	.61072632	-3.6×10^{-7}
.8	.67474094	.67473336	7.6×10^{-6}	.67473938	1.6×10^{-6}	.67474137	-4.3×10^{-7}
.9	.73281510	.73280581	9.3×10^{-6}	.73281330	1.8×10^{-6}	.73281556	-4.6×10^{-7}
1.0	.78539816	.78538785	1.0×10^{-5}	.78539642	1.7×10^{-6}	.78539862	-4.6×10^{-7}
2.0	1.1071487	1.1071434	5.3×10^{-6}	1.1071478	9.0×10^{-7}	1.1071490	-3.0×10^{-7}
3.0	1.2490458	1.2490442	1.6×10^{-6}	1.2490451	7.0×10^{-7}	1.2490458	0.0
4.0	1.3258177	1.3258166	1.1×10^{-6}	1.3258169	8.0×10^{-7}	1.3258177	0.0
5.0	1.3734008	1.3733999	9.0×10^{-7}	1.3734000	8.0×10^{-7}	1.3734009	-1.0×10^{-7}
6.0	1.4056476	1.4056473	3.0×10^{-7}	1.4056468	8.0×10^{-7}	1.4056478	-2.0×10^{-7}
7.0	1.4288993	1.4288989	4.0×10^{-7}	1.4288984	9.0×10^{-7}	1.4288993	0.0
8.0	1.4464413	1.4464410	3.0×10^{-7}	1.4464403	1.0×10^{-6}	1.4464413	0.0
9.0	1.4601391	1.4601390	1.0×10^{-7}	1.4601379	1.2×10^{-6}	1.4601393	-2.0×10^{-7}
10.0	1.4711277	1.4711278	-1.0×10^{-7}	1.4711264	1.3×10^{-6}	1.4711280	-3.0×10^{-7}
11.0	1.4801364	1.4801369	-5.0×10^{-7}	1.4801350	1.4×10^{-6}	1.4801367	-3.0×10^{-7}
12.0	1.4876551	1.4876561	-1.0×10^{-6}	1.4876535	1.6×10^{-6}	1.4876551	0.0
13.0	1.4940244	1.4940256	-1.2×10^{-6}	1.4940227	1.7×10^{-6}	1.4940242	2.0×10^{-7}
14.0	1.4994889	1.4994904	-1.5×10^{-6}	1.4994870	1.9×10^{-6}	1.4994882	7.0×10^{-7}
15.0	1.5042282	1.5042300	-1.8×10^{-6}	1.5042262	2.0×10^{-6}	1.5042272	1.0×10^{-6}
16.0	1.5083775	1.5083790	-1.5×10^{-6}	1.5083754	2.1×10^{-6}	1.5083761	1.4×10^{-6}
17.0	1.5120405	1.5120423	-1.8×10^{-6}	1.5120382	2.3×10^{-6}	1.5120388	1.7×10^{-6}
18.0	1.5152978	1.5152994	-1.6×10^{-6}	1.5152954	2.4×10^{-6}	1.5152958	2.0×10^{-6}
19.0	1.5182133	1.5182148	-1.5×10^{-6}	1.5182107	2.6×10^{-6}	1.5182110	2.3×10^{-6}
20.0	1.5208379	1.5208395	-1.6×10^{-6}	1.5208353	2.6×10^{-6}	1.5208354	2.5×10^{-6}

as y approaches $\pi/2$, thus making the truncation error almost zero so that the roundoff error, even though occurring in the eighth figure, is greater than the truncation error.   The roundoff properties of Milne's method are slightly better than those of Hamming's {51}, but because of the statistical nature of the roundoff, this is not enough to show up significantly in the results tabulated in Table 5.6.   Proper use of the error-estimation ability of predictor-corrector methods would have led us to increase the value of h when the roundoff error became dominant.   In fact, h should always be increased in the numerical solution of differential equations when roundoff becomes dominant, if values of the solution at the smaller spacing are not required (why?).

5.8   OTHER NUMERICAL INTEGRATION METHODS

5.8-1   Special methods for second-order equations

We have pointed out previously that general methods for the solution of a particular problem are usually adequate but that sometimes special cases can be handled significantly more efficiently by special methods.   In the realm of ordinary differential equations, second-order differential equations are both very common and appear often in a special form so that special methods for their solution are desirable.   The general form of such an equation is

$$y'' = f(x,y,y') \qquad y(x_0) = y_0 \qquad y'(x_0) = y_0' \tag{5.8-1}$$

This equation may be written as a system in the form

$$\begin{aligned} z' &= f(x,y,z) & z(x_0) &= y_0' \\ y' &= z & y(x_0) &= y_0 \end{aligned} \tag{5.8-2}$$

By taking into account the form of (5.8-1), it is possible to simplify somewhat the computation using predictor-corrector methods {53}, but no important improvement is obtained over applying one of the methods we have discussed previously in this chapter to (5.8-2).   When, however—and this is quite common—the y' term is missing from (5.8-1), significant improvements over using (5.8-2) can be made.

The equation then is

$$y'' = f(x,y) \qquad y(x_0) = y_0 \qquad y'(x_0) = y_0' \tag{5.8-3}$$

To derive a method for the solution of this equation directly, it is natural to consider methods of the form

$$y_{n+1} = \sum_{i=0}^{p} a_i y_{n-i} + h^2 \sum_{i=-1}^{p} b_i y_{n-i}'' \tag{5.8-4}$$

As before, with $b_{-1} = 0$, we have a predictor and, with $b_{-1} \neq 0$, a corrector. It is interesting to note that, if a method of the form (5.8-4) is exact for 1 and x, then the method never satisfies the conditions of Theorem 5.1 because there is always a double root of the stability equation at 1 when $h = 0$ (why?). The solution of the stability equation when $h = 0$ has, therefore, a term of the form cn in the error at the nth step (where c is a constant). Such error growth is unpleasant, but since c is usually small, in many problems it will not be significant.

As we have done previously, we may use the method of undetermined coefficients to specify the parameters in (5.8-4). Using this method, it is not difficult {54} to determine a fifth-order predictor-corrector pair of the form

Predictor: $\quad y_{n+1} = 2y_{n-1} - y_{n-3} + (4h^2/3)(y_n'' + y_{n-1}'' + y_{n-2}'')$

Corrector: $\quad y_{n+1} = 2y_n - y_{n-1} + (h^2/12)(y_{n+1}'' + 10y_n'' + y_{n-1}'')$

$$(5.8\text{-}5)$$

The truncation error in these two equations may be determined using the technique of Sec. 5.3. Using these truncation errors, we may estimate the error at each step, and we may augment the equations (5.8-5) by a modifier as in (5.5-27) {54}.

5.8-2 Methods based on higher derivatives

In this section we shall use derivatives higher than the first in formulas for the solution of first-order differential equations. One example of such a formula is readily derivable from the Euler-Maclaurin sum formula in the form (4.15-17). Replacing $f(x)$ with $y'(x)$, we get, after making some simple changes in notation,

$$y_{n+1} = y_1 + h \sum_{i=-1}^{n-1} y_{n-i}' - \frac{h}{2}(y_{n+1}' + y_1')$$

$$- \sum_{k=1}^{m} \frac{B_{2k}}{(2k)!} h^{2k-1}[y_{n+1}^{(2k)} - y_1^{(2k)}] \quad (5.8\text{-}6)$$

with the truncation error given by (4.15-16)

$$E_m = \frac{nh^{2m+2}B_{2m+2}}{(2m+2)!} Y^{(2m+3)}(\xi) \tag{5.8-7}$$

Our main interest in this section, however, is in a class of predictor and corrector formulas which use the second as well as the first derivative. The corrector formulas are generated by taking the Hermite interpolation formula (3.8-17) (or the modified Hermite formula) based on the points

x_{n+1}, x_n, . . . , x_{n-p} and integrating between x_n and x_{n+1} after replacing $f(x)$ by $y'(x)$. The result of this is

$$y_{n+1} = y_n + \sum_{i=-1}^{p} \left[\int_{x_n}^{x_{n+1}} h_{n-i}(x) \, dx \right] y'_{n-i}$$

$$+ \sum_{i=-1}^{p} \left[\int_{x_n}^{x_{n+1}} \bar{h}_{n-i}(x) \, dx \right] y''_{n-i} \quad (5.8\text{-}8)$$

The truncation error is given using (4.5-12) as

$$T_n = \frac{Y^{(2p+5)}(\eta)}{(2p+4)!} \int_{x_n}^{x_{n+1}} [(x - x_{n+1}) \cdots (x - x_{n-p})]^2 \, dx \quad (5.8\text{-}9)$$

With $p = 0$ in (5.8-8), we get the fourth-order corrector

$$y_{n+1} = y_n + (h/2)(y'_{n+1} + y'_n) + (h^2/12)(-y''_{n+1} + y''_n) \quad (5.8\text{-}10)$$

which has an error term

$$T_n = (h^5/720) Y^v(\eta) \quad (5.8\text{-}11)$$

The stability equation for (5.8-8) has only one root, $r_0 = 1$ at $h = 0$. Therefore, for some range of values of Kh, this class of methods is stable. In particular, (5.8-10) is stable for all values of Kh {57}. Moreover, note that the truncation-error term (5.8-11) is substantially smaller than that given by any of the correctors in Table 5.2. Thus, if the second derivative of y can be calculated easily, (5.8-10) may indeed be a good choice for a corrector. Indeed, when (5.1-1) is a single equation, the second derivative is given by

$$y'' = (d/dx)f(x,y) = (\partial f/\partial y)y' + \partial f/\partial x \quad (5.8\text{-}12)$$

It is often true that, having computed $f(x,y)$, the calculation of the partial derivatives of $f(x,y)$ can be done very quickly on a digital computer, in which case the second derivative as given by (5.8-12) is indeed easily calculable. Of course, for systems of equations, the calculation of the second derivative becomes substantially more complicated.

To get a class of predictors, we use a Hermite formula based on the points x_n, . . . , x_{n-p} and proceed as above {56}. A convenient predictor to use with (5.8-10) is

$$y_{n+1} = y_n + (h/2)(-y'_n + 3y'_{n-1}) + (h^2/12)(17y''_n + 7y''_{n-1}) \quad (5.8\text{-}13)$$

which has a truncation error

$$T_n = (31h^5/720) Y^v(\eta) \quad (5.8\text{-}14)$$

The set of equations analogous to (5.5-27) and (5.5-33) are

Predictor:
$$y_{n+1}^{(0)} = y_n + (h/2)(-y_n' + 3y_{n-1}') + (h^2/12)(17y_n'' + 7y_{n-1}'')$$

Modifier:
$$\bar{y}_{n+1}^{(0)} = y_{n+1}^{(0)} + \tfrac{31}{30}[y_n - y_n^{(0)}]$$
$$[\bar{y}_{n+1}^{(0)}]' = f[x_{n+1}, \bar{y}_{n+1}^{(0)}]$$

Corrector:
$$y_{n+1}^{(j+1)} = y_n + (h/2)\{[y_{n+1}^{(j)}]' + y_n'\} + (h^2/12)\{-[y_{n+1}^{(j)}]'' + y_n''\}$$

(5.8-15)

Example 5.7　Use (5.8-15) to perform the same calculations as in Sec. 5.7 on the same three examples.

The results for these calculations corresponding to those of Sec. 5.7 are given in the last two columns of Tables 5.3 to 5.6. Since the Hermite method is stable and has a smaller truncation error than either Hamming's or Milne's methods, we would expect it to give better results than Hamming's method for the differential equation (5.7-7) and better results than both Milne's and Hamming's methods for Eq. (5.7-10), and in fact it does. The importance of roundoff is again in evidence in the solution of the differential equation (5.7-11) where the Hermite method is initially best, but by the end of the computation, the errors in all three methods are similar in magnitude. In all the computations of this section, the same convergence factors were used as in the examples of Sec. 5.7, and in all cases one application of the corrector at each step was sufficient. Thus, when the second derivative is easy to calculate—it is very easy for the first two examples considered here and not quite so easy for the last—the Hermite method is to be recommended over Hamming's method.

5.9 BOUNDARY–VALUE PROBLEMS

Many problems in mathematical physics lead to second-order differential equations which are not initial-value problems but boundary-value problems of the form

$$y'' = f(x,y,y') \qquad y(a) = A \qquad y(b) = B \tag{5.9-1}$$

It is beyond the scope of this book to consider such problems in any generality. There is a wide literature on this subject, and in fact any intensive study of this subject should be preceded by a study of the material in Chaps. 9 and 10 of this book. Our object here is to point out when the techniques we have developed in this chapter thus far can be used to find a numerical solution of (5.9-1).

If the differential equation is linear

$$y'' = f_1(x)y' + f_2(x)y + f_3(x) \qquad y(a) = A \qquad y(b) = B \tag{5.9-2}$$

then (5.9-1) may be reduced to an initial-value problem. For suppose the differential equation (5.9-2) is solved subject to the initial conditions $y(a) = A$, $y'(a) = \alpha_1$ and then solved again with the conditions $y(a) = A$, $y'(a) = \alpha_2$ by any of the methods of this chapter. Call the two solutions

$y_1(x)$ and $y_2(x)$ and let $y_1(b) = \beta_1$, $y_2(b) = \beta_2$.   Then, if $\beta_1 \neq \beta_2$,

$$y(x) = \frac{1}{\beta_1 - \beta_2} [(B - \beta_2)y_1(x) + (\beta_1 - B)y_2(x)] \tag{5.9-3}$$

satisfies the differential equation and the boundary conditions of (5.9-2).

If the differential equation is not linear, then we may try to solve (5.9-1) by solving a sequence of initial-value problems using different values of $y'(a)$ and, by interpolating, try to find that value of $y'(a)$ which leads to a solution $y(x)$ for which $y(b) = B$.   This procedure would generally be extremely inefficient and is not to be recommended as a substitute for the well-established methods of solving (5.9-1).

BIBLIOGRAPHIC NOTES

The most complete, general reference on the numerical solution of ordinary differential equations is the book by Henrici (1962a).   Collatz (1960) and Milne (1953), although not so up to date as Henrici, are also good general references.   Fox (1962) has a recent survey of the field of the numerical solution of ordinary differential equations as well as integral and partial differential equations.

5.1   No student should approach the numerical solution of ordinary differential equations without a firm grounding in basic existence theory.   Henrici (1962a) contains an introduction to this subject.   More extensive references are Coddington and Levinson (1955) and Ince (1926).

5.2   The method of undetermined coefficients which is now widely used in the development of numerical integration formulas was introduced by Dahlquist (1956). A more accessible reference is Hamming (1959).   For other examples of its use, see Hull and Newbery (1959), Ralston (1961), and Crane and Lambert (1962).

5.3   The method of this section, particularly the use of the influence function, is due to Milne (1949).   Other examples of its use can be found in Hamming (1962) and Hildebrand (1956).   Hildebrand also considers some more sophisticated methods of deriving error terms.   Barrett (1952) considers some matters related to the material of this section.

5.4   It is possible to find almost as many definitions of stability as there are references on numerical integration methods.   Relative stability is considered by Hamming (1959) and Hull and Newbery (1962), and is discussed in detail by Ralston (1965).   Many authors define stability only for the case $h = 0$.   Henrici (1962a, b) has excellent discussions of this case; see also Hildebrand (1956).   Much of the material of Sec. 5.4-2 is from Hull and Newbery (1961).

5.5   The books by Milne (1953), Henrici (1962a), and Hamming (1962) and, in particular, the paper by Hamming (1959) are all good references on predictor-corrector methods.   The latter is the source of most of Sec. 5.5-4.   Other papers on the use of predictor-corrector methods are those of Hull and Newbery (1959, 1961), Ralston (1961), and Crane and Lambert (1962).   A technique to remove the instability of Milne's method is considered by Milne and Reynolds (1959, 1960).

5.6   For the use of Picard's method in existence theory, see Ince (1926). There is a good discussion of non-Runge-Kutta methods for starting the solution in Hildebrand (1956).   Much of the discussion of Runge-Kutta methods is taken from

Ralston (1962b). Kopal (1955) also has an extensive discussion of Runge-Kutta methods. The paper by Gill (1951) gives an interesting discussion of the use of Runge-Kutta methods on digital computers whose memory is limited.

5.7   Other examples of the use of predictor-corrector methods are given by Milne (1953), Henrici (1962a), Hildebrand (1956), and Hamming (1962); see also Ralston (1961). Nordsieck (1962) discusses the numerical solution of ordinary differential equations in an overall computational sense. Hull and Creemer (1963) offer confirmation of the view that two applications of the corrector at each stage should generally be sufficient.

5.8   Henrici (1962a), Hamming (1962), and Hildebrand (1956) all have discussions of methods for higher-order equations and methods based on higher derivatives.

5.9   The best reference on the numerical solution of boundary-value problems is Fox (1957). Some computational aspects are considered by Wachspress (1960).

BIBLIOGRAPHY

Barrett, W. (1952): On the Remainders of Numerical Formulae with Special References to Differentiation, *J. London Math. Soc.*, vol. 27, pp. 456–464.

Coddington, E. A., and N. Levinson (1955): *Theory of Ordinary Differential Equations*, McGraw-Hill Book Company, New York.

Collatz, L. (1960): *The Numerical Treatment of Differential Equations* (translated by P. G. Williams), 3d ed., Springer-Verlag OHG, Berlin.

Crane, R. L., and R. J. Lambert (1962): Stability of a Generalized Corrector Formula, *J. Assoc. Comput. Mach.*, vol. 9, pp. 104–117.

Dahlquist, G. (1956): Convergence and Stability in the Numerical Solution of Ordinary Differential Equations, *Math. Scand.*, vol. 4, pp. 33–53.

Emanuel, G. (1963): The Wilf Stability Criterion for Numerical Integration, *J. Assoc. Comput. Mach.*, vol. 10, pp. 557–561.

Fox, L. (1957): *The Numerical Solution of Two-point Boundary Problems in Ordinary Differential Equations*, Oxford University Press, Fair Lawn, N.J.

Fox, L. (1962): *Numerical Solution of Ordinary and Partial Differential Equations*, Addison-Wesley Publishing Company, Inc., Reading, Mass.

Galler, B. A., and D. P. Rozenberg (1960): A Generalization of a Theorem of Carr on Error Bounds for Runge-Kutta Procedures, *J. Assoc. Comput. Mach.*, vol. 7, pp. 57–60.

Gill, S. (1951): A Process for Step-by-Step Integration of a Differential Equation in an Automatic Digital Computing Machine, *Proc. Cambridge Philos. Soc.*, vol. 47, pp. 96–108.

Hamming, R. W. (1959): Stable Predictor-Corrector Methods for Ordinary Differential Equations, *J. Assoc. Comput. Mach.*, vol. 6, pp. 37–47.

Hamming, R. W. (1962): *Numerical Methods for Scientists and Engineers*, McGraw-Hill Book Company, New York.

Henrici, P. (1962a): *Discrete Variable Methods in Ordinary Differential Equations*, John Wiley & Sons, Inc., New York.

Henrici, P. (1962b): *Error Propagation for Difference Methods*, John Wiley & Sons, Inc., New York.

Hildebrand, F. B. (1956): *Introduction to Numerical Analysis*, McGraw-Hill Book Company, New York.

Hull, T. E., and A. L. Creemer (1963): The Efficiency of Predictor-Corrector Procedures, *J. Assoc. Comput. Mach.*, vol. 10, pp. 291–301.

Hull, T. E., and A. C. R. Newbery (1959): Error Bounds for a Family of Three-point
Integration Procedures, *J. Soc. Indust. Appl. Math.*, vol. 7, pp. 402–412.

Hull, T. E., and A. C. R. Newbery (1961): Integration Procedures Which Minimize
Propagated Errors, *J. Soc. Indust. Appl. Math.*, vol. 9, pp. 31–47.

Hull, T. E., and A. C. R. Newbery (1962): Corrector Formulas for Multi-step
Integration Formulas, *J. Soc. Indust. Appl. Math.*, vol. 10, pp. 351–369.

Ince, E. L. (1926): *Ordinary Differential Equations*, Dover Publications, Inc., New
York.

Kopal, Z. (1955): *Numerical Analysis*, John Wiley & Sons, Inc., New York.

Milne, W. E. (1949): The Remainder in Linear Methods of Approximation, *J. Res.
Nat. Bur. Standards*, vol. 43, pp. 501–511.

Milne, W. E. (1953): *Numerical Solution of Ordinary Differential Equations*, John
Wiley & Sons, Inc., New York.

Milne, W. E., and R. R. Reynolds (1959): Stability of a Numerical Solution of Differential Equations, I, *J. Assoc. Comput. Mach.*, vol. 6, pp. 196–203.

Milne, W. E., and R. R. Reynolds (1960): Stability of a Numerical Solution of Differential Equations, II, *J. Assoc. Comput. Mach.*, vol. 7, pp. 46–56.

Nordsieck, A. (1962): On Numerical Integration of Ordinary Differential Equations,
Math. Comput., vol. 16, pp. 22–49.

Ralston, A. (1961): Some Theoretical and Computational Matters Relating to Predictor-Corrector Methods of Numerical Integration, *Comput. J.*, vol. 4, pp. 64–67.

Ralston, A. (1962a): A Symmetric Matrix Formulation of the Hurwitz-Routh Stability Criterion, *IRE Trans. on Automatic Control*, vol. AC-7, pp. 50–51.

Ralston, A. (1962b): Runge-Kutta Methods with Minimum Error Bounds, *Math.
Comput.*, vol. 16, pp. 431–437.

Ralston, A. (1965): *Relative Stability in the Numerical Solution of Ordinary Differential
Equations*, *SIAM Rev.*, vol. 7, pp. 114–125.

Wachspress, E. L. (1960): The Numerical Solution of Boundary Value Problems in
Mathematical Methods for Digital Computers (A. Ralston and H. S. Wilf, eds.),
John Wiley & Sons, Inc., New York.

Wilf, H. S. (1957): An Open Formula for the Numerical Integration of First Order
Differential Equations, I, *MTAC*, vol. 11, pp. 201–203.

Wilf, H. S. (1958): An Open Formula for the Numerical Integration of First Order
Differential Equations, II, *MTAC*, vol. 12, pp. 55–58.

Wilf, H. S. (1959): A Stability Criterion for Numerical Integration, *J. Assoc. Comput.
Mach.*, vol. 6, pp. 363–365.

Wilf, H. S. (1960): Maximally Stable Numerical Integration, *J. Soc. Indust. Appl.
Math.*, vol. 8, pp. 537–540.

PROBLEMS

Section 5.1

1. (a) Prove that a system of ordinary differential equations may be written
in the form (5.1-1) if, and only if, the system can be rewritten with the highest-order
derivative in each variable appearing as the left-hand side of one equation and
nowhere else.

(b) Write the following system in the form (5.1-1):

$$\frac{d^3y}{dx^3} + \frac{dy}{dx}\frac{dz}{dx} + xy^2z\frac{d^2y}{dx^2} = \sin y$$

$$\frac{d^2z}{dx^2}\frac{dy}{dx} + y^3\frac{d^2y}{dx^2} + \left(\frac{dz}{dx}\right)^{3/2}\frac{dy}{dx} = e^{yz}$$

Section 5.2

2. (a) Derive a numerical integration method of the form (5.2-2) for $n = 1$ and any m by using a truncated Taylor series.

(b) Explain how you would use the method of part a to find the solution of $y' = xy^2$, $y(0) = 1$. With $m = 4$ and $h = .2$, find an approximate solution at $x = .2$ and .4 and compare with the true solution.

3. When the system (5.1-1) is linear, show that there is no computational difference between using a forward-integration formula and an iterative formula.

4. (a) Derive a fifth-order iterative formula of the form

$$y_{n+1} = ay_n + by_{n-1} + cy_{n-2} + dy_{n-3} + h(ey'_{n+1} + fy'_n + gy'_{n-1})$$

Express each coefficient in terms of b.   Find a value $0 < b \leq 1$ that leads to a simple set of coefficients.

(b) Repeat part a with the dy_{n-3} term replaced by a term dy'_{n-2}. [Ref.: Ralston (1961).]

5. (a) For $j = 0, 1, 2, 3$ use the method of undetermined coefficients to derive fourth-order forward-integration methods of the form

$$y_{n+1} = a_jy_{n-j} + h(by'_n + cy'_{n-1} + dy'_{n-2} + ey'_{n-3})$$

Show how each of these methods could have been derived by integrating the Lagrangian interpolation formula for $y'(x)$.

(b) Verify that Eqs. (5.5-29) are such that (5.5-28) will be fourth-order.

Section 5.3

6. Prove that, if the influence function $G(s)$ does change sign over the interval of integration $[a,b]$, then there exists some continuous function $y(s)$ for which

$$\int_a^b G(s)y(s)\ ds \neq y(\eta)\int_a^b G(s)\ ds$$

for any η in $[a,b]$.

7. Derive (5.3-13) and (5.3-14) from (4.6-1).

*8. (a) Use (5.3-13) to derive the error terms for the Newton-Cotes closed formulas with $n = 1, 2$ on an interval $[0,nh]$ and with $w(x) = 1$.

(b) Consider the quadrature method

$$\int_{-1}^1 f(x)\ dx = f(\alpha) + f(-\alpha) + E \qquad 0 \leq \alpha \leq 1$$

which is exact for 1 and x.. For what values of α is the influence function of constant sign in $[-1,1]$? Find E for those values of α.   Explain the behavior at $\alpha = 1/\sqrt{3}$. [Ref.: Hildebrand (1956), pp. 165–166.]

*9. (a) Using the notation of Prob. 44, Chap. 4, and (5.3-13) to (5.3-15), show that

$$E\left[\frac{1}{u - x}\right] = (n + 1)! \int_{-1}^{1} G(s) \frac{ds}{(u - s)^{n+2}}$$

where

$$n! G(s) = \int_{s}^{1} w(x)(x - s) \, dx - \frac{\lambda}{n} \sum_{a_j \geq s} (a_j - s)^n$$

(b) Use this to deduce that

$$Q(u) = n! \int_{-1}^{1} G(s) \frac{ds}{(u - s)^{n+1}}$$

and from this deduce that $Q(u)$ can be expanded in the form

$$Q(u) = \sum_{j=1}^{\infty} \frac{d_j}{u^{n+j}}$$

(c) When $n = 1$ and $w(x) = 1$, use the $G(s)$ in part a to find the form of the error for the Chebyshev quadrature formula.

*10. (a) By calculating $G(s)$ at x_{n-3}, x_{n-2}, x_{n-1}, x_n, and x_{n+1}, surmise for which values of b in Prob. 4a the error can be expressed in the form (5.3-2). Why is this technique not sufficient to *prove* that the error can be expressed in this form?

(b) For the values of b found in part a, calculate the explicit form of the error term.

*11. (a) For each value of j in Prob. 5a, use the influence function to determine if the error can be expressed in the form (5.3-2), and if so, find the error.

(b) Do both parts of Prob. 10 for the iterative formula (5.5-28) whose coefficients are given by (5.5-29).

Section 5.4

12. (a) Suppose that in place of (5.4-1) we have the system

$$[y^{(1)}]' = -K_{11}y^{(1)} - K_{12}y^{(2)} \qquad y^{(1)}(x_0) = y_{01}$$
$$[y^{(2)}]' = -K_{21}y^{(1)} - K_{22}y^{(2)} \qquad y^{(2)}(x_0) = y_{02}$$

Carry through an analysis similar to that in Eqs. (5.4-3) to (5.4-5) to show that the stability equation is now two coupled polynomial equations. Thus deduce that the analysis of Sec. 5.4 leads to generally intractable algebraic problems when more than one equation is being considered.

(b) However, show that the *convergence* of a numerical integration method is independent of whether a single equation or a system is being solved.

13. (a) By substituting (5.4-7) into (5.4-5) and using (5.2-6), show that $\beta_1 = -K$.

(b) Use Cramer's rule to express c_i, $i \neq 0$ in (5.4-4) in a form similar to (5.4-10), and use this result to show that, if $y_j \to y_0$, $j = 1, \ldots, p$ as $h \to 0$, then $c_i \to 0$ as $h \to 0$ for $i \neq 0$.

14. (a) Prove Theorem 5.1 in the case where (5.4-14) has simple complex roots. (*Hint:* If $r = Re^{i\theta}$ consider $w_k = hR^k \cos k\theta$ and $w_k^2 - w_{k+1}w_{k-1}$.)

(b) Use a similar technique to prove Theorem 5.1 in the case of multiple roots.

(c) Show that for the equation $y' = 0$, $y(0) = 0$ the condition of Theorem 5.1 is also sufficient for convergence. [Ref.: Henrici (1962a), pp. 218–219.]

15. (*a*) Show that the sequence (5.4-17) with A given by (5.4-18) satisfies (5.4-16).

(*b*) Give an example of a numerical integration method which is convergent and satisfies only the first two equations of (5.2-6).

*****16.** Suppose that $|f_y(x,y)| \leq -K$ and $|E_n| < E$ for all n and all $f(x,y)$ involved in calculating the solution of (5.1-1). Suppose further that $|Khb_{-1}| < 1$.

(*a*) Show that the solution of the difference equation

$$e_{n+1}(1 + h|b_{-1}|K) = \sum_{i=0}^{p} (|a_i| - h|b_i|K)e_{n-i} + E$$

is such that

$$|\epsilon_i| < e_i \qquad i = p + 1,\, p + 2,\, \ldots$$

where ϵ_i is the solution of (5.4-24), if the initial conditions for the difference equations are such that

$$|\epsilon_i| < e_i \qquad i = 0,\, \ldots,\, p$$

Thus deduce that the solution of the above difference equation dominates that of (5.4-24).

(*b*) Show that, if all the a_i's are positive, the difference equation of part a has a particular solution $E/Kh\sigma$ where $\sigma = \sum_{i=-1}^{k} |b_i|$.

(*c*) Show that, if again all the a_i's are positive, one solution of the homogeneous difference equation formed by setting $E = 0$ in part a is given by $e_n = r_0^n$ where

$$r_0 = 1 - \frac{Kh\sigma}{\sigma'} + 0(h^2) \qquad \sigma' = \sum_{i=-1}^{p} b_i$$

(*d*) Suppose $|\epsilon_i| < \lambda$, $i = 0,\, \ldots,\, p$. Show that

$$e_n = \lambda r_0^n - (E/Kh\sigma)(r_0^n - 1)$$

is a solution of the difference equation of part a which is greater in magnitude than ϵ_n for all n, and thus deduce a bound for the propagated error. [Ref.: Hildebrand (1956), pp. 209–211, and Hull and Newbery (1961).]

*****17.** (*a*) Show that the transformation

$$w = \frac{z - 1}{z + 1}$$

maps the unit circle in the z plane into the left half of the w plane.

(*b*) Show that the result of applying this transformation to the polynomial equation

$$c_0 z^n + c_1 z^{n-1} + \cdots + c_{n-1} z + c_n = 0$$

is a polynomial equation

$$d_0 w^n + d_1 w^{n-1} + \cdots + d_{n-1} w + d_n = 0$$

where

$$d_j = \sum_{i=0}^{n} c_i r^{(n)}_{n-i,n-j}$$

with the $r^{(n)}_{ij}$ defined by

$$(1 + x)^i(1 - x)^{n-i} = \sum_{j=0}^{n} r^{(n)}_{ij} x^j$$

(c) Deduce then that (5.4-5) has all its roots on or inside the unit circle if and only if the polynomial in w in part b has all its roots in the left half plane or on the imaginary axis where

$$d_j = \sum_{i=0}^{p+1} (-a_{i-1} + hKb_{i-1})r^{(p+1)}_{p+1-i,p+1+j} \qquad a_{-1} = 1$$

(d) The Hurwitz-Routh criterion states that the polynomial in w in part b has all its zeros in the left half plane or on the imaginary axis if and only if, when $d_0 > 0$ (<0) all the principal minors of the matrix $D = [D_{ij}]$ are nonnegative (nonpositive) where

$$D_{ij} = d_{2i+1-j} \qquad i, j = 0, 1 \ldots, n - 1 \qquad (d_k = 0 \text{ if } k < 0 \text{ or } k > n)$$

Use this criterion and the results of parts b and c to find those values of b for which the method of Prob. $5b$ is convergent.

(e) For $b = 0, \frac{1}{2}$, find those values of Kh for which the roots of the stability equation (5.4-5) lie within the unit circle. Does this help you to determine when the method is stable? Why? [Ref.: Ralston (1962a).]

*18. (a) A theorem of Schur states that the roots of the polynomial

$$c_0 z^n + c_1 z^{n-1} + \cdots + c_n = 0$$

will be on or within the unit circle if and only if the quadratic form

$$\sum_{j=0}^{n-1} [(c_0 x_j + c_1 x_{j+1} + \cdots + c_{n-j-1} x_{n-1})^2$$
$$- (c_n x_j + c_{n-1} x_{j+1} + \cdots + c_{j+1} x_{n-1})^2]$$

is nonnegative definite. From this derive the result that a sufficient condition for a numerical integration method (5.2-5) to be convergent is that the matrix with elements

$$A_{rs} = \sum_{l=0}^{\min(r,s)} (c_{r-l}c_{s-l} - c_{p+l+1-r}c_{p+l+1-s}) \qquad r, s = 0, 1 \ldots, p$$

where

$$c_j = -a_{j-1} \qquad j = 0, 1, \ldots, p + 1 \qquad a_{-1} = -1$$

be nonnegative definite. Why is this condition not necessary?

(b) Use this criterion to repeat the calculation of part d of the previous problem.

(c) If we wish to know for what values of Kh the roots of the polynomial equation related to (5.4-25) lie within the unit circle, then what do we have to replace c_j by in part a?

(d) Repeat part e of the previous problem using this criterion. Why is this method more difficult to use than that of the previous problem? [But, see Emanuel (1963).] [Ref.: Wilf (1959).]

*19. (a) For $b = \frac{2}{3}$ determine for what values of Kh the stability polynomial for the method of Prob. 4a has all its roots on or inside the unit circle.

(b) Show that, independent of the value of b, the iterative formula of Prob. 4b is never stable. [Ref.: Ralston (1961).]

20. (a) Show that, when $K < 0$, at least one root of the stability equation (5.4-5) always lies outside the unit circle for sufficiently small values of h.

(b) Discuss the merits and limitations of a definition of stability which requires only that the roots of (5.4-5) lie within the unit circle when $K > 0$.

Section 5.5

21. (a) With $b = \frac{2}{3}$ in the iterative formula of Prob. 4a, determine how large h may be in order that (5.5-10) will be satisfied for the differential equation $y' = -y$, $y(0) = 1$.

(b) For this value of h and $b = \frac{2}{3}$, use the result of Prob. 10b to determine the truncation error of the method for the same differential equation.

(c) Repeat parts a and b for the iterative formula of Prob. 5b with $b = 0, 1$ using the result of Prob. 11b. Show that when $b = 1$ this is Milne's corrector and when $b = 0$ Hamming's corrector.

(d) Give an intuitive argument to justify the assertion that, unless $|hK| \ll 1$, the truncation error will not be very small.

22. (a) Using the notation of (5.2-5), show that by integrating Newton's backward formula we may obtain a class of predictors of order $p + 1$ with $a_0 = 1$, $b_{-1} = 0$, and $a_i = 0$, $i \neq 0$.

(b) Using Newton's backward formula, derive (5.5-13) to (5.5-15).

(c) Using the error term in Newton's formula, derive the truncation errors for (5.5-13) to (5.5-15).

23. (a) Show how Newton's backward formula may be used to derive the class of correctors known as *Adams-Moulton correctors*

$$y_{n+1} = y_n + \sum_{i=-1}^{p} b_i y'_{n-i}$$

by suitably varying the limits of integration from those of the previous problem.

(b) Find an expression for the error term for this class of formulas.

(c) Display the formulas of this class and the error terms for $p = 0, 1, 2$.

24. (a) Show how Newton's backward formula may be used to generate *Nystrom's predictors*

$$y_{n+1} = y_{n-1} + \sum_{i=0}^{p} b_i y'_{n-i}$$

(b) Find an expression for the error term. Why does the problem of finding the error term differ from that in Probs. 22 and 23?

(c) Display the formulas of this class for $p = 0, 1, 2$. For $p = 0, 1$ display the error term by making use of open Newton-Cotes quadrature formulas.

25. (a) Show how the modified Hermite interpolation formula may be used to generate formulas of the form

$$y_{n+1} = \sum_{i=0}^{p} a_i y_{n-i} + \sum_{i=s}^{q} b_i y'_{n-i} \qquad q \leqq p$$

which have an order of accuracy $p + q + 1 - s$.

(b) In particular, derive the predictor P_6 of Table 5.1.

(c) With $p = 2$, $q = 2$, $s = 1$, derive the predictor and compare its error-term coefficient with that of P_6.

26. Use the error terms of the predictor and corrector of (5.5-11) to derive an estimate of the truncation error in both predictor and corrector. Use the estimate of the predictor error to get a method analogous to (5.5-27).

27. (a) Show that, if the estimate of the corrector error in (5.5-27) were used to modify the corrector, then the resulting method would be of fifth order.

(b) Generalize this result to prove that, if the estimate of the corrector error is used to modify the corrector, then the resulting predictor-corrector method always has an order one greater than that of the predictor and corrector.

*28. (a) If a term $b_2 y'_{n-2}$ is added to the corrector (5.5-28), derive the equations analogous to (5.5-29) if the corrector is still to be of order 4. Let a_1 and a_2 be the free parameters.

(b) If this corrector is used to compute the solution of $y' = 0$, $y(0) = 0$, but the initial conditions of the difference equation are $y_{-2} = y_{-1} = 0$, $y_0 = \epsilon$ (a roundoff error), show that the solution of the difference equation is

$$y_n = C_1 r_1^n + C_2 r_2^n + C_3$$

where

$$C_3 = \frac{\epsilon}{1 + a_1 + 2a_2}$$

(c) Thus deduce that, if the corrector is stable, then the growth of this single roundoff error (in fact, of course, a new roundoff error will be introduced at each step) is determined by $1 + a_1 + 2a_2$. If $1 + a_1 + 2a_2$ is positive (it usually is; see Table 5.2), show that there will be no magnification of the roundoff error if

$$a_2 \geqq (-a_1/2)$$

Which methods in Table 5.2 satisfy this condition?

(d) The above indicates that the accumulated roundoff error is correlated (not completely random) because of the relation between successive values of y_n through the corrector. What factor should be kept small to control the random component of the error? Compare this quantity for the correctors of Table 5.2.

(e) Assuming that the influence function $G(s)$ for the corrector of part a is of constant sign over the necessary interval, find the form of the error term.

(f) Use the result of Prob. 11b to deduce that, with $b_2 = 0$ and $-.6 \leqq a_1 \leqq 1$, $G(s)$ is of constant sign, and thus calculate the last row in Table 5.2. [Ref.: Hamming (1962), pp. 176–177, 195–201.]

*29. Consider the corrector (5.3-10).

(a) Use Prob. 17 to show that, if the corrector is convergent, then $-1 \leqq a \leqq 1$.

(b) For these values of a show that, if the roots of (5.4-5) are to lie within the unit circle when $K > 0$, then $Kh \leqq (6 - 6a)/(1 + a)$

(c) Find the value of a which maximizes the range of Kh in part b and is such that part a and (5.5-10) are satisfied. For this value of a, determine the other coefficients. This method has been called the maximally stable formula of this type of third order. (Note, however, that here stability is defined as in Prob. 20b.) [Ref.: Wilf (1960).]

30. (a) Use the errors in the predictor and corrector of (5.5-33) to derive the modifier equation in (5.5-33).

(b) Find the expression for the truncation error in (5.5-17).

(*c*) Display the system of equations analogous to (5.5-27) and (5.5-33) for the corrector of Prob. 4*a* with $b = \frac{2}{3}$, using as a predictor (5.5-17).   Use the results of Prob. 10*b*.   [Ref.: Hamming (1959) and Ralston (1961).]

31. (*a*) Derive (5.5-1) and (5.5-2) using the method of undetermined coefficients.

(*b*) Derive the same formulas by integrating the proper Lagrangian interpolation formula.

(*c*) Can integration of the Lagrangian interpolation formula be used to derive all formulas of the form (5.2-5) with only one value of y_i on the right-hand side? Why?

*32. Obrechkoff's method.   Suppose we wish to find an equation for the numerical integration of $y' = f(x,y)$ which has an error of the form

$$E = \frac{1}{(2r)!} \int_0^h x^r(x - h)^r Y^{(2r+1)}(x)\, dx$$

where h is the step size.

(*a*) Integrate by parts r times to obtain

$$E = \frac{1}{(2r)!} \int_0^h Y^{(r+1)}(x) \frac{d^r}{dx^r} [x^r(h - x)^r]\, dx$$

(*b*) Integrate by parts r additional times and translate the origin to x_n to obtain the desired numerical integration formula

$$y_{n+1} = y_n + \frac{r!}{(2r)!} \sum_{j=1}^{r} (-1)^{j-1} \frac{(2r - j)!h^j}{(r - j)!j!} [y_{n+1}^{(j)} + (-1)^{j-1}y_n^{(j)}] + E$$

where $x_{n+1} = x_n + h$.

(*c*) Show that the error term can be expressed in the form

$$E = (-1)^r \frac{h^{2r+1}}{2r + 1} \left(\frac{r!}{(2r)!}\right)^2 Y^{(2r+1)}(\eta)$$

with $x_n < \eta < x_{n+1}$.   [Ref.: Hildebrand (1956), pp. 231–232.]

33. In order to avoid a calculation of $f(x,y)$, it is possible to predict y' directly.

(*a*) Display an extrapolation formula which predicts y'_{n+1} using $y_n,\ y_{n-1},\ \ldots,\ y_{n-r}$.

(*b*) What is the error in this formula?

(*c*) Discuss the relative merits of this type of prediction and the prediction of y as discussed in Sec. 5.5.   Can an estimate of the error at each step be found when y' is being predicted?   [Ref.: Ralston (1961).]

34. (*a*) Use Eqs. (4.2-16) without the error terms to derive the corrector of (5.5-11) by solving the second equation for f_1, inserting the result in the first equation and making the appropriate changes in notation.

(*b*) Derive the formulas analogous to (4.2-16) for $n = 4$.   That is, derive formulas for y'_i, $i = 0, 1, 2, 3$ in terms of y_i, $i = 0, 1, 2, 3$.   For each equation also derive the error term.

(*c*) Eliminate y_2 and y_3 from the first three of the equations derived in part *b* to get

$$y_1 - y_0 = (h/12)(5y'_0 + 8y'_1 - y'_2)$$

(*d*) Eliminate y_3 from the first two equations in part *b* to get

$$y_2 = 5y_0 - 4y_1 + 2h(y_0' + 2y_1')$$

(*e*) Show how the equations of part *c* and *d* together form a self-starting numerical integration method by using part *d* to "guess" the value of y_2' required in part *c*. Show that the error term of the overall method is $O(h^4)$. Is this method a special case of the numerical integration equation obtained from the general numerical integration operator? Why? [Ref.: Wilf (1957).]

Section 5.6

35. (*a*) Show that starting values for a numerical integration method may be found by letting

$$y(x) = \sum_{k=0}^{\infty} A_k(x - x_0)^k$$

substituting this in (5.1-1), letting $x - x_0 = hs$, and getting a recurrence relation for the A_k's, A_0 being determined from the initial condition. For what types of functions $f(x,y)$ is this method most applicable?

(*b*) Show that this method gives results identical to the Taylor-series method of Sec. 5.6-1.

36. (*a*) Complete the calculation of Example 5.6 to get values of $y(.01s)$, $s = 1$, 2, 3 using terms through the third derivative. Compare these results with the true values.

(*b*) Repeat the calculation of part *a* for $h = .1$.

37. (*a*) Derive Eqs. (5.6-3).

(*b*) Show that the truncation error in all the equations is $O(h^5)$. For which equation may a truncation error of the form (5.3-2) be easily calculated? Why?

(*c*) Use these equations to find initial values for the differential equation $y' = y$, $y(0) = 1$ with $h = .1$. Use 1.1, 1.2, and 1.3 as initial guesses of y_1, y_2, and y_3, respectively. Carry eight decimal places and compare the answers with the true values.

*38. (*a*) Derive Eqs. (5.6-18) to (5.6-21).

(*b*) If the w_i's, α_i's, and β_{ij}'s are to be independent of $f(x,y)$, why must the expressions in brackets on the left-hand sides of (5.6-24) and (5.6-25) equal the corresponding operators on the right-hand sides?

39. (*a*) Verify that, for Runge-Kutta methods of order 2 and 3, *m* must be at least 2 and 3, respectively.

(*b*) Prove that $m \geqq M$ for all orders by showing that the coefficient of h_n^M on the right-hand side of (5.6-4) always contains a term $cw_M(f_y)^{M-2}D_2f$ (where *c* is a constant) and no other terms of this form in w_j, $j < M$.

*40. (*a*) Starting from (5.6-19) to (5.6-21), derive the error bounds (5.6-35) to (5.6-37).

(*b*) Show that $\alpha_2 = \frac{2}{3}$ minimizes γ_2.

(*c*) Show that $\alpha_2 = \frac{1}{2}$, $\alpha_3 = \frac{3}{4}$ minimizes γ_3. [Ref.: Ralston (1962b).]

41. (*a*) Verify (5.6-44).

(*b*) Show that, when $\alpha_2 = 0$, there are no Runge-Kutta third-order methods.

(*c*) Derive the one-parameter family of third-order Runge-Kutta methods when $\alpha_2 = \alpha_3$ and when $\alpha_3 = 0$. [Ref.: Ralston (1962b).]

42. (*a*) Use the results of Prob. 40 to verify that (5.6-41) is that second-order Runge-Kutta method for which the bound on γ_2 is minimized.

(b) Verify that (5.6-45) is that third-order Runge-Kutta method for which the bound on γ_3 is minimized. [Ref.: Ralston (1962b).]

43. For fourth-order Runge-Kutta methods

(a) Verify (5.6-47).

(b) Show that no solutions are possible when $\alpha_2 = 0$ or $\alpha_3 = 1$. Why is it reasonable to require $\alpha_2 \neq 0$ in any Runge-Kutta method?

(c) Find the one-parameter family of solutions when

$$\alpha_2 = \alpha_3 \qquad \alpha_2 = 1 \qquad \alpha_3 = 0$$

[Ref.: Kopal (1955), pp. 206–209.]

44. (a) For what values of α_2 and α_3 other than the special cases of the previous problem can β_{32}, β_{42}, or β_{43} be infinite?

(b) What happens to the corresponding weights in these cases?

(c) Even if the corresponding weight is zero and this term is dropped in (5.6-4), will the method be fourth-order?

45. (a) Compare the errors in the second-order Runge-Kutta method (5.6-41) and the second-order corrector of (5.5-11) when $f(x,y)$ is x^2 and when $f(x,y) = y$. Use (5.6-31) for the Runge-Kutta error.

(b) Do the same for the fourth-order Runge-Kutta method (5.6-49) and the fourth-order corrector in (5.5-33) for $f(x,y) = x^4$ and y.

(c) Why do the results of part b indicate that it is very difficult to assess the truncation error in a particular Runge-Kutta method using simple examples of this type? How does the higher-order term in (5.6-30) affect the comparative error estimates? Which of the two functions $f(x,y) = y$ and $f(x,y) = x^m$ is a more realistic test of the value of a method?

*46. For a system of two simultaneous differential equations

$$dy/dx = f(x,y,z) \qquad dz/dx = g(x,y,z)$$

the Runge-Kutta equations corresponding to (5.6-4) are

$$y_{n+1} - y_n = \sum_{i=1}^{m} w_i k_i \qquad z_{n+1} - z_n = \sum_{i=1}^{m} v_i m_i$$

where

$$k_i = h_n f\left(x_n + \alpha_i h_n, \; y_n + \sum_{j=1}^{i-1} \beta_{ij} k_j, \; z_n + \sum_{j=1}^{i-1} \gamma_{ij} m_j \right)$$

$$m_i = h_n g\left(x_n + \alpha_i h_n, \; y_n + \sum_{j=1}^{i-1} \beta_{ij} k_j, \; z_n + \sum_{j=1}^{i-1} \gamma_{ij} m_j \right)$$

(a) Use the analog of (5.6-17) to show that the coefficient of h_n^t in k_i and m_i contains no term which includes a product of a β_{ij} and γ_{ij} for $t \leq 4$.

(b) Deduce then that a Runge-Kutta method of order $m \leq 4$ for the above system is given by using w_i, α_i, β_{ij} as for a single equation and by having $v_i = w_i$, $\beta_{ij} = \gamma_{ij}$.

(c) Can this result be generalized for a system of N equations? Why?

47. For the equation

$$d^2y/dx^2 = f(x,y,y')$$

use the equations in the previous problem to write the equations for the fourth-order

Runge-Kutta method corresponding to (5.6-48).   How are these equations simplified when f is independent of $\dot{y}'$?

48. (*a*) If a Lagrangian interpolation formula is used to halve the interval in a numerical integration using the predictor-corrector method (5.5-33), how many points should be used in the interpolation?   If $y(x_n)$ has just been computed using the interval h and $y(x_n + \frac{1}{2}h)$ is to be calculated next using (5.5-33), what interpolated values have to be computed?

(*b*) If the interval is to be doubled, show that no restarting is necessary if enough past values have been saved.   For the method (5.5-33), how many past values (i.e., y_{n-1}, y_{n-2}, etc.) must be available for this method?

49. For the differential equations

$$(A)\ y' + y = 0 \qquad\qquad y(0) = 1$$
$$(B)\ y' + 2xy = 2x^3 \qquad\quad y(0) = 0$$
$$(C)\ y' + y + xy^2 = 0 \qquad y(0) = 1$$
$$(D)\ y' - 2y\tan x = 2\tan x \qquad y(0) = 1$$

(*a*) Use five terms of a Taylor series to obtain values of y at $x = 0.1, 0.2, 0.3$.

(*b*) Solve (A) using Picard's method.

(*c*) Compute starting values for equation (A) at $x = 0.1, 0.2, 0.3$ using the method of Sec. 5.6-2.   Use initial values $y_1 = .9$, $y_2 = .8$, $y_3 = .7$, and do three iterations.

(*d*) Repeat part *a* using the Runge-Kutta method of (i) second order (5.6-41), (ii) third order (5.6-45), (iii) fourth order (5.6-49).

Section 5.7

50. (*a*) Use the data of Table 5.3 for $x = .1, .2, .3, .4$ to calculate y at $x = .5$ using Hamming's and Milne's methods (skipping the modifier step in both cases since this is the first predictor-corrector step).   Estimate the error using the technique of Sec. 5.5-3 and compare with the actual error.

(*b*) As in part *a*, calculate y at $x = .6$, this time including the modifier step.

51. (*a*) Compare the roundoff properties of Milne's and Hamming's methods (cf. Prob. 28).   Would you expect the difference to be significant in the calculations of Table 5.6?

(*b*) Show that roundoff error dominates in the calculation of Table 5.6 for large x.

(*c*) Why should the interval be increased if possible when roundoff is the dominant error?

52. For the four differential equations of Prob. 49, using the results of *d* (iii) of Prob. 49, continue the solution from $x = 0.3$ to $x = 1.0$ with $h = 0.1$, using (*a*) the trapezoidal rule method (5.5-11); (*b*) Euler's method (5.5-13); (*c*) Adams's method with $p = 2$ (5.5-15); (*d*) Milne's method (5.5-27); (*e*) Hamming's method (5.5-33). In *a*, *d*, and *e* estimate the truncation error at each step.   In all five cases compare the calculated and true values.   How do you account for the uniformly poor results for equation (D)?

Section 5.8

53. (*a*) For the two equations

$$y' = f(x,y,z) \qquad z' = g(x,y,z)$$

indicate the sequence of calculations at each step using a predictor-corrector method.

(*b*) If these equations were obtained from $y'' = f(x,y,y')$, show how one of the predictions and modifications at each step can be avoided.

(*c*) Explain how you would use convergence factors with simultaneous equations.

54. (a) With $p = 2$ in (5.8-4) use the method of undetermined coefficients to derive a fifth-order corrector.   Express the coefficients in terms of a_2.   Use this result to derive the corrector (5.8-5).

(b) Calculate the three roots of the convergence equation (5.4-14) in terms of a_2. Why is $a_2 = 0$ a good choice from the stability point of view?

(c) Show that the corrector in (5.8-5) is also fifth-order.

(d) As in Prob. 10 use the technique of Sec. 5.3 to find the error terms in (5.8-5).

(e) Use the results of part d to find an estimate of the error at each step and to derive a method of the form (5.5-33).   Also derive an estimate of the truncation error at each step.   [Ref.: Hamming (1962), pp. 213–214.]

55. (a) For use in integrating $y'' = f(x,y)$ derive a predictor of the form

$$y_{n+1} = a_0 y_n + a_1 y_{n-1} + h^2 (b_0 y_n'' + b_1 y_{n-1}'')$$

and a corrector of the form

$$y_{n+1} = a_0 y_n + a_1 y_{n-1} + h^2 (b_{-1} y_{n+1}'' + b_1 y_{n-1}'')$$

both of which are to be exact for polynomials of degree 3 or less.

(b) Repeat parts d and e of the previous problem for this predictor and corrector.

56. (a) Verify (5.8-10) and (5.8-11) using (5.8-8) and (5.8-9).

(b) Use the Hermite interpolation formula to derive (5.8-13) and (5.8-14).

(c) Verify the modifier equation in (5.8-15) and find an estimate of T_n.

57. (a) Derive the equation analogous to (5.4-5) for Eq. (5.8-8).

(b) Deduce that any method of the form (5.8-8) is stable for some range of values of Kh.

(c) Deduce in particular that (5.8-10) is stable for all values of Kh.

58. For the differential equation $y'' = y$, $y(0) = 1$, $y'(0) = -1$

(a) Use Hamming's method with $h = 0.1$ applied to two first-order equations to take the solution to $x = 1.0$.

(b) Use (5.8-5) in the form derived in Prob. 54 with $h = 0.1$ to take the solution to $x = 1.0$.

In both cases use (5.6-49) to get starting values.

59. Use (5.8-15) to calculate the solutions of the four differential equations in Prob. 49.   Use $h = .1$ and the results of d (iii) of Prob. 49 to carry the solution from $x = .3$ to $x = 1.0$.   Compare the results with those of Prob. 52.   Instead of starting the computation at $x = .4$, where could you have started it?

chapter 6

FUNCTIONAL APPROXIMATION—
LEAST-SQUARES TECHNIQUES

6.1 INTRODUCTION

Polynomial interpolation is a method of approximating the value of a function at a point by means of a polynomial passing through known functional values.   A major virtue of this method of approximation is its ease of implementation.   Another virtue is that it leads to an expression for the truncation error in the approximation which can often be estimated or bounded.   Implicit in our discussion of polynomial interpolation in Chap. 3 was the assumption that truncation and not roundoff error was the major source of error.

In this chapter we consider the problem of approximating a function whose values at a sequence of points are generally known only empirically and thus are subject to inherent errors which may be large.   Thus roundoff will be a serious source of error and often is the controlling source. Moreover, it is often the case that an approximation to such a function is desired which can be manipulated analytically—in particular differentiated—with a reasonable degree of accuracy.   This we saw in Chap. 4 is generally difficult with exact polynomial approximations.   In fact, the $1/h^k$ factor in the numerical differentiation formula (4.1-12) means that, if the inherent error in the functional value is large, then differentiation will cause a serious "noise" problem.   This is in contrast to the case where the functional value can be calculated to the full word length (say 10 decimals) of a digital computer so that the roundoff error will be small. The subject of this chapter—least-squares approximations—is concerned with a technique by which "noisy" functional values may be used to generate a "smooth" approximation to the function. This smooth approximation can then, for example, be used to approximate the derivative of the function more accurately than exact approximations.

The reader may be familiar with the principle of least squares as applied to continuous functions over an interval $[a,b]$. In this chapter, we shall be concerned entirely with the principle of least squares as applied to functions known only at a discrete set of points. However, the derivation of the principle of least squares in the next section for a discrete set of points is precisely analogous to the derivation in the continuous case.

Our reason for emphasizing the discrete rather than the continuous case is that this is the case of interest in numerical applications. Approximating continuous functions by least-squares approximations is, of course, of great theoretical interest. In the case where the approximating functions are polynomials, such approximations of continuous functions lead naturally to the development of the orthogonal polynomials discussed in Chap. 4. As we shall see in Sec. 6.4, orthogonal polynomials also play an important role in discrete least-squares approximations.

6.2 THE PRINCIPLE OF LEAST SQUARES

We are now ready to make precise our heuristic definition of least-squares approximations in Sec. 2.1-2. Let $f(x)$ be a function and $\{x_i\}$, $i = 1$, . . . , n be a sequence of *data points* at which we have observed values of $f(x)$ which generally will be in error. We denote $f(x_i)$, the true value at x_i, by f_i, and we denote the observed value at x_i by $\bar{f}_i$. We define $E_i = f_i - \bar{f}_i$. Throughout this chapter we shall assume that the errors at different data points are uncorrelated (i.e., independent).

Let $\{\phi_j(x)\}$, $j = 0, 1, \ldots$ be a (generally finite) sequence of functions defined for every x_i. Then our object is to approximate $\bar{f}_i$ by a linear combination of the $\{\phi_j(x)\}$

$$\bar{f}_i \approx \sum_{j=0}^{m} a_j^{(m)} \phi_j(x_i) \qquad i = 1, \ldots, n \tag{6.2-1}$$

with the $a_j^{(m)}$ to be determined so that

$$H(a_0^{(m)}, \ldots, a_m^{(m)}) \equiv \sum_{i=1}^{n} w(x_i) \left[\bar{f}_i - \sum_{j=0}^{m} a_j^{(m)} \phi_j(x_i) \right]^2$$

$$= \sum_{i=1}^{n} w(x_i) R_i^2 \tag{6.2-2}$$

is minimized. The function $w(x)$ is called the *weight function* and is assumed to be such that $w(x_i) \geqq 0$, $i = 1, \ldots, n$. The quantity R_i is called the *residual* at x_i. The superscript m on $a_j^{(m)}$ denotes the fact that the coefficient of $\phi_j(x)$ will generally depend on m, although in Sec. 6.4 we shall see that this is not always the case. Having determined the $a_j^{(m)}$ so as to satisfy (6.2-2), we have then an approximation

$$y_m(x) = \sum_{j=0}^{m} a_j^{(m)} \phi_j(x) \tag{6.2-3}$$

which is called a least-squares approximation to $f(x)$ over $\{x_i\}$. We may use this approximation not only at the points $\{x_i\}$ but also at other values of x. In this sense, our development is analogous to that of Chap. 3 in which functional values at a discrete set of points were used to derive an approximation to be used over an interval. Nevertheless, in most applications of least-squares approximations, we shall be interested in the values of $y(x)$ and its derivatives at the points $\{x_i\}$.

If $\phi_j(x) = x^j$ and there are no more data points than parameters in the approximating polynomial (i.e., $n \leq m + 1$), then, by making the summation in (6.2-3) the Lagrangian interpolation polynomial corresponding to the points $\{x_i\}$, we would have $y_i = \bar{f_i}$, $i = 1, \ldots, n$ [where $y_i = y(x_i)$]. Since (6.2-2) would then be zero, this would be the desired minimum. In this chapter, however, we shall be concerned with the case $n > m + 1$; that is, we use a number of approximating functions less than the number of data points. Thus, for example, we might approximate a function known at five data points by a polynomial of degree 1 (i.e., $m = 1$). We could derive a polynomial of degree 4 passing through these five points, but such a fifth-degree polynomial will not enable us to "smooth" the empirical data. However, as we shall see, such smoothing is possible in general when $m + 1 < n$.

Graphically, this is illustrated by Fig. 6.1. Suppose we have empir-

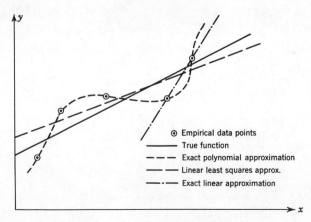

Fig. 6.1   Least squares and exact approximations.

ical data at five points on a function which is in fact linear as shown. The errors in the empirical data as such are much too great to allow approximating the true function by an *exact* linear approximation using any two points (although, if we knew which two points to choose—which we never shall—we could get quite a good approximation this way!). If we pass a fourth-degree polynomial through the five points, then we get an approximation whose deviation from the true function is not too bad but whose derivatives are much different from those of the true function.   On the other hand, the linear least-squares approximation not only lies close to the true function but also has a similar slope.

Although the considerations above were for the case where the set $\{\phi_j(x)\}$ is the powers of x, the points we have made are equally true for other sets of functions, in particular for the functions $\{\sin jx, \cos jx\}$ which we shall also consider in this chapter.

The use of Eq. (6.2-2) as the one to be minimized instead of

$$\sum_{i=1}^{n} w(x_i)|R_i| \tag{6.2-4}$$

or

$$\max_{i=1,\ldots,n} w(x_i)|R_i| \tag{6.2-5}$$

is motivated by an analytical consideration.   If the magnitude of the error is the quantity in which we are directly interested, then minimizing (6.2-4) would be more desirable than minimizing H.   Minimizing (6.2-5) (the so-called *minimax* approximation) has the advantage of giving us a sure bound on the error at any data point.   The desirability in some circumstances of having such a sure bound on the error, not just at a discrete set of points but over a whole interval, is the motivation behind the whole of Chap. 7.   But for general application with empirical data, the thing that rules out (6.2-4) and (6.2-5) is the fact that the absolute value is not a differentiable function of x.   Therefore, the determination of the constants a_j would be extremely difficult in general using either (6.2-4) or (6.2-5).

To calculate the $a_j^{(m)}$'s, we take the partial derivative of H in (6.2-2) with respect to $a_k^{(m)}$ and set it equal to zero, thereby obtaining

$$\frac{\partial H}{\partial a_k^{(m)}} = -2 \sum_{i=1}^{n} w_i \left[\bar{f}_i - \sum_{j=0}^{m} a_j^{(m)} \phi_j(x_i) \right] \phi_k(x_i) = 0$$
$$k = 0, \ldots, m; \, w_i = w(x_i) \tag{6.2-6}$$

Equation (6.2-6) is a system of $m + 1$ linear equations for the $m + 1$ unknown $a_j^{(m)}$'s.   This system is called the *normal equations*.   If the determinant of the coefficients does not vanish, we can solve for the $a_j^{(m)}$'s.

By considering $H[a_0^{(m)} + \Delta a_0, \ldots, a_m^{(m)} + \Delta a_m]$ it is not hard to show that this solution is indeed a minimum.

Our basic assumption in this chapter is that for some unknown value of m, say M, the true function $f(x)$ can be expressed as a finite linear combination of the set of functions $\{\phi_j(x)\}$. That is, we assume

$$f(x) = \sum_{j=0}^{M} a_j^{(M)} \phi_j(x) \tag{6.2-7}$$

Now clearly this assumption will not always be satisfied in practice, but if the assumption is a good approximation to reality, then the results we shall derive based on this assumption will be useful.

6.3 POLYNOMIAL LEAST–SQUARES APPROXIMATIONS

In this and the next section, we consider the case in which $\phi_j(x)$ is a polynomial of degree j. In particular, in this section we shall consider the case $\phi_j(x) = x^j$ and $w(x) = 1$. For this case Eq. (6.2-6) becomes, after canceling the -2,

$$\sum_{i=1}^{n} \left[\bar{f}_i - \sum_{j=0}^{m} a_j^{(m)} x_i^j \right] x_i^k = 0 \qquad k = 0, \ldots, m \tag{6.3-1}$$

Interchanging summations, we may rewrite (6.3-1) as

$$\sum_{j=0}^{m} a_j^{(m)} \left(\sum_{i=1}^{n} x_i^{j+k} \right) = \sum_{i=1}^{n} \bar{f}_i x_i^k \qquad k = 0, \ldots, m \tag{6.3-2}$$

Using the notation

$$g_{jk} = \sum_{i=1}^{n} x_i^{j+k} \qquad \rho_k = \sum_{i=1}^{n} \bar{f}_i x_i^k \tag{6.3-3}$$

the normal equations may be written

$$\sum_{j=0}^{m} g_{jk} a_j^{(m)} = \rho_k \qquad k = 0, \ldots, m \tag{6.3-4}$$

Using matrix calculus, it can be proved that the least-squares problem and, thus, the system (6.3-4) has a unique solution. We leave the proof to a problem {2}.

6.3-1 Solution of the normal equations

We seem at this point to have solved the least-squares problem for the case $\phi_j(x) = x^j$, $w(x) = 1$. All we need do is perform the perhaps tedious calculations required to solve the normal equations (6.3-4).   And indeed for small values of m, say up to 5 or 6, experience indicates that the solution of (6.3-4) produces quite good least-squares approximations.   But for greater values of m, the solutions found by solving (6.3-4) generally lead to progressively poorer least-squares approximations.   Moreover, this is quite independent of which of the many methods available for the solution of (6.3-4) (see Chap. 9) is used.   An explanation of this may be found using the following argument.

For convenience let us assume that the points x_i are all in the interval (0,1).   Further, let us assume that they are distributed fairly uniformly in this interval.   Then g_{jk} as defined in (6.3-3) has the form of n times a Riemann sum.   For large n then the approximation

$$g_{jk} = \sum_{i=1}^{n} x_i^{j+k} \approx n \int_0^1 x^{j+k} \, dx = \frac{n}{j+k+1} \qquad j, k = 0, \ldots, m$$

$$(6.3-5)$$

should be a good one.   Let $G = [g_{jk}]$ be the matrix of coefficients in (6.3-4). Using (6.3-5) we approximate G by n times the matrix H where

$$H = \begin{bmatrix} 1 & \frac{1}{2} & \frac{1}{3} & \cdots & & \frac{1}{m+1} \\ \frac{1}{2} & \frac{1}{3} & \frac{1}{4} & \cdots & & \frac{1}{m+2} \\ \frac{1}{3} & \cdots & \cdots & \cdots & & \frac{1}{m+3} \\ \cdots & \cdots & \cdots & \cdots & \cdots & \cdots \\ \frac{1}{m+1} & & \cdots & & & \frac{1}{2m+1} \end{bmatrix} \qquad (6.3-6)$$

This matrix is the principal minor of order $m + 1$ of the infinite *Hilbert matrix*.   This matrix is a classical example of an *ill-conditioned matrix*. We shall consider the meaning of ill conditioning in some detail in Chap. 9. But suffice it to say here that a matrix is ill-conditioned if, when it has been normalized so that its largest element has order of magnitude 1 [as, for example, in (6.3-6)], its inverse has very large elements.   Thus, for example, when $m = 9$, the inverse of (6.3-6) has elements of magnitude 3×10^{12}.   The result of this is that, in calculating the solution of (6.3-4) by any method whatsoever, any roundoff error committed will result in a greatly magnified error in the solution.   Therefore, in order to get an accurate solution to a set of linear equations whose matrix of coefficients is ill-conditioned, a very large number of decimal places must be carried in the computation, a number which, for the Hilbert matrix, soon becomes prohibitively large.

For m even as large as 9, the situation as we have presented it is so bad that, even though G is only an approximation to a Hilbert matrix, we still expect to have a great deal of difficulty in solving the normal equations. Some actual examples to illustrate how hard it is to solve the system (6.3-4) with any degree of accuracy are considered in the problems {5}.

The previous argument is a cogent one against using $\phi_j(x) = x^j$ for all but very small values of m. But to make the case even stronger, we now consider this class of functions from another standpoint.

6.3-2 Choosing the degree of the polynomial

Given a value of n how is one to choose m, the degree of the polynomial approximation? This problem is analogous to choosing the order of an interpolation or quadrature formula as discussed in previous chapters. But whereas in those cases we were interested in making an error term small and at the same time being able to estimate it, here the considerations are different.

Our basic hypothesis is that the true function $f(x)$ is a polynomial of degree $M < n$ or at least can be accurately represented by such a polynomial. A priori we do not know what M is; our problem is to find it. If we choose a value of $m < M$, then clearly it is impossible to get a good representation of the true function. On the other hand, choosing a value of $m > M$ also defeats our purpose. We have pointed out that by choosing $m = n - 1$ we can make

$$\delta_m^2 = \sum_{i=1}^n w_i R_i^2 = \sum_{i=1}^n w_i \left[\bar{f_i} - \sum_{j=0}^m a_j^{(m)} x_i^j \right]^2 \tag{6.3-7}$$

equal to zero. But in so doing, we shall have lost all smoothing properties of least-squares approximations. In fact, any value of $m > M$ sacrifices some smoothing.

When we are using powers of x, (6.2-7) becomes

$$f(x) = \sum_{j=0}^M a_j^{(M)} x^j \tag{6.3-8}$$

Therefore, if we knew M and calculated the least-squares approximation

$$y_{M+1}(x) = \sum_{j=0}^{M+1} a_j^{(M+1)} x^j \tag{6.3-9}$$

using the observed data $\{\bar{f_i}\}$, then *statistically* $a_{M+1}^{(M+1)}$ should be zero. That is, if there were no errors in the data, it would be zero, but because of these errors, it will not be zero even if the assumption that $f(x)$ has the form (6.3-8) is correct. We should like then to test the statistical hypothesis that $a_{M+1}^{(M+1)} = 0$. In order to be able to do this, we make the one further assumption that the errors E_i are normally distributed with zero mean and variance σ^2/w_i. This assumption is reasonable because more accurate measurements (i.e., those with small variance) will usually be more heavily weighted.

This statistical hypothesis that we wish to test is often called the *null hypothesis*. It can be tested using maximum-likelihood statistical methods, a discussion of which is beyond the scope of this book [see Wilks (1962)]. Here we only state the result that, if the null hypothesis is correct, then the expected value of

$$\sigma_m^2 = \delta_m^2/(n - m - 1) \tag{6.3-10}$$

will be independent of m for $m = M, M + 1, \ldots, n - 1$. Thus in practice, since we do not know M, we would wish to solve the normal equations (6.3-4) for $m = 1, 2, \ldots$, compute σ_m^2, and continue as long as σ_m^2 decreases significantly with increasing m. As soon as a value of m is reached after which no significant decrease occurs in σ_m^2, then this m is that of the null hypothesis, and we have the desired least-squares approximation.

Computationally, this means that we must compute the solution of the normal equations for a sequence of values of m,† since the solutions for $m \leq r$ are of no use in computing the solution for $m = r + 1$. This situation is analogous to the problem of adding a point to the Lagrangian interpolation formula which necessitated recalculation of each $l_j(x)$. Thus, even if the problems of Sec. 6.3-1 did not exist, the need to solve the normal equations a number of times would itself be a strong case against using $\phi_j(x) = x^j$. In the case of Lagrangian interpolation, we solved the computational problem by introducing iterated interpolation (Sec. 3.6). Here we shall solve both the computational problem of this section and the analytic problem of Sec. 6.3-1 by the use of orthogonal polynomials.

6.4 ORTHOGONAL POLYNOMIAL APPROXIMATIONS

If $p_j(x)$ is a polynomial of degree j, then the least-squares approximation of degree m may be written

$$y_m(x) = \sum_{j=0}^{m} b_j^{(m)} p_j(x) \tag{6.4-1}$$

† In practice, using our knowledge of the problem, we would often start with a value of $m > 1$.

In order to minimize

$$H[b_0^{(m)}, \ldots, b_m^{(m)}] \equiv \sum_{i=1}^{n} w_i[\bar{f}_i - y_m(x_i)]^2 \tag{6.4-2}$$

we proceed as in the previous section. We get, corresponding to (6.3-4),

$$\sum_{j=0}^{m} d_{jk} b_j^{(m)} = \omega_k \qquad k = 0, \ldots, m \tag{6.4-3}$$

where

$$d_{jk} = \sum_{i=1}^{n} w_i p_j(x_i) p_k(x_i) \qquad \omega_k = \sum_{i=1}^{n} w_i \bar{f}_i p_k(x_i) \tag{6.4-4}$$

For arbitrary choice of the $\{p_j(x)\}$, the computational problems involved in solving these normal equations can be just as serious as before. If, however, the $\{p_j(x)\}$ are chosen so that the nondiagonal terms of the matrix $D = [d_{jk}]$ are small compared with the diagonal elements, then the matrix D, unlike G, will not be nearly singular. In particular, if the $\{p_j(x)\}$ are *orthogonal* over the set of points $\{x_i\}$, then the off-diagonal terms will all be zero. By definition, a set of polynomials $\{p_j(x)\}$ is *orthogonal* over a set of points $\{x_i\}$ with respect to a weight function $w(x)$ if

$$\sum_{i=1}^{n} w_i p_j^{(n)}(x_i) p_k^{(n)}(x_i) = 0 \qquad \text{if } j \neq k \tag{6.4-5}$$

where the superscript denotes the fact that the polynomial will depend on the number of points n. We assume in what follows that $w(x_i) > 0$ for all i. If the $\{p_j^{(n)}(x)\}$ are orthogonal, then, as defined in (6.4-4), $d_{jk} = 0, j \neq k$. The system (6.4-3) then becomes

$$d_{kk} b_k^{(m)} = \omega_k \qquad k = 0, \ldots, m \tag{6.4-6}$$

which has the immediate solution

$$b_k^{(m)} = \omega_k / d_{kk} \qquad k = 0, \ldots, m \tag{6.4-7}$$

thereby eliminating the problems of solving an ill-conditioned system of normal equations. Moreover, the solution with m replaced by $m + 1$ is given by

$$b_k^{(m+1)} = \omega_k / d_{kk} \qquad k = 0, \ldots, m + 1 \tag{6.4-8}$$

with ω_k and d_{kk} again given by (6.4-4). Thus

$$b_k^{(m)} = b_k^{(m+1)} \qquad k = 0, \ldots, m \tag{6.4-9}$$

Therefore, to compute the solution for $m + 1$, we need only compute

ω_{m+1} and $d_{m+1,m+1}$. Since (6.4-9) indicates that b_k is in fact independent of m, we shall from now on drop the superscript.

The development above indicates that the use of orthogonal polynomials enables us to avoid the difficulties of both Secs. 6.3-1 and 6.3-2. We now proceed to consider the generation of polynomials orthogonal over discrete sets of points. We consider first the case in which the data points are equally spaced. To derive the orthogonal polynomials in this case, we use a method directly analogous to that considered in Prob. 13 of Chap. 4 for the generation of polynomials orthogonal over continuous intervals. We shall then show that these polynomials satisfy a three-term recurrence relation analogous to that in Prob. 16, Chap. 4. In fact we shall show that any polynomials satisfying (6.4-5) satisfy such a recurrence relation.

For later notational convenience, we assume that we have $N + 1$ equally spaced data points

$$x_i = x_0 + ih \qquad i = 0, \ldots, N \tag{6.4-10}$$

We rewrite (6.4-5) as

$$\sum_{i=0}^{N} w_i p_j^{(N+1)}(x_0 + ih) p_k^{(N+1)} (x_0 + ih) = 0 \qquad j \neq k \tag{6.4-11}$$

We expect that there will be at most $N + 1$ independent polynomials in the sequence $\{p_j^{(N+1)}(x)\}$ (why?). To make the notation more convenient, we replace $p_j^{(N+1)}(x_0 + ih)$ by $p_j(i,N)$. To derive the orthogonal polynomials, we set

$$w_i p_j(i,N) = \Delta^j U_j(i,N) \tag{6.4-12}$$

where Δ is the forward-difference operator of Sec. 3.3-2-1 and $U_j(i,N)$ is a function to be determined. Then if $q_{j-1}(x)$ is any polynomial of degree $j - 1$ or less, the condition (6.4-11) is equivalent to

$$\sum_{i=0}^{N} q_{j-1}(i)\Delta^j U_j(i,N) = 0 \tag{6.4-13}$$

where $q_{j-1}(i)$ denotes $q_{j-1}(x_0 + ih)$. Now we apply the formula for summation by parts {7}

$$\sum_{i=R}^{S} u_i \, \Delta v_i = u_i v_i \Big|_R^{S+1} - \sum_{i=R}^{S} v_{i+1} \, \Delta u_i \tag{6.4-14}$$

j times to (6.4-13). We get

$$[\Delta^{j-1}U_j(i,N)q_{j-1}(i)] - [\Delta^{j-2}U_j(i + 1, N) \, \Delta q_{j-1}(i)] + \cdots$$
$$+ (-1)^{j-1}[U_j(i + j - 1, N)\Delta^{j-1}q_{j-1}(i)]_{i=0}^{i=N+1} = 0 \tag{6.4-15}$$

since $\Delta^j q_{j-1}(i) = 0$ (why?). This boundary condition is satisfied if

$$U_j(j-1, N) = \Delta U_j(j-2, N) = \cdots = \Delta^{j-1}U_j(0,N) = 0$$
$$U_j(N+j, N) = \Delta U_j(N+j-1, N) = \cdots \qquad (6.4\text{-}16)$$
$$= \Delta^{j-1}U_j(N+1, N) = 0$$

which can be restated as

$$U_j(k,N) = 0 \qquad k = 0, \ldots, j-1$$
$$U_j(N+k, N) = 0 \qquad k = 1, \ldots, j \qquad (6.4\text{-}17)$$

Although more general conditions on $U_j(i,N)$ satisfying (6.4-15) could be stated, those in (6.4-17) serve to determine $p_j(i,N)$ uniquely (cf. part b of Prob. 13, Chap. 4).

Now since $p_j(i,N)$ is to be a polynomial of degree j in i, we must have from (6.4-12)

$$\Delta^{j+1}[p_j(i,N)] = \Delta^{j+1}[(1/w_i)\Delta^j U_j(i,N)] = 0 \qquad (6.4\text{-}18)$$

But this is a difference equation of order $2j+1$ for $U_j(i,N)$ which is subject to the $2j$ boundary conditions (6.4-17). Thus, because the number of boundary conditions (6.4-17) is one less than the order of the equation (6.4-18), they determine $U_j(i,N)$ only to within a multiplicative constant (why?).

For the particular case $w(x) = 1$, Eq. (6.4-18) becomes

$$\Delta^{2j+1}U_j(i,N) = 0 \qquad (6.4\text{-}19)$$

so that $U_j(i,N)$ is a polynomial of degree $2j$ in i (why?). The conditions (6.4-17) give the $2j$ zeros of this polynomial. Therefore,

$$U_j(i,N) = A_{jN}[i(i-1) \cdots (i-j+1)]$$
$$\times [(i-N-1)(i-N-2) \cdots (i-N-j)] \qquad (6.4\text{-}20)$$

Using the factorial functions defined in Sec. 4.15-2, this may be written

$$U_j(i,N) = A_{jN}i^{(j)}(i-N-1)^{(j)} \qquad (6.4\text{-}21)$$

Using (6.4-12) and by suitable manipulation of the factorial functions {9}, we may show that

$$p_j(i,N) = B_{jN} \sum_{k=0}^{j} (-1)^k \frac{(j+k)^{(2k)}}{(k!)^2} \frac{i^{(k)}}{N^{(k)}} \qquad (6.4\text{-}22)$$

with

$$B_{jN} = (-1)^j j! N^{(j)} A_{jN} \qquad (6.4\text{-}23)$$

Thus, since A_{jN} is at our disposal, we may choose B_{jN} to be anything we wish. For ease of calculation, it is convenient to choose B_{jN} so that $p_j(N,N) = 1$. We leave to a problem {10} the result that this will be so if $B_{jN} = (-1)^j$, as we shall take it to be in what follows.

In least-squares approximations with equally spaced data, it is convenient where possible to use an odd number of points and to let zero be the midpoint of the range of the abscissas. Thus we let $N = 2L$ and define a new variable s such that

$$i = L + s \tag{6.4-24}$$

With this change of variable, the orthogonal polynomials (6.4-22) become

$$p_j(s,2L) = \sum_{k=0}^{j} (-1)^{k+j} \frac{(j+k)^{(2k)}}{(k!)^2} \frac{(L+s)^{(k)}}{2L^{(k)}} \tag{6.4-25}$$

The polynomials $p_j(s,2L)$ are known as the Gram polynomials (or sometimes, confusingly, as Chebyshev polynomials). For purposes of tabulation, it is convenient to write $p_j(s,2L)$ as

$$p_j(s,2L) = \epsilon_j \sum_{k=0}^{j} \delta_{jk}s^k \qquad \delta_{jj} = 1 \tag{6.4-26}$$

The coefficients in (6.4-26) for $j = 1, 2, 3, 4, 5$ are given in Table 6.1. All δ_{jk}'s not shown are zero.

Table 6.1   Coefficients of $p_j(s,2L)$ as defined in (6.4-26)

$j = 1$:	$\epsilon_1 = 1/L$
$j = 2$:	$\epsilon_2 = \dfrac{3}{L(2L-1)}$
	$\delta_{20} = -\dfrac{L(L+1)}{3}$
$j = 3$:	$\epsilon_3 = \dfrac{5}{L(L-1)(2L-1)}$
	$\delta_{31} = -\dfrac{3L^2+3L-1}{5}$
$j = 4$:	$\epsilon_4 = \dfrac{35}{2L(L-1)(2L-1)(2L-3)}$
	$\delta_{40} = \dfrac{3L(L^2-1)(L+2)}{35}$
	$\delta_{42} = -\dfrac{6L^2+6L-5}{7}$
$j = 5$:	$\epsilon_5 = \dfrac{63}{2L(L-1)(L-2)(2L-1)(2L-3)}$
	$\delta_{51} = \dfrac{15L^4+30L^3-35L^2-50L+12}{63}$
	$\delta_{53} = -\dfrac{5(2L^2+2L-3)}{9}$

From our derivation the Gram polynomials are such that

$$\sum_{s=-L}^{L} p_i(s,2L)p_j(s,2L) = 0 \qquad i \neq j \tag{6.4-27}$$

Thus, if we are given values of a function $f(s)$ at $s = -L, -L+1,$ $\ldots, 0, 1, \ldots, L$, the least-squares approximation to $f(s)$ given by the first m Gram polynomials is, using (6.4-4),

$$y_m(s) = \sum_{j=0}^{m} b_j p_j(s,2L) \tag{6.4-28}$$

with

$$b_j = \omega_j/\gamma_j \tag{6.4-29}$$

where

$$\omega_j = \sum_{s=-L}^{L} \tilde{f}_s p_j(s,2L) \tag{6.4-30}$$

and {11}

$$\gamma_j = d_{jj} = \sum_{s=-L}^{L} p_j^2(s,2L) = \frac{(2L+j+1)!(2L-j)!}{(2j+1)[(2L)!]^2} \tag{6.4-31}$$

As we have noted, to get the least-squares approximation $y_{m+1}(s)$, it is necessary only to compute b_{m+1} since the b_j's are independent of m. To convert the approximation (6.4-28) to one in terms of x we need only make the change of variable

$$s = \frac{x - x_0}{h} - L \tag{6.4-32}$$

This follows from (6.4-10) and (6.4-24).

When the data points are not equally spaced, a derivation using divided-difference techniques (see Prob. 25 of Chap. 3) may be given, but it is extremely cumbersome. A more convenient method of derivation which is also applicable to the case of equally spaced data is to use recurrence relations. Suppose then that $\{p_j(x)\}$ is any sequence of polynomials satisfying the orthogonality relationship (6.4-5) with respect to some positive weight function $w(x)$ and some sequence of data points $\{x_i\}$, where we now return to the previous notation of n points labeled 1 to n. We shall show by induction that there exists a relation of the form

$$p_{j+1}(x) = (x - \alpha_{j+1})p_j(x) - \beta_j p_{j-1}(x)$$
$$j = 0, 1, \ldots \qquad p_0(x) = 1, \ p_{-1}(x) = 0 \tag{6.4-33}$$

where α_{j+1} and β_j are constants to be determined. For $j = 0$ (6.4-33) becomes

$$p_1(x) = (x - \alpha_1) \tag{6.4-34}$$

The relation (6.4-5) requires that

$$\sum_{i=1}^{n} w_i p_0(x_i) p_1(x_i) = \sum_{i=1}^{n} w_i(x_i - \alpha_1) = 0 \tag{6.4-35}$$

from which it follows that

$$\alpha_1 = \sum_{i=1}^{n} w_i x_i \Big/ \sum_{i=1}^{n} w_i \tag{6.4-36}$$

Let us suppose that for $j = 0, 1, \ldots, k$ the polynomials $p_j(x)$ satisfy a relationship of the form (6.4-33) and the orthogonality relationship (6.4-5). Then we wish to show that we can choose α_{k+1} and β_k so that with $p_{k+1}(x)$ defined by (6.4-33)

$$\sum_{i=1}^{n} w_i p_j(x_i) p_{k+1}(x_i) = 0 \qquad j = 0, 1, \ldots, k \tag{6.4-37}$$

Using (6.4-33) with $j = k$ in (6.4-37) we have

$$\sum_{i=1}^{n} w_i x_i p_j(x_i) p_k(x_i) - \alpha_{k+1} \sum_{i=1}^{n} w_i p_j(x_i) p_k(x_i)$$

$$- \beta_k \sum_{i=1}^{n} w_i p_j(x_i) p_{k-1}(x_i) = 0 \qquad j = 0, 1, \ldots, k \tag{6.4-38}$$

For $j = 0, 1, \ldots, k - 2$ the last two terms on the left-hand side of (6.4-38) are identically zero by the induction hypothesis. Moreover, for these values of j, $x_i p_j(x_i)$ in the first term is a polynomial of degree no greater than $k - 1$ and thus can be expressed as a linear combination of the $p_j(x)$, $j = 0, \ldots, k - 1$. Therefore, again by the induction hypothesis, the first term is also zero. For $j = 0, 1, \ldots, k - 2$ then (6.4-5) is satisfied for *any* choice of α_{k+1} and β_k.

For $j = k - 1$ the second term is still zero, and so we get the requirement that

$$\beta_k = \sum_{i=1}^{n} w_i x_i p_{k-1}(x_i) p_k(x_i) \Big/ \sum_{i=1}^{n} w_i [p_{k-1}(x_i)]^2$$

$$= \sum_{i=1}^{n} w_i [p_k(x_i)]^2 \Big/ \sum_{i=1}^{n} w_i [p_{k-1}(x_i)]^2 \tag{6.4-39}$$

the second form following from use of (6.4-33).   For $j = k$ the third term vanishes and we get

$$\alpha_{k+1} = \sum_{i=1}^{n} w_i x_i [p_k(x_i)]^2 \Big/ \sum_{i=1}^{n} w_i [p_k(x_i)]^2 \qquad (6.4\text{-}40)$$

We have the result then that, with β_k and α_{k+1} given by (6.4-39) and (6.4-40), the polynomial of degree $k + 1$, $p_{k+1}(x)$, defined by (6.4-33), satisfies the orthogonality relation (6.4-5).   This proves our assertion that a recurrence relation of the form (6.4-33) exists.   We have assumed in the above that the denominators in (6.4-39) and (6.4-40) do not vanish. A denominator can vanish only if

$$p_j(x_i) = 0 \qquad i = 1, \ldots, n \qquad (6.4\text{-}41)$$

for some j.   If (6.4-41) held for no j then we could generate an unending sequence of polynomials $p_j(x)$.   Given n data points we expect to be able to generate at most n independent polynomials $p_0(x), \ldots, p_{n-1}(x)$. Therefore, it is no surprise that we can show {13} that, if (6.4-33) is used to generate $p_n(x)$, then $p_n(x_i) = 0$, $i = 1, \ldots, n$.

Corresponding to (6.4-28) to (6.4-31) we have, for the polynomials generated using (6.4-33), the least-squares approximation

$$y_m(x) = \sum_{j=0}^{m} b_j p_j(x) \qquad (6.4\text{-}42)$$

with

$$b_j = \omega_j / \gamma_j \qquad (6.4\text{-}43)$$

where

$$\omega_j = \sum_{i=1}^{n} w_i \bar{f}_i p_j(x_i) \qquad (6.4\text{-}44)$$

and

$$\gamma_j = \sum_{i=1}^{n} w_i [p_j(x_i)]^2 \qquad (6.4\text{-}45)$$

This technique of generating orthogonal polynomials is a very powerful one and, since it is easily mechanized, is very useful on digital computers. The technique can, as we mentioned above, be used for generating the Gram polynomials.   In fact, for the Gram polynomials α_{j+1} in (6.4-33) is zero for all j {12}.   In deriving the recurrence relation for the Gram polynomials we must remember that the above derivation leads to a sequence of polynomials in which the coefficient of the highest power of x is 1, whereas in our derivation of the Gram polynomials this was not so. Taking this into account, the recurrence relation for the Gram polynomials is {12}

$$(1/\epsilon_{j+1})p_{j+1}(s,2L) = (s/\epsilon_j)p_j(s,2L) - (\beta_j/\epsilon_{j-1})p_{j-1}(s,2L)$$
$$j = 0, 1, \ldots \qquad p_0(s,2L) = 1 \qquad p_{-1}(s,2L) = 0 \qquad (6.4\text{-}46)$$

where

$$\beta_j = \frac{j^2[(2L+1)^2 - j^2]}{4(4j^2 - 1)} \qquad \epsilon_j = \frac{(2j)!}{(j!)^2}\frac{1}{(2L)^{(j)}} \qquad (6.4\text{-}47)$$

The quantity ϵ_j is the same as that given in (6.4-26).   Equation (6.4-46) may be used to derive the values in Table 6.1 {12}.

In the next section we shall present some examples which illustrate the use of orthogonal polynomials in generating least-squares approximations, and we shall contrast these with the use of nonorthogonal polynomial approximations.

6.5 AN EXAMPLE OF THE GENERATION OF LEAST–SQUARES APPROXIMATIONS

Suppose we are given the empirical data

x_i:	.1	.2	.3	.4	.5	.6	.7	.8	.9
$\bar{f}_i$:	5.1234	5.3057	5.5687	5.9378	6.4370	7.0978	7.9493	9.0253	10.3627

and we wish to find the best least-squares polynomial approximation to $f(x)$.   Since the data points are equally spaced, it is convenient to use the Gram polynomials.   Putting the origin in the s coordinate system at $x = .5$, we have

$$x = .5 + .1s \qquad (6.5\text{-}1)$$

Using Table 6.1 and dropping the $2L$ in (6.4-26) for convenience, we get the orthogonal polynomials

$$\begin{aligned}
&p_0(s) = 1 \qquad p_1(s) = s/4 \\
&p_2(s) = (3s^2 - 20)/28 \qquad p_3(s) = (5s^3 - 59s)/84 \\
&p_4(s) = (7s^4 - 115s^2 + 216)/168 \\
&p_5(s) = (9s^5 - 185s^3 + 716s)/240
\end{aligned} \qquad (6.5\text{-}2)$$

In Table 6.2 we have the values of $p_j(s)$, $j = 0, \ldots, 5$ evaluated at the relevant values of s together with the values of γ_j.   Using these values

Table 6.2   Values of $p_j(s)$

s	p_0	p_1	p_2	p_3	p_4	p_5
-4	1	-1	1	-1	1	-1
-3	1	$-\tfrac{3}{4}$	$\tfrac{1}{4}$	$\tfrac{1}{2}$	$-\tfrac{3}{2}$	$1\tfrac{1}{4}$
-2	1	$-\tfrac{1}{2}$	$-\tfrac{2}{7}$	$1\tfrac{3}{14}$	$-1\tfrac{1}{14}$	-1
-1	1	$-\tfrac{1}{4}$	$-1\tfrac{7}{28}$	$\tfrac{9}{14}$	$\tfrac{9}{14}$	$-\tfrac{9}{4}$
0	1	0	$-5\tfrac{5}{7}$	0	$\tfrac{9}{7}$	0
1	1	$\tfrac{1}{4}$	$-1\tfrac{7}{28}$	$-\tfrac{9}{14}$	$\tfrac{9}{14}$	$\tfrac{9}{4}$
2	1	$\tfrac{1}{2}$	$-\tfrac{2}{7}$	$-1\tfrac{3}{14}$	$-1\tfrac{1}{14}$	1
3	1	$\tfrac{3}{4}$	$\tfrac{1}{4}$	$-\tfrac{1}{2}$	$-\tfrac{3}{2}$	$-1\tfrac{1}{4}$
4	1	1	1	1	1	1
γ_i	9	$15\tfrac{1}{4}$	$9\tfrac{9}{28}$	$49\tfrac{5}{98}$	$14\tfrac{3}{14}$	$11\tfrac{7}{4}$

and (6.4-28) and (6.4-29) we calculate

$$
\begin{aligned}
\omega_0 &= 62.80770 & b_0 &= 6.97863 \\
\omega_1 &= 9.50930 & b_1 &= 2.53581 \\
\omega_2 &= 2.69424 & b_2 &= .76201 \\
\omega_3 &= .42323 & b_3 &= .08379 \\
\omega_4 &= .02449 & b_4 &= .00240 \\
\omega_5 &= .00100 & b_5 &= .00003
\end{aligned}
\tag{6.5-3}
$$

Using these results and (6.5-2) we may, as in (6.3-7), calculate

$$
\delta_m^2 = \sum_{s=-4}^{4} \left[\bar{f}_s - \sum_{j=0}^{m} b_j p_j(s) \right]^2
\tag{6.5-4}
$$

We get

$$
\begin{array}{ccc}
\delta_0^2 = 26.202 & \delta_1^2 = 2.089 & \delta_2^2 = .0355 \\
\delta_3^2 = .000059 & \delta_4^2 = .00000049 & \delta_5^2 = .00000045
\end{array}
\tag{6.5-5}
$$

Then using (6.3-10) we calculate

$$
\begin{array}{ccc}
\sigma_0^2 = 3.275 & \sigma_1^2 = .298 & \sigma_2^2 = .0059 \\
\sigma_3^2 = .000012 & \sigma_4^2 = .00000012 & \sigma_5^2 = .00000015
\end{array}
\tag{6.5-6}
$$

from which we conclude that $m = 4$ gives us the best least-squares approximation. This approximation is

$$
y_4(s) = \sum_{j=0}^{4} b_j p_j(s)
\tag{6.5-7}
$$

with the b_j's given by (6.5-3) and $p_j(s)$ given by (6.5-2). Now using

(6.5-1) and (6.5-2) we convert back to x and get

$$y_4(x) = 1.0000x^4 + 2.9875x^3 + 2.0188x^2 + .9915x + 5.0010$$

$$(6.5\text{-}8)$$

In fact the values given in the table at the start of the section are perturbations of the values of

$$f(x) = x^4 + 3x^3 + 2x^2 + x + 5 \tag{6.5-9}$$

The true values of $f(x)$ at the points given in the table are

x_i:	.1	.2	.3	.4	.5	.6	.7	.8	.9
f_i:	5.1231	5.3056	5.5691	5.9376	6.4375	7.0976	7.9491	9.0256	10.3631

In order to show the effect of the ill condition of the matrix G, let us now repeat the above computation using powers of x instead of orthogonal polynomials. Using (6.3-3) and (6.3-4) we wish to calculate $a_j^{(4)}$, $j = 0, \ldots, 4$. We get for G, the matrix of the g_{jk},

$$G = \begin{bmatrix} 9.0 & 4.5 & 2.85 & 2.025 & 1.5333 \\ 4.5 & 2.85 & 2.025 & 1.5333 & 1.20825 \\ 2.85 & 2.025 & 1.5333 & 1.20825 & .978405 \\ 2.025 & 1.5333 & 1.20825 & .978405 & .8080425 \\ 1.5333 & 1.20825 & .978405 & .8080425 & .67731333 \end{bmatrix}$$

$$= 9 \begin{bmatrix} 1.00000 & .50000 & .31667 & .22500 & .17037 \\ .50000 & .31667 & .22500 & .17037 & .13425 \\ .31667 & .22500 & .17037 & .13425 & .10871 \\ .22500 & .17037 & .13425 & .10871 & .08978 \\ .17037 & .13425 & .10871 & .08978 & .07526 \end{bmatrix} \tag{6.5-10}$$

From (6.5-10) we see that $\tfrac{1}{9}G$ is quite close to (6.3-6), as we would expect since the points x_i are all in the interval (0,1). For the determinant of G we get

$$\det(G) = .000000014 \tag{6.5-11}$$

Therefore, we expect to lose a great deal of significance in solving the normal equations. We emphasize that the orthogonal polynomial and powers of x formulations are two ways of starting precisely the same problem. Therefore, any difference between (6.5-8) and the solution of (6.3-4) will be entirely due to different computational techniques.

Using (6.3-3) the right-hand side of (6.3-4) is

$$\rho_0 = 62.8077 \qquad \rho_1 = 35.20757 \qquad \rho_2 = 23.944287$$
$$\rho_3 = 17.8176647 \qquad \rho_4 = 13.93266027 \tag{6.5-12}$$

If we solve the normal equations using Gaussian elimination (see Sec.

9.3-1) and carry six decimal places throughout the computation we get, rounding the results to four decimal places,

$$a_0^{(4)} = .9672 \qquad a_1^{(4)} = 3.0522 \qquad a_2^{(4)} = 1.9763$$
$$a_3^{(4)} = 1.0020 \qquad a_4^{(4)} = 5.0003 \tag{6.5-13}$$

which in the cases of $a_0^{(4)}$ and $a_1^{(4)}$ have errors far larger than those in (6.5-8). Note that the coefficients of (6.5-8) are an equally good solution of the normal equations as those of (6.5-13). That is, the difference between the right-hand side of (6.3-4) [as given by (6.5-12)] and the left-hand side is not significantly different whether (6.5-13) or the coefficients of (6.5-8) are used {17}. The large errors of (6.5-13) are entirely due to the ill condition of the matrix G. The smallness of the determinant of G causes a great loss of significance in the calculation of the $a_j^{(4)}$. In fact $a_0^{(4)}$ was calculated as the ratio of .000059/.000061. That is, only two of the digits remaining at this point are significant. If instead of six decimals we had carried eight throughout the computation, then the values of the $a_j^{(4)}$ would have been very close to those of (6.5-8) {17}. But for values of m greater than 5 or 6, the number of decimal places that must be carried to avoid this loss of significance becomes prohibitively large. Therefore, the use of orthogonal polynomials (which requires less computation anyway) is indicated.

A possible source of loss of significance when using orthogonal polynomials is in the computation of the b_j's. If, for example, the magnitude of $p_j(x_i)$ is small for all x_i, then the calculation of the quotient ω_j/γ_j may result in a substantial loss of significance particularly in fixed point calculations {21}. When using the Gram polynomials with the normalized variable s, this is not a problem. But it can be a serious problem when using the recurrence relation technique. To avoid loss of significance in this latter case, it is desirable to scale and shift the data points from their original interval to a more convenient one (i.e., in effect to normalize the independent variable). Such a convenient interval [Forsythe (1957)] when $w(x) = 1$ is $[-2,2]$.

It is important that the reader clearly distinguish the two types of errors considered here. On the one hand the ill condition of G causes the difference between the calculated coefficients given by (6.5-8) and (6.5-13). On the other hand the difference between the coefficients in (6.5-8) and the true coefficients (6.5-9) is due to the inherent empirical errors in the data. Now suppose that we know the probability distribution of these errors. Can we show that the coefficients in (6.5-8) are approximations to those in (6.5-9) within an expected error due to the empirical errors? More generally, given a least-squares approximation to an unknown function, what can be said about the accuracy of the coefficients? We shall try to answer this question in the next section.

6.6 ERRORS IN LEAST–SQUARES APPROXIMATIONS

We begin by considering the errors in coefficients generated using orthogonal polynomials. Let us denote by $\bar{b}_k$ the coefficients calculated using the observed data and by b_k the coefficients that would result if true values were used. Then from Sec. 6.4

$$\bar{b}_k = \frac{1}{\gamma_k} \sum_{i=1}^{n} w_i \bar{f}_i p_k(x_i) \tag{6.6-1}$$

and

$$b_k = \frac{1}{\gamma_k} \sum_{i=1}^{n} w_i f_i p_k(x_i) \tag{6.6-2}$$

with γ_k defined by (6.4-45). Then

$$\Delta b_k = b_k - \bar{b}_k = \frac{1}{\gamma_k} \sum_{i=1}^{n} w_i E_i p_k(x_i) \tag{6.6-3}$$

As in Sec. 6.3-2 we assume that the E_i are distributed with zero mean and variance σ^2/w_i. The mean or *expected value* of Δb_k is therefore zero; our object here is to determine the variance of Δb_k, $\sigma^2_{\Delta b_k}$ which is the expected value of $(\Delta b_k)^2$.

Denoting expected value by M (for mean) we have

$$\sigma^2_{\Delta b_k} = M\left\{ \frac{1}{\gamma_k^2} \left[\sum_{i=1}^{n} w_i E_i p_k(x_i) \right]^2 \right\}$$

$$= M\left[\frac{1}{\gamma_k^2} \sum_{i=1}^{n} \sum_{j=1}^{n} w_i w_j E_i E_j p_k(x_i) p_k(x_j) \right]$$

$$= \frac{1}{\gamma_k^2} \sum_{i=1}^{n} \sum_{j=1}^{n} M(w_i w_j E_i E_j) p_k(x_i) p_k(x_j)$$

$$= \frac{1}{\gamma_k^2} \sum_{i=1}^{n} w_i M(w_i E_i^2)[p_k(x_i)]^2$$

$$= \sigma^2/\gamma_k \tag{6.6-4}$$

where, in going from the third to the fourth line, we used the assumption that the errors at distinct data points are uncorrelated.

We may now quite easily derive the result corresponding to (6.6-4) when powers of x instead of orthogonal polynomials are used. We write [cf. (6.4-26)]

$$p_j(x) = \sum_{r=0}^{j} \beta_{jr} x^r \qquad j = 0, 1, \ldots \qquad (6.6\text{-}5)$$

Then we may rewrite (6.4-42) with $\bar{b}_j$ in place of b_j as

$$y_m(x) = \sum_{j=0}^{m} \sum_{r=0}^{j} \bar{b}_j \beta_{jr} x^r = \sum_{r=0}^{m} \sum_{j=r}^{m} \bar{b}_j \beta_{jr} x^r \qquad (6.6\text{-}6)$$

The coefficient of x^k in (6.6-6) must be identical to $\bar{a}_k^{(m)}$, the coefficient of x^k in the least-squares approximation generated using powers of x (why?). Therefore,

$$\bar{a}_k^{(m)} = \sum_{j=k}^{m} \beta_{jk} \bar{b}_j \qquad (6.6\text{-}7)$$

Let $a_k^{(m)}$ be the value that would result if true values of $f(x)$ were used and let $\Delta a_k^{(m)} = a_k^{(m)} - \bar{a}_k^{(m)}$. Because of the assumption of uncorrelated errors at distinct data points, all the covariances of the Δb_j's are zero. Thus, using (6.6-4),

$$\sigma_{\Delta a_k^{(m)}}^2 = M \left(\sum_{j=k}^{m} \beta_{jk} \Delta b_j \right)^2 = \sum_{j=k}^{m} \beta_{jk}^2 M(\Delta b_j^2) = \sigma^2 \sum_{j=k}^{m} \frac{\beta_{jk}^2}{\gamma_j} \qquad (6.6\text{-}8)$$

If we have an estimate of σ^2, then (6.6-4) or (6.6-8) may be used to estimate the variance. More commonly we shall not have such an estimate. But using the residuals at the data points, we may obtain the desired estimate. Assume we have calculated the approximation using orthogonal polynomials. Then

$$R_i = \bar{f}_i - \sum_{j=0}^{m} \bar{b}_j p_j(x_i) \qquad (6.6\text{-}9)$$

The expected value of the residual is zero (why?). The variance of $\bar{f}_i$ is the same as that of E_i (why?) so that, denoting covariance by cov, we have

$$M(R_i^2) = \frac{\sigma^2}{w_i} - 2 \sum_{j=0}^{m} \text{cov}\,(\bar{f}_i, \bar{b}_j) p_j(x_i) + \sum_{j=0}^{m} \sigma_{\Delta b_j}^2 [p_j(x_i)]^2 \qquad (6.6\text{-}10)$$

Now

$$\text{cov}\,(\bar{f}_i, \bar{b}_j) = M(E_i \Delta b_j) = M \left[\frac{E_i}{\gamma_j} \sum_{r=1}^{n} w_r E_r p_j(x_r) \right] = \frac{\sigma^2 p_j(x_i)}{\gamma_j} \qquad (6.6\text{-}11)$$

Using this result and (6.6-4) in (6.6-10) we obtain

$$M(R_i^2) = \frac{\sigma^2}{w_i} \left\{ 1 - \sum_{j=0}^{m} \frac{w_i[p_j(x_i)]^2}{\gamma_j} \right\} \tag{6.6-12}$$

Finally

$$M\left(\sum_{i=1}^{n} w_i R_i^2 \right) = \sigma^2 \left\{ n - \sum_{j=0}^{m} \sum_{i=1}^{n} \frac{w_i[p_j(x_i)]^2}{\gamma_j} \right\}$$

$$= \sigma^2 \left\{ n - \sum_{j=0}^{m} \frac{1}{\gamma_j} \sum_{i=1}^{n} w_i[p_j(x_i)]^2 \right\} = (n - m - 1)\sigma^2 \tag{6.6-13}$$

Therefore,

$$\frac{1}{n - m - 1} \sum_{i=1}^{n} w_i R_i^2 = \frac{\delta_m^2}{n - m - 1} = \sigma_m^2 \tag{6.6-14}$$

provides the desired estimate of σ^2 [cf. (6.3-10)].

Example 6.1   Apply the results of this section to the example of the previous section.

We suppose first that we have no a priori estimate of σ^2.   Using (6.5-8) and the given values of $\bar{f}_i$, we first calculate the residuals

x_i:	.1	.2	.3	.4	.5	.6	.7	.8	.9
R_i:	$-.0001$	.0001	$-.0003$	.0003	$-.0005$	.0001	.0001	$-.0003$	.0000

Since $n = 9$, $m = 4$, and $w(x) = 1$, our estimate of σ^2 from (6.6-14) is given by σ_4 in (6.5-6) as $\sigma^2 \approx 12 \times 10^{-8}$.   Since the data are equally spaced the values of γ_k are those tabulated in Table 6.2.   Using these values in (6.6-4) we calculate

$\sigma_{\Delta b_0}^2 = (^{14}\!\!/_9) \times 10^{-8} = 1.56 \times 10^{-8}$
$\sigma_{\Delta b_1}^2 = (^{56}\!\!/_{15}) \times 10^{-8} = 3.73 \times 10^{-8}$
$\sigma_{\Delta b_2}^2 = (^{392}\!\!/_{99}) \times 10^{-8} = 3.96 \times 10^{-8}$
$\sigma_{\Delta b_3}^2 = (^{1372}\!\!/_{495}) \times 10^{-8} = 2.77 \times 10^{-8}$
$\sigma_{\Delta b_4}^2 = (^{196}\!\!/_{143}) \times 10^{-8} = 1.37 \times 10^{-8}$

so that the standard deviations are

$\sigma_{\Delta b_0} = 1.25 \times 10^{-4}$
$\sigma_{\Delta b_1} = 1.93 \times 10^{-4}$
$\sigma_{\Delta b_2} = 1.99 \times 10^{-4}$
$\sigma_{\Delta b_3} = 1.66 \times 10^{-4}$
$\sigma_{\Delta b_4} = 1.17 \times 10^{-4}$

These values would lead us to expect that the errors in the b_k's given by (6.5-3) would be of the order of about 1 or 2 in the fourth decimal place.   To check this we must convert (6.5-9) to a linear combination of the $p_j(s)$.   This can be done by expressing each power of s as a linear combination of the $p_j(s)$ {22}.   In particular

$$s = 4p_1(s) \qquad s^2 = 28\tfrac{2}{3}p_2(s) + 20\tfrac{2}{3}$$
$$s^3 = 84\tfrac{2}{5}p_3(s) + 236\tfrac{2}{5}p_1(s) \qquad s^4 = 24p_4(s) + 460\tfrac{2}{3}p_2(s) + 236\tfrac{2}{3} \tag{6.6-15}$$

Using these and (6.5-1) in (6.5-9), we get

$$F(s) = f(.5 + .1s) = 6.97870p_0(s) + 2.53600p_1(s)$$
$$+ .76200p_2(s) + .08400p_3(s) + .00240p_4(s)$$

Comparing these coefficients with (6.5-3), we find no error in the coefficient of $p_4(s)$, an error of 10^{-5} in the coefficients of $p_0(s)$ and $p_2(s)$, and errors of -1.9×10^{-4} and -2.1×10^{-4}, respectively, in the coefficients of $p_1(s)$ and $p_3(s)$. The latter two errors are both of the expected order of magnitude while the others are much smaller. The simplest explanation of this is that the data at the beginning of Sec. 6.5 are such that most of the error in $f(x)$ is in the *odd* component of the function.

6.7 SMOOTHING

Our results of the previous sections indicate that the most appropriate least-squares polynomial approximation to a function $f(x)$ must have two characteristics: (1) it must be of sufficiently high degree so that the approximating polynomial provides a good approximation to the *true* function, but (2) it must not be of so high a degree that it fits the *observed* data too closely in the sense that the "noise" or inaccuracies in the observed data are retained in the least-squares approximation. If the least-squares approximation has these two properties then it may be said to *smooth* the observed data in the sense that the *information* on the true function in the observed data is retained but the noise has been "smoothed out." For a given degree least-squares approximation, we get more *smoothing* the greater the number of points that we use in (6.2-2). That is, because of our assumption that the errors E_i (i.e., the noise) are distributed with zero mean about the true function, the larger the sample n the more nearly these errors will be "averaged" out in the least-squares approximation.

A common aim in least-squares approximation is to use the approximation to generate the smoothed value at the data points. For example, using the example of Sec. 6.5, the smoothed values at the points $x = .1, \ldots, .9$ are given by substituting these values of x into (6.5-8) or the corresponding values of s, $-4, -3, \ldots, 3, 4$ into (6.5-7). Doing the latter we get

s:	-4	-3	-2	-1	0	1	2	3	4
$y_4(s)$:	5.1235	5.3056	5.5690	5.9375	6.4375	7.0977	7.9492	9.0256	10.3627

The table of residuals in Sec. 6.6 is just the difference between the table at the beginning of Sec. 6.5 and the above table.

Because of the commonness of this problem, it is convenient to tabulate the formulas which give the smoothed values at the data points in terms of the observed data. Such formulas are generally called *smoothing formulas*. These formulas must be tabulated in terms of two parameters, m, the degree of the approximation, and n, the number of data points.

We consider in what follows the case $w(x) = 1$. To derive the smoothing formulas, it is necessary only to use (6.4-28)

$$y_m(s) = \sum_{j=0}^{m} b_j p_j(s, 2L) \tag{6.7-1}$$

where the b_j's are given by (6.4-29). This assumes that $n = 2L + 1$ is odd, which, as we have mentioned before, is the usual case. The smoothed value at x_i is given then by evaluating (6.7-1) at that value of s corresponding to x_i. Using (6.4-29) to (6.4-31) in (6.7-1) we have

$$
\begin{aligned}
y_m(s) &= \sum_{j=0}^{m} \sum_{t=-L}^{L} \left\{ \bar{f}_t p_j(t, 2L) p_j(s, 2L) \bigg/ \frac{(2L+j+1)!(2L-j)!}{(2j+1)[(2L)!]^2} \right\} \\
&= \sum_{t=-L}^{L} \sum_{j=0}^{m} \left\{ \frac{(2j+1)[(2L)!]^2}{(2L+j+1)!(2L-j)!} p_j(t, 2L) p_j(s, 2L) \right\} \bar{f}_t
\end{aligned}
\tag{6.7-2}
$$

which is the desired expression for $y_m(s)$ as a linear combination of the observed values $\bar{f}_t$. For example, if $m = 1$ and $n = 3$ ($L = 1$) (6.7-2) yields

$$y_1(-1) = \tfrac{1}{6}(5\bar{f}_{-1} + 2\bar{f}_0 - \bar{f}_1) \qquad y_1(0) = \tfrac{1}{3}(\bar{f}_{-1} + \bar{f}_0 + \bar{f}_1)$$
$$y_1(1) = \tfrac{1}{6}(-\bar{f}_{-1} + 2\bar{f}_0 + 5\bar{f}_1) \tag{6.7-3}$$

Actually, because of the symmetry with respect to $s = 0$, it is not necessary to give the equation for $y_1(1)$. Thus, for $m = 1$, $n = 5$ ($L = 2$), it is sufficient to give

$$
\begin{aligned}
y_1(-2) &= \tfrac{1}{5}(3\bar{f}_{-2} + 2\bar{f}_{-1} + \bar{f}_0 - \bar{f}_2) \\
y_1(-1) &= \tfrac{1}{10}(4\bar{f}_{-2} + 3\bar{f}_{-1} + 2\bar{f}_0 + \bar{f}_1) \\
y_1(0) &= \tfrac{1}{5}(\bar{f}_{-2} + \bar{f}_{-1} + \bar{f}_0 + \bar{f}_1 + \bar{f}_2)
\end{aligned}
\tag{6.7-4}
$$

Some other examples of formulas for particular values of m and n are considered in the problems {23}. These smoothing formulas can be conveniently written in terms of central differences {24}.

Given a set of observed data points which we wish to approximate with a least-squares polynomial, it is clearly not necessary to fit one polynomial to all the data. Instead, it is possible to fit part of the data with one polynomial and another part with another polynomial. This is often desirable when, for example, a function which is by no means linear over its whole range can nevertheless be approximated well by a straight line over subranges of the data. An example illustrating this as well as some other aspects of smoothing has the data shown in the second column of Table 6.3. These data are plotted in Fig. 6.2. Now these data surely do not appear linear over the whole range. But various subsets of the data points do appear to be nearly linear, and so, having no other a priori knowledge of the true function $f(x)$, we might try to make a linear least-squares fit over subranges of the data. As a first try we use the second of Eqs. (6.7-3) to calculate $y_1(0)$ for $x = 1, 2,$ $\ldots, 24$. At the end points $x = 0, 25$ where we cannot use $y_1(0)$ (why?), we use the first and third equations of (6.7-3), respectively. Note that we use the central equation where possible (why?). The results of this are shown in the third column of Table 6.3 and are plotted in Fig. 6.2. In the fourth column are the corresponding results using (6.7-4). For all x except 0, 1, 24, 25, $y_1(0)$ was used. At these four points, respectively, $y_1(-2)$, $y_1(-1)$, $y_1(1)$, and $y_1(2)$ were calculated.

How can we compare these two sets of smoothed data? In the first place, we get more smoothing from the five-point formula than the three-point formula, but this of itself does not mean that the five-point

Table 6.3   **Examples of data smoothing**

x_i	$\bar{f}_i$	y_i $(n = 3)$	y_i $(n = 5)$	y_i $(n = 5)$ second time
0	431	424	402	405
1	409	423	423	422
2	429	420	444	439
3	422	460	459	456
4	530	486	469	472
5	505	498	483	485
6	459	488	504	499
7	499	495	510	516
8	526	529	527	536
9	563	559	554	557
10	587	582	584	585
11	595	610	612	616
12	647	637	649	650
13	669	687	683	684
14	746	725	720	720
15	760	761	756	752
16	778	789	792	784
17	828	817	810	815
18	846	837	841	847
19	836	866	876	880
20	916	903	914	922
21	956	962	960	966
22	1014	1015	1019	1012
23	1076	1075	1061	1060
24	1134	1111	1106	1107
25	1124	1135	1152	1154

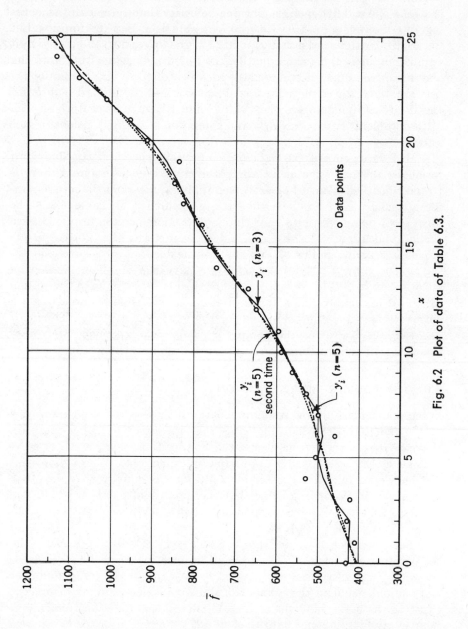

Fig. 6.2 Plot of data of Table 6.3.

253

formula is to be preferred. For if so, why not use seven, nine, or more points? Only if the assumption of linearity over five consecutive points is a good one will five-point smoothing be better than three-point smoothing. If, however, linearity over five points is a bad assumption but linearity over three consecutive points is a good one, then the three-point approximation will be superior. In the absence of definitive knowledge about the true function, the answer to which of these approximations is best is in the realm of the art rather than the science of numerical analysis. Intuition—meaning experience, really—and general physical knowledge of the problem must be used by the computor to make decisions of this nature.

Having smoothed the data once by either the three- or five-point formulas, we may once again apply the smoothing formulas, this time to the smoothed data. For example, applying five-point linear smoothing a second time results in the data in column 5 of Table 6.3. The purpose of doing this is to smooth the data more than is provided by a single application of (6.7-4), and indeed, comparing the plotted results of columns 4 and 5 in Fig. 6.2, we see that the result of the second smoothing is "smoother." But here again we have the problem of knowing when to stop. For if we continue this process—that is, take the results of (6.7-4) and apply (6.7-4) again and again—we shall eventually get a single straight-line approximation for the whole range {25}. Thus it is necessary here also for the computor to use his experience and other knowledge of the true function in order to decide when to stop.

6.8 THE FOURIER APPROXIMATION

Often, particularly in real-time applications, there is physical knowledge of the function $f(x)$ which indicates that the function is periodic. In this case it is advantageous to use the Fourier functions instead of polynomials as the least-squares approximating functions. Throughout this section we assume that the set of points $\{x_i\}$ is equally spaced. Also, we shall, as in Sec. 6.4, assume that the number of points n is odd and equal to $2L + 1$. The corresponding results when n is even are considered in a problem {29}.

For convenience we set $x_i = 2\pi i/(2L + 1)$, $i = 0, \ldots, 2L$. The set of functions $\{\phi_j(x)\}$ that we shall use are the $2L + 1$ functions, 1, $\cos x, \ldots, \cos Lx, \sin x, \ldots, \sin Lx$. We limit ourselves to a number of functions equal to the number of data points because, as before, we expect to have no more than $2L + 1$ independent functions on $2L + 1$ points. In fact, it is not hard to show {27} that $\sin kx$ or $\cos kx$ where k is an integer greater than L can be simply expressed in terms of one of the above functions on the set $\{x_i\}$.

Just as the Fourier functions satisfy an orthogonality relationship over the interval $[0,\pi]$ so do the above functions satisfy an orthogonality relationship over the discrete set of points $\{x_i\}$. In fact, we may show that {28}

$$\sum_{i=0}^{2L} \sin jx_i \sin kx_i = \begin{cases} 0 & j \neq k \\ \dfrac{2L+1}{2} & j = k \neq 0 \\ 0 & j = k = 0 \end{cases} \qquad (6.8\text{-}1)$$

$$\sum_{i=0}^{2L} \cos jx_i \cos kx_i = \begin{cases} 0 & j \neq k \\ \dfrac{2L+1}{2} & j = k \neq 0 \\ 2L+1 & j = k = 0 \end{cases} \qquad (6.8\text{-}2)$$

$$\sum_{i=0}^{2L} \cos jx_i \sin kx_i = 0 \qquad \text{all } j, k \qquad (6.8\text{-}3)$$

where j and k are restricted to run between 0 and L.

With $2L + 1$ functions we would expect to be able to fit exactly the $2L + 1$ points $\{x_i\}$, but in the least-squares context, this again is just what we do not wish to do. As before we want to use enough functions to provide a good approximation to the true function $f(x)$ but not too many so that we lose smoothing. Suppose then as before that $\bar{f}_i$ is the observed value of $f(x)$ at x_i. We approximate $f(x)$ by

$$y_m(x) = \tfrac{1}{2}a_0 + \sum_{j=1}^{m} (a_j \cos jx + b_j \sin jx) \qquad m < L \qquad (6.8\text{-}4)$$

in direct analogy with standard Fourier-series notation. Again we determine the a_j's and b_j's so that the sum of the squares of the differences $\bar{f}_i - y_m(x_i)$ will be minimized. Using the orthogonality relations (6.8-1) to (6.8-3) the normal equations (6.2-6) yield

$$a_j = \frac{2}{2L+1} \sum_{i=0}^{2L} \bar{f}_i \cos jx_i = \frac{2}{2L+1} \sum_{i=0}^{2L} \bar{f}_i \cos \frac{2\pi ij}{2L+1}$$
$$j = 0, \ldots, m \qquad (6.8\text{-}5)$$

$$b_j = \frac{2}{2L+1} \sum_{i=1}^{2L} \bar{f}_i \sin jx_i = \frac{2}{2L+1} \sum_{i=1}^{2L} \bar{f}_i \sin \frac{2\pi ij}{2L+1}$$
$$j = 1, \ldots, m \qquad (6.8\text{-}6)$$

In order to compute the coefficients in (6.8-5) and (6.8-6) we may, of course, evaluate the summations directly. But a much more efficient algorithm which, because of its recursive nature, is particularly well adapted to calculation on a digital computer is the following.   Define

$$V_k(x) = \sum_{i=k}^{2L} \bar{f}_i \sin (i - k + 1)x \qquad k = 1, \ldots, 2L$$

$$V_{2L+1}(x) = V_{2L+2}(x) = 0$$

(6.8-7)

The motivation behind this definition is that, because of (6.8-6), $V_1(x_j) = [(2L + 1)/2]b_j$.   Our object is to derive a recurrence relation for $V_k(x)$ which will enable us to calculate $V_L(x)$, $V_{L-1}(x)$, $\ldots$, $V_1(x)$. As we shall see, this relation may be used to calculate the a_j's as well as the b_j's.   Such a recurrence relation is

$$\bar{f}_k \sin x + 2 \cos x V_{k+1}(x) - V_{k+2}(x)$$

$$= \bar{f}_k \sin x + \sum_{i=k+1}^{2L} \bar{f}_i[2 \cos x \sin (i - k)x - \sin (i - k - 1)x]$$

$$= \bar{f}_k \sin x + \sum_{i=k+1}^{2L} \bar{f}_i \sin (i - k + 1)x = V_k(x) \quad (6.8\text{-}8)$$

where the last line follows from the identity

$$\sin nx = 2 \sin (n - 1)x \cos x - \sin (n - 2)x \tag{6.8-9}$$

The left-hand side of the recurrence (6.8-8) requires two multiplications at each step.   To avoid one of these we define

$$U_{kj} \sin x_j = V_k(x_j) \qquad j = 1, \ldots, 2L \tag{6.8-10}$$

and use the definition of $V_k(x)$ to write

$$U_{kj} \sin x_j = \sum_{i=k}^{2L} \bar{f}_i \sin (i - k + 1)x_j \qquad \begin{matrix} k = 1, \ldots, 2L \\ j = 1, \ldots, 2L \end{matrix} \tag{6.8-11}$$

$$U_{2L+1,j} = U_{2L+2,j} = 0$$

Then we may rewrite the recurrence relation (6.8-8) as

$$U_{kj} = \bar{f}_k + 2 \cos x_j U_{k+1,j} - U_{k+2,j} \tag{6.8-12}$$

Using (6.8-12) we may, for any j, calculate U_{kj} starting with $k = 2L$, using the initial conditions in (6.8-11) and calculating successively $U_{2L,j}$, $U_{2L-1,j}$, $\ldots$, U_{1j}.   From (6.8-11) we have

$$U_{1j} \sin x_j = \sum_{i=1}^{2L} \bar{f}_i \sin ix_j = \sum_{i=1}^{2L} \bar{f}_i \sin \frac{2\pi ij}{2L + 1}$$

$$= \sum_{i=1}^{2L} \bar{f}_i \sin jx_i = \frac{2L + 1}{2} b_j \quad (6.8\text{-}13)$$

Therefore,

$$b_j = \frac{2}{2L + 1} U_{1j} \sin \frac{2\pi j}{2L + 1} \tag{6.8-14}$$

Also from (6.8-11) we have

$$(\bar{f}_0 + U_{1j} \cos x_j - U_{2j}) \sin x_j$$

$$= \bar{f}_0 \sin x_j + \sum_{i=1}^{2L} \bar{f}_i [\sin ix_j \cos x_j - \sin (i - 1)x_j]$$

$$= \bar{f}_0 \sin x_j + \sum_{i=1}^{2L} \bar{f}_i \cos ix_j \sin x_j$$

$$= \left(\sum_{i=0}^{2L} \bar{f}_i \cos ix_j \right) \sin x_j = \left(\sum_{i=0}^{2L} \bar{f}_i \cos jx_i \right) \sin x_j$$

$$= \frac{2L + 1}{2} a_j \sin x_j \tag{6.8-15}$$

so that

$$a_j = \frac{2}{2L + 1} \left(\bar{f}_0 + U_{1j} \cos \frac{2\pi j}{2L + 1} - U_{2j} \right) \tag{6.8-16}$$

Although the above derivation was for values of j from 1 to $2L$, it is not hard to show that, if (6.8-12) is used with the initial conditions (6.8-11) for $j = 0$, then (6.8-16) correctly gives a_0. Thus using (6.8-12), (6.8-14), and (6.8-16), we may calculate all the a_j's and b_j's. This algorithm is efficient as well as convenient. To calculate U_{2j} and U_{1j} using (6.8-12) requires about $2L$ multiplications and $4L$ additions for each j (why?), which is, because of (6.8-14) and (6.8-16), the approximate number of additions and multiplications required to calculate a_j and b_j. In contrast, the use of (6.8-5) and (6.8-6) requires $4L$ multiplications and additions for a_j and b_j.

Although calculation of the a_j's and b_j's using (6.8-14) and (6.8-16) requires knowledge of $\sin [2\pi j/(2L + 1)]$ and $\cos [2\pi j/(2L + 1)]$, $j = 1$, $\ldots$, m, this does not in fact mean that we must calculate each of these values of the sine and cosine using the appropriate trigonometric subroutine. Instead we calculate only $\sin [2\pi/(2L + 1)]$ and $\cos [2\pi/(2L + 1)]$ using the subroutine and then use the recurrence relations [where θ denotes $2\pi/(2L + 1)$]

$$\begin{aligned} \sin (j + 1)\theta &= \sin j\theta \cos \theta + \cos j\theta \sin \theta \\ \cos (j + 1)\theta &= \cos j\theta \cos \theta - \sin j\theta \sin \theta \end{aligned} \qquad j = 1, \ldots, m - 1$$

$$\tag{6.8-17}$$

These same relations may of course be used to calculate the sines and cosines needed in (6.8-5) and (6.8-6).

The results of Sec. 6.3 can be applied to approximations of the form (6.8-4) just as they were to polynomial approximations. In particular, we may calculate

$$\delta_m^2 = \sum_{i=0}^{2L} \left\{ \bar{f}_i - \left[\frac{1}{2} a_0 + \sum_{j=1}^{m} (a_j \cos jx_i + b_j \sin jx_i) \right] \right\}^2$$

$$= \sum_{i=0}^{2L} \bar{f}_i^2 - \frac{2L+1}{2} \left[\frac{a_0^2}{2} + \sum_{j=1}^{m} (a_j^2 + b_j^2) \right] \quad (6.8\text{-}18)$$

by making use of the orthogonality relations (6.8-1) to (6.8-3) {28}. Also we may use the techniques of Sec. 6.6 to estimate the accuracy of the coefficients {30}.

Example 6.2   Use the data in the following table:

x_i:	0	$2\pi/9$	$4\pi/9$	$2\pi/3$	$8\pi/9$	$10\pi/9$	$4\pi/3$	$14\pi/9$	$16\pi/9$
$\bar{f}_i$:	3.0004	5.7203	3.1993	-1.0981	$-.8679$	2.9890	4.0985	1.1477	$-.1882$

to calculate Fourier least-squares approximations with $m = 1, 2, 3$.

We have

$$\sin \frac{2\pi}{9} = .64279$$

$$\cos \frac{2\pi}{9} = .76604$$

Using (6.8-17) we get

$$\sin \frac{4\pi}{9} = .98481 \qquad \cos \frac{4\pi}{9} = .17364$$

$$\sin \frac{2\pi}{3} = .86602 \qquad \cos \frac{2\pi}{3} = -.50001$$

Then using (6.8-12) we calculate

$$U_{10} = 51.41730 \qquad U_{20} = 36.41670$$
$$U_{11} = -.00200 \qquad U_{21} = -1.50102$$
$$U_{12} = 13.70810 \qquad U_{22} = 5.38018$$
$$U_{13} = .00008 \qquad U_{23} = 2.99912$$

Finally, from (6.8-14) and (6.8-16) we get

$$a_0 = 4.00022$$
$$a_1 = .99998 \qquad b_1 = .00029$$
$$a_2 = .00011 \qquad b_2 = 2.99997$$
$$a_3 = .00023 \qquad b_3 = .00002$$

Using the second equality in (6.8-18) we calculate

$$\delta_0^2 = 44.99932$$
$$\delta_1^2 = 40.49950$$
$$\delta_2^2 = .00031$$
$$\delta_3^2 = .00031$$

To find the value of m which results in the best least-squares approximation, we would generally use (6.3-10) with $2(L - m)$ in the denominator (why?). In this example, however, it is clear—as indeed the coefficients a_i and b_i indicated—that $m = 2$ gives the desired least-squares approximation. In fact, the data in the table are slightly perturbed values of $f(x) = 2 + \cos x + 3 \sin 2x$. The techniques of Sec. 6.6 may be used to get estimates of the accuracy of the coefficients as before {30}.

6.8-1   Trigonometric interpolation

We have noted that a least-squares approximation in which the number of functions used equals the number of data points results in an exact approximation. In particular, in the polynomial case, we get the Lagrangian interpolation formula. When our approximating functions are the trigonometric functions, we get a formula for trigonometric interpolation. In common with our approach to interpolation in Chap. 3, we shall assume in this section that the given functional values are exact (except perhaps for some roundoff error).

When $m = L$, Eq. (6.8-4) becomes the discrete Fourier series for the function defined by the set of values $\{f_i\}$

$$y_L(x) = \tfrac{1}{2}a_0 + \sum_{j=1}^{L} (a_j \cos jx + b_j \sin jx) \tag{6.8-19}$$

with the a_j's and b_j's again given by (6.8-5) and (6.8-6). Now, however, δ_L^2 as given by (6.8-18) is zero. To prove this we substitute (6.8-5) and (6.8-6) into (6.8-19) to get

$$y_L(x) = \frac{2}{2L + 1} \sum_{i=0}^{2L} f_i \left[\frac{1}{2} + \sum_{j=1}^{L} (\cos jx_i \cos jx + \sin jx_i \sin jx) \right]$$

$$= \frac{2}{2L + 1} \sum_{i=0}^{2L} f_i \left[\frac{1}{2} + \sum_{j=1}^{L} \cos j(x_i - x) \right] \tag{6.8-20}$$

We wish to show that $y_L(x_k) = f_k$. First we note that

$$\cos j(x_i - x_k) = \cos \frac{2\pi}{2L + 1} j(i - k)$$

$$= \cos \left[\frac{2\pi}{2L + 1} (i - k)(2L + 1 - j) \right]$$

$$= \cos [(2L + 1 - j)(x_i - x_k)] \tag{6.8-21}$$

Using this we rewrite (6.8-20) at $x = x_k$ as

$$
\begin{aligned}
y_L(x_k) &= \frac{2}{2L+1} \sum_{i=0}^{2L} f_i \left[\frac{1}{2} + \frac{1}{2} \sum_{j=1}^{L} \cos j(x_i - x_k) \right. \\
&\qquad\qquad\qquad \left. + \frac{1}{2} \sum_{j=L+1}^{2L} \cos j(x_i - x_k) \right] \\
&= \frac{1}{2L+1} \sum_{i=0}^{2L} f_i \sum_{j=0}^{2L} \cos j(x_i - x_k)
\end{aligned}
\tag{6.8-22}
$$

But using (6.8-1) and (6.8-2) we may show that {31}

$$
\sum_{j=0}^{2L} \cos j(x_i - x_k) = \begin{cases} 2L+1 & i = k \\ 0 & i \neq k \end{cases}
\tag{6.8-23}
$$

from which it follows that in (6.8-22)

$$
y_L(x_k) = f_k
\tag{6.8-24}
$$

as we wished to prove.

Equation (6.8-19) or, equivalently, (6.8-20) is an equation for trigonometric interpolation which agrees with the observed data at $x = x_i$, $i = 0, \ldots, 2L$ and can be used to interpolate at values of $x \neq x_i$. In the form (6.8-20) the formula is the trigonometric analog to the Lagrangian interpolation formula in the polynomial case. The coefficient of f_i

$$
\frac{2}{2L+1} \left[\frac{1}{2} + \sum_{j=1}^{L} \cos j(x_i - x) \right]
\tag{6.8-25}
$$

is therefore the trigonometric analog of the Lagrangian interpolation polynomial $l_j(x)$. By suitably manipulating the term in brackets in (6.8-25), we may show that {31}

$$
\frac{1}{2} + \sum_{j=1}^{L} \cos j(x_i - x) = \frac{\sin (L + \frac{1}{2})(x_i - x)}{2 \sin \frac{1}{2}(x_i - x)}
\tag{6.8-26}
$$

and thus (6.8-20) may be written

$$
y_L(x) = \frac{1}{2L+1} \sum_{i=0}^{2L} \frac{\sin (L + \frac{1}{2})(x_i - x)}{\sin \frac{1}{2}(x_i - x)} f_i
\tag{6.8-27}
$$

In contrast to the polynomial case, we cannot derive any very useful closed form for the error in the approximation (6.8-27); see, however, {32} for one expression for the error.

BIBLIOGRAPHIC NOTES

There is a wide literature on methods for fitting curves to numerical data. For a general reference covering the subject matter of this chapter as well as the statistical background and many related subjects we recommend Guest (1961).

6.1–6.2   Most numerical analysis texts contain some material on least-squares approximation; in particular, see Hildebrand (1956) and Hamming (1962). The former also includes a good deal of material on least-squares approximations over continuous intervals. Davis (1963) and Rice (1964) consider least-squares approximation in the context of linear spaces; the latter also considers discrete least-squares approximations and the problem of minimizing (6.2-4).

6.3   Much of the material from this section is from Forsythe (1957). For more information on the ill condition of Hilbert matrix, see Todd (1954). Guest (1961) discusses methods for the solution of the normal equations; see also Chap. 9.

6.4   Guest (1961) has an excellent chapter on the generation and use of orthogonal polynomials in least-squares approximations. Another good source is the paper by Birge and Weinberg (1947); see also Forsythe (1957) and Aitken (1932). The derivation of the Gram polynomials is given by Hildebrand (1956). These polynomials have been tabulated by De Lury (1950).

6.6   Most of the material in this section is from Guest (1961). Hildebrand (1956) also treats errors in least-squares approximations; see also Lewis (1947).

6.7   Most of the material in this section is from Hildebrand (1956). Table 6.3 was given originally by Spencer (1904) and has been used by other authors. Whittaker and Robinson (1940) discuss a number of smoothing techniques. For an interesting smoothing technique see Rhodes (1921).

6.8   The computational algorithm is due to Goertzel (1958). For a much fuller discussion of the numerical analysis of periodic functions, see Hamming (1962). A good discussion of trigonometric interpolation may be found in Lanczos (1956); see also Lanczos (1938). The standard text on the subject of trigonometric series in general is Zygmund (1952).

BIBLIOGRAPHY

Aitken, A. C. (1932): On the Graduation of Data by the Orthogonal Polynomials of Least Squares, *Proc. Roy. Soc. Edinburgh*, vol. 53, pp. 54–78.

Birge, R. T., and J. W. Weinberg (1947): Least Squares Fitting of Data by Means of Polynomials, *Rev. Mod. Phys.*, vol. 19, pp. 298–360.

Davis, P. J. (1963): *Interpolation and Approximation*, Blaisdell Publishing Company, New York.

De Lury, D. B. (1950): *Values and Integrals of Orthogonal Polynomials Up to n = 26*, University of Toronto Press, Toronto, Canada.

Forsythe, G. E. (1957): Generation and Use of Orthogonal Polynomials for Data-fitting on a Digital Computer, *J. Soc. Indust. Appl. Math.*, vol. 5, pp. 74–88.

Goertzel, G. (1958): An Algorithm for the Evaluation of Finite Trigonometric Series, *Amer. Math. Monthly*, vol. 65, pp. 34–35.

Guest, P. G. (1961): *Numerical Methods of Curve Fitting*, Cambridge University Press, New York.

Hamming, R. W. (1962): *Numerical Methods for Scientists and Engineers*, McGraw-Hill Book Company, New York.

Hildebrand, F. B. (1956): *Introduction to Numerical Analysis*, McGraw-Hill Book Company, New York.

Lanczos, C. (1938): Trigonometric Interpolation of Empirical and Analytic Functions, *J. Math. and Phys.*, vol. 17, pp. 123–199.

Lanczos, C. (1956): *Applied Analysis*, Prentice-Hall, Inc., Englewood Cliffs, N.J.

Lewis, D. C. (1947): Polynomial Least Square Approximation, *Amer. J. Math.*, vol. 69, pp. 273–278.

Rhodes, E. C. (1921): *Smoothing*, Tracts for Computers, VI, Cambridge University Press, New York.

Rice, J. R. (1964): *The Approximation of Functions*, vol. 1, Addison-Wesley Publishing Company, Inc., Reading, Mass.

Savage, I. R., and E. Lukacs (1954): Tables of Inverses of Finite Segments of the Hilbert Matrix in *Contributions to the Solution of Systems of Linear Equations and the Determination of Eigenvalues* (O. Taussky, ed.), vol. 39, National Bureau of Standards Applied Mathematics Series.

Shannon, C. E. (1949): Communication in the Presence of Noise, *Proc. I.R.E.*, vol. 37, pp. 10–21.

Spencer, J. (1904): On the Graduation of the Rate of Sickness and Mortality Presented by the Experience of the Manchester Unity of Oddfellows during the Period 1893–1897, *J. Inst. Actuar.*, vol. 38, pp. 334–343.

Todd, J. (1954): The Condition of Finite Segments of the Hilbert Matrix in *Contributions to the Solution of Systems of Linear Equations and the Determination of Eigenvalues* (O. Taussky, ed.), vol. 39, National Bureau of Standards Applied Mathematics Series.

Whittaker, E. T., and G. Robinson (1940): *The Calculus of Observations*, 3d ed., Blackie & Son, Ltd., Glasgow.

Wilks, S. S. (1962): *Mathematical Statistics*, rev. ed., John Wiley & Sons, Inc., New York.

Zygmund, A. (1952): *Trigonometric Series*, 2d ed., Chelsea Publishing Company, New York.

PROBLEMS

Section 6.2

1. Given the data

x_i:	-1.00	$-.75$	$-.50$	$-.25$	0	$.25$	$.50$	$.75$	1.00
$\bar{f}_i$:	$-.2209$	$.3295$	$.8826$	1.4392	2.0003	2.5645	3.1334	3.7061	4.2836

calculate the coefficients in the normal equations for $m = 3, 4, 5$ with (a) $\phi_j(x) = x^i$; (b) $\phi_j(x) = P_j(x)$, the Legendre polynomial of degree j.   Use $w(x) = 1$.

Section 6.3

*2. Let $\mathbf{v}$ be a column vector such that $\mathbf{v}^T = (v_1, \ldots, v_n)$ where T denotes the transpose.   Define the norm of $\mathbf{v}$ to be $\|\mathbf{v}\| = (v_1^2 + v_2^2 + \cdots + v_n^2)^{1/2}$.

(a) Show that the least-squares problem for polynomials with $w(x) = 1$ may be written in the form

$$\|\mathbf{f} - Q\mathbf{a}^{(m)}\|^2 = \text{minimum}$$

where $\mathbf{f}^T = (f_1, \ldots, f_n)$, $\mathbf{a}^{(m)T} = [a_0^{(m)}, \ldots, a_m^{(m)}]$ and Q is an $n \times m + 1$ matrix with columns $\mathbf{q}_j = (x_1^j, x_2^j, \ldots, x_n^j)$, $j = 0, \ldots, m$.

(b) If $n > m$ and $\mathbf{c}$ is a column vector with $m + 1$ components, show that

$$\mathbf{c}^T Q^T Q \mathbf{c} \geq 0$$

with the equality holding only if $\mathbf{c} = \mathbf{0}$.

(c) Show that the minimum problem of part a is equivalent to minimizing

$$[\mathbf{a}^{(m)} - G^{-1}\mathbf{g}]^T G[\mathbf{a}^{(m)} - G^{-1}\mathbf{g}] + \mathbf{f}^T\mathbf{f} - \mathbf{g}^T(G^{-1})^T\mathbf{g}$$

where $G = Q^T Q$ and $\mathbf{g} = Q^T\mathbf{f}$.

(d) Use this result and part b to show that

$$\mathbf{a}^{(m)} = G^{-1}Q^T\mathbf{f}$$

is the unique solution of the minimum problem.   [Ref.: Forsythe (1957).]

3. (a) If the set of points $\{x_i\}$ are symmetrically placed with respect to zero, show that the system of normal equations (6.3-4) can be "decoupled" into two sets of equations with $(m + 1)/2$ equations in each set if m is odd and $m/2$ and $(m/2) + 1$ equations in the two sets if m is even.

(b) Display these two sets of equations for the normal equations derived in Prob. 1a.

(c) Can the systems derived in Prob. 1b be decoupled?   What is the general rule?

*4. A theorem of Cauchy states that if $a_1, \ldots, a_n, b_1, \ldots, b_n$ are $2n$ numbers, the determinant with elements $(a_i + b_k)^{-1}$, $i = 1, \ldots, n$, $k = 1, \ldots, n$ has the value

$$\left| \frac{1}{a_i + b_k} \right| = \frac{\displaystyle\prod_{i>k=1}^{n} (a_i - a_k)(b_i - b_k)}{\displaystyle\prod_{i=1}^{n} \prod_{k=1}^{n} (a_i + b_k)}$$

(a) Use this theorem to show that Δ_n, the determinant of H_n, is given by

$$\Delta_n = \frac{\left(\displaystyle\prod_{k=1}^{n-1} k!\right)^2}{n^n \displaystyle\prod_{k=1}^{n-1} (n^2 - k^2)^{n-k}}$$

(b) If Δ_n^{ij} is the minor of the element in the ith row and jth column of H_n, show that

$$\Delta_n^{ij} = \frac{(n + i - 1)!(n + j - 1)!}{[(i - 1)!(j - 1)!]^2 n!(n - i)!(n - j)!} \frac{\left(\displaystyle\prod_{k=1}^{n-1} k!\right)^3}{\displaystyle\prod_{k=1}^{n-1} (n + k)!} \frac{1}{i + j - 1}$$

(c) Use induction to show that

$$\frac{n^n}{n!} \prod_{k=1}^{n-1} \frac{(n^2 - k^2)^{n-k} k!}{(n + k)!} = 1$$

(d) Use the results of parts a, b, and c to show that h_n^{ij}, the element in the ith row and jth column of H_n^{-1}, is given by

$$h_n^{ij} = \frac{(-1)^{i+j}}{i + j - 1} \frac{(n + i - 1)!(n + j - 1)!}{[(i - 1)!(j - 1)!]^2(n - i)!(n - j)!}$$

(e) Use this result to show that

$$h_{n+1}^{ij} = \frac{(n + i)(n + j)}{(n + 1 - i)(n + 1 - j)} h_n^{ij} \qquad i, j = 1, \ldots, n$$

$$h_{n+1}^{n+1,j} = h_{n+1}^{j,n+1} = \frac{(-1)^{n+j+1}}{(n + j)} \frac{(2n + 1)!(n + j)!}{[n!(j - 1)!]^2(n + 1 - j)!}$$

(f) Use the results of part e to calculate H_n^{-1}, $n = 2, 3, 4, 5$. [Ref.: Savage and Lukacs (1954).]

5. Using equations derived in Prob. 1, compute the coefficients of the least-squares approximations for $m = 3, 4, 5$ for the case $\phi_j(x) = x^j$. Use any technique to solve the normal equations. Also calculate the determinant of the coefficients in the normal equations (see Probs. 16 and 20).

6. (a) Repeat the calculations of the previous problem for the case $\phi_j(x) = P_j(x)$.

(b) Convert the Legendre polynomial approximations to the form of approximations in powers of x. Compare the coefficients with those found in the previous problem. How do you account for the differences? Which coefficients do you expect to be more accurate? Why? (See Probs. 16 and 20.)

Section 6.4

7. (a) Show that

$$\Delta(u_i v_i) = u_i \, \Delta v_i + v_{i+1} \, \Delta u_i$$

(b) Use this to derive the formula for summation by parts (6.4-14).
(c) Derive also the alternative formula

$$\sum_{i=R}^{S} u_i \, \Delta v_i = u_{i-1} v_i \Big|_R^{S+1} - \sum_{i=R}^{S} v_i \, \Delta u_{i-1}$$

8. (a) Use the series expansions for $(1 + x)^p$ and $(1 + x)^m$ to derive the identity

$$\binom{m + p}{n} = \sum_{k=0}^{n} \binom{p}{k}\binom{m}{n - k} = \sum_{k=0}^{n} \binom{p}{n - k}\binom{m}{k}$$

(b) If we define

$$\binom{-p}{q} = \frac{(-p)^{(q)}}{q!}$$

where p and q are positive integers, show that

$$\binom{-p}{q} = (-1)^q \binom{p + q - 1}{q}$$

(c) Use the results of parts a and b to derive the identity

$$\binom{m - p}{n} = \sum_{k=0}^{n} (-1)^k \binom{p + k - 1}{k} \binom{m}{n - k}$$

$$= \sum_{k=0}^{n} (-1)^{n+k} \binom{p + n - k - 1}{n - k} \binom{m}{k}$$

*9. (a) Use the result of the previous problem to show that

$$(i - N - 1)^{(i)} = (-1)^i j! \sum_{k=0}^{j} (-1)^k \binom{N - k}{j - k} \binom{i - j}{k}$$

(b) Derive the relation

$$(i)^{(n)}(i - n)^{(k)} = (i)^{(n+k)}$$

(c) Use the results of parts a and b and (6.4-21) to show that

$$U_j(i,N) = (-1)^i j! A_{jN} \sum_{k=0}^{j} \frac{(-1)^k}{k!} \binom{N - k}{j - k} i^{(i+k)}$$

(d) Then with $w(x) = 1$ use (6.4-12) to derive

$$p_j(i,N) = (-1)^i j! A_{jN} \sum_{k=0}^{j} (-1)^k \frac{(j + k)^{(i)}}{k!} \binom{N - k}{j - k} i^{(k)}$$

and from this derive (6.4-22).

10. Use the results of Prob. 8 and the previous problem to show that $p_j(N,N) = 1$ if B_{jN} as defined in (6.4-23) equals $(-1)^i$.

*11. (a) If we define $\gamma_j(N) = \sum_{j=0}^{n} w_i[p_j(i,N)]^2$, show that

$$\gamma_j(N) = (-1)^i j! c_j \sum_{i=0}^{N} U_j(i + j, N)$$

where c_j is the coefficient of i^j in $p_j(i,N)$ and U_j is as defined in (6.4-12).

(b) Use this result and summation by parts to show that when $w(x) = 1$

$$\sum_{i=0}^{N} [p_j(i,N)]^2 = \frac{(-1)^i (2j)!}{[j! N^{(j)}]^2} \sum_{i=0}^{N} (j + i)^{(j)}(j + i - N - 1)^{(j)}$$

$$= \frac{1}{[N^{(j)}]^2} \sum_{i=0}^{N} (j + i)^{(2j)}$$

(c) Finally use this result to derive (6.4-31).

12. (a) Use (6.4-25) to show that ϵ_j in Table 6.1 is as given in (6.4-47). (b) Using an argument based on symmetry, show that in the recurrence relation for the Gram polynomials $\alpha_{j+1} = 0$. (c) Use these results to derive (6.4-46) and (6.4-47). (d) Use (6.4-46) to verify the entries in Table 6.1.

*13. (a) Prove that any polynomial of degree j satisfying the orthogonality relationship (6.4-5) with $w_i \geqq 0$ for all i has j distinct zeros interior to the interval spanned by the points $\{x_i\}$.

(b) Show that, if $p_j^{(n)}(x)$, $j = 0, 1, \ldots, n$ are a set of polynomials of degree j satisfying (6.4-5), then $p_n^{(n)}(x_i) = 0$, $i = 1, \ldots, n$.

14. (a) Let $p_j(s,2L) = \displaystyle\sum_{k=1}^{j} \delta_{jk}s^k$, $j = 1, \ldots, J$ be a sequence of polynomials orthogonal over a set of $2L$ points $\{s_i\}$ with respect to a weight function $w(x)$. Show how the Gram-Schmidt orthogonalization procedure can be used to generate $p_{J+1}(s,2L)$ using the base function s^{J+1}. Compare the usefulness of this and the recurrence-relation technique of Sec. 6.4.

(b) Use the recurrence-relation technique to generate polynomials through degree 4 orthogonal over the set of points $x_i = .1i$, $i = 4, \ldots, 10$.

*15. (a) Use induction to prove that if s in $p_j(s,2L)$ as given by (6.4-25) is replaced by sL, then

$$\lim_{L \to \infty} p_j(sL,2L) = P_j(s)$$

(b) Use this result to derive the equations analogous to (6.4-28) to (6.4-31) for the continuous least-squares approximation to $f(x)$ over the interval $[-1,1]$ with a weight function $w(x) = 1$.

16. (a) Use the data of Prob. 1 and orthogonal polynomials generated using (6.4-46) to generate a least-squares approximation for $m = 1, 2, 3, 4, 5$. Express the approximations as sums of powers of x. Compare these results with those of Probs. 5 and 6 and discuss the differences.

(b) From these results which, if any, of these values of m would you choose to be M in (6.2-7)? (See Prob. 20.)

Sections 6.5, 6.6

17. Solve the system (6.3-4) with $m = 4$ for the data of Sec. 6.5 using any method and carrying (a) six decimal places; (b) eight decimal places. In both cases substitute the results back into the system of equations to see how well they satisfy the system.

18. For the data of Sec. 6.5

(a) Use a Lagrangian five-point formula (see Sec. 4.1) to differentiate the data numerically at $x = .3, .4, .5, .6, .7$. In each case center the Lagrangian formula at the point at which the derivative is to be calculated.

(b) Calculate the derivatives at these points using the least-squares approximation (6.5-8).

(c) Calculate the derivatives using the true function (6.5-9). Compare these results with those of parts a and b and discuss the reasons for the errors.

19. (a) Use (6.5-1) to convert the polynomials in (6.5-2) to powers of x.

(b) Use (6.6-8) to compute the standard deviations of the errors in the coefficients of (6.5-8). (Use the estimate of σ^2 found in Example 6.1.)

(c) Why are the estimates calculated in part b very conservative? What general rule can you state about converting an approximation in s to one in x when the interval of the data in x is small (cf. Prob. 21)?

20. (*a*) Calculate the standard deviations of the errors in the coefficients found in Prob. 16 for $m = 3$. Assume you have no estimate of σ^2.

(*b*) If the true function is

$$f(x) = e^{\frac{1}{4}x} + 2x + 1$$

are the errors within expected bounds?

(*c*) Repeat parts a and b using the coefficients of powers of x calculated in Prob. 6 for $m = 3$.

21. Given the data

x_i:	.4	.5	.6	.7	.8	.9	1.0
$\bar{f}_i$:	$-.9435$	$-.9996$	$-.9362$	$-.7284$	$-.3517$	.2164	.9998

(*a*) Make an appropriate change of variable and then use the Gram polynomials to find the best least-squares orthogonal polynomial approximation to these data.

(*b*) Use the orthogonal polynomials generated in Prob. 14b to find the best least-squares approximation to these data.

(*c*) Calculate the residuals at the data points using the approximations of parts a and b. Which approximation appears to be better? Did you expect this? Why?

(*d*) Using the approximation of part a, calculate the standard deviations of the coefficient errors. If the true function is $f(x) = T_3(x)$, are your estimates within expected limits?

22. (*a*) Use Table 6.1 to derive relations of the form (6.6-15) in terms of L (where the number of points is $2L + 1$) for the powers of s through s^4. (*b*) Use these results to verify (6.6-15).

Section 6.7

23. Derive formulas for smoothing data at the tabular points for (*a*) $m = 1$, $n = 7$; (*b*) $m = 3$, $n = 5$; (*c*) $m = 3$, $n = 7$; (*d*) $m = 5$, $n = 7$. [Ref.: Hildebrand (1956), pp. 295–296.]

24. (*a*) Express the smoothed values in (6.7-3) as the sum of the value at the corresponding data point plus a multiple of the second central difference of $\bar{f}(s)$ at $s = 0$.

(*b*) Do the same for the formulas of parts b and d of the previous problem using fourth and sixth differences, respectively. [Ref.: Hildebrand (1956), pp. 295–296.]

*25. (*a*) Let $\{\bar{f}_i\}$ be a set of n data points as in Table 6.3. Let $\{y_i^{(1)}\}$ be the points that result from applying m-point ($m < n$) linear smoothing to $\{\bar{f}_i\}$. In general, let $\{y_i^{(k+1)}\}$ be the result of m-point linear smoothing applied to $\{y_i^{(k)}\}$. Prove that $\{y_i^{(k)}\}$ converges and that in the limit all the points lie on one straight line. Is this the same straight line they would lie on if n-point linear smoothing were applied once?

(*b*) Apply five-point least-squares smoothing to the data in the last column of Table 6.3 once more and note how close the final result is to linearity.

26. (*a*) Use the data of Prob. 21 and the results of Prob. 23c to compute smoothed values at the data points.

(*b*) Using $f(x) = T_3(x)$ compute the residuals given by these values and compare them with those computed in Prob. 21c.

Section 6.8

27. (*a*) With $x_i = 2\pi i/(2L + 1)$ show that

$$\cos kx_i = \cos (2L + 1 - k)x_i$$
$$\sin kx_i = -\sin (2L + 1 - k)x_i$$

(b) Thus deduce that for any $k > L$, $\cos kx_i$ and $\sin kx_i$, $i = 0, \ldots, 2L$ may be expressed in terms of, respectively, $\cos jx_i$ and $\sin jx_i$ for $j \leq L$.

28. (a) Derive the result

$$\sum_{k=0}^{2L} e^{ik\alpha} = \begin{cases} e^{i\alpha L} \dfrac{\sin (L + \frac{1}{2})\alpha}{\sin \alpha/2} & \alpha \neq 2\pi\nu \\ 2L + 1 & \alpha = 2\pi\nu \end{cases}$$

where ν is any integer.

(b) Deduce from this that

$$\sum_{k=0}^{2L} \cos k\alpha = \begin{cases} \dfrac{\cos L\alpha \sin (L + \frac{1}{2})\alpha}{\sin \alpha/2} & \alpha \neq 2\pi\nu \\ 2L + 1 & \alpha = 2\pi\nu \end{cases}$$

$$\sum_{k=0}^{2L} \sin k\alpha = \frac{\sin L\alpha \sin (L + \frac{1}{2})\alpha}{\sin \alpha/2}$$

(c) Then letting $\alpha = 2\pi j/(2L + 1)$ deduce that

$$\sum_{k=0}^{2L} \cos jx_k = \begin{cases} 0 & j \neq \nu(2L + 1) \\ 2L + 1 & j = \nu(2L + 1) \end{cases}$$

$$\sum_{k=0}^{2L} \sin jx_k = 0$$

where $x_k = 2\pi k/(2L + 1)$.

(d) Use these results and the identities for the products of two sines, two cosines, and one sine and one cosine to derive (6.8-1) to (6.8-3) and (6.8-18).

29. (a) Derive the relations corresponding to (6.8-1) to (6.8-3) when the number of points n is even.

(b) Derive the relations corresponding to (6.8-5), (6.8-6), and (6.8-18) when n is even.

(c) When n is even consider replacing the L in (6.8-19) by $L - 1$ and adding a term $\frac{1}{2}a_L \cos Lx$. Find an expression for a_L analogous to (6.8-5). Why is it not reasonable to add a term in $\sin Lx$?

***30.** (a) Derive the relations corresponding to (6.6-4) for the coefficients a_j and b_j in (6.8-4).

(b) Derive the estimate of σ^2 corresponding to (6.6-14).

(c) Use these results to get estimates of the accuracy of the coefficients in Example 6.2.

***31.** (a) Verify (6.8-23) and from this deduce (6.8-24). (b) Derive (6.8-26) and thus deduce (6.8-27). (c) Derive the analog of (6.8-27) when the number of points is even. [Ref.: Hamming (1962), pp. 280–283.]

***32.** (a) Show that the error $\epsilon_L = f(x) - y_L(x)$ in the approximation (6.8-27) may be expressed in the form

$$\epsilon_L = \frac{1}{2L + 1} \sum_{i=0}^{2L} \frac{\sin (L + \frac{1}{2})(x_i - x)}{\sin \frac{1}{2}(x_i - x)} [f(x) - f_i]$$

(b) Deduce from this that, particularly if $f(x)$ does not change rapidly, the major contribution to the error comes from the term or terms with x_i nearest to x. [Ref.: Hamming (1962), pp. 280–283.]

33. (a) Suppose $f(x)$ is a periodic function of period 2π. Show that the coefficients of the discrete Fourier expansion, (6.8-5) and (6.8-6), are what would be obtained if the trapezoidal rule were used to approximate the coefficients of the continuous Fourier series for $f(x)$ on $[0,2\pi]$.

(b) Show that for any periodic function the trapezoidal-rule correction terms in the Euler-Maclaurin sum formula drop out if the interval of integration is a multiple of the period. Does this indicate that the trapezoidal rule is exact for periodic functions? Why? [Ref.: Hildebrand (1956), p. 375.]

34. Given the data

x_i:	0	$2\pi/7$	$4\pi/7$	$6\pi/7$	$8\pi/7$	$10\pi/7$	$12\pi/7$
$\bar{f}_i$:	1.0004	−.1190	1.5987	.2115	−.6567	−.3514	−1.6824

(a) Find the best least-squares Fourier approximation to these data. (b) Calculate the residuals at the data points. (c) With $m = 3$ calculate δ_m^2 using both forms of (6.8-18), and discuss the difference.

35. (a) Use (6.8-4) to (6.8-6) to derive an equation analogous to (6.7-2).

(b) Use this result to derive smoothing formulas for (i) $m = 1$, $n = 5$; (ii) $m = 1$, $n = 7$. Why doesn't it make sense to derive a smoothing formula for $m = 1$, $n = 3$ or $m = 3$, $n = 7$?

36. (a) Why doesn't it make sense to use either of the formulas of the previous problem to smooth the data of Prob. 34?

(b) Compute smoothed values at the data points of Prob. 34 using the least-squares approximation calculated in that problem.

37. Let $f(x)$ be a function whose discrete Fourier series $y_L(x)$ corresponding to a set of values $\{\bar{f}_i\}$, $i = 0, \ldots, 2L$ is given by (6.8-19). Let the continuous Fourier-series expansion of the observed function $\bar{f}(x)$ on $[0,2\pi]$ be given by

$$\bar{f}(x) = \tfrac{1}{2}A_0 + \sum_{j=1}^{\infty} (A_j \cos jx + B_j \sin jx)$$

(a) By summing both sides of the above equation for $x = x_i$, $i = 0, \ldots, 2L$ and using (6.8-5), prove that

$$a_0 = A_0 + 2 \sum_{j=1}^{\infty} A_{(2L+1)j}$$

(b) Now by multiplying the continuous Fourier series by, respectively, $\cos kx$ and $\sin kx$ and summing as above, prove that

$$a_k = A_k + \sum_{j=1}^{\infty} [A_{(2L+1)j-k} + A_{(2L+1)j+k}] \qquad k > 0$$

$$b_k = B_k + \sum_{j=1}^{\infty} [B_{(2L+1)j+k} - B_{(2L+1)j-k}] \qquad k > 0$$

The importance of this result is that, when the function $f(x)$ is *sampled* at the equally spaced points $\{x_i\}$, the calculated discrete Fourier series includes in its coefficients the effects of higher frequencies than the *sampling rate*. This "folding" back of the higher frequencies on the lower ones is often called "aliasing." [Ref.: Hamming (1962), pp. 278–280.]

*38. A function $f(x)$ is called band-limited if its Fourier transform

$$F(\lambda) = \int_{-\infty}^{\infty} f(t)e^{-2\pi i\lambda t}\, dt$$

vanishes outside the open interval $(-\Omega, \Omega)$.

(a) Show that, if $f(x)$ is band-limited, then

$$F(\lambda) = F_1(\lambda)P(\lambda)$$

where $F_1(\lambda)$ is periodic with period Ω and

$$P(\lambda) = \begin{cases} 1 & |\lambda| < \Omega \\ 0 & |\lambda| \geq \Omega \end{cases}$$

(b) Show that

$$F_1(\lambda) = \sum_{k=-\infty}^{\infty} c_k e^{(i\pi/\Omega)k\lambda}$$

where

$$c_k = \frac{1}{2\Omega} f\left(\frac{-k}{2\Omega}\right)$$

and thus deduce that

$$F(\lambda) = \sum_{k=-\infty}^{\infty} f\left(\frac{k}{2\Omega}\right) \frac{P(\lambda)}{2\Omega} e^{-(i\pi/\Omega)k\lambda}$$

(c) Show that $P(\lambda)$ is the Fourier transform of

$$P(x) = \frac{\sin 2\pi\Omega x}{\pi x}$$

(d) Use part c to take the inverse transform of $F(\lambda)$ in part b and thus show that

$$f(x) = \sum_{k=-\infty}^{\infty} f\left(\frac{k}{2\Omega}\right) \frac{\sin \pi(2\Omega x - k)}{\pi(2\Omega x - k)}$$

This result is known as the *sampling theorem* and is due to Shannon (1949). It implies that if $f(x)$ is sampled at equal intervals with a frequency greater than the band width Ω of the function, then the entire function can be reconstructed from this infinite set of samples. When we approximate the infinite sum above by a finite sum, we have the analog for nonperiodic functions to the approximation (6.8-27) for periodic functions. [See Hamming (1962), pp. 308–310, for a good discussion of the sampling theorem and its importance.]

chapter 7

FUNCTIONAL APPROXIMATION— MINIMUM MAXIMUM ERROR TECHNIQUES

7.1 GENERAL REMARKS

One way of evaluating a mathematical function—trigonometric, logarithmic, exponential, Bessel, etc.—on a digital computer would be to store a table of the function in the memory of the computer and to use an interpolation formula to evaluate the function at nontabulated points. But not only is this technique extremely wasteful of the memory of the computer but also it generally has no advantages in speed or accuracy over the techniques to be discussed in this chapter. These techniques all involve approximating a function $f(x)$ by a rational function.† We noted in Chap. 2 that a rational function is the most general function of a variable x that can be evaluated directly on a digital computer. But why use rational functions rather than the more familiar polynomial approximations (which are, of course, just a special case of rational functions)? To answer this we need to consider our aims in approximating functions on a computer.

The general situation is this: A computation is to be performed in which a certain mathematical function is to be evaluated many—perhaps millions—of times. It is known a priori that the arguments of this function will be in some interval (perhaps infinite), but it is not known a priori what the arguments will be. Thus the function must be approxi-

† We may, however, use a different rational function on different intervals.

mated over the entire interval. The property of this approximation of most importance to us is the error between it and the true function, an error which will vary over the interval.

Generally, in the overall computation, it is desirable to be able to bound the error in the result. To bound this error without a priori knowledge of what the numbers involved will be, we must consider the worst possible case. Thus, in an approximation to a function to be used in such a computation, the property of the error that is of most importance is the maximum error (in magnitude) on the interval.† Therefore, the major aim of a computer approximation to a function is to make the maximum error as small as possible. Our final goal in this chapter will be to develop a technique for generating a rational approximation to a function which, among all rational approximations with the same degree polynomial in numerator and denominator, has the *minimum maximum error*. We shall call such an approximation the Chebyshev or, more often, the *minimax* approximation. Before this, however, we shall develop techniques for generating good, if not minimax, approximations.

If an approximation is to be evaluated millions of times, another aim of a computer approximation must certainly be to achieve maximum speed. We shall as usual estimate the speed with which an approximation can be evaluated by considering the number of multiplications and divisions required. We shall assume as before that multiplication and division are equally time-consuming. It is important to note, however, that, while this is a good rule of thumb, on some computers division is more time-consuming than multiplication {9}. Moreover, as we noted in Sec. 1.5-5, on a few computers addition and subtraction are as or almost as time-consuming as multiplication and division, particularly in floating-point computations. Nevertheless, our conclusions based only on a consideration of multiplications and divisions will usually be valid in this case also.

The first of the above aims—minimum maximum error—is the major reason for preferring rational approximations to polynomial approximations. For a given amount of computation, rational approximations lead to smaller maximum errors than polynomial approximations for the functions most commonly approximated on a digital computer. This empirical result will be illustrated by examples in this chapter. The above assertion implies the need to compare the computation required to evaluate one rational function with that required to evaluate another rational function or a polynomial. Since the means by which rational functions are evaluated is of both interest and significance, we shall, in

---

† This also covers the case of bounding the error in $g(x) = f(x)/x$ by using $g(x)$ as the function to be approximated.

the next section, consider the computational aspects of the evaluation of rational approximations.

7.2 RATIONAL FUNCTIONS, POLYNOMIALS, AND CONTINUED FRACTIONS

Let

$$R_{mk}(x) = \frac{P_m(x)}{Q_k(x)} \qquad (7.2\text{-}1)$$

be a rational approximation to a function $f(x)$ where $P_m(x)$ and $Q_k(x)$ are polynomials of degree at most m and k, respectively. We shall call $N = m + k$ the index of $R_{mk}(x)$. The number of coefficients at our disposal in $R_{mk}(x)$ is $N + 1$ since one of the $N + 2$ coefficients in the numerator and denominator is redundant. In general it is true that the greater the index, the higher the accuracy of the approximation. Moreover, for a particular function over intervals of interest to us, all approximations with the same index, in contrast to approximation with other indices, require similar amounts of computation and achieve similar accuracy. In this section we shall consider the computational and not the accuracy aspect of rational approximations.

Let us consider first the evaluation of the polynomial

$$p_n(x) = x^n + a_{n-1}x^{n-1} + \cdots + a_1 x + a_0 \qquad (7.2\text{-}2)$$

To evaluate $p_n(x)$ by computing all the powers of x and then multiplying by the coefficients and adding would require $2n - 2$ multiplications. A much better technique is to write

$$p_n(x) = x(x(\cdots (x(x + a_{n-1}) + a_{n-2}) + \cdots + a_2) + a_1) + a_0 \qquad (7.2\text{-}3)$$

and then use Horner's rule

$$b_k = a_{k+1} + xb_{k+1} \qquad k = n - 2, \ldots, 0, -1 \qquad b_{n-1} = 1 \qquad (7.2\text{-}4)$$

from which it is easily verified that $b_{-1} = p_n(x)$. The number of multiplications required using (7.2-4) is $n - 1$. When the coefficients themselves are the result of some computation or when the polynomial is not going to be evaluated many times, the use of Eq. (7.2-4) is the recommended way to evaluate polynomials. But if $p_n(x)$ is part of a rational approximation to a function to be used in a computer subroutine, then neither of the above conditions holds. For this case, we shall now develop an algorithm which generally results in a better computational procedure than the use of (7.2-4).

By making the change of variable $y = x + (a_{n-1} - 1)/n$, we convert the polynomial $p_n(x)$ to

$$q_n(y) = y^n + y^{n-1} + b_{n-2}y^{n-2} + \cdots + b_1 y + b_0 \qquad (7.2\text{-}5)$$

If the polynomial $q_n(y)$ is divided by $(y^2 - \alpha_1)$ the result is

$$q_n(y) = (y^2 - \alpha_1)(y^{n-2} + y^{n-3} + c_{n-4}y^{n-4} + \cdots \\ + c_1 y + c_0) + \gamma_1 y + \beta_1 \qquad (7.2\text{-}6)$$

where

$$c_j = b_{j+2} + \alpha_1 c_{j+2} \qquad j = n - 4, n - 5, \ldots, 0, -1, -2 \\ c_{n-2} = c_{n-3} = 1 \qquad (7.2\text{-}7)$$

with $c_{-1} = \gamma_1$, $c_{-2} = \beta_1$. Our interest here is in γ_1. Using (7.2-7) we write {1}

$$\begin{aligned} \gamma_1 = c_{-1} &= b_1 + \alpha_1 c_1 = b_1 + \alpha_1(b_3 + \alpha_1 c_3) \\ &= b_1 + \alpha_1 b_3 + \alpha_1^2(b_5 + \alpha_1 c_5) \\ &= b_1 + \alpha_1 b_3 + \alpha_1^2 b_5 + \cdots + \alpha_1^{r-1} b_{2r-1} + \alpha_1^r \end{aligned} \qquad (7.2\text{-}8)$$

where $2r = n - 2$ if n is even and $n - 1$ if n is odd. Setting $\gamma_1 = 0$ in (7.2-8) gives us a polynomial equation for α_1. Suppose this equation has a real root. Let α_1 in (7.2-6) be this real root. Then

$$q_n(y) = (y^2 - \alpha_1)(y^{n-2} + y^{n-3} + \cdots + c_1 y + c_0) + \beta_1 \qquad (7.2\text{-}9)$$

Now consider the polynomial of degree $n - 2$ in parentheses in (7.2-9). Dividing this polynomial by $(y^2 - \alpha_2)$ and proceeding as above, we then get

$$q_n(y) = (y^2 - \alpha_1)[(y^2 - \alpha_2)(y^{n-4} + y^{n-5} + d_{n-6}y^{n-6} \\ + \cdots + d_0) + \beta_2] + \beta_1 \qquad (7.2\text{-}10)$$

if the polynomial corresponding to that in (7.2-8) has a real root α_2. Continuing in this way, if the polynomial corresponding to that in (7.2-8) has a real root at every stage, we get finally

$$q_n(y) = (\cdots \{[(\delta_n y^2 + y + \alpha_s)(y^2 - \alpha_{s-1}) + \beta_{s-1}](y^2 - \alpha_{s-2}) \\ + \beta_{s-2}\} \cdots)(y^2 - \alpha_1) + \beta_1 \qquad (7.2\text{-}11)$$

where

$$\delta_n = \begin{cases} 1 & n \text{ even} \\ 0 & n \text{ odd} \end{cases} \qquad s = \begin{cases} \dfrac{n}{2} & n \text{ even} \\ \dfrac{n+1}{2} & n \text{ odd} \end{cases} \qquad (7.2\text{-}12)$$

The algorithm to compute $p_n(x)$ is then

$$y = x + \frac{a_{n-1} - 1}{n}$$
$$z = y^2$$
$$w_s = \delta_n z + y + \alpha_s \qquad (7.2\text{-}13)$$
$$w_j = w_{j+1}(z - \alpha_j) + \beta_j \qquad j = s - 1, \ldots, 1$$

so that $w_1 = p_n(x)$. The total number of multiplications is s (one to get y^2 and $s - 1$ to calculate the w_j). Note that the initial change of variable from x to y is significant only when n is even. For without this change of variable, the $y^2 + y + \alpha_s$ term in (7.2-11) would be $y^2 + \tau y + \alpha_s$ with $\tau \neq 1$ and thus would require another multiplication. When n is odd, the leading term is of the form $y + \alpha_s$ regardless of the change of variable {3}.

Of course, the above assumes the existence of a real solution of the polynomial equation (7.2-8) obtained by setting $\gamma_1 = 0$ at each stage. At every second stage,† the degree of this polynomial is odd and a real solution exists. But when the degree is even, a real solution may not exist. If a real solution does not exist, then we may apply one step of the procedure of (7.2-3) and continue as before. For example, if the polynomial of degree $n - 2$ in (7.2-9) were such that the polynomial of (7.2-8) had no real roots, we would write (7.2-5) as

$$q_n(y) = (y^2 - \alpha_1)[y(y^{n-3} + y^{n-4} + \cdots + c_1) + c_0] + \beta_1 \quad (7.2\text{-}14)$$

and then attempt to apply this procedure to the polynomial of degree $n - 3$ in (7.2-14). After at most two steps of the type (7.2-14), the polynomial of (7.2-8) will be of odd degree {2}. The following table indicates the number of multiplications required to evaluate a polynomial by this quadratic factor algorithm as a function of its degree and compares these numbers with those obtained using Horner's rule {4}:

Degree	Quadratic factor algorithm	Horner's rule
2	1	1
3	2	2
4	2	3
5	3	4
6	3 or 4	5
7	4	6
8	4 or 5	7
9	5 or 6	8
10	5, 6 or 7	9

† If we allow complex numbers in (7.2-11) then the algorithm always works. But since each multiplication of two complex numbers requires four real multiplications, it is clearly desirable to require that all the parameters be real.

Where there is more than one entry in the second column, the number of multiplications depends on the solvability of the polynomial in (7.2-8) at each stage. While the above table indicates that the quadratic factor algorithm is superior to Horner's rule, it should be realized that in specific instances, the quadratic factor algorithm will itself not be the best possible algorithm. For example, it is possible to evaluate every polynomial of sixth degree with three multiplications {5}, but the quadratic factor algorithm will sometimes require four. Nevertheless, this algorithm does give best possible results for all polynomials of degree 2, 3, 4, 5, and 7 and for a large class of polynomials of other degrees.

The analytic effort required to express $p_n(x)$ in the form (7.2-14) becomes considerable as n increases. But it is clearly worthwhile when the polynomial in question is part of an approximation to a function which once found can be used forever. In the remainder of this section, we shall assume that all polynomials are evaluated using the form (7.2-14).

Example 7.1   Apply the technique above to the polynomial

$$p_4(x) = x^4 + 5x^3 + 3x^2 + 2.$$

Since $a_3 = 5$ the change of variable is $y = x + 1$ and

$$q_4(y) = y^4 + y^3 - 6y^2 + 5y + 1$$

With $\gamma_1 = 0$, Eq. (7.2-8) is then

$$0 = 5 + \alpha_1$$

Thus $\alpha_1 = -5$ and we get

$$q_4(y) = (y^2 + 5)(y^2 + y - 11) + 56$$

In order to evaluate $R_{mk}(x)$ then, one approach would be to evaluate $P_m(x)$ and $Q_k(x)$ as described above and then to take their quotient. Another approach is to write $R_{mk}(x)$ in the form of a continued fraction. To convert a rational function to a continued fraction, we perform a series of divisions and reciprocations. For example,

$$\frac{2x^3 + x^2 + x + 3}{x^2 - x + 4} = 2x + 3 - \frac{4x + 9}{x^2 - x + 4}$$

$$= 2x + 3 - \cfrac{4}{\cfrac{x^2 - x + 4}{x + \cfrac{9}{4}}}$$

$$= 2x + 3 - \cfrac{4}{x - \cfrac{13}{4} + \cfrac{\frac{181}{16}}{x + \frac{9}{4}}}$$

An algorithm for performing this conversion in general is considered in {7}. Here we consider explicitly only the cases $m = k$ or $k + 1$ and leave the other cases to a problem {8}. For these cases, the continued-fraction form of $R_{mk}(x)$ is (except in certain degenerate cases {7})

$$R_{mk}(x) = C_0 x + D_0$$
$$+ \cfrac{C_1}{x + D_1 + \cfrac{C_2}{x + D_2 + \cfrac{C_3}{x + D_3 + \cfrac{\ddots}{\ddots + \cfrac{C_k}{x + D_k}}}}}$$

$$\text{(7.2-15)}$$

$$= C_0 x + D_0 + \frac{C_1|}{|x + D_1} + \frac{C_2|}{|x + D_2} + \cdots + \frac{C_k|}{|x + D_k}$$

where $C_0 = 0$ when $m = k$. The computation of (7.2-15) requires k divisions and, if $m = k + 1$, one multiplication. In the following table we compare the number of multiplications and divisions required to evaluate $R_{mk}(x)$ first by evaluating the numerator and denominator polynomials using the quadratic factor algorithm discussed above and second by using continued fractions.†

(m,k)	Polynomial evaluations		Continued fraction	
	Mult.	Div.	Mult.	Div.
(2,2)	2	1	0	2
(3,2)	3	1	1	2
(3,3)	4	1	0	3
(4,3)	4	1	1	3
(4,4)	4	1	0	4
(5,4)	5	1	1	4
(5,5)	6	1	0	5
(6,5)	6 or 7	1	1	5
(6,6)	6, 7, or 8	1	0	6

Thus, if division and multiplication are equally time-consuming, the continued-fraction approach is superior using this comparison, but if multiplication is somewhat faster than division, then this may not be true {9}. Comparing the number of additions and subtractions re-

† Note that in evaluating the two polynomials and then dividing, we may assume one polynomial is in the form (7.2-2) but the other will in general have a coefficient multiplying the highest power of x which adds one multiplication to the total.

quired by the two techniques also favors the continued-fraction method {4}.

We considered the continued-fraction formulation with $m = k$ or $k + 1$ because these generally give the most accurate approximations among all rational approximations with the same index. In conclusion it is only fair to point out that the continued-fraction approach may lead to certain computational difficulties, the main one being loss of significance due to the subtraction of nearly equal quantities. This difficulty can, however, often be overcome quite easily {12, 13}.

7.3   PADÉ APPROXIMATIONS

Our first approach toward generating approximations of the form (7.2-1) will be, for a given m and k, to choose $P_m(x)$ and $Q_k(x)$ so that $f(x)$ and $P_m(x)/Q_k(x)$ are equal at $x = 0$ and have as many derivatives as possible equal at $x = 0$. In the case $k = 0$, the approximation is then just the Maclaurin expansion for $f(x)$. Implicit in what follows will be the assumption that the Maclaurin series for $f(x)$ exists in some neighborhood of $x = 0$. There are two reasons for the arbitrary choice of $x = 0$: (1) It makes the manipulations below substantially simpler than for any other x. (2) The interval over which we wish to approximate most functions will contain zero, and when it does not, a simple change of variable can be used to make the interval contain zero. We also assume that $P_m(x)$ and $Q_k(x)$ have no common factors. Now let

$$
\begin{aligned}
P_m(x) &= \sum_{j=0}^{m} a_j x^j \\
Q_k(x) &= \sum_{j=0}^{k} b_j x^j \qquad (b_0 = 1)
\end{aligned}
\tag{7.3-1}
$$

It is permissible to let the constant term in $Q_k(x)$ equal 1 because (1) the constant term cannot be zero if the approximation is to exist at $x = 0$; (2) the value of $R_{mk}(x)$ is unchanged if numerator and denominator are divided by the same constant.

Now let $f(x)$ have a Maclaurin series

$$
f(x) = \sum_{j=0}^{\infty} c_j x^j
\tag{7.3-2}
$$

Then we consider the difference

$$
f(x) - \frac{P_m(x)}{Q_k(x)} = \frac{\left(\sum\limits_{j=0}^{\infty} c_j x^j \right) \left(\sum\limits_{j=0}^{k} b_j x^j \right) - \sum\limits_{j=0}^{m} a_j x^j}{\sum\limits_{j=0}^{k} b_j x^j}
\tag{7.3-3}
$$

Since we have $N + 1$ constants—$m + 1$ a_j's and k b_j's—at our disposal, we would hope to make $f(x) - R_{mk}(x)$ and its first N derivatives equal to zero at $x = 0$. We shall achieve this if the numerator of the right-hand side of (7.3-3) is such that its leading power is of degree $N + 1$ (why?). Thus we write

$$\left(\sum_{j=0}^{\infty} c_j x^j \right) \left(\sum_{j=0}^{k} b_j x^j \right) - \sum_{j=0}^{m} a_j x^j = \sum_{j=N+1}^{\infty} d_j x^j \qquad (7.3\text{-}4)$$

The vanishing of the coefficients of the first $N + 1$ powers of x on the left-hand side of (7.3-4) is equivalent to the equations $\{10\}$

$$\sum_{j=0}^{k} c_{N-s-j} b_j = 0 \qquad \begin{array}{l} s = 0, 1, \ldots, N - m - 1 \\ (c_j = 0 \text{ if } j < 0,\ b_0 = 1) \end{array}$$

$$a_r = \sum_{j=0}^{r} c_{r-j} b_j \qquad \begin{array}{l} r = 0, 1, \ldots, m \\ (b_j = 0 \text{ if } j > k) \end{array} \qquad (7.3\text{-}5)$$

When this set of $N + 1$ linear equations in the $N + 1$ unknowns has a solution, it provides us with the desired approximation of the form (7.2-1) $\{10\}$.

One disadvantage of this derivation is that it does not provide us with an error term in closed form. Such an error term can be derived using other techniques $\{14$ to $19\}$. But since our emphasis here is on finding the maximum error on an interval, error terms which contain a derivative of the function which we can bound or estimate but not evaluate are not of basic interest to us. Rather we must be able to find the error at any point in the interval, and this we shall do by actual evaluation of the approximation and comparison with the true function.

Estimates of the error are useful, however, in indicating how good a given approximation is likely to be in the minimum maximum error context. For the case of approximations as we have derived them in this section, it is often true that the coefficients $d_i, i = N + 1, \ldots$ and $b_i, i = 1, 2, \ldots, k$ in (7.3-4) decrease very rapidly in magnitude. Thus a good estimate of the error in (7.2-1) may be given by the first term on the right-hand side of (7.3-4), which is $d_{N+1} x^{N+1}$ with d_{N+1} given by

$$d_{N+1} = \sum_{j=0}^{k} c_{N+1-j} b_j \qquad (7.3\text{-}6)$$

This approximation to the error illustrates the fact that, in common with Maclaurin-series approximations, rational approximations of the kind we have developed have errors which are small near zero and increase away from zero. This is just what we would expect because of our requirement that the approximation agree with $f(x)$ and its first N derivatives at $x = 0$. This means that in practice, if $x = 0$ is not the center of the interval over which we are approximating, then we should make a change of variable so that zero becomes the center of the interval.

The development of approximations of the form (7.2-1) by the method of this section is due to the French mathematician Padé. The approximation $R_{mk}(x)$ is called the (m,k) entry in the Padé table of $f(x)$. We note the important empirical fact that, for most functions for which approximations are desired on computers, the entries in the Padé table for $m = k$ or $m = k + 1$ give the smallest minimum maximum error for a given N.

7.4   AN EXAMPLE

Let us consider the problem of approximating e^x on the interval $(-\infty, \infty)$. The first thing we must consider is the infinite interval. We cannot expect to approximate a function over an infinite interval with good error behavior over the whole interval. Our first step then will be to convert the problem to that of approximating e^x on some finite interval.

We suppose that the approximation is going to be used on a digital computer which uses the decimal system internally. (The argument for a binary computer is precisely analogous.)

For any x in $(-\infty, \infty)$ we write

$$x \log_{10} e = X + F \tag{7.4-1}$$

where X is an integer and F a fraction such that $0 \leqq F < 1$. From (7.4-1) we have

$$10^{x \log_{10} e} = e^x = 10^X \times 10^F = 10^X \times e^{F \ln 10} \tag{7.4-2}$$

Since X is an integer, on a decimal computer multiplication by 10^X represents a shift of a fixed-point number or a change in the exponent of a floating-point number, both of which are very simple operations. Thus we are left with the problem of approximating the exponential over the interval $[0, \ln 10] \approx [0, 2.3026]$. Since zero is not at the center of this interval, we would first make a change of variable to get as the new interval $[-1.1513, 1.1513]$. Then after the approximation has been found, we would change back to the original variable.

Thus we have reduced our original problem to that of finding an approximation to e^x on the interval $[-1.1513, 1.1513]$. For illustrative purposes, we consider the case $N = 4$. For $m = k = 2$ we shall now perform the calculations of Sec. 7.3 in detail. From the Maclaurin expansion for e^x, we have $c_0 = 1$, $c_1 = 1$, $c_2 = \frac{1}{2}$, $c_3 = \frac{1}{6}$, $c_4 = \frac{1}{24}$.

Using these values, Eqs. (7.3-5) become

$$\frac{1}{24} + \frac{1}{6}b_1 + \frac{1}{2}b_2 = 0 \qquad \frac{1}{6} + \frac{1}{2}b_1 + b_2 = 0$$
$$a_0 = 1 \qquad a_1 = 1 + b_1 \qquad a_2 = \frac{1}{2} + b_1 + b_2 \tag{7.4-3}$$

Solving the first two equations for b_1 and b_2 and then using the last three to calculate a_0, a_1, and a_2, we find

$$b_1 = -\frac{1}{2} \qquad b_2 = \frac{1}{12}$$
$$a_0 = 1 \qquad a_1 = \frac{1}{2} \qquad a_2 = \frac{1}{12}$$

so that

$$R_{2,2}(x) = \frac{12 + 6x + x^2}{12 - 6x + x^2} \tag{7.4-4}$$

Similarly we may calculate the other entries of the Padé table for $N = 4$ {20}:

$$R_{4,0}(x) = 1 + x + \frac{1}{2}x^2 + \frac{1}{6}x^3 + \frac{1}{24}x^4$$
$$R_{3,1}(x) = \frac{24 + 18x + 6x^2 + x^3}{24 - 6x}$$
$$R_{1,3}(x) = \frac{24 + 6x}{24 - 18x + 6x^2 - x^3} \tag{7.4-5}$$
$$R_{0,4}(x) = \frac{1}{1 - x + \frac{1}{2}x^2 - \frac{1}{6}x^3 + \frac{1}{24}x^4}$$

The approximation $R_{m,0}(x)$ is always just the truncated Maclaurin-series expansion of the function. Note also that in this example, we have $R_{mk}(x) = 1/R_{km}(-x)$ (why would we expect this?).

Our interest is in the errors in these various approximations over the interval $[-1.1513, 1.1513]$. In Fig. 7.1 we have plotted $e^x - R_{mk}(x)$ and in Table 7.1 we have listed some sample values of this error. We note first that over the entire range $[-1.1513, 1.1513]$ $R_{3,1}(x)$ has the minimum maximum error, which is contrary to our previous assertion that approximations with $m = k$ or $k + 1$ would generally be best. However, over the smaller interval $[-.75, .75]$ $R_{2,2}(x)$ is indeed the best approximation in a minimum maximum error sense. Note also that, as the ends of the interval are approached, the errors grow very rapidly. This suggests that where possible we shall approximate functions over quite small intervals. Indeed our assertion about approximations with $m = k$ or $k + 1$ was made with small intervals in mind.

In the present case, we could do the following: (1) break up the interval into two intervals $[0, 1.1513]$ and $[1.1513, 2.3026]$ and (2) use a different approximation over each interval. To find the proper approxi-

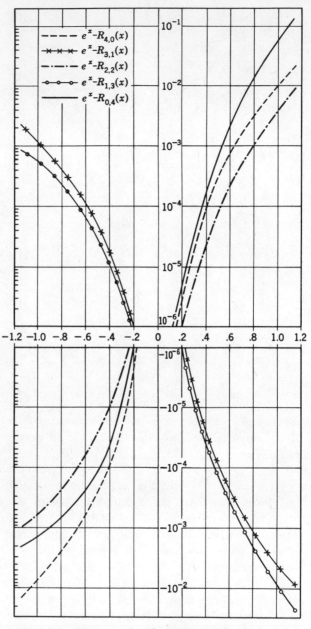

Fig. 7.1   Errors in Padé approximations to e^x.

Table 7.1   Errors in Padé approximations to e^x: $e^x - R_{mk}(x)$

(m,k) \ x	(4,0)	(3,1)	(2,2)	(1,3)	(0,4)
-1.15	$-.01401$	$.00226$	$-.00096$	$.00088$	$-.00208$
-1.00	$-.00712$	$.00121$	$-.00054$	$.00053$	$-.00135$
$-.75$	$-.00175$	$.00033$	$-.00016$	$.00018$	$-.00050$
$-.50$	$-.000240$	$.000049$	$-.000027$	$.000032$	$-.000104$
$-.25$	$-.0000078$	$.0000018$	$-.0000011$	$.0000014$	$-.0000052$
$.25$	$.0000086$	$-.0000023$	$.0000018$	$-.0000029$	$.0000129$
$.50$	$.000284$	$-.000088$	$.000073$	$-.000134$	$.000653$
$.75$	$.00225$	$-.00079$	$.00072$	$-.00147$	$.00783$
1.00	$.00995$	$-.00394$	$.00400$	$-.00899$	$.05162$
1.15	$.02059$	$-.00882$	$.00950$	$-.02274$	$.13381$

mations, we transform both intervals to $[-.57565, .57565]$ by, respectively, the changes of variable $x \to x - .57565$ and $x \to x - 1.72695$. Then, since $R_{2,2}(x)$ is the best approximation for $N = 4$ over $[-.57565, .57565]$, we would, from (7.4-4), use

$$\frac{12 + 6(x + .57565) + (x + .57565)^2}{12 - 6(x + .57565) + (x + .57565)^2}$$

in $[0, 1.1513]$ and

$$\frac{12 + 6(x + 1.72695) + (x + 1.72695)^2}{12 - 6(x + 1.72695) + (x + 1.72695)^2}$$

in $[1.1513, 2.3026]$.   In actual practice, we would store in the computer only the approximation (7.4-4) and would first make the proper change of variable and then evaluate (7.4-4).

In general we have two alternatives when an approximation for a given N is not sufficiently good over the whole interval: (1) Break up the interval into one or more subintervals as we have done above and use an appropriate approximation over each subinterval.   (2) Use a larger value of N so as to get more accuracy.   The disadvantage of the latter method is that the greater the value of N, the more multiplications and divisions are required.   But if different approximations are used on different subintervals, this is very wasteful of the memory of the computer.   Moreover, the time required to find the proper subinterval for a given argument grows with the number of subintervals.   General rules for choosing the value of N and the number of subintervals are quite difficult to give.

With Padé approximations, the error increases rapidly away from the center of the interval, but as we shall see, for minimum maximum error approximations, this is not the case. In the latter case, the argument for subintervals, while it still exists, is not nearly so cogent as for Padé approximations. Thus on digital computers most approximations are for the whole interval. In this case the accuracy desired—that is, the maximum error that can be tolerated—determines N.

If we were using the approximation (7.4-4), we would, of course, not compute it in that form but rather in one of the forms of Sec. 7.2. Using the results of Sec. 7.2, we find that $R_{2,2}(x)$ requires two divisions to calculate as a continued fraction while all the other approximations with $N = 4$ require at least three operations. Because both numerator and denominator polynomials have a coefficient of the highest power of 1, $R_{2,2}(x)$ requires two multiplications and one division using the quadratic factor algorithm. The other approximations require at least three operations also [although $R_{4,0}(x)$ requires no division] {22}.

7.5 CHEBYSHEV POLYNOMIALS

We would not expect Padé approximations to be best or even nearly best in a minimax sense. The basis for their derivation—equality of a function and its derivatives at a point—does not, as we have seen, give good error behavior over a whole interval. In the remainder of this chapter, we shall develop methods which lead to approximations which are better in the minimax sense than Padé approximations. In particular in Sec. 7.7 we shall use Padé approximations as the starting point from which to develop better approximations. As a fundamental tool in the rest of this chapter, we shall use the Chebyshev polynomials which were mentioned briefly in Chap. 4 and which we now discuss in some detail here.

Before so doing, however, let us consider the motivation for the use of Chebyshev polynomials. The problem with using approximations based on Maclaurin series is that the error over an interval centered at zero is extremely nonuniform—small near the center but growing very rapidly near the end points. It would seem more reasonable to use as approximating functions, instead of powers of x, polynomials whose behavior over an interval centered at zero would be in some sense uniform. We would hope that rational functions formed from combinations of these polynomials would exhibit a more uniform error behavior. As we shall now show, the Chebyshev polynomials have ideal properties for these aims.

The Chebyshev polynomial of degree r is given by (see Prob. 26, Chap. 4)

$$T_r(x) = \cos (r \cos^{-1} x) \tag{7.5-1}$$

These polynomials satisfy the orthogonality relationship

$$\int_{-1}^{1} \frac{1}{(1-x^2)^{\frac{1}{2}}} T_r(x) T_s(x)\, dx = \begin{cases} 0 & r \neq s \\ \pi & r = s = 0 \\ \pi/2 & r = s \neq 0 \end{cases} \tag{7.5-2}$$

and the recurrence relationship (see Prob. 26, Chap. 4)

$$T_{r+1}(x) = 2x T_r(x) - T_{r-1}(x) \qquad T_0(x) = 1 \qquad T_1(x) = x \tag{7.5-3}$$

In this and the next two sections we shall assume that the interval over which we wish to approximate a function is $[-1,1]$. This will be convenient in the development here and involves no loss of generality.

From (7.5-1), it follows that in $[-1,1]$ $T_r(x)$ has r zeros at

$$x = \cos \frac{(2j+1)\pi}{2r} \qquad j = 0, \ldots, r-1 \tag{7.5-4}$$

and $r + 1$ extrema of magnitude 1 at

$$x = \cos (j\pi/r) \qquad j = 0, \ldots, r \tag{7.5-5}$$

where (7.5-5) includes the $r - 1$ places where $T_r'(x) = 0$ as well as the two end points. For $T_6(x)$ this is illustrated in Fig. 7.2.

That property of the Chebyshev polynomials of particular interest to us here is expressed by the following theorem:

Theorem 7.1 (Chebyshev)   Of all polynomials of degree r with coefficient of x^r equal to 1, the Chebyshev polynomial of degree r multiplied by $1/2^{r-1}$ oscillates with minimum maximum amplitude on the interval $[-1,1]$.

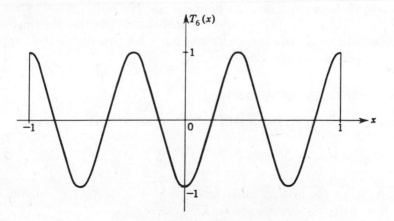

Fig. 7.2 Graph of $T_6(x)$.

Proof   From (7.5-3) it follows that the coefficient of x^r in $T_r(x)$ is 2^{r-1}. Thus

$$Q_r(x) = \frac{1}{2^{r-1}} T_r(x) \tag{7.5-6}$$

satisfies the conditions of the theorem.   The requirement that the coefficient of x^r be 1 has the effect of "normalizing" all polynomials of degree r. Without this normalization the theorem would be meaningless.

The proof is by contradiction.   Suppose there exists a polynomial $q_r(x)$ of degree r with leading coefficient 1 which has a smaller minimum maximum amplitude than $Q_r(x)$ on $[-1,1]$.   We consider

$$p_{r-1}(x) = Q_r(x) - q_r(x) \tag{7.5-7}$$

which is a polynomial of degree $r - 1$.   The $r + 1$ extrema of the polynomial $Q_r(x)$ each of magnitude $1/2^{r-1}$ are given by (7.5-5).   By our hypothesis $q_r(x)$ has a smaller magnitude than $Q_r(x)$ at each of these extrema.   From the definition of $T_r(x)$, it follows that the $r + 1$ extrema of $T_r(x)$ and thus of $Q_r(x)$ alternate in sign.   It follows then that $p_{r-1}(x)$ alternates in sign from one extremum of $Q_r(x)$ to the next, which means that $p_{r-1}(x)$ has r zeros in $[-1,1]$.   But $p_{r-1}(x)$ is a polynomial of degree $r - 1$.   Therefore, we have a contradiction.   Now suppose there exists a polynomial $q_r(x)$ with minimum maximum amplitude equal to $Q_r(x)$. Unless $q_r(x) = Q_r(x)$ at an extremum of $Q_r(x)$ we get a contradiction as above.   But, if $q_r(x) = Q_r(x)$ at such an extremum, then $p_{r-1}(x)$ has a double zero at this extremum and, proceeding as above to count the zeros of $p_{r-1}(x)$, we again arrive at a contradiction which completes the proof of the theorem.

The Chebyshev polynomials are sometimes called *equal-ripple polynomials* because they oscillate between positive and negative extrema of the same magnitude.   In the next two sections, we shall use the Chebyshev polynomials to derive approximations which are superior to Padé approximations in the minimax sense.

7.6   CHEBYSHEV EXPANSIONS

The expansion of $f(x)$ in a series of Chebyshev polynomials is given by

$$f(x) = \tfrac{1}{2}c_0 + \sum_{j=1}^{\infty} c_j T_j(x) \tag{7.6-1}$$

where, using the orthogonality property of the Chebyshev polynomials, we may write the coefficients in (7.6-1) as

$$c_j = \frac{2}{\pi} \int_{-1}^{1} \frac{f(x)T_j(x)}{(1 - x^2)^{1/2}} \, dx \qquad j = 0, 1, \ldots \tag{7.6-2}$$

Our first object is to approximate $f(x)$ by truncating the expansion (7.6-1) after a finite number of terms.   We shall call the approximation formed by truncating at $j = m$, $T_{m,0}(x)$.   Having calculated $T_{m,0}(x)$ using (7.6-1), we shall then convert it to power-series form by writing each $T_j(x)$ in its polynomial form.

   Example 7.2   Let $f(x) = e^x$.   Use (7.6-1) to calculate $T_{4,0}(x)$ and compare this with $R_{4,0}(x)$ in (7.4-5).

   With $f(x) = e^x$, the integrals in (7.6-2) can be evaluated to give [see Watson (1962, p. 20, Eq. 5)]

$$c_j = 2I_j(1) \qquad\qquad\qquad (7.6\text{-}3)$$

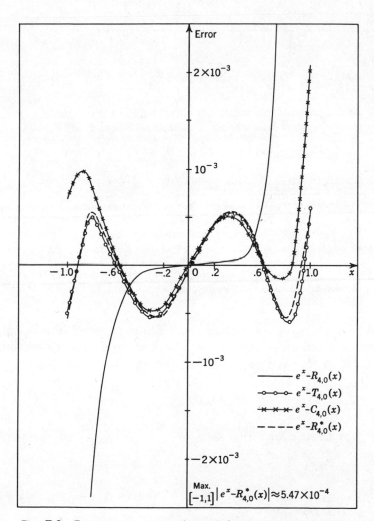

Fig. 7.3   Errors in various polynomial approximations to e^x.

Table 7.2   Errors in various polynomial approximations to e^x

x	$e^x - R_{4,0}(x)$	$e^x - T_{4,0}(x)$	$e^x - C_{4,0}(x)$
-1.00	$-.00712$	$-.00050$	$.00069$
$-.75$	$-.00175$	$.00047$	$.00069$
$-.50$	$-.000240$	$-.00023$	$-.00024$
$-.25$	$-.0000078$	$-.00052$	$-.00050$
0	$.0000000$	$-.00004$	$.00000$
$.25$	$.0000085$	$.00051$	$.00050$
$.50$	$.000284$	$.00032$	$.00028$
$.75$	$.00225$	$-.00050$	$-.00019$
1.00	$.00994$	$.00059$	$.00214$

where $I_j(x)$ is the modified Bessel function of the first kind.   Using this result and truncating (7.6-1) after five terms, we have

$$T_{4,0}(x) = 1.266066 + 1.130318T_1(x) + .271495T_2(x) \\ + .044337T_3(x) + .005474T_4(x) \quad (7.6\text{-}4)$$

which, converted to a power series, becomes

$$T_{4,0}(x) = 1.000044 + .997310x + .499200x^2 + .177344x^3 + .043792x^4 \quad (7.6\text{-}5)$$

In Fig. 7.3 and Table 7.2 the errors in this approximation and $R_{4,0}(x)$ are compared on the interval $[-1,1]$.[†]   From the figure and table the improved accuracy of $T_{4,0}(x)$ is clear.   As we might expect, this is particularly notable near the end points, thus bearing out our hope that the smoothness of the Chebyshev polynomials would result in improved error behavior near the end points.   For later reference (see Sec. 7.8) we note that the error has six maxima and minima, including the end points. Starting from -1, the values of these extrema are (multiplied by 10^4) -5.03, 5.08, -5.28, 5.56, -5.82, 5.92.

We shall now use the expansion (7.6-1) to generate rational approximations in a manner analogous to that used to generate Padé approximations from Maclaurin expansions.   We wish to find approximations of the form

$$T_{mk}(x) = \frac{\displaystyle\sum_{j=0}^{m} a_j T_j(x)}{\displaystyle\sum_{j=0}^{k} b_j T_j(x)} \quad (7.6\text{-}6)$$

[†] We could compare over the interval $[-1.1513,1.1513]$ by changing variable from $x \to x/1.1513$ in (7.6-5).

where the a_j's and b_j's are to be determined so that in

$$f(x) - T_{mk}(x) = \frac{\left[\tfrac{1}{2}c_0 + \sum\limits_{j=1}^{\infty} c_j T_j(x)\right]\left[\sum\limits_{j=0}^{k} b_j T_j(x)\right] - \sum\limits_{j=0}^{m} a_j T_j(x)}{\sum\limits_{j=0}^{k} b_j T_j(x)}$$

(7.6-7)

the coefficients of $T_j(x)$, $j = 0, \ldots, N$ in the numerator of the right-hand side vanish [cf. (7.3-3) and (7.3-4)]. Thus we write

$$\left[\tfrac{1}{2}c_0 + \sum_{j=1}^{\infty} c_j T_j(x)\right]\left[\sum_{j=0}^{k} b_j T_j(x)\right] - \sum_{j=0}^{m} a_j T_j(x) = \sum_{j=N+1}^{\infty} h_j T_j(x)$$

(7.6-8)

In order to get equations for the a_j's and b_j's, we use the identity {25}

$$T_{i+j}(x) + T_{|i-j|}(x) = 2T_i(x)T_j(x)$$

(7.6-9)

and with this rewrite (7.6-8) as

$$\frac{1}{2}c_0 \sum_{j=0}^{k} b_j T_j(x) + \frac{1}{2} \sum_{j=1}^{\infty} \sum_{i=0}^{k} b_i c_j [T_{i+j}(x) + T_{|i-j|}(x)]$$

$$- \sum_{j=0}^{m} a_j T_j(x) = \sum_{j=N+1}^{\infty} h_j T_j(x) \quad (7.6\text{-}10)$$

From (7.6-10) we get the following set of equations for the a_j's and b_j's {25}:

$$a_0 = \frac{1}{2} \sum_{i=0}^{k} b_i c_i$$

$$a_r = \frac{1}{2} \sum_{i=0}^{k} b_i(c_{|r-i|} + c_{r+i}) \qquad \begin{aligned} &r = 1, \ldots, N \\ &a_r = 0, r > m \end{aligned}$$

(7.6-11)

These are $N + 1$ equations in the $N + 2$ constants a_j and b_j. This is what we would expect since one coefficient in (7.6-6) is redundant. We shall set $b_0 = 1$ in all cases where this leads to a system (7.6-11) which is solvable.

The first nonzero coefficient on the right-hand side of (7.6-8) is given by

$$h_{N+1} = \frac{1}{2} \sum_{i=0}^{k} b_i(c_{N+1-i} + c_{N+1+i})$$

(7.6-12)

In analogy with (7.3-6), this coefficient multiplied by $T_{N+1}(x)$ is often a good approximation of the error in $T_{mk}(x)$.

Example 7.3   Let $f(x) = e^x$. Find $T_{2,2}(x)$ and compare with $R_{2,2}(x)$ as given by (7.4-4).

Equations (7.6-11) are

$$a_0 = \tfrac{1}{2}(c_0 + b_1 c_1 + b_2 c_2) \qquad (b_0 = 1)$$
$$a_1 = c_1 + \tfrac{1}{2}[b_1(c_0 + c_2) + b_2(c_1 + c_3)]$$
$$a_2 = c_2 + \tfrac{1}{2}[b_1(c_1 + c_3) + b_2(c_0 + c_4)]$$
$$0 = c_3 + \tfrac{1}{2}[b_1(c_2 + c_4) + b_2(c_1 + c_5)]$$
$$0 = c_4 + \tfrac{1}{2}[b_1(c_3 + c_5) + b_2(c_2 + c_6)]$$

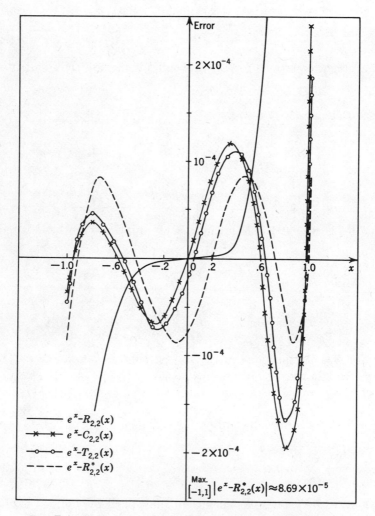

Fig. 7.4   Errors in various rational approximations to e^x.

Table 7.3   Errors in various rational
approximations to e^x

x	$e^x - R_{2,2}(x)$	$e^x - T_{2,2}(x)$	$e^x - C_{2,2}(x)$
-1.00	$-.00054$	$-.000042$	$-.000032$
$-.75$	$-.00016$	$.000047$	$.000036$
$-.50$	$-.000027$	$-.000018$	$-.000027$
$-.25$	$-.0000011$	$-.000070$	$-.000063$
0	$.0000000$	$-.000020$	$.000000$
$.25$	$.0000018$	$.000088$	$.000105$
$.50$	$.000073$	$.000084$	$.000073$
$.75$	$.00072$	$-.000122$	$-.000163$
1.00	$.00400$	$.000189$	$.000239$

where for $j = 0, \ldots, 4$ the c_j's are given by (7.6-4) and $c_5 = .000543$, $c_6 = .000045$. Solving the last two equations for b_1 and b_2 and then solving the first three for a_0, a_1, and a_2, we get

$a_0 = 1.0009875$
$a_1 = .4825306$
$a_2 = .0397096$
$b_1 = -.4783387$
$b_2 = .0387418$

Converting $T_{2,2}(x)$ to a rational function, we get†

$$T_{2,2}(x) = \frac{1.0000205 + .5019781x + .0826200x^2}{1.0 - .4976173x + .0806064x^2} \tag{7.6-13}$$

In Fig. 7.4 and Table 7.3, the errors in this approximation are compared with those of $R_{2,2}(x)$ over $[-1,1]$. Again, we note that the Chebyshev approximation is substantially better than the Padé approximation, particularly near the ends of the interval. Note, however, that $T_{2,2}(x)$, while it also has six maxima and minima, including the end points, is not nearly so smooth as $T_{4,0}(x)$ over the whole interval. Since no condition at $x = 0$ is imposed in deriving $T_{mk}(x)$, it is not surprising that neither $T_{2,2}(x)$ nor $T_{4,0}(x)$ gives exact results at $x = 0$.

Our examples have illustrated the general empirical result that rational approximations derived using the Chebyshev expansion of a function give a smaller maximum error than Padé approximations. The chief drawback to the approach as we have presented it thus far is the necessity of evaluating the integrals (7.6-2), which cannot be done analytically in most cases. One way to avoid evaluation of the integrals (7.6-2)

† Here and hereafter in this chapter, we shall normalize our approximations by setting $b_0 = 1$ in order to conform to the notation of (7.3-1). However, in actual computational practice, we would always normalize the approximation so that the coefficient of some, usually the highest, power of x in the denominator (or numerator) is equal to 1, for so doing always saves at least one multiplication (cf. Sec. 7.2).

is to use trigonometric interpolation to approximate the first $L + 1$ coefficients in (7.6-1). We make the change of variable $x = \cos\theta$, and remembering that $T_j(\cos\theta) = \cos j\theta$, (7.6-1) becomes

$$g(\theta) = f(\cos\theta) = \tfrac{1}{2}c_0 + \sum_{j=1}^{\infty} c_j \cos j\theta \qquad (7.6\text{-}14)$$

and (7.6-2) becomes

$$c_j = \frac{2}{\pi} \int_0^{\pi} g(\theta) \cos j\theta\, d\theta \qquad (7.6\text{-}15)$$

Equation (7.6-14) is just the Fourier-series expansion of $g(\theta)$. Therefore, the Fourier and Chebyshev expansions of a function are related to each other through the change of variable $x = \cos\theta$.

Our interest here is in approximating $g(\theta)$ by

$$y_L(\theta) = \tfrac{1}{2}\bar{c}_0 + \sum_{j=1}^{L} \bar{c}_j \cos j\theta \qquad (7.6\text{-}16)$$

which is precisely equivalent to (6.8-19) since $b_j = 0$ for all j when the function being approximated is even. Therefore, applying the techniques of Sec. 6.8-1, we get approximations $\bar{c}_0, \bar{c}_1, \ldots, \bar{c}_L$ to the true coefficients $c_0, c_1, \ldots, c_L$.

Another approach which avoids evaluating the integrals (7.6-2), which is easy to mechanize and which can achieve as much accuracy as desired, is to use the Maclaurin expansion of $f(x)$ to calculate the coefficients in the Chebyshev expansion. This can be done by substituting the Maclaurin series into (7.6-2) and integrating term by term {27}. The resulting infinite series for c_j usually converges sufficiently rapidly to make the calculation of the c_j's quite feasible. In fact, this procedure can be mechanized on a digital computer so that the computer in effect generates the approximations to be used by the computer. This procedure does, however, involve a great deal of calculation even in the power-series case $(k = 0)$, and when we try to extend the method to rational functions, the amount of calculation becomes very great. In the next section we present another method of improving on Padé approximations using Chebyshev polynomials, which leads to approximations which are generally almost as good as those of this section and which are much easier to generate.

7.7   ECONOMIZATION OF RATIONAL FUNCTIONS

Our object here is to take the Padé approximations of Sec. 7.3 and perturb them so that the resulting approximation has a smaller minimum maximum error on the desired interval. Without losing generality, we shall assume that the interval is of the form $[-\alpha, \alpha]$ since a change of variable can always be used to bring any other interval into this form.   We shall first consider the problem for $k = 0$, that is, for power-series approximations, and then shall extend it to general rational functions.

7.7-1   Economization of power series

Given N we begin with the Padé approximation with $m = N$, $k = 0$ which is just the first $N + 1$ terms of the Maclaurin expansion of $f(x)$. We write this as

$$R_{N,0}(x) = \sum_{j=0}^{N} d_j x^j \qquad (7.7\text{-}1)$$

In order to get an improvement over this approximation, we shall use

$$R_{N+1,0} = \sum_{j=0}^{N+1} d_j x^j \qquad (7.7\text{-}2)$$

Then

$$C_{N,0}(x) = R_{N+1,0}(x) - d_{N+1} \frac{\alpha^{N+1}}{2^N} T_{N+1}\left(\frac{x}{\alpha}\right) \qquad (7.7\text{-}3)$$

is a polynomial of degree N since the leading term of the Chebyshev polynomial $T_{N+1}(x/\alpha)$ is $x^{N+1}2^N/\alpha^{N+1}$.   Moreover, since $|T_{N+1}(x)| \leqq 1$ for $x \, \varepsilon \, [-1,1]$, the error in $C_{N,0}(x)$ is greater than that in $R_{N+1,0}(x)$ by no more than $(d_{N+1}\alpha^{N+1})/2^N$.   Since α will be less than or equal to 1 in virtually all applications and d_{N+1} will be decreasing as N increases, this added error will be very small in general.   What we have done then is to take the power-series approximation of degree $N + 1$ and from it derive an approximation of degree N whose maximum error is very little greater than that of the $(N + 1)$st degree approximation.   Thus we have "economized" the power series in the sense of using fewer terms to achieve almost the same result.

Our object here, though, is to compare $C_{N,0}(x)$ with $R_{N,0}(x)$; that is, we wish to compare corresponding approximations of the same degree. We let $x = \alpha u$ so that the interval for u is $[-1,1]$.   We have from (7.7-1)

$$\lim_{\alpha \to 0} \frac{f(\alpha u) - R_{N,0}(\alpha u)}{\alpha^{N+1}} = d_{N+1}u^{N+1} \qquad (7.7\text{-}4)$$

From (7.7-2) and (7.7-3)

$$\lim_{\alpha \to 0} \frac{f(\alpha u) - C_{N,0}(\alpha u)}{\alpha^{N+1}} = \lim_{\alpha \to 0} \frac{d_{N+1}(\alpha^{N+1}/2^N)T_{N+1}(u) + \sum\limits_{j=N+2}^{\infty} d_j(\alpha u)^j}{\alpha^{N+1}}$$

$$= d_{N+1}\frac{T_{N+1}(u)}{2^N} \qquad (7.7\text{-}5)$$

Comparing (7.7-4) and (7.7-5) and using Theorem 7.1, we conclude that, in the limit as $\alpha \to 0$, $C_{N,0}(x)$ has a smaller maximum error on $[-\alpha, \alpha]$ than $T_{N,0}(x)$. Therefore, for sufficiently small α, the economized approximation $C_{N,0}(x)$ is a better approximation than $R_{N,0}(x)$ in the minimax sense. In practice "sufficiently small α" includes almost all intervals of interest.

Example 7.4   Let $f(x) = e^x$. With $\alpha = 1$ find $C_{4,0}(x)$ and compare with $R_{4,0}(x)$ and $T_{4,0}(x)$.

We have

$$R_{5,0}(x) = 1 + x + \frac{x^2}{2} + \frac{x^3}{6} + \frac{x^4}{24} + \frac{x^5}{120}$$

and

$$T_5(x) = 16x^5 - 20x^3 + 5x$$

so that (7.7-3) becomes

$$C_{4,0}(x) = R_{5,0}(x) = \frac{-1}{120} \times \frac{1}{16}(16x^5 - 20x^3 + 5x)$$

$$= 1 + \frac{383}{384}x + \frac{x^2}{2} + \frac{17}{96}x^3 + \frac{x^4}{24}$$

In Fig. 7.3 and Table 7.2, the errors in this approximation are compared with those of $R_{4,0}(x)$ and $T_{4,0}(x)$. We note that (1) $C_{4,0}(x)$ is a much better approximation than $R_{4,0}(x)$. (2) Near $x = 0$, $C_{4,0}(x)$ and $T_{4,0}(x)$ are about equally good, but near the end points, $T_{4,0}(x)$ is substantially better. But as $\alpha \to 0$, the approximation using the Chebyshev expansion and that using the economized power series would be more nearly equivalent over the whole interval.

7.7-2   Generalization to rational functions

Corresponding to (7.7-4), we have for any Padé approximation $R_{mk}(x) = P_m(x)/Q_k(x)$

$$\lim_{\alpha \to 0} \frac{f(\alpha u) - R_{mk}(\alpha u)}{\alpha^{N+1}} = d_{N+1}^{(m,k)} u^{N+1} \tag{7.7-6}$$

The superscripts have been added to $d_{N+1}^{(m,k)}$ for later reference. Our object is, in analogy with (7.7-5), to find a rational approximation $C_{mk}(x)$ such that

$$\lim_{\alpha \to 0} \frac{f(\alpha u) - C_{mk}(\alpha u)}{\alpha^{N+1}} = d_{N+1}^{(m,k)} \frac{T_{N+1}(u)}{2^N} \tag{7.7-7}$$

because, if we can do so, we shall again have a better approximation than $R_{mk}(x)$ for sufficiently small α.

To find such a $C_{mk}(x)$, we use a sequence of Padé approximations to $f(x)$ of the form

$$R_{i,j-i}^{(j)}(x) = \frac{P_i^{(j)}(x)}{Q_{j-i}^{(j)}(x)} \qquad j = 0, \ldots, N-1 \tag{7.7-8}$$

where the only restrictions on i are that $0 \leq i \leq m$ and $0 \leq j - i \leq k$. Therefore, i is not uniquely determined except when $m = 0$, $k = 0$ and, for all m and k, when $j = 0$.   Analogously to (7.7-6), we have

$$\lim_{\alpha \to 0} \frac{f(\alpha u) - R_{i,j-i}^{(j)}(\alpha u)}{\alpha^{j+1}} = d_{j+1}^{(i,j-i)} u^{j+1} \tag{7.7-9}$$

Now we define

$$C_{mk}(x) = \frac{P_m(x) + \displaystyle\sum_{j=0}^{N-1} \gamma_{j+1} P_i^{(j)}(x) + \gamma_0}{Q_k(x) + \displaystyle\sum_{j=0}^{N-1} \gamma_{j+1} Q_{j-i}^{(j)}(x)} \tag{7.7-10}$$

with

$$\gamma_{j+1} = \frac{d_{N+1}^{(m,k)}}{d_{j+1}^{(i,j-i)}} \frac{\alpha^{N-j}}{2^N} t_{j+1} \qquad j = 0, \dots, N - 1 \tag{7.7-11}$$
$$\gamma_0 = -d_{N+1}^{(m,k)} \alpha^{N+1} t_0 / 2^N$$

where t_j is the coefficient of u^j in $T_{N+1}(u)$.   Then we have

$$f(x) - C_{mk}(x)$$

$$= \frac{\left[Q_k(x) + \displaystyle\sum_{j=0}^{N-1} \gamma_{j+1} Q_{j-i}^{(j)}(x) \right] f(x) - P_m(x) - \displaystyle\sum_{j=0}^{N-1} \gamma_{j+1} P_i^{(j)}(x) - \gamma_0}{Q_k(x) + \displaystyle\sum_{j=0}^{N-1} \gamma_{j+1} Q_{j-i}^{(j)}(x)}$$

$$= \frac{Q_k(x) f(x) - P_m(x) + \displaystyle\sum_{j=0}^{N-1} \gamma_{j+1} [Q_{j-i}^{(j)}(x) f(x) - P_i^{(j)}(x)] - \gamma_0}{Q_k(x) + \displaystyle\sum_{j=0}^{N-1} \gamma_{j+1} Q_{j-i}^{(j)}(x)}$$

$$\tag{7.7-12}$$

Since $Q_r(0) = 1$ in all Padé approximations (why?), we may write, using (7.7-6), (7.7-9), and (7.7-11),

$$\lim_{\alpha \to 0} \frac{f(\alpha u) - C_{mk}(\alpha u)}{\alpha^{N+1}} = d_{N+1}^{(m,k)} \left(u^{N+1} + \sum_{j=0}^{N-1} \frac{t_{j+1}}{2^N} u^{j+1} + \frac{t_0}{2^N} \right)$$

$$= d_{N+1}^{(m,k)} \frac{T_{N+1}(u)}{2^N} \tag{7.7-13}$$

Thus $C_{mk}(x)$ is in fact the desired economized rational function and will, for sufficiently small α, have a smaller maximum error than $R_{mk}(x)$.

From (7.7-11) it would seem that this procedure will fail if $d_{j+1}^{(i,j-i)} = 0$ for any j.   When this happens, it will often be possible to choose another member of the sequence (7.7-8).   Note also that the foregoing derivation requires the use of only those γ_{j+1} for which t_{j+1} is nonzero.   Thus, when $t_{j+1} = 0$ [as it is for every other coefficient of $T_{N+1}(u)$], the value of $d_{j+1}^{(i,j-i)}$ is immaterial {31}.

Example 7.5   Let $f(x) = e^x$. With $\alpha = 1$ find $C_{2,2}(x)$ and compare with $R_{2,2}(x)$ and $T_{2,2}(x)$.

For the sequence (7.7-8), we choose $R_{0,0}^{(0)}(x)$, $R_{1,0}^{(1)}(x)$, $R_{1,1}^{(2)}(x)$, and $R_{2,1}^{(3)}(x)$.   Performing the calculations analogous to those in Sec. 7.4, we find

$$R_{0,0}^{(0)}(x) = 1$$
$$R_{1,0}^{(1)}(x) = 1 + x$$
$$R_{1,1}^{(2)}(x) = \frac{1 + \frac{1}{2}x}{1 - \frac{1}{2}x}$$
$$R_{2,1}^{(3)}(x) = \frac{1 + \frac{2}{3}x + \frac{1}{6}x^2}{1 - \frac{1}{3}x}$$

and rewriting $R_{2,2}(x)$ so that $b_0 = 1$, we have

$$R_{2,2}(x) = \frac{1 + \frac{1}{2}x + \frac{1}{12}x^2}{1 - \frac{1}{2}x + \frac{1}{12}x^2}$$

Then using (7.3-6), we calculate

$$d_1^{(0,0)} = 1$$
$$d_2^{(1,0)} = \frac{1}{2}$$
$$d_3^{(1,1)} = -\frac{1}{12}$$
$$d_4^{(2,1)} = -\frac{1}{72}$$
$$d_5^{(2,2)} = \frac{1}{720}$$

Further

$$T_5(x) = 16x^5 - 20x^3 + 5x$$

so from (7.7-11) with $N = 4$ and $\alpha = 1$

$$\gamma_0 = 0$$
$$\gamma_1 = \frac{\frac{1}{720}}{1} \times \frac{1}{16} \times 5 = \frac{1}{2304}$$
$$\gamma_2 = 0$$
$$\gamma_3 = \frac{\frac{1}{720}}{-\frac{1}{12}} \times \frac{1}{16} \times (-20) = \frac{1}{48}$$
$$\gamma_4 = 0$$

Then from (7.7-10)

$$C_{2,2}(x) = \frac{(1 + \frac{1}{2}x + \frac{1}{12}x^2) + \frac{1}{48}(1 + \frac{1}{2}x) + \frac{1}{2304}}{(1 - \frac{1}{2}x + \frac{1}{12}x^2) + \frac{1}{48}(1 - \frac{1}{2}x) + \frac{1}{2304}}$$
$$= \frac{2353 + 1176x + 192x^2}{2353 - 1176x + 192x^2} = \frac{1.0 + .49978751x + .08159796x^2}{1.0 - .49978751x + .08159796x^2}$$

In Fig. 7.4 and Table 7.3 the errors in this approximation are compared with $R_{2,2}(x)$ and $T_{2,2}(x)$. As in the case with the economized power series, the economized rational function is not quite so good as that derived using a Chebyshev expansion, but it is much superior to the Padé approximation.

This completes our discussion of the economization of rational functions. Although we have come close, we have not yet succeeded in deriving true minimax approximations. In the next section, we shall prove a theorem which gives a characterization that must be possessed by the true minimax approximation to a function over an interval.

7.8   CHEBYSHEV'S THEOREM ON MINIMAX APPROXIMATIONS

Let $f(x)$ be the continuous function we wish to approximate over the finite interval $[a,b]$ in the form (7.2-1). Let

$$r_{mk} = \max_{a \leq x \leq b} |f(x) - R_{mk}(x)| \tag{7.8-1}$$

for any rational function

$$R_{mk}(x) = \frac{P_m(x)}{Q_k(x)} = \frac{\displaystyle\sum_{j=0}^{m} a_j x^j}{\displaystyle\sum_{j=0}^{k} b_j x^j} \tag{7.8-2}$$

Then we may prove†

Theorem 7.2 (Chebyshev)   There exists a unique rational function $R_{mk}(x)$ which minimizes r_{mk} (if two rational functions are considered identical if they are equal when reduced to their lowest terms). Moreover, if we write this unique rational function as

$$R_{mk}^*(x) = \frac{\displaystyle\sum_{j=0}^{m-\nu} a_{j+\nu} x^j}{\displaystyle\sum_{j=0}^{k-\mu} b_{j+\mu} x^j} = \frac{P_m^*(x)}{Q_k^*(x)} \tag{7.8-3}$$

where

$$0 \leq \mu \leq k \qquad 0 \leq \nu \leq m \qquad a_m, b_k \neq 0 \tag{7.8-4}$$

and $P_m^*(x)/Q_k^*(x)$ is irreducible, then, if $r_{mk}^* \neq 0$, the number of consecutive points of $[a,b]$ at which $f(x) - R_{mk}^*(x)$ takes on its maximum value of magnitude r_{mk}^* with alternate change of sign is not less than $L = m + k + 2 - d$ where $d = \min(\mu, \nu)$.

† Chebyshev proved only the characterization and uniqueness parts of the theorem. The existence portion was proved much later by Walsh.

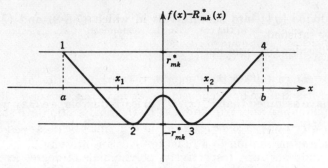

Fig. 7.5   An example of alternating extrema of $f(x) - R_{mk}^*(x)$.

In particular, the theorem says that, when $k = 0$, the number of points at which the error attains its maximum value is at least $m + 2$. Note how nearly $T_{4,0}(x)$ as given by (7.6-5) meets this requirement.

We shall leave the existence and uniqueness parts of the proof to the problems {37, 38} and here will prove only that $R_{mk}(x)$ has the characteristic form stated in the theorem.   We note here that both this theorem and Theorem 7.3 below are true if we consider approximations to $f(x)$ of the form $s(x)R_{mk}(x)$ where $s(x)$ is a given continuous function which does not vanish in (a,b) {39}.

Proof   We suppose that L', the number of points at which $f(x) - R_{mk}^*(x)$ takes on its maximum value r_{mk}^* with alternating sign, is such that

$$L' < L$$

so that

$$L' \leqq m + k + 1 - d \tag{7.8-5}$$

Note, for example, that if $f(x) - R_{mk}^*(x)$ has the form of Fig. 7.5, then the number of points at which it takes on its extreme value *with alternating sign* is only 3 since the extrema labeled 2 and 3 have the same sign.

We may then subdivide the interval $[a,b]$ into L' subintervals

$$[a,x_1], [x_1,x_2], \ldots, [x_{L'-1},b] \tag{7.8-6}$$

such that, in alternate intervals, the inequalities

$$-r_{mk}^* \leqq f(x) - R_{mk}^*(x) < r_{mk}^* - \alpha \tag{7.8-7}$$

and

$$-r_{mk}^* + \alpha < f(x) - R_{mk}^*(x) \leqq r_{mk}^* \tag{7.8-8}$$

are satisfied for some positive number α.†   In Fig. 7.5 the points a,

† That such a subdivision exists is not quite trivial; see Davis (1964, pp. 149–151).

x_1, x_2, b divide $[a,b]$ into subintervals in which (7.8-8) and (7.8-7) are alternately satisfied.

We consider the function

$$A(x) = (x - x_1)(x - x_2) \cdots (x - x_{L'-1}) \tag{7.8-9}$$

Since we have assumed that $P_m^*(x)/Q_k^*(x)$ is irreducible, we may write {36}

$$A(x) = Q_k^*(x)a(x) - P_m^*(x)b(x) \tag{7.8-10}$$

where $a(x)$ and $b(x)$ are, respectively, polynomials of degree less than or equal to m and k.

We shall now display a function $R_{mk}(x)$ which achieves a smaller minimum maximum error than $R_{mk}^*(x)$ on $[a,b]$ under the assumption that $L' < L$. This contradiction will prove the theorem. Let

$$R_{mk}(x) = \frac{P_m^*(x) - \beta a(x)}{Q_k^*(x) - \beta b(x)} \tag{7.8-11}$$

where β is a real number. The numerator is then a polynomial of degree $\leq m$, and the denominator is a polynomial of degree $\leq k$. Now we may write

$$f(x) - R_{mk}(x) = f(x) - R_{mk}^*(x) + \frac{\beta A(x)}{Q_k^*(x)[Q_k^*(x) - \beta b(x)]} \tag{7.8-12}$$

by making use of (7.8-10), (7.8-11), and (7.8-3). Since $Q_k^*(x)$ must be bounded away from zero in $[a,b]$ [for, if not, $R_{mk}^*(x)$ will certainly not be a minimax approximation], by choosing β sufficiently small in magnitude, the denominator of the last term on the right-hand side of (7.8-12) will also be bounded away from zero in $[a,b]$. The numerator changes sign at each point x_i because of (7.8-9) and is of constant sign in each subinterval (7.8-6). Thus we may choose β so that

$$\left| \frac{\beta A(x)}{Q_k^*(x)[Q_k^*(x) - \beta b(x)]} \right| < \alpha \qquad x \, \varepsilon \, [a,b] \tag{7.8-13}$$

and such that this term has sign opposite to $f(x) - R_{mk}^*(x)$ in each subinterval (7.8-6). With β chosen in this way (7.8-7), (7.8-8), and (7.8-13) imply that $R_{mk}(x)$ in (7.8-11) has a smaller minimum maximum error than $R_{mk}^*(x)$ on $[a,b]$, which is the desired contradiction. Therefore, we have proved that $L' \geq m + k + 2 - d$.

Theorem 7.2 gives us no way of constructing minimax approximations. Nor does it enable us to judge how close to the minimax approximation a given approximation is. The plot of $e^x - R_{4,0}^*(x)$ in Fig. 7.3 implies that $T_{4,0}(x)$ is very nearly a minimax approximation. Conversely the plot of $e^x - R_{2,2}^*(x)$ in Fig. 7.4 indicates that $T_{2,2}(x)$ deviates a good deal from the minimax approximation. We might surmise then that, if L alternating extrema of the error in a given approximation are of nearly equal magnitude, this approximation achieves nearly as small a maximum error as the minimax approximation. The following theorem confirms this.

Theorem 7.3   Let

$$R_{mk}(x) = \frac{P_m(x)}{Q_k(x)} = \frac{\displaystyle\sum_{j=0}^{m-\nu} a_{j+\nu}x^j}{\displaystyle\sum_{j=0}^{k-\mu} b_{j+\mu}x^j} \tag{7.8-14}$$

be irreducible and let the difference

$$f(x) - R_{mk}(x)$$

remain finite in $[a,b]$.   Further, let

$$x_1 < x_2 < \cdots < x_L$$

be in $[a,b]$ and let

$$f(x_i) - R_{mk}(x_i) = (-1)^i\lambda_i \qquad i = 1, \ldots, L \tag{7.8-15}$$

where $\lambda_i > 0$ for all i and $L = m + k + 2 - d$ with $d = \min(\mu,\nu)$. Let $S_{mk}(x) = p_m(x)/q_k(x)$ be any rational approximation to $f(x)$ with degrees of numerator and denominator less than or equal to, respectively, m and k and let

$$s_{mk} = \max_{[a,b]} |f(x) - S_{mk}(x)| \tag{7.8-16}$$

Then

$$s_{mk} \geqq \min_i \lambda_i \tag{7.8-17}$$

Proof   Suppose that

$$s_{mk} < \min_i \lambda_i \tag{7.8-18}$$

Consider the difference

$$\delta(x) = S_{mk}(x) - R_{mk}(x) = [f(x) - R_{mk}(x)] - [f(x) - S_{mk}(x)]$$

From (7.8-15), (7.8-16), and (7.8-18) we have the result that the numbers $\delta(x_i)$ are nonzero and alternate in sign. Since $\delta(x)$ is continuous in $[a,b]$, it has at least $L - 1 = m + k + 1 - d$ zeros in $[a,b]$.   But

$$\delta(x) = \frac{P_m(x)}{Q_k(x)} - \frac{p_m(x)}{q_k(x)} = \frac{P_m(x)q_k(x) - p_m(x)Q_k(x)}{Q_k(x)q_k(x)}$$

has a numerator of degree $\leq m + k - d$ (why?) and thus cannot have $m + k + 1 - d$ zeros. This contradiction proves the theorem.

By identifying $S_{mk}(x)$ with $R^*_{mk}(x)$, this theorem says that the error in the minimax approximation is greater than the magnitude of the smallest extremum in the error of $R_{mk}(x)$. Since the minimax error is certainly smaller than the magnitude of the largest extremum in the error of $R_{mk}(x)$, we thereby obtain an upper and lower bound on the minimax error from any approximation $R_{mk}(x)$ which satisfies the conditions of Theorem 7.3. For example, from Fig. 7.3 the six extrema of $T_{4,0}(x)$ vary in magnitude between 5.03×10^{-4} and 5.92×10^{-4} with the minimax error given by 5.47×10^{-4}. In Fig. 7.4 the extrema of $T_{2,2}(x)$ vary in magnitude between 4.20×10^{-5} and 18.88×10^{-5} and the minimax error is equal to 8.69×10^{-5}.

It remains now only to consider some means for constructing the minimax approximation. This is the subject of the last section of this chapter.

7.9 CONSTRUCTING MINIMAX APPROXIMATIONS

A number of algorithms are known by which the true Chebyshev approximation to a function for a given m and k may be calculated. All of them have this much in common: They start from an initial approximation, and from this a sequence of approximations is derived which in the limit converges to the Chebyshev approximation. In this section, we shall content ourselves with presenting one of these algorithms, called the second algorithm of Remes, in which the calculations may be easily mechanized on a digital computer. We shall present this method without out proof of convergence; a proof may be found in Ralston (196–).

For simplicity, we shall assume in this section that the minimax approximation to $f(x)$ on $[a,b]$ of the form (7.8-3) has at least

$$N + 2 = m + k + 2$$

points at which the extreme value of the error is attained. That is, we assume that d in Theorem 7.2 is zero.† We also assume, without loss of generality, that the interval $[a,b]$ includes $x = 0$ so that we may set $b_0 = 1$. The problem then is:

Given: A continuous function $f(x)$ on an interval $[a,b]$ including zero and m and k

---

† Degeneracy (i.e., $d \neq 0$) can occur when $f(x)$ is even or odd on $[a,b]$ {40}. Except in trivial cases like this, it occurs in only some quite pathological cases. But near degeneracy, in which $P^*_m(x)$ and $Q^*_k(x)$ have a nearly common factor, is more common and can cause severe computational difficulties.

Find: $R_{mk}^*(x)$, the minimax approximation to $f(x)$ on $[a,b]$ of the form (7.8-3).

Let us suppose that we have somehow obtained (see comments after algorithm) an approximation

$$R_{mk}^{(0)}(x) = \frac{\sum_{j=0}^{m} a_j x^j}{\sum_{j=0}^{k} b_j x^j} \qquad (b_0 = 1) \qquad (7.9\text{-}1)$$

such that $f(x) - R_{mk}^{(0)}(x)$ has $N + 2$ extrema which alternate in sign. Then the second algorithm of Remes is as follows:

1. Let $x_0^{(0)} < x_1^{(0)} < \cdots < x_{N+1}^{(0)}$ be $N + 2$ points at which $f(x) - R_{mk}^{(0)}(x)$ has local extrema which alternate in sign.
2. Solve the system of $N + 2$ nonlinear equations

$$f[x_i^{(0)}] - \frac{\sum_{j=0}^{m} a_j [x_i^{(0)}]^j}{\sum_{j=0}^{k} b_j [x_i^{(0)}]^j} = (-1)^i E \qquad i = 0, \ldots, N + 1$$

$$(b_0 = 1) \quad (7.9\text{-}2)$$

for the $N + 2$ unknowns $a_0, \ldots, a_m, b_1, \ldots, b_k,$ and E. Call the solution $a_0^{(0)}, \ldots, a_m^{(0)}, b_1^{(0)}, \ldots, b_k^{(0)}, E^{(0)}$. Note that $E^{(0)}$ is the magnitude of the error in the approximation at each of the points $x_i^{(0)}$.
3. Define

$$h_0(x) = f(x) - \frac{\sum_{j=0}^{m} a_j^{(0)} x^j}{\sum_{j=0}^{k} b_j^{(0)} x^j} \qquad [b_0^{(0)} = 1] \qquad (7.9\text{-}3)$$

The function $h_0(x)$ then has magnitude $|E^{(0)}|$ with alternating sign at the points $x_i^{(0)}, i = 0, \ldots, N + 1$. It is not hard to show, therefore, that, in the neighborhood of each $x_i^{(0)}$, there is a point $x_i^{(1)}$ at which $h_0(x)$ has an extremum of the same sign as that of $f(x) - R_{mk}^{(0)}(x)$ at $x_i^{(0)}$. Replace each $x_i^{(0)}$ by the corresponding $x_i^{(1)}$. If $\bar{x}$, the point at which $h_0(x)$ has its maximum magnitude, is one of the points $x_i^{(1)}$, proceed to step 4. If not, then replace one of the points $x_i^{(1)}$ by $\bar{x}$ in such a way that $h_0(x)$ still alternates in sign on the points $x_i^{(1)}$. This can always be done (why?).

4. Repeat steps 2 and 3 using the points $x_0^{(1)}, \ldots, x_{N+1}^{(1)}$ in (7.9-2). This process then generates a sequence of rational approximations of the form (7.9-1) which converge uniformly to $R_{mk}^*(x)$ if the initial extrema $x_i^{(0)}$, $i = 0, \ldots, N + 1$ are sufficiently close (see below) to the corresponding extrema of $R_{mk}^*(x)$.

We make the following comments on this algorithm:

(i) If $k = 0$, then the iteration will converge for an arbitrary choice of the $N + 2$ abscissas in step 1. That is, an initial approximation of the form (7.9-1) is not necessary [Novodvorskii and Pinsker (1951)]. However, when $k \neq 0$ all that can be said is that there exists an $\epsilon > 0$ such that, if each extremum of $f(x) - R_{mk}^{(0)}(x)$ lies within ϵ of the corresponding extremum of $f(x) - R_{mk}^*(x)$, then the algorithm will converge. Thus what is really required is not an approximation $R_{mk}^{(0)}(x)$ but a set of extrema lying sufficiently close to the corresponding extrema of $f(x) - R_{mk}^*(x)$. For example we might use the $N + 2$ extrema of the Chebyshev polynomial $T_{N+1}(x)$, suitably related to $[a,b]$. But in many cases, in order to obtain a set of $N + 2$ $x_i^{(0)}$ for which the algorithm will converge, it is necessary to first derive an approximation $R_{mk}^{(0)}(x)$. When $f(x) - C_{mk}(x)$ has $N + 2$ extrema, $C_{mk}(x)$ may almost always be used for $R_{mk}^{(0)}(x)$. In some particularly difficult cases a technique due to Werner (1962) may be used to generate an appropriate $R_{mk}^{(0)}(x)$.

(ii) When $k = 0$, the equations of step 2 of the algorithm are, in fact, linear (why?) and thus are easily solvable (see, for example, Sec. 9.3). When $k \neq 0$, the nonlinear system may be solved as follows:

(a) Write the system (7.9-2) as

$$\sum_{j=0}^{m} a_j [x_i^{(0)}]^j - \{f[x_i^{(0)}] - (-1)^i E_r\} \sum_{j=1}^{k} b_j [x_i^{(0)}]^j$$
$$= f[x_i^{(0)}] - (-1)^i E_{r+1} \qquad \begin{matrix} i = 0, \ldots, N + 1 \\ r = 0, 1, \ldots \end{matrix} \qquad (7.9\text{-}4)$$

(b) Starting from an assumed initial value of E_0, solve the *linear* system (7.9-4) in the unknowns $a_0, \ldots, a_m, b_1, \ldots, b_k$ and E_{r+1} for $r = 0, 1, \ldots$, until two successive values of E_r are in agreement. In the absence of other information (cf. Example 7.6 below), $E_0 = 0$ may be used. In practice, convergence of this method has seldom proved to be a problem.

(iii) The problem of finding the extrema of $h_0(x)$ is computationally intractable if we wish the exact solution. However, since the extrema of $h_0(x)$ will be close to those of $f(x) - R_{mk}^{(0)}(x)$ (and similarly at subsequent stages of the algorithm), it is sufficient in practice to search in the neighborhood of $x_i^{(0)}$ with a mesh of points until the approximate location of the extremum is found. Then $x_i^{(1)}$ is chosen, using a single stage of linear or quadratic inverse interpolation (cf. Sec. 3.7) as the point where the derivative of the error is zero.

(iv) This algorithm is also applicable to the case in which an approximation of the form $s(x)R_{mk}(x)$ is desired where $s(x)$ is a given continuous function which does not vanish in (a,b) {39}.

Example 7.6   Let $f(x) = e^x$. Starting with $C_{2,2}(x)$ as found in Example 7.5, use the above algorithm to find the minimax approximation to e^x on $[-1,1]$ with $m = k = 2$.

Arbitrarily, we divide the interval $[-1,1]$ into 201 points, equally spaced at an interval of .01. The six of these points at which $e^x - C_{2,2}(x)$ has its extreme values are (see Fig. 7.4)

$$-1.00, \ -.80, \ -.27, \ +.35, \ +.82, \ +1.00$$

Of these extrema, the one at $+1.00$ has the greatest magnitude, 2.39×10^{-4}. We expect the maximum error in the minimax approximation to be somewhat less than 2.39×10^{-4}. (In fact, we know from the previous section that $r_{mk}^* < 1.89 \times 10^{-4}$.) Therefore, as E_0 in (7.9-4), we choose -2.0×10^{-4}, the minus sign being used because the error at -1.00 [i.e., $i = 0$ in (7.9-2)] is negative. Then solving (7.9-2) by the algorithm given above, we get

$a_0 = 1.00007407$
$a_1 = .50802883$
$a_2 = .08549199$
$b_1 = -.49166131$
$b_2 = .07792980$
$E = -.745 \times 10^{-4}$

The maximum error on $[-1,1]$ is $.978 \times 10^{-4}$ at $x = .47333$. The six extrema of this approximation are at

-1.00
$- .73773$
$- .13475$
$.47333$
$.86488$
1.00

The next stage of the algorithm gives

$a_0 = 1.00007275$
$a_1 = .50864603$
$a_2 = .08583370$
$b_1 = -.49108231$
$b_2 = .07770411$
$E = -.867 \times 10^{-4}$

Now the maximum error is $.870 \times 10^{-4}$ at $x = -.11898$.   Note that this maximum error is very little greater than E so that the process has almost converged.   The extrema are now at

    −1.00
    − .72601
    − .11898
      .47363
      .86571
     1.00

A third application of the algorithm gives

$a_0 = 1.00007255$
$a_1 = .50863618$
$a_2 = .08582937$
$b_1 = -.49109193$
$b_2 = .07770847$
$E = -.8689990 \times 10^{-4}$

The maximum error is now $.8689996 \times 10^{-4}$ at $x = .47357$.   Thus, for all practical purposes, these coefficients give the Chebyshev approximation to e^x on $[-1,1]$.

We conclude this chapter by pointing out that the calculation of minimax approximations can be entirely mechanized on a digital computer using the methods of this chapter.   This is illustrated in Fig. 7.6. The only input required is the function m, k, the interval $[a,b]$, and the first $N + 1$ Maclaurin coefficients.   By saying the function is a required

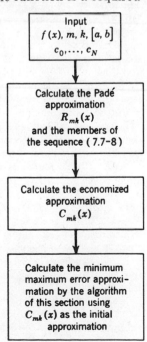

Fig. 7.6 Calculation of minimax approximations.

Input
$f(x)$, m, k, $[a, b]$
$c_0, \ldots, c_N$

Calculate the Padé approximation
$R_{mk}(x)$
and the members of the sequence (7.7-8)

Calculate the economized approximation
$C_{mk}(x)$

Calculate the minimum maximum error approximation by the algorithm of this section using $C_{mk}(x)$ as the initial approximation

input, we mean there must be available a program to compute values of $f(x)$. This program itself will use some approximation to $f(x)$. To be useful then, this approximation must have a maximum error which is small compared with that in the minimax approximation we are deriving. If no better approximation is available, a power-series approximation using the truncated Maclaurin expansion can be used.

No other input is *required*. The program could make a standard decision as to which members of the sequence (7.7-8) to use, or this could be optional input. The value of E_0 to be used in (7.9-4) could also be chosen in a prescribed manner [e.g., based on the maximum error in $C_{mk}(x)$], or it could be optional input. When $C_{mk}(x)$ cannot be used as $R_{mk}^{(0)}(x)$ in (7.9-1), the program could, for example, automatically choose the extrema of the Chebyshev polynomial $T_{N+1}(x)$, suitably related to the interval $[a,b]$, as the set of points $\{x_i^{(0)}\}$. For particularly difficult cases, the algorithm of Werner mentioned on p. 303 would have to be part of the program.

BIBLIOGRAPHIC NOTES

7.1   The need to approximate functions on digital computers has given a great impetus to the well-established mathematical field of approximation theory. The texts by Achieser (1956), Cheney (1966), Davis (1963), and Rice (1964) all contain valuable material. Some of the earliest work on approximations for digital computers was done by Hastings (1955). The most up-to-date compilation of approximations for digital computers is contained in the handbook by Hart (196–). Recent surveys of the field have been given by Kogbetliantz (1960), Stiefel (1959), and Cheney and Southard (1963).

7.2   The algorithm for evaluating polynomials is due to Knuth (1962). The standard text on continued fractions is that of Wall (1948). For techniques of converting rational functions to continued fractions, see Maehly (1959).

7.3-7.4   The Padé table is extensively discussed by Wall (1948). Much of the material of these sections can be found in Kogbetliantz (1960). Lawson (1964) considers the problem of using different approximations on different subintervals.

7.5   The best reference on the Chebyshev polynomials and their many applications is Lanczos (1956).

7.6   Much of the material in this section is due to Maehly and is discussed by Kogbetliantz (1960). Minnick (1957) discusses the use of the Maclaurin series to evaluate the coefficients in the Chebyshev expansion, and Spielberg (1961) uses this technique to mechanize the procedure on a digital computer.

7.7   The concept of economization of power series is due to Lanczos (1938) [see also Lanczos (1956)] and is discussed by Kogbetliantz (1960). The extension to rational functions was done by Maehly (1960) and in the form presented here by Ralston (1963).

7.8   The proof of Chebyshev's theorem here is from Achieser (1956).

7.9   For rational functions the proofs of the convergence of the second algorithm of Remes and the related exchange algorithm of Remes are given by Ralston

(196-). Werner (1962) has given a proof of the convergence of a modified form of the second algorithm. A proof of the convergence of the exchange algorithm for a class of functions including polynomials but not rational functions has been given by Novodvorskii and Pinsker (1951). Murnaghan and Wrench (1959) discuss the second algorithm in the polynomial case. Fraser and Hart (1962) and Shenitzer (1957) have applied the exchange algorithm to rational and polynomial approximations, respectively. Other algorithms for generating Chebyshev approximations are discussed by Cheney and Loeb (1962) and by Cheney and Southard (1963). The method used to solve (7.9-2) is due to Fraser and Hart (1962).

BIBLIOGRAPHY

Achieser, N. I. (1956): *Theory of Approximation* (translated by C. J. Hyman), Frederick Ungar Publishing Co., New York.

Cheney, E. W. (1966): *Introduction to Approximation Theory*, McGraw-Hill Book Company, New York.

Cheney, E. W., and H. L. Loeb (1962): On Rational Chebyshev Approximation, *Numer. Math.*, vol. 4, pp. 124–127.

Cheney, E. W., and T. H. Southard (1963): A Survey of Methods for Rational Approximation, with Particular Reference to a New Method Based on a Formula of Darboux, *SIAM Rev.*, vol. 5, pp. 219–231.

Davis, P. J. (1963): *Interpolation and Approximation*, Blaisdell Publishing Company, New York.

Fraser, W., and J. F. Hart (1962): On the Computation of Rational Approximations to Continuous Functions, *Comm. ACM*, vol. 5, pp. 401–403.

Hart, J. F., et al. (1968): *Handbook of Computer Approximations*, SIAM Series in Applied Mathematics.

Hastings, C. (1955): *Approximations for Digital Computers*, Princeton University Press, Princeton, N.J.

Knuth, D. E. (1962): Evaluation of Polynomials by Computer, *Comm. ACM*, vol. 5, pp. 595–599.

Kogbetliantz, E. G. (1960): Generation of Elementary Functions in *Mathematical Methods for Digital Computers* (A. Ralston and H. S. Wilf, eds.), John Wiley & Sons, Inc., New York.

Lanczos, C. (1938): Trigonometric Interpolation of Empirical and Analytic Functions, *J. Math. and Phys.*, vol. 17, pp. 123–199.

Lanczos, C. (1956): *Applied Analysis*, Prentice-Hall, Inc., Englewood Cliffs, N.J.

Lawson, C. L. (1964): Characteristic Properties of the Segmented Rational Minimax Approximation Problem, *Numer. Math.*, vol. 6, pp. 293–301.

Maehly, H. J. (1959): Report on Rational and Polynomial Approximations in *Proceedings of the First International Conference on Information Processing*, UNESCO, Paris.

Maehly, H. J. (1960): Methods for Fitting Rational Approximations, *J. Assoc. Comput. Mach.*, I, vol. 7, pp. 150–162.

Maehly, H. J. (1963): Methods for Fitting Rational Approximations, *J. Assoc. Comput. Mach.*, II, III, vol. 10, pp. 257–277.

Milne-Thomson, L. M. (1933): *Calculus of Finite Differences*, Macmillan & Co., Ltd., London.

Minnick, R. C. (1957): Tshebysheff Approximation for Power Series, *J. Assoc. Comput. Mach.*, vol. 4, pp. 487–504.

Murnaghan, F. J., and J. W. Wrench, Jr. (1959): The Determination of the Chebyshev Approximating Polynomial for a Differentiable Function, *MTAC*, vol. 13, pp. 185–193.

Novodvorskii, E. N., and I. S. Pinsker (1951): On a Process of Equalization of Maxima, *Uspehi Mat. Nauk.*, vol. 6, pp. 174–181 (translation by A. Shenitzer available from New York University library).

Ralston, A. (1963): On Economization of Rational Functions, *J. Assoc. Comput. Mach.*, vol. 10, pp. 278–282.

Ralston, A. (196–): Rational Chebyshev Approximation by Remes' Algorithms, *Numer. Math.* (to appear).

Rice, J. R. (1964): *The Approximation of Functions*, vol. 1, Addison-Wesley Publishing Company, Inc., Reading, Mass.

Shenitzer, A. (1957): Chebyshev Approximation of a Continuous Function by a Class of Functions, *J. Assoc. Comput. Mach.*, vol. 4, pp. 30–35.

Spielberg, K. (1961): Representation of Power Series in Terms of Polynomials, Rational Approximations and Continued Fractions, *J. Assoc. Comput. Mach.*, vol. 8, pp. 613–627.

Stiefel, E. (1959): Numerical Methods of Tchebysheff Approximation in *On Numerical Approximation* (R. E. Langer, ed.), The University of Wisconsin Press, Madison, Wis.

Wall, H. S. (1948): *Analytic Theory of Continued Fractions*, D. Van Nostrand Company, Inc., Princeton, N.J.

Watson, G. N. (1962): *Theory of Bessel Functions*, Cambridge University Press, New York.

Werner, H. (1962): Die konstruktive Ermittlung der Tschebyscheff-Approximierenden im Bereich der rationalen Funktionen, *Arch. Rational Mech. Anal.*, vol. 11, pp. 368–384.

PROBLEMS

Section 7.2

1. (a) Verify Eq. (7.2-7). (b) Use (7.2–7) to derive (7.2–8).

2. (a) Use the quadratic factor algorithm to factor the polynomials (i) $x^6 - 5x^5 + 9x^4 - 9x^3 + 10x^2 - x + 7$; (ii) $x^5 + 11x^4 + 38x^3 + 36x^2 - 15x + 44$.

(b) Show that, if at any time the equation $\gamma_1 = 0$ does not have a real root α_1, then at most two applications of synthetic division will lead to an equation $\gamma_1 = 0$ which does have a real root.

3. (a) For odd-degree polynomials, show that the quadratic factor algorithm can be applied without the initial change of variable and that in this case α_s in (7.2-11) is equal to a_{n-1}. What change must be made in (7.2-6) in this case?

(b) Apply this modified algorithm to the polynomial $x^5 + 11x^4 + 38x^3 + 36x^2 - 39x + 44$.

4. (a) Verify the values in the tables on pages 275 and 277.

(b) Derive a table analogous to that on page 277 which compares the number of additions and subtractions for the two methods. Are the differences significant?

*5. (a) Given A, B, C, D, E show how the equations

$$2p + 1 = A$$
$$p(p + 1) + 2q + a = B$$
$$p(2q + a) + q + r + s = C$$
$$p(r + s) + r + q(q + a) = D$$
$$ar + q(r + s) = E$$

can be solved for a, p, q, r, and s by finding a real root of a certain cubic equation in q.

(b) Then defining $b = q - ac$, $c = p - a$, $d = s - bc$, $e = r - bc$, $f = F - rs$, show that

$$P(x) = x^6 + Ax^5 + Bx^4 + Cx^3 + Dx^2 + Ex + F$$

can be evaluated with three multiplications by the algorithm

$$y = x(x + a)$$
$$w = (y + b)(x + c)$$
$$P(x) = (w + y + d)(w + e) + f$$

(c) Show how this algorithm can be used to evaluate $x^6 + 13x^5 + 49x^4 + 33x^3 - 61x^2 - 37x + 3$. [Ref.: Knuth (1962).]

*6. Consider the following algorithm for computing x^n (when no lower powers are required):

(a) Write n as a binary number (e.g., $9 = 1001$).

(b) Cancel the high-order 1 (001).

(c) Replace each zero by S (square) and each 1 by SX (square, multiply by x) $(001 \rightarrow SSSX)$.

(d) Starting from the left with x compute by squaring or multiplying by x as specified in the "code word" $\{x^9 = [(x^2)^2]^2 x\}$.

Prove that this algorithm is valid for any n. (Hint: Use induction.) [Ref.: Knuth (1962).]

*7. (a) Show that any rational function

$$R_{mk}(x) = \frac{\sum\limits_{j=0}^{m} a_j x^j}{\sum\limits_{j=0}^{k} b_j x^j} \qquad m \geq k, \, b_k \neq 0$$

may be written as

$$R_{mk}(x) = x \left(\sum\limits_{j=0}^{m-k-1} s_j x^j \right) + \frac{\sum\limits_{j=0}^{k} p_j x^{k-j}}{\sum\limits_{j=0}^{k} q_j x^{k-j}} \qquad (q_0 = 1)$$

Find a recurrence relation for the p_j's and s_j's in terms of the a_j's and b_j's.

(b) Except in certain degenerate cases, show that we may write

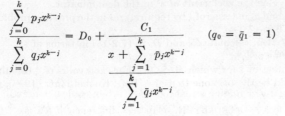

$$\frac{\sum_{j=0}^{k} p_j x^{k-j}}{\sum_{j=0}^{k} q_j x^{k-j}} = D_0 + \frac{C_1}{x + \dfrac{\sum_{j=1}^{k} \bar{p}_j x^{k-j}}{\sum_{j=1}^{k} \bar{q}_j x^{k-j}}} \qquad (q_0 = \bar{q}_1 = 1)$$

Find D_0 and C_1 in terms of p_0, p_1, and q_1.   When do the degenerate cases occur?

(c) Derive recurrence relations for the $\bar{p}_j$ and $\bar{q}_j$ in terms of the p_j and q_j.   Indicate how you would solve these relations.

(d) Thus deduce the correctness of (7.2-15) in nondegenerate cases.

8. (a) Use the previous problem to derive the relation analogous to (7.2-15) when $m > k + 1$.

(b) Do the same for $m < k$ by considering $1/R_{mk}(x)$.

(c) In both cases, how many multiplications and divisions are required to evaluate $R_{mk}(x)$?

(d) Use the recurrence relations of the previous problem to transform $(x^4 - 5x^3 + 12x^2 - 11x + 2)/(x^2 - 3x + 4)$ to the form of part a.

9. Consider computers on which the division time is, respectively, 1, $1\frac{1}{4}$, $1\frac{1}{2}$, $1\frac{3}{4}$, . . . , $2\frac{3}{4}$, 3 times the multiplication time.   For $m = 2$, 3, 4, 5, considering multiplications and divisions only, determine whether it is more efficient on each of these computers to compute $R_{mm}(x)$ as a rational function or as a continued fraction.

Section 7.3

10. (a) Derive Eqs. (7.3-5) using (7.3-4).

(b) For $m = k = 1$, show that the Padé approximation to $\cos x$ does not exist.

11. Let the Padé approximation $R_{mk}(x)$ be written

$$R_{mk}(x) = \frac{P_m(x)}{Q_k(x)} = \frac{P_m^{(m,k)}}{Q_k^{(m,k)}}$$

Assuming the existence of all relevant Padé approximations, show that the following recurrence relations exist:

$$P_m^{(m,k)} = P_{m-1}^{(m-1,k)} + Dx P_{m-1}^{(m-1,k-1)}$$
$$Q_k^{(m,k)} = Q_k^{(m-1,k)} + Dx Q_{k-1}^{(m-1,k-1)}$$
$$P_m^{(m,k)} = P_m^{(m,k-1)} + Ex P_{m-1}^{(m-1,k-1)}$$
$$Q_k^{(m,k)} = Q_{k-1}^{(m,k-1)} + Ex Q_{k-1}^{(m-1,k-1)}$$

where D and E are constants which also depend upon k and m.   Find expressions for D and E in terms of the Maclaurin coefficients and the constants in the Padé approximations.   [Ref.: Wall (1948), p. 15, and Chap. 20.]

*12. (a) Show that there exists a Padé approximation $R_{mk}(x)$ to $\cos x$ which contains only even powers of x for any m and k.

(b) Thus find $R_{6,6}(x) = R_{3,3}(z)$ ($z = x^2$).

(c) In the continued-fraction form of $R_{3,3}(z)$ given by (7.2-15), calculate D_0. From the value of D_0, deduce that, in calculating $\cos x$ using this approximation, there will be a loss of significance of about two digits.

(d) For $R_{3,3}(z)$, calculate d_7 as given by (7.3-6).

*13. In the notation of the previous problem, consider adding a term $-\xi b_3 z^4$ to the numerator of $R_{3,3}(z)$ where b_3 is the coefficient of z^3 in the denominator.

(a) Calculate b_1, b_2, b_3, and a_3 in terms of ξ by requiring, as in the previous problem, that $d_j = 0$, $j = 0, \ldots, 6$ in (7.3-4).

(b) For this approximation, calculate C_0 and D_0 in (7.2-15) in terms of ξ.

(c) Calculate d_7 in terms of ξ.

(d) Calculate those values of ξ for which $D_0 = 0$. For each value of ξ calculate d_7. Which value of ξ would be the best one to use? [Ref.: Kogbetliantz (1960), pp. 14, 25.]

14. Reciprocal differences. Define the kth reciprocal difference of $f(x)$ as

$$\rho_k(x_0, x_1, \ldots, x_k) = \frac{x_0 - x_k}{\rho_{k-1}(x_0, \ldots, x_{k-1}) - \rho_{k-1}(x_1, \ldots, x_k)} \\ + \rho_{k-2}(x_1, \ldots, x_{k-1}) \qquad k \geq 2$$

$$\rho_1(x_0, x_1) = \frac{x_0 - x_1}{f(x_0) - f(x_1)} \qquad \rho_0(x_0) = f(x_0)$$

(a) Show that, if the two end arguments of ρ_k are interchanged or if any two interior arguments are interchanged, then the value of the reciprocal difference is unchanged.

(b) Deduce then that, if the value is unchanged if the first two arguments are interchanged, then the value of a reciprocal difference is independent of the order of any of its arguments. [Reciprocal differences are in fact symmetric in all their arguments, but the proof of this result is quite difficult; see Milne-Thomson (1933) for one such proof.]

15. (a) Show how a reciprocal-difference table may be set up analogously to a finite-difference table.

(b) Given values of $\ln x$ at an interval of .1 from $x = .3$ to .9 (see Example 3.3, p. 48), calculate the reciprocal-difference table.

16. (a) Use the definition of reciprocal differences with $x_0 = x$ to derive the identity

$$f(x) = f(x_1) + \frac{x - x_1|}{|\phi_1(x_1, x_2)} + \frac{x - x_2|}{|\phi_2(x_1, x_2, x_3)} \\ + \cdots + \frac{x - x_n|}{|\rho_n(x, x_1, \ldots, x_n) - \rho_{n-2}(x_1, \ldots, x_{n-1})}$$

where

$$\phi_k(x_1, x_2, \ldots, x_{k+1}) = \rho_k(x_1, x_2, \ldots, x_{k+1}) - \rho_{k-2}(x_1, x_2, \ldots, x_{k-1})$$

(b) Show that, even if the last term on the right-hand side in this identity is deleted, the above is still an equality when $x = x_i$, $i = 1, \ldots, n$. This *interpolation formula* is called *Thiele's interpolation formula*.

(c) Use this interpolation formula and the table of part b of the previous problem to estimate $\ln .54$ (cf. Example 3.2). Do this by computing successive *convergents* of the continued fraction (i.e., using first one reciprocal difference, then two, etc.).

*17. Reciprocal derivatives. Define the jth reciprocal derivative of $f(x)$ at a as

$$R_j f(a) = \lim_{x_1, \ldots, x_{j+1} \to a} \rho_j(x_1, \ldots, x_{j+1})$$

(a) Show that $R_1 f(a) = 1/f'(a)$.

(b) Using the definition of ϕ_k in the previous problem, show that

$$\lim_{x_1, \ldots, x_{j+1} \to a} \phi_j(x_1, \ldots, x_{j+1}) = R_j f(a) - R_{j-2} f(a)$$

$$= \lim_{x_{j+1} \to a} \frac{x_{j+1} - a}{\rho_{j-1}(x_{j+1}, a, \ldots, a) - \rho_{j-1}(a, \ldots, a)} = \frac{1}{(\partial/\partial x)\rho_{j-1}(x, \ldots, x)} \Big|_{x=a}$$

if the various limits exist.

(c) Thus deduce that

$$R_j f(a) - R_{j-2} f(a) = j R_1 R_{j-1} f(a)$$

(d) Assuming that $f(x)$ has reciprocal derivatives of all orders, use the previous problem to show that as $n \to \infty$

$$f(x) = f(a) + \frac{x - a|}{|R_1 f(a)} + \frac{x - a|}{|2R_1 R_1 f(a)} + \cdots + \frac{x - a|}{|kR_1 R_{k-1} f(a)} + \cdots$$

This result, known as *Thiele's theorem*, is the continued-fraction analog of Taylor's theorem.

*18. (a) Show that the reciprocal derivatives of $f(x)$ may be conveniently calculated using the recurrence relation

$$R_j(x) = R_{j-2}(x) + r_{j-1}(x) \qquad r_j(x) = \frac{j+1}{R'_j(x)} \qquad R_0(x) = f(x) \qquad R_{-1}(x) = 0$$

and that r_{j-1} therefore becomes the jth denominator in Thiele's theorem.

(b) Use Thiele's theorem to derive a continued-fraction expansion of $\ln(1 + x)$ about $x = 0$. Derive a general form for $r_j(0)$. Use the first four convergents of this result to estimate $\ln .54$, and compare with the result of Prob. 16c.

(c) Similarly, derive a continued-fraction expansion about $x = 0$ for e^x. Find the general form for $r_j(0)$. Use the first five convergents of this expansion to approximate e.

*19. (a) Write Thiele's interpolation formula as

$$f(x) = y(x) + E(x) = \frac{P(x)}{Q(x)} + E(x)$$

where $P(x)$ and $Q(x)$ are the polynomials that result when the continued fraction with terms through that in ϕ_{n-1} is converted to a rational function. By considering

$$F(z) = Q^2(z)[f(z) - y(z)] - Q^2(x)[f(x) - y(x)] \frac{p_n(z)}{p_n(x)}$$

with $p_n(x) = (x - x_1) \cdots (x - x_n)$ show that

$$E(x) = \frac{p_n(x)}{n! Q^2(x)} \frac{d^n}{dx^n} [Q^2(x) f(x)]_{x=\xi}$$

with ξ in the interval spanned by $x_1, \ldots, x_n$.

(b) By taking the limit as $x_i \to a$, $i = 1, \ldots, n$ find the error incurred by truncating the continued-fraction expansion in part d of Prob. 17 after the term in $(n - 1)R_1 R_{n-2}(a)$.

(c) Deduce from the limiting form of the error term that the limiting form of the rational function in part a when $a = 0$ is identical to a Padé approximation with the same degree polynomials in numerator and denominator, and thus find a general form for the error in a Padé approximation.   [Ref.: Probs. 14 to 19, Milne-Thomson (1933).]

Section 7.4

20. (*a*) Derive each of the Padé approximations (7.4-5).

(*b*) Use (7.3-6) to estimate the errors in the approximations (7.4-4) and (7.4-5). In each case determine how good these estimates are by comparing them with the values of the errors in Table 7.1.

21. (*a*) Find all Padé approximations for (i) $f(x) = \sin x$ with $N = 5$; (ii) $f(x) = \cos x$ with $N = 4$.

(*b*) Display an algorithm for the calculation of $\sin x$ on $(-\infty, \infty)$ by first showing how any value of x outside of $[-(\pi/2),\pi/2]$ can be reduced to this interval.   Then show how one of the approximations of part a can be applied with an argument less than $\pi/4$ in magnitude followed by an adjustment of the sign if necessary.   Do the same for $\cos x$ on $(-\infty, \infty)$.   What is the advantage of keeping the argument of the Padé approximation small?

(*c*) Draw a graph of the error on $[-(\pi/4),\pi/4]$ for each of the approximations of part a.

22. (*a*) Use the technique of Probs. 7 and 8 to express each of the approximations (7.4-4) and (7.4-5) in the form of a polynomial plus a continued fraction.

(*b*) Use the results of Sec. 7.2 to determine how many multiplications and divisions are required to evaluate each of these five approximations (i) in continued-fraction form; (ii) in rational-function form.

(*c*) Which approximation can be computed most rapidly if the division time is (i) the same as the multiplication time; (ii) $1\frac{1}{2}$ times as great as the multiplication time; (iii) twice as great as the multiplication time?

Section 7.5

23. (*a*) By making an appropriate change of variable from $[-1,1]$ to $[0,1]$, derive the *shifted* Chebyshev polynomials $T_r^*(x)$ which are such that

$$T_r^*(x) = \cos r\theta \qquad x = \cos^2(\theta/2)$$

(*b*) Find a recurrence relation for the shifted Chebyshev polynomials and use it to generate $T_r^*(x)$, $r = 1, \ldots, 6$.

(*c*) State and prove a theorem similar to Theorem 7.1 for the shifted Chebyshev polynomials.

*24. (*a*) With the Chebyshev polynomial of degree i written as

$$T_i(x) = \sum_{j=0}^{i} t_j^{(i)} x^j$$

show that the nonzero $t_j^{(i)}$ are given by

$$t_j^{(i)} = 2^{j-1} \left[2 \binom{\frac{1}{2}(i+j)}{\frac{1}{2}(i-j)} - \binom{\frac{1}{2}(i+j)-1}{\frac{1}{2}(i-j)} \right] (-1)^{(i-j)/2}$$

(*b*) Similarly, writing

$$T_i^*(x) = \sum_{j=0}^{i} u_j^{(i)} x^j$$

show that

$$u_j^{(i)} = 2^{2j-1} \left[2 \binom{i+j}{i-j} - \binom{i+j-1}{i-j} \right] (-1)^{i+j}$$

[Ref.: Lanczos (1956), pp. 454–457.]

Section 7.6

25. (a) Derive the identity (7.6-9).   (b) Use this result to derive (7.6-10) and (7.6-11).

26. (a) With $f(x) = e^x$, use trigonometric interpolation to calculate $y_L(\theta)$ as given by (7.6-16) with $L = 4$.   Compare this result with (7.6-4).

(b) Convert the result of part a to a power series analogous to (7.6-5).   Plot the error in this approximation on $[-1,1]$ and compare with the error in $T_{4,0}(x)$.

*27. (a) Let $f(x) = \displaystyle\sum_{j=0}^{\infty} a_j x^j$ be the Maclaurin series for $f(x)$ and let

$$T_i(x) = \sum_{j=0}^{i} t_j^{(i)} x^j$$

By substituting these series in (7.6-2), show that

$$c_{2n} = \sum_{j=0}^{\infty} R_{2j}^{(2n)} a_{2j} \qquad c_{2n+1} = \sum_{j=0}^{\infty} R_{2j+1}^{(2n+1)} a_{2j+1}$$

where

$$R_{2j}^{(2n)} = \frac{(2j)!}{2^{2j-1}(j!)^2} \left[t_0^{(2n)} + t_2^{(2n)} \frac{2j+1}{2j+2} + \cdots \right.$$
$$\left. + t_{2n}^{(2n)} \frac{(2j+1)(2j+3) \cdots (2j+2n-1)}{(2j+2)(2j+4) \cdots (2j+2n)} \right]$$

$$R_{2j+1}^{(2n+1)} = \frac{(2j)!}{2^{2j-1}(j!)^2} \left[t_1^{(2n+1)} \frac{2j+1}{2j+2} + t_3^{(2n+1)} \frac{(2j+1)(2j+3)}{(2j+2)(2j+4)} \right.$$
$$\left. + \cdots + t_{2n+1}^{(2n+1)} \frac{(2j+1)(2j+3) \cdots (2j+2n+1)}{(2j+2)(2j+4) \cdots (2j+2n+2)} \right]$$

(b) Approximate the coefficients in (7.6-4) by truncating the series for c_{2n} and c_{2n+1} after the term in $j = 3$, and then convert the approximation to a power series.

(c) As in part b of the previous problem, compare this approximation with $T_{4,0}(x)$. [Ref.: Minnick (1957).]

28. (a) Derive the Chebyshev expansions for $\sin x$ and $\cos x$.   By drawing a graph of the error on $[-\pi/4, \pi/4]$, compare the approximations obtained by truncating these expansions with the corresponding results of Prob. 21 [see Watson (1962, p. 21) for the integrals (7.6-2)].

(b) Calculate $T_{3,2}(x)$ for $f(x) = \sin x$.   Convert the result to rational-function form.   Draw a graph of the error on $[-\pi/4, \pi/4]$ and compare the result with $R_{3,2}(x)$ derived in Prob. 21.

(c) Calculate $T_{2,2}(x)$ for $f(x) = \cos x$.   Convert the result to rational-function form, draw a graph of the error on $[-\pi/4, \pi/4]$, and compare with $R_{2,2}(x)$ derived in Prob. 21.

29. For $f(x) = e^x$, calculate $T_{3,1}(x)$ and $T_{1,3}(x)$. Draw a graph of the error on $[-1,1]$ and compare with the corresponding Padé approximations.

Section 7.7

30. (a) When the Maclaurin expansion of $f(x)$ contains only even powers or only odd powers, how should (7.7-3) be modified?

(b) Use this result to calculate $C_{5,0}(x)$ for $f(x) = \sin x$ with $\alpha = \pi/4$. Draw a graph of the error on $[-(\pi/4),\pi/4]$ and compare with the corresponding results of Probs. 21 and 28.

(c) Calculate $C_{4,0}(x)$ for $f(x) = \cos x$ with $\alpha = \pi/4$. Draw a graph of the error on $[-(\pi/4),\pi/4]$ and compare with the corresponding results of Probs. 21 and 28.

31. For $f(x) = e^x$ derive an approximation $C_{2,2}(x)$ with $\alpha = 1$ as in Example 7.5, using as the sequence (7.7-8) (a) $R_{0,0}^{(0)}(x)$, $R_{1,0}^{(1)}(x)$, $R_{2,0}^{(2)}(x)$, $R_{3,0}^{(3)}(x)$; (b) $R_{0,0}^{(0)}(x)$, $R_{1,0}^{(1)}(x)$, $R_{0,2}^{(2)}(x)$, $R_{3,0}^{(3)}(x)$. Why doesn't the choice of the second and fourth rational functions make any difference? In each case compare the resulting approximation with $T_{2,2}(x)$, $R_{2,2}(x)$, and the approximation of Example 7.5.

32. (a) Calculate $C_{3,1}(x)$ and $C_{1,3}(x)$ for e^x with $\alpha = 1$. By drawing graphs of the errors on $[-1,1]$, compare the errors with the corresponding Padé and Chebyshev approximations. [Use any convenient sequence (7.7-8).]

(b) Show that the derivation of $C_{1,1}(z)$ for $\sin (\sqrt{|z|})/\sqrt{|z|}$ on $[-(\pi^2/16),\pi^2/16]$ requires substantially less effort than the derivation of $C_{3,2}(x)$ for $\sin x$ on $[-(\pi/4),\pi/4]$. Is $xC_{1,1}(x^2)$ equal to $C_{3,2}(x)$?

(c) Actually derive $xC_{1,1}(x^2)$ with $\alpha = \pi/4$. By drawing the graph of the error on $[-(\pi/4),\pi/4]$, compare this approximation with corresponding Padé and Chebyshev approximations.

(d) Similarly derive $C_{1,1}(x^2)$ for $\cos x$ on $[-(\pi/4),\pi/4]$ and compare this approximation with corresponding Padé and Chebyshev approximations.

*33. A commonly used iterative method to compute $\sqrt{a}$ for a in $(0, \infty)$ is (cf. Prob. 10, Chap. 2)

$$x_{n+1} = \tfrac{1}{2}(x_n + a/x_n)$$

This iteration converges very rapidly if the initial approximation x_1 is sufficiently close to $\sqrt{a}$ (see Sec. 8.4). To get a good initial approximation, it is convenient to use a rational approximation. We begin by writing $a = 10^{2m} \times b$ where $.01 < b \leqq 1$.

(a) Derive a Padé approximation $R_{2,2}(x)$ to $\sqrt{x}$ on $[.01,1]$ by first making a change of variable so that the new interval is centered at the origin.

(b) Similarly, derive $C_{2,2}(x)$ with $\alpha = .495$ using $R_{0,0}^{(0)}(x)$, $R_{1,0}^{(1)}(x)$, $R_{1,1}^{(2)}(x)$, $R_{2,1}^{(3)}(x)$. By drawing a graph compare the errors in the approximations of parts a and b. [Ref.: Kogbetliantz (1960), pp. 33–35.]

34. (a) How must the development in Sec. 7.7 be modified if the interval $[-\alpha,\alpha]$ is replaced by the interval $[0,\alpha]$?

(b) Use these modifications to derive an economized approximation $C_{2,2}^*(x)$ to e^x on $[0,1]$. Draw a graph of the error.

*35. The τ method. Consider the differential equation

$$L(y) = p_n(x) \frac{d^n y}{dx^n} + p_{n-1}(x) \frac{d^{n-1} y}{dx^{n-1}} + \cdots + p_0(x)y + P(x) = 0$$
$$y(0) = y_0 \qquad y^{(i)}(0) = y_i \qquad i = 1, \ldots, n-1$$

where $p_j(x)$ is a polynomial of degree d_j and $P(x)$ is a polynomial of degree d.

(a) Assume a solution

$$y(x) = \sum_{j=0}^{m} a_j x^j \qquad m \geqq n$$

and let

$$D = \max (d, d_0 + m, d_1 + m - 1, \ldots, d_n + m - n)$$

Show that substituting this solution into the differential equation leads in general to a system of $D + 1 + n$ equations in $m + 1$ unknowns if the initial conditions are to be satisfied.

(b) Show that, in general, the differential equation

$$L(y) = \sum_{i=1}^{D-m+n} \tau_i T^*_{m-n+i} (x)$$

does have a solution of the form of part a where the τ_i's are real numbers and T^*_{m-n+i} is the shifted Chebyshev polynomial of degree $m + n + i$ (see Prob. 23). Thus deduce that, if the τ_i's are small, the solution of this differential equation is a good approximation to the solution of $L(y) = 0$.

(c) Use this method with $m = 4$ to approximate e^x. Draw a graph of the error on [0,1] and compare this with the error in $R_{4,0}(x)$ on [0,1]. [This method is of particular value when $f(x)$ does not have a convergent polynomial or continued-fraction expansion.] [Ref.: Lanczos (1956), pp. 464–469.]

Sections 7.8, 7.9

36. Let $P^*_m(x)/Q^*_k(x)$ be irreducible where $P^*_m(x)$ and $Q^*_k(x)$ are polynomials of degree m and k, respectively. Prove that any polynomial $A(x)$ of degree $m + k$ or less may be written

$$A(x) = Q^*_k(x)a(x) - P^*_m(x)b(x)$$

where $a(x)$ and $b(x)$ are polynomials of degree less than or equal to m and k, respectively.

*37. (a) Let r be the greatest lower bound of all r_{mk} in (7.8-1) for given $f(x)$, [a,b], m, and k. Why does an infinite sequence of rational approximations $R^{(i)}_{mk}(x) = P^{(i)}_m(x)/Q^{(i)}_k(x)$ exist such that $r^{(i)}_{mk} \to r$ as $i \to \infty$?

(b) Normalize $Q^{(i)}_k(x)$ so that $\sum_{j=0}^{k} [b^{(i)}_j]^2 = 1$ and prove that for this normalization,

$\sum_{j=0}^{m} [a^{(i)}_j]^2$ is bounded. Thus deduce that a subsequence $\{R^{(i_k)}_{mk}(x)\}$ exists such that

$$\lim_{i \to \infty} a^{(i_k)}_j = A_j \qquad \lim_{i \to \infty} b^{(i_k)}_j = B_j$$

for some constants A_j and B_j.

(c) Let $R(x) = \sum_{j=0}^{m} A_j x^j / \sum_{j=0}^{k} B_j x^j$ and let

$$\bar{r} = \max_{a \leq x \leq b} |f(x) - R(x)|$$

Prove that $\{R^{(i)}_{mk}(x)\}$ converges uniformly to $R(x)$.

(d) Use this result to show that $\bar{r} \leqq r$, and thus deduce the existence of the Chebyshev approximation.

*38. Suppose there exist two rational approximations $R_{mk}^{(1)}(x)$ and $R_{mk}^{(2)}(x)$ which minimize r_{mk} as given in Eq. (7.8-1). Let L_1 and L_2 be, respectively, the number of alternating extrema of the errors in $R_{mk}^{(1)}(x)$ and $R_{mk}^{(2)}(x)$. Assume $L_2 \geqq L_1$ and let $\alpha_1, \ldots, \alpha_{L_2}$ be the abscissas of the error extrema for $R_{mk}^{(2)}(x)$.

(a) Define $\Delta(x) = R_{mk}^{(1)}(x) - R_{mk}^{(2)}(x)$. Show that

$$\text{sgn} \left[f(\alpha_j) - R_{mk}^{(2)}(\alpha_j) \right] = \text{sgn} \, \Delta(\alpha_j)$$

if $\Delta(\alpha_j) \neq 0$.

(b) Suppose $\Delta(\alpha_{i-1}) \neq 0$, $\Delta(\alpha_j) = 0$, $j = i, \ldots, i+k$ and $\Delta(\alpha_{i+k+1}) \neq 0$. Show that the number of zeros of $\Delta(x)$ (counting multiplicities) in $[\alpha_{i-1}, \alpha_{i+k+1}]$ is even if k is even and odd if k is odd. Thus deduce that the number of zeros (counting multiplicities) in this interval is at least $k + 2$.

(c) Thus deduce that $\Delta(x)$ has at least $L_2 - 1$ zeros in (a,b).

(d) From this deduce a contradiction and, therefore, the uniqueness of the Chebyshev approximation.   [Ref.: Probs. 37 and 38, Achieser (1956), pp. 53–57.]

39. (a) Show that the results of Sec. 7.8 and the previous three problems are unchanged if we consider $s(x)R_{mk}(x)$ as the approximation to $f(x)$ where $s(x)$ is continuous and does not vanish in (a,b).

(b) How does the algorithm of Sec. 7.9 need to be modified for approximations of the form $s(x)R_{mk}(x)$ where $s(x)$ is a continuous function which does not vanish in (a,b)?

40. Consider approximating $f(x) = x^2 - 1$ on $[-1,1]$ by a rational function with $m = k = 1$.   Show that the Chebyshev approximation of this type is a constant and thus deduce that d in Theorem 7.2 is one.

41. Calculate the Chebyshev approximation to e^x on $[-1,1]$ of the form

$$\frac{a_0 + a_1 x}{1 + b_1 x}$$

by (a) calculating the Padé approximation $R_{1,1}(x)$; (b) calculating the economized approximation $C_{1,1}(x)$; (c) calculating $R_{1,1}^*(x)$ using the algorithm of Sec. 7.9.

chapter 8

THE SOLUTION OF
NONLINEAR EQUATIONS

8.1 INTRODUCTION

The remaining three chapters of this book will be concerned with the solution of linear and nonlinear equations and systems of equations.   In this chapter we shall be concerned with the solution of nonlinear algebraic and transcendental equations.   It might seem illogical to discuss the solution of nonlinear before linear equations, but the relation between the two subjects is tenuous indeed.   And since the solution of simultaneous linear equations provides the gateway to many of the advanced topics in numerical analysis that are not discussed in this book, it seems reasonable to leave linear equations to the last.

This chapter is divided naturally into two main sections which consider the not unrelated but mainly separate problems:

1. The search for *real* roots of the equation

$$f(x) = 0 \tag{8.1-1}$$

   where x is a real variable and $f(x)$ is any reasonably well-behaved function.

2. The search for *real and complex* roots of

$$P(x) = 0 \tag{8.1-2}$$

   where $P(x)$ is a polynomial.

This is not to say that we are never interested in complex roots of the general equation $f(x) = 0$, but this is a comparatively rare problem. Except in Sec. 8.8, we shall restrict ourselves to single equations. One reason for this is that this case is much more common than that of simultaneous nonlinear equations. An equally important reason, however, is that the solution of simultaneous nonlinear equations is an extremely difficult problem about which comparatively little is known.

In the case of the solution of simultaneous linear equations, the problem is not to find a closed form for the solution but rather to find an efficient algorithm for *computing* the known solution. For the single nonlinear equations of interest here, we assume no solution in closed form can be found, for if so, it would generally be easy to compute the solution (e.g., quadratic equations). Thus we must seek methods which lead to approximate solutions. Our technique throughout this chapter will be to develop iterative techniques for the solution of (8.1-1) and (8.1-2) (cf. Sec. 5.5-1). In considering these iterative techniques, we shall wish to answer two basic questions: (1) Does the iteration converge? (2) If so, how fast does it converge? Perhaps surprisingly to the reader, the first of these questions will occupy us much less than the second in our consideration of (8.1-1). This is because the convergence question is in one sense very easy to answer and in another sense too hard to answer. It is easy to answer because there is generally little difficulty in showing that, if the initial approximation(s) to a root of α of (8.1-1) are sufficiently close to the root, then the iteration will converge to α. (In a very few cases the iteration will converge independent of the initial approximation.) But the phrase "sufficiently close" points the way to the hard part of the question. How close the initial approximation(s) have to be to α for convergence depends generally upon the value of a derivative of $f(x)$ at some unknown point on the interval spanned by the initial approximation(s) and α. This presents the same problems we have found previously in the estimation of error terms.

Moreover, in practical problems, it is often the case that enough a priori knowledge of the desired root of the equation is known so that convergence of the iterations is not a problem. When a priori knowledge is poor, it is often advisable to use a method which converges independent of the starting values (but, alas, usually slowly) until a good approximation is obtained and then to switch over to a more rapidly converging method. Thus we conclude that, among those methods whose convergence depends upon the initial approximation, it is difficult to compare the convergence properties of various methods and often it is not significant.

However, it is both possible and important to compare the relative *rates* of convergence of various iteration methods. As we shall indicate, analogously to the case of the numerical solution of ordinary differential equations, the computational efficiency of a method depends upon the number of evaluations of $f(x)$ and its derivatives.

In the special case of polynomial equations, good a priori knowledge is often not available and, moreover, whereas often only a single root of $f(x) = 0$ is desired, all the roots of $P(x) = 0$ may be desired. We shall therefore place more emphasis on methods whose convergence is assured independent of the starting value in the case of polynomial equations than in the general case.

It is worth noting that, if an iterative method for the solution of (8.1-1) converges, then the only limitation on the accuracy of the root is in the number of digits carried in the computation. That is, the roundoff error *in a single iteration* is the only inherent limitation on the accuracy. This seldom creates any problems in the solution of (8.1-1).

8.2 FUNCTIONAL ITERATION

Let $f(x)$ be a continuous real-valued function with as many derivatives as are required in what follows. Furthermore, we assume that, in some neighborhood of the desired root α of $f(x) = 0$, the function $f(x)$ has an inverse (i.e., we assume α is a simple root). Our approach here is to derive iterative methods for the solution of $f(x) = 0$ by using inverse interpolation, a subject which we introduced briefly in Sec. 3.7.

Let $g(y)$ be the function inverse to $f(x)$. Given the points y_j, $j = 1, \ldots, n$ we may approximate $g(y)$ using a Lagrangian interpolation formula as

$$g(y) \approx h(y) = \sum_{j=1}^{n} l_j(y)g(y_j) = \sum_{j=1}^{n} l_j(y)x_{i+1-j} \tag{8.2-1}$$

using, for later convenience, the notation $x_{i+1-j} = g(y_j)$. Our object is to find a value α of x at which $y = 0$. Since $\alpha = g(0)$, we get from (8.2-1) an approximation x_{i+1} for α given by

$$x_{i+1} = h(0) = \sum_{j=1}^{n} l_j(0)x_{i+1-j} \tag{8.2-2}$$

where, using (3.2-3),

$$l_j(0) = \frac{(-1)^{n-1}y_1y_2y_3 \cdots y_{j-1}y_{j+1} \cdots y_n}{(y_j - y_1)(y_j - y_2) \cdots (y_j - y_{j-1})(y_j - y_{j+1}) \cdots (y_j - y_n)} \tag{8.2-3}$$

From (3.2-9)

$$\alpha - x_{i+1} = \frac{g^{(n)}(\eta)}{n!}(-1)^n y_1y_2 \cdots y_n \tag{8.2-4}$$

with η in the interval spanned by $y_1, \ldots, y_n$ and 0. The derivative of the inverse function can be calculated in terms of derivatives of $f(x)$ {1}.

Equation (8.2-2) defines an iterative method for finding a root of (8.1-1) if the iteration converges. That is, using the points $x_i, \ldots, x_{i-n+1}$, we calculate x_{i+1}, and then, replacing one of the points $x_i, \ldots, x_{i-n+1}$ by x_{i+1}, we calculate x_{i+2} using the remaining n points, and so on. This method is one example of an *n-point iteration function* whose most general form is

$$x_{i+1} = F_i(x_i, x_{i-1}, \ldots, x_{i-n+1}) \tag{8.2-5}$$

where the iteration function F_i will in general involve not only $x_i, \ldots, x_{i-n+1}$ but also values of $f(x)$ and some of its derivatives evaluated at one or more of the points x_j. For example, in (8.2-2) $l_j(0)$ involves values of $f(x)$ at the points x_j, $j = 1, \ldots, n$. We shall assume throughout this chapter that F_i has as many continuous derivatives as required in a neighborhood of α.

Methods for finding the roots of (8.1-1) based on (8.2-5) are called *functional iteration methods;* all the methods we shall consider for the solution of (8.1-1) are of this form. The subscript i on F_i is necessary only when the iteration function itself may change from one iteration to the next; generally the iteration function will be *stationary* (i.e., independent of i), in which case we shall write F instead of F_i. If the iteration using a stationary iteration function converges to a root α then we must have

$$\alpha = F(\alpha, \alpha, \ldots, \alpha) \tag{8.2-6}$$

A concept which will be basic to our discussion of iteration methods is that of the *order* of the method. First we define the error in the ith iterate to be

$$\epsilon_{i+1} = \alpha - x_{i+1} \tag{8.2-7}$$

Now assume that the iteration (8.2-5) converges so that $\lim\limits_{i \to \infty} x_i = \alpha$. Then, if there exists a real number $p \geq 1$ such that

$$\lim_{i \to \infty} \frac{|x_{i+1} - \alpha|}{|x_i - \alpha|^p} = \lim_{i \to \infty} \frac{|\epsilon_{i+1}|}{|\epsilon_i|^p} = C \neq 0 \tag{8.2-8}$$

we say that the method is of order p at α {2}. The constant C is called the asymptotic error constant; it depends on $f(x)$. The requirement that $C \neq 0$ is to be interpreted to mean that $C \neq 0$ for a general function $f(x)$. This assures the uniqueness of p. For a particular function $f(x)$, C may be zero, in which case, for this function, the iteration will converge more rapidly than usual. When $p = 1$ then C must be less than or equal to 1 in order for the method to converge {2}, but for $p > 1$, C need not be less than 1 for convergence.

We assumed in the foregoing that α is a simple root. But we shall often apply iteration methods derived using this assumption to functions which have multiple roots. We shall see that the order of the iteration will depend on the multiplicity of the root.

8.2-1 Computational efficiency

We could compare methods of functional iteration on the basis of how fast they converge (i.e., on their order), but it makes more sense to compare their *computational efficiency*, which is a measure of how much computation must be done to arrive at a given accuracy in a root. In order to arrive at a definition of computational efficiency, let us consider trying to find a root of (8.1-1) using two different iteration methods, both starting from the same initial approximation. Let the two methods have orders p_1 and p_2, respectively. For large enough i (i.e., as we near convergence), the approximations

$$|\epsilon_{i+1}^{(1)}| = C_1|\epsilon_i^{(1)}|^{p_1} \qquad |\epsilon_{i+1}^{(2)}| = C_2|\epsilon_i^{(2)}|^{p_2} \tag{8.2-9}$$

are valid where C_1 and C_2 are the asymptotic error constants of the two methods. Let

$$S_i = -\ln|\epsilon_i^{(1)}| \qquad T_i = -\ln|\epsilon_i^{(2)}| \tag{8.2-10}$$

Then

$$S_{i+1} = -\ln C_1 + p_1 S_i \qquad T_{i+1} = -\ln C_2 + p_2 T_i \tag{8.2-11}$$

The solutions of these difference equations are {3}

$$S_i = S_1 p_1^i - \ln\{C_1^{[(p_1{}^i-1)/(p_1-1)]}\} \qquad T_i = T_1 p_2^i - \ln\{C_2^{[(p_2{}^i-1)/(p_2-1)]}\} \tag{8.2-12}$$

where the initial values S_1 and T_1 are equal. Let the number of steps required to get the desired degree of convergence be I and J, respectively, for methods 1 and 2. Hence $|\epsilon_I^{(1)}|$ and $|\epsilon_J^{(2)}|$ and, therefore, S_I and T_J are essentially equal. Then using (8.2-12) we get

$$S_1(p_1^I - p_2^J) + \ln\frac{C_2^{[(p_2{}^J-1)/(p_2-1)]}}{C_1^{[(p_1{}^I-1)/(p_1-1)]}} = 0 \tag{8.2-13}$$

If θ and ϕ are, respectively, the costs per iteration (i.e., the amount of computation required per iteration) of the two methods, then the total costs of the computation are θI and ϕJ, respectively. The quantities θ and ϕ can be estimated from the iteration function, but (8.2-13) gives us no obvious way of relating I and J. It is, however, often a good assumption that the second term in (8.2-13) is small compared with the first (as will happen, for example, if C_1 and C_2 are both close to unity). In this case we get

$$\frac{I}{1/\ln p_1} \approx \frac{J}{1/\ln p_2} \tag{8.2-14}$$

Therefore, a measure of the cost of a method is the product of θ, the cost per iteration, and the reciprocal of the logarithm of the order p. The efficiency index, which is the reciprocal of the cost, may be defined as $\ln p/\theta$ or, to use the more usual definition,

$$EI = p^{1/\theta} \tag{8.2-15}$$

A particular case in which (8.2-13) may be used directly to estimate I/J is considered in $\{14\}$.

It is worth noting that, since the order of a method is a property local to the neighborhood of a root, the efficiency index measures only how good a method is when it is near convergence. A determination of the efficiency of a method outside of the neighborhood of a root is generally extremely difficult (cf. Sec. 8.10-4).

The cost per iteration will, in analogy with our argument in Chap. 5, depend mainly on the number of evaluations of $f(x)$ and its derivatives required at each step and not on the arithmetic operations required to combine these quantities in the iteration function F_i of (8.2-5). We noted in Sec. 5.8-2 that, having computed $f(x)$, $f'(x)$ is often quite cheap to compute on a digital computer. For example, if $f(x)$ is composed of elementary functions, the chief cost of evaluating $f(x)$ is in the evaluation of these elementary functions. Thus, since $f'(x)$ will also be some combination of these elementary functions, the evaluation of $f'(x)$ is simple $\{4\}$.

8.3 THE SECANT METHOD

This is one of the oldest methods known for the solution of $f(x) = 0$, but it has been surprisingly neglected until recently when its important advantages, particularly for use on computers, have again been realized. For this reason and because it serves to illustrate various aspects of iteration methods, we shall discuss it before considering some more general aspects of functional iteration. In this section and the following two we assume that α is a simple root of (8.1-1).

Our approach in this section will be to use linear inverse interpolation [i.e., (8.2-2) with $n = 2$] to derive methods of the form (8.2-5). One such method, illustrated in Fig. 8.1, is the *method of false position*. Suppose we can find two points x_1 and x_2 such that $f(x_1)f(x_2) < 0$. The chord joining y_1 and y_2 intersects the x axis at a point x_3. Then choosing

x_3 and x_i, $i = 1$ or 2, such that $f(x_3)f(x_i) < 0$ (in the case shown $i = 1$), we repeat the above procedure to obtain x_4 and so on. From a study of Fig. 8.1 it is clear that this method converges for any continuous function $f(x)$; we leave the details of the proof to a problem $\{5\}$. Also considered in a problem $\{6\}$ is the method of bisection, which also converges for all continuous functions.

The method of false position is a nonstationary iteration method in general. From Fig. 8.1 we have

$$x_3 = \frac{y_2}{y_2 - y_1}\, x_1 + \frac{y_1}{y_1 - y_2}\, x_2$$

$$x_4 = \frac{y_3}{y_3 - y_1}\, x_1 + \frac{y_1}{y_1 - y_3}\, x_3 \tag{8.3-1}$$

$$x_5 = \frac{y_4}{y_4 - y_3}\, x_3 + \frac{y_3}{y_3 - y_4}\, x_4$$

Therefore,

$$F_i = \frac{y_i}{y_i - y_{i-1}}\, x_{i-1} + \frac{y_{i-1}}{y_{i-1} - y_i}\, x_i \qquad i = 2, 4$$

$$F_i = \frac{y_i}{y_i - y_{i-2}}\, x_{i-2} + \frac{y_{i-2}}{y_{i-2} - y_i}\, x_i \qquad i = 3 \tag{8.3-2}$$

For certain functions, however, the method of false position is a stationary method of functional iteration. For example, if $f(x)$ is convex between x_1 and x_2, then the method is stationary. From Fig. 8.2 we see that the point x_1 is always one of the two points used to get the next iterate.

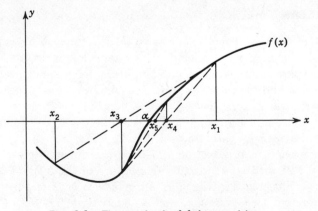

Fig. 8.1   The method of false position.

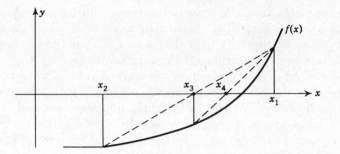

Fig. 8.2   The method of false position for convex functions.

Therefore, we have

$$x_{i+1} = \frac{y_i}{y_i - y_1} x_1 + \frac{y_1}{y_1 - y_i} x_i \tag{8.3-3}$$

for all i.

Since the method of false position is just a sequence of linear inverse interpolations, the error may be written down using (8.2-4) as

$$\epsilon_{i+1} = \alpha - x_{i+1} = \frac{g''(\eta)}{2} y_i y_1 = \frac{-f''(\xi)}{2[f'(\xi)]^3} y_i y_1 \tag{8.3-4}$$

since {1}

$$g''(y) = -\frac{f''(x)}{[f'(x)]^3} \tag{8.3-5}$$

Now since $f(\alpha) = 0$ we have, using the mean-value theorem

$$y_1 = f(x_1) = f(x_1) - f(\alpha) = (x_1 - \alpha)f'(\xi_1) \tag{8.3-6}$$

and similarly

$$y_i = (x_i - \alpha)f'(\xi_i) \tag{8.3-7}$$

with ξ_1 and ξ_i in appropriate intervals.   Using these two equations in (8.3-4) we have

$$\epsilon_{i+1} = \frac{-f''(\xi)f'(\xi_1)f'(\xi_i)}{2[f'(\xi)]^3} \epsilon_i \epsilon_1 \tag{8.3-8}$$

Therefore,

$$\lim_{i \to \infty} \frac{|\epsilon_{i+1}|}{|\epsilon_i|} = \left| \frac{-f''(\bar{\xi})f'(\xi_1)f'(\alpha)}{2[f'(\bar{\xi})]^3} \right| |\epsilon_1| \tag{8.3-9}$$

since ξ_i approaches α and ξ approaches some limiting value $\bar{\xi}$ as $i \to \infty$. We have assumed that $f'(x)$ is bounded away from zero in a neighborhood of α. From this it follows that $p = 1$. Thus the method of false position has *linear* convergence for convex functions.

The method of false position is an excellent method when the a priori information on the location of the root is poor. In such a case, we would first search for two points at which $f(x)$ has opposite signs and then apply the method. However, it converges slowly. If we let the cost of evaluating $f(x)$ equal 1 (as we shall hereafter also), then from (8.2-15) we have†

$$EI = 1 \tag{8.3-10}$$

which, as we shall see, can be substantially improved upon. In fact, it can be improved upon using linear inverse interpolation if we drop the requirement that $f(x)$ have opposite signs at the two points used to generate the next point. If instead we always use x_i and x_{i-1} to generate x_{i+1}, we have

$$x_{i+1} = \frac{y_i}{y_i - y_{i-1}} x_{i-1} + \frac{y_{i-1}}{y_{i-1} - y_i} x_i \tag{8.3-11}$$

This stationary iteration method is called the *secant method*. It is a substantial improvement over the method of false position except in one respect, namely, that it may not converge. This is, of course, the price we would expect to have to pay for an increase in efficiency.

For (8.3-11) the analogous equation to (8.3-8) is

$$\epsilon_{i+1} = \frac{-f''(\xi)f'(\xi_i)f'(\xi_{i-1})}{2[f'(\xi)]^3} \epsilon_i \epsilon_{i-1} \tag{8.3-12}$$

If the initial approximations x_1 and x_2 are sufficiently close to α, then, since the term in brackets in (8.3-12) is bounded in some neighborhood of α, the iteration will converge to α. Assume now that the iteration does converge so that all iterates are contained in some interval I. On this interval let

$$0 < m_1 \leqq |f'(x)| \leqq M_1 \qquad |f''(x)| \leqq M_2 \tag{8.3-13}$$

Then from (8.3-12)

$$|\epsilon_{i+1}| \leqq K|\epsilon_i| \, |\epsilon_{i-1}| \tag{8.3-14}$$

where $K = M_2 M_1^2 / 2m_1^3$. Now let $K|\epsilon_i| = d_i$. Then we may write (8.3-14) as

$$d_{i+1} \leqq d_i d_{i-1} \tag{8.3-15}$$

† Here and hereafter in this chapter we shall estimate the cost of evaluating the iteration function F by considering only the evaluations of $f(x)$ and its derivatives.

Now let "sufficiently close" above mean that d_1 and d_2 are both less than or equal to $d < 1$.   Then from (8.3-15)

$$d_3 \leqq d^2 \qquad d_5 \leqq d^5$$
$$d_4 \leqq d^3 \qquad d_6 \leqq d^8 \tag{8.3-16}$$

and in general

$$d_{i+1} \leqq d^{\gamma_i} \tag{8.3-17}$$

where

$$\gamma_{i+1} = \gamma_i + \gamma_{i-1} \qquad i = 1, 2, \ldots \qquad \gamma_0 = \gamma_1 = 1 \tag{8.3-18}$$

Equation (8.3-18) is the difference equation for the Fibonacci numbers. The indicial equation for (8.3-18) is

$$\rho^2 = \rho + 1 \tag{8.3-19}$$

which has the solutions $(1 + \sqrt{5})/2$ and $(1 - \sqrt{5})/2$.   Therefore, the solution of (8.3-18) is {7}

$$\gamma_i = \frac{1}{\sqrt{5}} \left[\left(\frac{1 + \sqrt{5}}{2} \right)^{i+1} - \left(\frac{1 - \sqrt{5}}{2} \right)^{i+1} \right] \tag{8.3-20}$$

Furthermore,

$$\lim_{i \to \infty} \frac{\gamma_{i+1}}{\gamma_i} = \frac{1 + \sqrt{5}}{2} \approx 1.618 \tag{8.3-21}$$

Now from (8.3-17) and the definition of d_i, we have

$$|\epsilon_i| \leqq (1/K) \, d^{\gamma_i} \tag{8.3-22}$$

This together with (8.3-21) suggests the result that {7}

$$\lim_{i \to \infty} \frac{|\epsilon_{i+1}|}{|\epsilon_i|^{(1+\sqrt{5})/2}} = \left| \frac{f''(\alpha)}{2f'(\alpha)} \right|^{(\sqrt{5}-1)/2} \tag{8.3-23}$$

since as x_i approaches α, the coefficient of $\epsilon_i \epsilon_{i-1}$ in (8.3-12) approaches $|f''(\alpha)/2f'(\alpha)|$.   Hopefully, however, the reader has noted that the foregoing by no means constitutes a proof of (8.3-23).   A rigorous proof of (8.3-23) is beyond our scope here but may be found in Ostrowski (1960).   From (8.3-23) it follows that the order of the secant method is $(1 + \sqrt{5})/2$ and that

$$EI = (1 + \sqrt{5})/2 \tag{8.3-24}$$

Not only is this a substantial improvement over (8.3-10), but as we shall see, the efficiency of the secant method compares favorably with many seemingly more sophisticated methods.

The fact that the secant method does not require the evaluation of any derivatives can be a great advantage in certain problems. For example, a not uncommon problem is to find a root of

$$f(x;y_1,y_2, \ldots ,y_k) = 0 \qquad\qquad (8.3\text{-}25)$$

where

$$y_j = g_j(x) \qquad j = 1, \ldots , k \qquad\qquad (8.3\text{-}26)$$

Evaluating derivatives of f with respect to x is often impractical in such a case.

A disadvantage of the secant method would seem to be that multiple-precision arithmetic would be required as the iteration nears convergence because (8.3-11) then involves the difference of two nearly equal quantities. But let us rewrite (8.3-11) as

$$x_{i+1} = x_i - \frac{x_i - x_{i-1}}{y_i - y_{i-1}} y_i \qquad\qquad (8.3\text{-}27)$$

The second term may be considered a correction term to x_i and as such requires only a very few significant digits as convergence is neared (why?). Therefore, although the quotient $(x_i - x_{i-1})/(y_i - y_{i-1})$ will have very few significant digits if multiple-precision arithmetic is not used, there will nevertheless generally be enough significant figures to compute α to nearly full single-precision accuracy.

Example 8.1   Find the positive root of $\sin x - x/2 = 0$ using both the method of false position and the secant method.

Since the root lies between $\pi/2$ and π (see Fig. 8.3), we use $x_1 = \pi$, $x_2 = \pi/2$. Using (8.3-3) and (8.3-11), we get (note that $f''(x) \leqq 0$ in $[\pi/2, \pi]$)

	Method of false position	Secant method
x_3	1.75960	1.75960
x_4	1.84420	1.93200
x_5	1.87701	1.89242
x_6	1.88895	1.89543
x_7	1.89320	1.89549
x_8	1.89469	
x_9	1.89521	
x_{10}	1.89540	
x_{11}	1.89546	
x_{12}	1.89548	
x_{13}	1.89549	

and, as we would expect, the secant method converges substantially faster to the true value 1.89549. Note particularly the slow convergence of the method of false position as the root is approached.

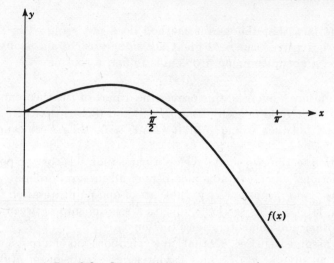

Fig. 8.3   Graph of $f(x) = \sin x - x/2$.

8.4   ONE–POINT ITERATION FORMULAS

Equation (8.3-11) is a two-point iteration method; that is, to compute x_{i+1} we use information at two previous values. Formulas of the class which use information at only one point are naturally called one-point iteration formulas. In this section we shall consider only stationary one-point iteration formulas which have the form

$$x_{i+1} = F(x_i) \tag{8.4-1}$$

with $\alpha = F(\alpha)$ if the method converges. We prove first

Theorem 8.1   The order of any one-point iteration function $F(x)$ is a positive integer. More specifically $F(x)$ has order p if and only if $F(\alpha) = \alpha$; $F^{(j)}(\alpha) \equiv 0$, $1 \leq j < p$; $F^{(p)}(\alpha) \neq 0$.

Proof   We expand $F(x_i)$ in a Taylor series about α

$$F(x_i) = \alpha + (x_i - \alpha)F'(\alpha) + \cdots + \frac{(x_i - \alpha)^{p-1}}{(p-1)!} F^{(p-1)}(\alpha)$$
$$+ \frac{(x_i - \alpha)^p}{p!} F^{(p)}(\xi) = \alpha + \frac{(x_i - \alpha)^p}{p!} F^{(p)}(\xi) \tag{8.4-2}$$

where ξ lies between x_i and α. Since $F(x_i) = x_{i+1}$, we have

$$x_{i+1} - \alpha = \frac{(x_i - \alpha)^p}{p!} F^{(p)}(\xi) \tag{8.4-3}$$

Therefore,

$$\lim_{i \to \infty} \frac{|x_{i+1} - \alpha|}{|x_i - \alpha|^p} = \frac{1}{p!} |F^{(p)}(\alpha)| \neq 0 \qquad (8.4\text{-}4)$$

if the iteration converges; this proves the if part of the theorem. On the other hand, it follows easily from (8.4-2) and (8.4-4) that, if $F^{(j)}(\alpha) \neq 0$ for some j between 0 and p or if $F^{(p)}(\alpha) \equiv 0$, then $F(x)$ cannot be of order p.

In this section we shall develop a particular class of one-point iteration functions which contains members of all integral orders. Although this class by no means exhausts the class of one-point iteration functions, we shall, later in this section, indicate a relationship between this class and all other one-point iteration functions.

We assume as in Sec. 8.2 that, in a neighborhood of a root α of (8.1-1), $f(x)$ has an inverse $g(y)$. The Taylor-series expansion of $g(y)$ about a point y_i is given by

$$x = g(y) = \sum_{j=0}^{m+1} \frac{(y - y_i)^j}{j!} g^{(j)}(y_i) + \frac{(y - y_i)^{m+2}}{(m+2)!} g^{(m+2)}(\eta)$$

$$= x_i + \sum_{j=1}^{m+1} \frac{(y - y_i)^j}{j!} g^{(j)}(y_i) + \frac{(y - y_i)^{m+2}}{(m+2)!} g^{(m+2)}(\eta)$$

$$g^{(j)}(y_i) = \frac{d^j}{dy^j} g(y) \Big|_{y=y_i} \qquad (8.4\text{-}5)$$

where η is between y and y_i. Since $\alpha = g(0)$ we have

$$\alpha = x_i + \sum_{j=1}^{m+1} \frac{(-1)^j}{j!} y_i^j g^{(j)}(y_i) + \frac{(-1)^{m+2} y_i^{m+2}}{(m+2)!} g^{(m+2)}(\eta)$$

$$= x_i + \sum_{j=1}^{m+1} \frac{(-1)^j}{j!} f_i^j g_i^{(j)} + \frac{(-1)^{m+2}}{(m+2)!} f_i^{m+2} g^{(m+2)}(\eta) \quad (8.4\text{-}6)$$

where we have written $y_i = f(x_i) = f_i$ and $g^{(j)}(y_i) = g_i^{(j)}$. If we now define

$$Y_j(x_i) \equiv Y_j = \frac{(-1)^j}{(j+1)!} (f_i')^{j+1} g^{(j+1)} \qquad \text{and} \qquad u_i = \frac{f_i}{f_i'}$$

$$j = 0, 1, \ldots \quad (8.4\text{-}7)$$

then (8.4-6) becomes

$$\alpha = x_i - u_i \sum_{j=0}^{m} u_i^j Y_j + \frac{(-1)^{m+2}}{(m+2)!} f_i^{m+2} g^{(m+2)}(\eta) \qquad (8.4\text{-}8)$$

Equation (8.4-8) suggests consideration of the iteration formula

$$x_{i+1} = x_i - u_i \sum_{j=0}^{m} u_i^j Y_j \qquad (8.4\text{-}9)$$

The value of (8.4-9) will depend partly on whether the Y_j's can be easily calculated. From (8.4-7) we have $Y_0 = 1$ (why?). By differentiating $Y(x)$ as defined in (8.4-7), we calculate $\{9\}$

$$Y_j = \frac{1}{j+1} (j D_2 Y_{j-1} - Y'_{j-1}) \qquad j > 0$$

$$Y'_j = \frac{d}{dx} Y_j(x) \Big|_{x=x_i} \qquad (8.4\text{-}10)$$

where

$$D_j(x_i) \equiv D_j = f_i^{(j)} / f'_i \qquad (8.4\text{-}11)$$

From (8.4-11) we have by differentiating $D_j(x)$

$$D_1 = 1$$
$$D_j = D_2 D_{j-1} + D'_{j-1} \qquad j > 1 \qquad D'_j = \frac{d}{dx} D_i(x) \Big|_{x=x_i} \qquad (8.4\text{-}12)$$

Using (8.4-11) and (8.4-12) in (8.4-10), we have in particular

$$Y_1 = \tfrac{1}{2} D_2$$
$$Y_2 = \tfrac{1}{3}[D_2^2 - \tfrac{1}{2}(d/dx)D_2] = \tfrac{1}{3}[D_2^2 - \tfrac{1}{2}(D_3 - D_2^2)]$$
$$\qquad\qquad = \tfrac{1}{6}(3D_2^2 - D_3) \qquad (8.4\text{-}13)$$
$$Y_3 = \tfrac{1}{4}\{\tfrac{1}{2}D_2(3D_2^2 - D_3) - \tfrac{1}{6}[6D_2(D_3 - D_2^2)$$
$$\qquad - (D_4 - D_2 D_3)]\} = \tfrac{1}{24}(15D_2^3 - 10D_2 D_3 + D_4)$$

We leave to a problem $\{9\}$ the proof of the general result that Y_j is a polynomial in $D_2, D_3, \ldots, D_{j+1}$. Thus the main problem in evaluating (8.4-9) is to evaluate u_i and $D_j, j = 1, \ldots, m + 1$.

Subtracting (8.4-9) from (8.4-8) we have

$$\epsilon_{i+1} = \frac{(-1)^{m+2}}{(m+2)!} f_i^{m+2} g^{(m+2)}(\eta) \qquad (8.4\text{-}14)$$

Since

$$f_i = f(x_i) = f(x_i) - f(\alpha) = (x_i - \alpha)f'(\xi_1) \qquad (8.4\text{-}15)$$

with ξ_1 between x_i and α, we have

$$\epsilon_{i+1} = \frac{1}{(m+2)!} \{[f'(\xi_1)]^{m+2} g^{(m+2)}(\eta)\} \epsilon_i^{m+2} \qquad (8.4\text{-}16)$$

If the root is simple the term in braces in (8.4-16) is bounded in some neighborhood of α. Therefore, the order of (8.4-9) is $m + 2$, and if the initial approximation is sufficiently good, the iteration will converge. (Even for a bad initial approximation it may converge; see Sec. 8.7.)

The evaluation of (8.4-9) requires the evaluation of $f(x_i)$ and its first $m + 1$ derivatives (why?). If θ_j is the cost of evaluating $f^{(j)}(x_i)$ relative to the cost of evaluating $f(x)$, which as before we take to be 1, then the efficiency index of (8.4-9) is given by

$$EI = (m + 2)^{1/\left(1 + \sum\limits_{j=1}^{m+1} \theta_j\right)} \tag{8.4-17}$$

One important and familiar special case of (8.4-9) is that for $m = 0$. We have

$$x_{i+1} = x_i - u_i = x_i - \frac{f(x_i)}{f'(x_i)} \tag{8.4-18}$$

which is the familiar Newton-Raphson iteration. The error is given by (8.4-16) as

$$\epsilon_{i+1} = \tfrac{1}{2}[f'(\xi_1)]^2 g''(\eta)\epsilon_i^2 = -\frac{f''(\xi)[f'(\xi_1)]^2}{2[f'(\xi)]^3}\,\epsilon_i^2 \tag{8.4-19}$$

In fact it can be shown {13} that the terms in $f'(x)$ can be canceled as if $\xi = \xi_1 = x_i$ so that

$$\epsilon_{i+1} = -\frac{1}{2}\frac{f''(\xi)}{f'(x_i)}\,\epsilon_i^2 \tag{8.4-20}$$

From (8.4-17) the efficiency index of the Newton-Raphson method is $2^{1/1+\theta_1}$ where θ_1 is the cost of evaluating $f'(x)$. A straightforward calculation leads to the result that if $\theta_1 < .44$ the efficiency of the Newton-Raphson method is greater than that of the secant method (8.3-11). As we pointed out previously, the cost of evaluating the derivative is often much less than that of evaluating the function, a notable exception being polynomials. If a decision is to be made on whether to use (8.3-11) or (8.4-18) to solve (8.1-1), then a perfectly reasonable basis for this decision is to estimate θ_1 and use (8.3-11) if it is greater than .44 and (8.4-18) otherwise.

Example 8.2   Repeat the calculation of Example 8.1 using the Newton-Raphson method starting with, first, $x_1 = \pi$ and, second, $x_1 = \pi/2$.

The results are

	$x_1 = \pi$	$x_1 = \pi/2$
x_2	2.09440	2.00000
x_3	1.91322	1.90100
x_4	1.89567	1.89551
x_5	1.89549	1.89549

The convergence in both cases requires one less iteration than the secant method. Since $f'(x) = \cos x - \frac{1}{2}$ the derivative is somewhat, but not a great deal, easier to compute than the function (because to compute the cosine from the sine a square root will have to be calculated). But if, for example, we had $f(x) = e^x - x$ then the derivative would be much easier to calculate than the function.

8.4-1   Rational one-point iteration formulas

Equation (8.4-9) may be rewritten as

$$x_{i+1} = x_i - u_i U_m(u_i) \qquad U_m(u_i) = \sum_{j=0}^{m} u_i^j Y_j \qquad (8.4-21)$$

where $U_m(u_i)$ is a polynomial of degree m in u_i. Now drawing on the theory of rational approximations discussed in the previous chapter, we ask: Can we improve upon (8.4-21) using rational functions in place of $U_m(u_i)$? To investigate this we consider iterations of the form

$$x_{i+1} = x_i - u_i[P(u_i)/Q(u_i)] \qquad (8.4-22)$$

where

$$P(u_i) = \sum_{j=0}^{p} P_j u_i^j \qquad Q(u_i) = \sum_{j=0}^{q} Q_j u_i^j \qquad (8.4-23)$$

Our interest here will not be in Chebyshev approximations, since we are not approximating on some *fixed* interval about α, but rather in Padé approximations since they will be more accurate the nearer we are to α. (Note that $u_i = 0$ at $x_i = \alpha$.) In the limit as $m \to \infty$ the iteration (8.4-21) becomes

$$\alpha = x_i - u_i U(u_i) \qquad (8.4-24)$$

where

$$U(u_i) = \sum_{j=0}^{\infty} Y_j u_i^j \qquad (8.4-25)$$

Our object is to choose the coefficients P_j and Q_j in (8.4-23) so that $U(u_i)$ and $P(u_i)/Q(u_i)$ have as many derivatives as possible equal at $u_i = 0$.

Therefore, as in Chap. 7 we assume that $Q_0 = 1$ and we consider

$$U(u_i) - \frac{P(u_i)}{Q(u_i)} = \frac{\left(\sum_{j=0}^{\infty} Y_j u_i^j\right)\left(1 + \sum_{j=1}^{q} Q_j u_i^j\right) - \sum_{j=0}^{p} P_j u_i^j}{1 + \sum_{j=1}^{q} Q_j u_i^j}$$

$$= \frac{\sum_{j=0}^{\infty} H_j u_i^j}{1 + \sum_{j=1}^{q} Q_j u_i^j} \qquad (8.4\text{-}26)$$

Then using equations analogous to (7.3-5) we determine the P_j and Q_j so that $H_j = 0, j = 0, \ldots, p + q$. The result is an iteration formula of the form (8.4-22) which we denote by

$$x_{i+1} = I_{pq}(x_i) \qquad (8.4\text{-}27)$$

with $q = 0$ corresponding to (8.4-21). For $p + q = 0, 1, 2$ these iteration formulas are {15}

$$
\begin{aligned}
p + q = 0: \quad & I_{00} = x_i - u_i && \text{(Newton's method)} \\
p + q = 1: \quad & I_{10} = x_i - u_i(1 - Y_1 u_i) \\
& I_{01} = x_i - \frac{u_i}{1 - Y_1 u_i} && \text{(Halley's method)} \\
p + q = 2: \quad & I_{20} = x_i - u_i(1 + Y_1 u_i + Y_2 u_i^2) && (8.4\text{-}28) \\
& I_{11} = x_i - u_i \frac{Y_1 + (Y_1^2 - Y_2)u_i}{Y_1 - Y_2 u_i} \\
& I_{02} = x_i - \frac{u_i}{1 - Y_1 u_i + (Y_1^2 - Y_2)u_i^2}
\end{aligned}
$$

In order to consider the error in an iteration formula of the form (8.4-27), we introduce the notation

$$\epsilon_{i+1}^{(p,q)} = \alpha - x_{i+1} \qquad (8.4\text{-}29)$$

Subtracting (8.4-22) from (8.4-24) we get

$$\epsilon_{i+1}^{(p,q)} = u_i\left[\frac{P(u_i)}{Q(u_i)} - U(u_i)\right] = -\frac{u_i^{m+2}\sum_{j=0}^{\infty} H_{m+1+j}u_i^j}{1 + \sum_{j=1}^{q} Q_j u_i^j}$$

$$m = p + q \quad (8.4\text{-}30)$$

In analogy with (7.3-6) we shall estimate the error by $-H_{m+1}u_i^{m+2}$, the first nonzero term in the numerator of (8.4-30). For example, with

$m = 2$ we may calculate $\{15\}$

$$\epsilon_{i+1}^{(2,0)} \approx -Y_3 u_i^4 \qquad \epsilon_{i+1}^{(1,1)} \approx -(Y_3 - Y_2^2/Y_1)u_i^4$$
$$\epsilon_{i+1}^{(0,2)} \approx -(Y_3 - 2Y_1Y_2 + Y_1^3)u_i^4 \tag{8.4-31}$$

Furthermore, using the mean-value theorem

$$u_i = \frac{f_i}{f_i'} = \frac{f(x_i) - f(\alpha)}{f'(x_i)} = \frac{(x_i - \alpha)f'(\xi)}{f'(x_i)} \tag{8.4-32}$$

It follows then from (8.4-30) that the order of $I_{pq}(x_i)$ is $m + 2$ since H_{m+1} is in general nonzero. For the case $q = 0$ we already knew this. The efficiency index of $I_{pq}(x_i)$ is therefore also given by (8.4-17).

Since the Y_j's depend on $f(x)$, the estimates (8.4-31) do not in themselves indicate which of the three iterative methods with $p + q = 2$ is to be preferred; in fact there is no one which is always best. In Chap. 7 we concluded that the Padé approximation with degrees of numerator and denominator most nearly equal was generally to be preferred; the example below supports this conclusion for the current case also.

Example 8.3   Compare the errors (8.4-31) when $f(x) = x^n - A$.

Using (8.4-13) in (8.4-31) we may calculate $\{16\}$ the coefficients of $-u_i^4$ at $x_i = \alpha$ to be, respectively,

$$C_{20} = \frac{(n-1)(2n-1)(3n-1)}{24\alpha^3} \qquad C_{11} = \frac{(n^2 - 1)(2n - 1)}{72\alpha^3}$$
$$C_{02} = \frac{n(n^2 - 1)}{24\alpha^3} \tag{8.4-33}$$

For various values of n we have the comparison

n	C_{20}/C_{11}	C_{02}/C_{11}
2	5	2
3	6	$1\frac{4}{5}$
4	$6\frac{3}{5}$	$1\frac{5}{7}$
5	7	$1\frac{2}{3}$
.	.	.
.	.	.
.	.	.
∞	9	$1\frac{1}{2}$

so that for this $f(x)$, $I_{11}(x_i)$ is the best and $I_{20}(x_i)$ the worst of the three iteration functions. If, for example, $f(x) = x^2 - 2$ and $x_1 = 2$, then for x_2 we get, using $I_{20}(x_i)$, $I_{11}(x_i)$, and $I_{02}(x_i)$, respectively, 1.4218750, 1.4166667, 1.4181818 whereas the true value $\sqrt{2} = 1.4142136$ so that $I_{11}(x_i)$ does indeed give the best result. In this example, because of the fourth-order convergence of the methods, a calculation of x_3 would give the $\sqrt{2}$ correct to seven decimal places in all three methods $\{16\}$.

The class of one-point iteration formulas we have considered here are all of order $m + 2$, and because of (8.4-16), they will all converge if the starting value x_1 is sufficiently close to a simple root α. However, the difficulty of estimating the coefficient of ϵ_i^{m+2} in (8.4-16) will generally make it very difficult to determine how close to the root the initial value must be for convergence. But if a priori knowledge of the root is at all good, convergence is seldom a problem. When it is we could, for example, use the method of false position to get a reasonable starting value for the iteration (8.4-1).

We have by no means considered all possible one-point iteration formulas. However, it can be shown, and we leave the proof to a problem {20}, that the most general one-point iteration function of order $m + 2$ at a simple root is given by

$$F(x_i) = I_{m0}(x_i) + U(x_i)u_i^{m+2} \qquad (8.4\text{-}34)$$

where $U(x_i)$ is an arbitrary function which may depend on $f(x_i)$ and its derivatives except that it must be bounded at $x_i = \alpha$ and not equal to $-I_{m0}^{(m+2)}(\alpha)/(m + 2)!$ at α.

Among all one-point iteration formulas, the decision on which to use should generally be determined (assuming that on a digital computer a variety of programs are available) by computational efficiency. If, for example, the function $f(x)$ is known to satisfy a second-order differential equation then θ_2 would be quite small; in this case, $I_{11}(x_i)$ might be a very good choice.

8.5   MULTIPOINT ITERATION FORMULAS†

In this section we shall consider some examples of stationary multipoint iteration functions. Such iteration functions have the form (8.2-5) with $n > 1$. Of the various possible approaches to the derivation of multipoint iteration functions, we shall consider two in this section, the first because of its general theoretical interest and the second because it leads to some particularly interesting and useful formulas. Again we shall assume that α is a simple root.

8.5-1   Iteration formulas using general inverse interpolation

In Sec. 8.2 we used inverse Lagrangian interpolation to derive a class of methods of functional iteration. Here we shall generalize this technique using the general polynomial interpolation formula (3.9-5). As in Sec. 8.2 we assume that $f(x)$ has an inverse $g(y)$. As usual we assume that f and, therefore, g have as many continuous derivatives as we require.

† Traub (1964, Chap. 8) uses "multipoint" in a different context. He calls the iteration functions of this section "one-point iteration functions with memory."

Using (3.9-6) with the a_j's replaced by the approximations $x_{i+1-j}, j = 1,$ $\ldots, n$ we have

$$f(x) = y(x) + \frac{f^{(\beta+1)}(\xi)}{(\beta + 1)!} \prod_{j=1}^{n} (x - x_{i+1-j})^{r_i+1}$$

$$\beta = n - 1 + \sum_{i=1}^{n} r_i \quad (8.5\text{-}1)$$

where ξ lies in the interval spanned by $x_i, \ldots, x_{i-n+1}$ and x and $y(x)$ is as given in (3.9-5). For a direct application of this formula to functional iteration, see {26 to 28}. Our interest here, however, is in interpolating using the inverse function g. Corresponding to (8.2-1) we have

$$g(y) = q(y) + \frac{g^{(\beta+1)}(\eta)}{(\beta + 1)!} \prod_{j=1}^{n} (y - y_j)^{r_i+1} \quad (8.5\text{-}2)$$

where $y_j = f(a_j)$ and η lies in the interval spanned by $y_1, \ldots, y_n$ and y. Since $\alpha = g(0)$ we get, by analogy with (8.2-2), an iteration formula given by $x_{i+1} = q(0)$ where $q(0)$ is a linear combination of $x_{i+1-j} = g(y_j)$, $j = 1, \ldots, n$ and derivatives of g evaluated at $y_j, j = 1, \ldots, n$. For example, if $r_j = 1$ for all j, then from the Hermite interpolation formula we get

$$x_{i+1} = \sum_{j=1}^{n} h_j(0)x_{i+1-j} + \sum_{j=1}^{n} \bar{h}_j(0)g'(y_j) \quad (8.5\text{-}3)$$

This formulation of multipoint iteration formulas includes as a special case the one-point iteration formulas of the previous section. The Taylor-series expansion (8.4-5) is identical with the generalized interpolation formula when $n = 1$ (i.e., only one point is used). Note that the Newton-Raphson method is given by (8.5-3) with $n = 1$. Almost all the well-known methods of stationary functional iteration are derivable as special cases of this general approach. Besides the Newton-Raphson method another example of this that we have seen is the secant method, which is an application of linear inverse Lagrangian interpolation.

Of particular interest to us here is the order of an iteration formula derived from (8.5-2). Analogous to (8.2-4) we have

$$\alpha - x_{i+1} = (-1)^{\beta+1} \frac{g^{(\beta+1)}(\eta)}{(\beta + 1)!} \prod_{j=1}^{n} y_j^{r_i+1} \quad (8.5\text{-}4)$$

Now since

$$y_j = f(x_{i+1-j}) = f(x_{i+1-j}) - f(\alpha)$$
$$= -f'(\xi_j)\epsilon_{i+1-j} = \frac{-\epsilon_{i+1-j}}{g'(\eta_j)} \qquad j = 1, \ldots, n \quad (8.5\text{-}5)$$

we may rewrite (8.5-4) as

$$\epsilon_{i+1} = \frac{g^{(\beta+1)}(\eta)}{(\beta+1)!} \frac{\prod\limits_{j=1}^{n} \epsilon_{i+1-j}^{r_j+1}}{\prod\limits_{j=1}^{n} [g'(\eta_j)]^{r_j+1}} \qquad (8.5\text{-}6)$$

We assume the iteration converges so that all iterates lie on some interval I. Let K be such that

$$\left| \frac{g^{(\beta+1)}(\eta)}{(\beta+1)!} \frac{1}{\prod\limits_{j=1}^{n} [g'(\eta_j)]^{r_j+1}} \right| < K \qquad (8.5\text{-}7)$$

for all η and η_j. Then

$$|\epsilon_{i+1}| \leqq K \prod\limits_{j=1}^{n} |\epsilon_{i+1-j}|^{r_j+1} \qquad (8.5\text{-}8)$$

This equation is reminiscent of (8.3-14). Indeed we may show that {24}

$$d_{i+1} \leqq d^{\gamma_i} \qquad i = 1, 2, \ldots \qquad (d < 1) \qquad (8.5\text{-}9)$$

where $d_i = K^{1/\beta}\epsilon_i$ and the γ_i's satisfy

$$\gamma_{i+1} = \sum\limits_{j=1}^{n} (r_j + 1)\gamma_{i-j+1} \qquad i = n - 1, n, \ldots$$
$$(\gamma_0 = \gamma_1 = \cdots = \gamma_{n-1} = 1) \quad (8.5\text{-}10)$$

The indicial equation of (8.5-10) is

$$\rho^n = \sum\limits_{j=1}^{n} (r_j + 1)\rho^{n-j} \qquad (8.5\text{-}11)$$

so that γ_i is given by some linear combination of the zeros of the polynomial (8.5-11). From these zeros we might expect to be able to indicate the order of convergence of the iteration as we did in Sec. 8.3, and indeed this can be done. We shall content ourselves with stating the result that, in the case $r_j = r$ for all j, the order of the iteration defined by $x_{i+1} = q(0)$, with $g(y)$ as in (8.5-2), is given by the only real root of (8.5-11) with magnitude greater than 1. This root is real and positive. The derivation of this result may be found in Traub (1964, pp. 62–67).

8.5-2   Derivative estimated iteration formulas

Consider the Newton-Raphson method (8.4-18). Let us replace the derivative term by its approximation found by differentiating a two-point Lagrangian formula for $f(x)$ with the two points being x_i and x_{i-1}. We have

$$f(x) \approx \frac{x - x_i}{x_{i-1} - x_i} f(x_{i-1}) + \frac{x - x_{i-1}}{x_i - x_{i-1}} f(x_i) \tag{8.5-12}$$

so that

$$f'(x_i) \approx \frac{f(x_{i-1}) - f(x_i)}{x_{i-1} - x_i} \tag{8.5-13}$$

If we substitute (8.5-13) into the Newton-Raphson method we get precisely the secant method, which is not a very interesting result {29}.

Now consider the method (8.4-9) with $m = 1$ which is

$$x_{i+1} = x_i - \frac{f(x_i)}{f'(x_i)} - \frac{1}{2} \frac{[f(x_i)]^2 f''(x_i)}{[f'(x_i)]^3} \tag{8.5-14}$$

Let us replace the second derivative in (8.5-14) by its approximation found by differentiating a two-point Hermite interpolation formula for $f(x)$ with the two points being x_i and x_{i-1}. We have {29}

$$f(x) \approx \frac{1}{(x_i - x_{i-1})^2} \left[\left(1 - 2\frac{x - x_i}{x_i - x_{i-1}}\right)(x - x_{i-1})^2 f(x_i) \right.$$
$$+ \left(1 - 2\frac{x - x_{i-1}}{x_{i-1} - x_i}\right)(x - x_i)^2 f(x_{i-1})$$
$$\left. + (x - x_i)(x - x_{i-1})^2 f'(x_i) + (x - x_{i-1})(x - x_i)^2 f'(x_{i-1}) \right] \tag{8.5-15}$$

so that

$$f''(x_i) \approx \frac{-6}{(x_i - x_{i-1})^2} [f(x_i) - f(x_{i-1})]$$
$$+ \frac{2}{x_i - x_{i-1}} [2f'(x_i) + f'(x_{i-1})] \tag{8.5-16}$$

Substituting the right-hand side of (8.5-16) into (8.5-14) we obtain an iteration formula

$$x_{i+1} = x_i - \frac{f(x_i)}{f'(x_i)} - \frac{1}{2}\frac{[f(x_i)]^2}{[f'(x_i)]^3}\bar{f}''(x_i) \qquad (8.5\text{-}17)$$

where

$$\bar{f}''(x_i) = -(6/h_i^2)[f(x_i) - f(x_{i-1})] + (2/h_i)[2f'(x_i) + f'(x_{i-1})]$$
$$h_i = x_i - x_{i-1} \qquad (8.5\text{-}18)$$

which, like the Newton-Raphson method, depends upon $f(x)$ and its first derivative. The order of (8.5-14) is 3. Of interest to us here is the order of the modified formula (8.5-17).

Let us call the right-hand side of (8.5-14) $F_1(x_i)$ and the right-hand side of (8.5-17) $F_2(x_i,x_{i-1})$. Then

$$F_1(x_i) - F_2(x_i,x_{i-1}) = \frac{f(x_i)^2}{2[f'(x_i)]^3}\left[\frac{(x_i - x_{i-1})^2}{12}f^{iv}(\xi)\right] \qquad (8.5\text{-}19)$$

where the term in brackets on the far right is the result of twice differentiating the error term of the Hermite interpolation formula and then evaluating the result at $x = x_i$. Now using (8.4-16) we have

$$\alpha - F_1(x_i) = \tfrac{1}{6}\{[f'(\xi_1)]^3 g'''(\eta)\}\epsilon_i^3 \qquad \epsilon_i = \alpha - x_i \qquad (8.5\text{-}20)$$

Then from (8.5-19) and (8.5-20)

$$\epsilon_{i+1} = \alpha - F_2(x_i,x_{i-1}) = \frac{[f(x_i)]^2}{2[f'(x_i)]^3}\left[\frac{(x_i - x_{i-1})^2}{12}f^{iv}(\xi)\right]$$
$$+ \tfrac{1}{6}\{[f'(\xi_1)]^3 g'''(\eta)\}\epsilon_i^3 \qquad (8.5\text{-}21)$$

Now

$$(x_i - x_{i-1})^2 = (\alpha - x_{i-1} + x_i - \alpha)^2 = (\epsilon_i - \epsilon_{i-1})^2 \qquad (8.5\text{-}22)$$

Substituting this into (8.5-21) and using (8.4-15) we have

$$\epsilon_{i+1} = \frac{f^{iv}(\xi)[f'(\xi_2)]^2}{2[f'(x_i)]^3}\epsilon_i^2(\epsilon_i - \epsilon_{i-1})^2 + \tfrac{1}{6}\{[f'(\xi_1)]^3 g'''(\eta)\}\epsilon_i^3 \qquad (8.5\text{-}23)$$

As we near convergence the errors in (8.5-23) will be monotonically decreasing in magnitude. The dominant term in (8.5-23) is either ϵ_i^3 or $\epsilon_i^2\epsilon_{i-1}^2$ (why?). Our object is to show that the $\epsilon_i^2\epsilon_{i-1}^2$ term is in fact dominant. To do this, it is sufficient to consider the order of a hypothetical formula with an error†

$$\bar{\epsilon}_{i+1} = \frac{f^{iv}(\xi)[f'(\xi_2)]^2}{2[f'(x_i)]^3}\bar{\epsilon}_i^2\bar{\epsilon}_{i-1}^2 \qquad (8.5\text{-}24)$$

Proceeding as we have previously we obtain

$$|\bar{\epsilon}_{i+1}| \leqq K|\bar{\epsilon}_i|^2|\bar{\epsilon}_{i-1}|^2 \qquad (8.5\text{-}25)$$

† The bars in (8.5-24) and (8.5-25) are to distinguish the errors in this hypothetical formula from the errors in (8.5-23).

where K is such that

$$\left| \frac{f^{\text{iv}}(\xi)[f'(\xi_2)]^2}{2[f'(x_i)]^3} \right| < K \tag{8.5-26}$$

on some interval including α. With $d_i = K^{\frac{1}{3}}|\epsilon_i|$ we get, using (8.5-8) to (8.5-11), that {29}

$$d_{i+1} \leqq d^{\gamma_i} \qquad i = 1, 2, \ldots \qquad (d < 1) \tag{8.5-27}$$

where

$$\gamma_i = \tfrac{1}{2}[(1 + \sqrt{3})^i + (1 - \sqrt{3})^i] \tag{8.5-28}$$

Therefore, by reasoning similar to that in Sec. 8.3, we conclude, but again do not prove, that

$$\lim_{i \to \infty} \frac{|\epsilon_{i+1}|}{|\epsilon_i|^{1+\sqrt{3}}} = \left| \frac{f^{\text{iv}}(\alpha)}{2f'(\alpha)} \right|^{1/\sqrt{3}} \tag{8.5-29}$$

Therefore, the order of (8.5-17) is $1 + \sqrt{3} \approx 2.732$ and the efficiency index is given by

$$EI = (1 + \sqrt{3})^{1/(1+\theta_1)} \tag{8.5-30}$$

which means that (8.5-17) is a distinct improvement over the Newton-Raphson method, its only relative disadvantage being the need for two starting values.†

The procedure described above may be generalized in a number of directions. One way would be to approximate the $(m + 1)$st-order derivative in the iteration (8.4-9) using an interpolation formula based on the first m derivatives. Another generalization would be to use more than two points in approximating $f''(x_i)$ in (8.5-16) {30}. All such methods of functional iteration are called *derivative estimated iteration formulas*.

Example 8.4 Repeat the calculations of Example 8.1 using the iteration formula (8.5-17) with $x_1 = \pi$, $x_2 = \pi/2$.

The calculations give

i	x_i	$\bar{f}''(x_i)$	$f''(x_i)$
2	$\pi/2$	-1.15847	-1.00000
3	1.78659	$-.98064$	$-.97681$
4	1.89414	$-.94910$	$-.94818$
5	1.89549	$-.96230$	$-.94775$

† Note that we are assuming here that the additions and multiplications needed to evaluate (8.5-17) and (8.5-18) require a negligible amount of time compared with the evaluation of $f(x_i)$ and $f'(x_i)$. This assumption is not unreasonable in general.

This method converges after three iterations compared with four with the Newton-Raphson method in Example 8.2.   This is as we would expect because the order of (8.5-17) is 2.732 while that of (8.4-18) is 2.   The last two columns in the table give the approximation to the second derivative given by (8.5-18) and the true value. Note that as the root is approached, the difference between the approximate and true values of the derivative first decreases and then increases.   This is a phenomenon of numerical differentiation that we discussed in Chap. 4.   When $x_i - x_{i-1}$ is comparatively large, truncation error dominates and decreases as $x_i - x_{i-1}$ decreases.   But when $x_i - x_{i-1}$ gets very small, roundoff dominates and grows as $x_i - x_{i-1}$ decreases. Note, however, that as $x_i \to \alpha$ the coefficient of $\bar{f}''(x_i)$ gets very small; therefore, the loss of significance in $\bar{f}''(x_i)$ is not important.

8.6   FUNCTIONAL ITERATION AT A MULTIPLE ROOT

All the results of the past three sections depend upon the root α being simple.   In particular, if α is a root of multiplicity $r > 1$, all our derivations based on inverse interpolation are invalid because the inverse function does not exist in any neighborhood of $x = \alpha$.

Nevertheless, we may still consider the behavior of such formulas in the neighborhood of a multiple root.   We consider here the class of methods (8.4-9) with Y_j given by (8.4-10).

We show first that, independent of m, (8.4-9) converges linearly when α is a root of multiplicity greater than 1.

From (8.4-9) we have

$$\epsilon_{i+1} = \alpha - x_{i+1} = \alpha - x_i + u_i \sum_{j=0}^{m} u_i^j Y_j = \epsilon_i + \sum_{j=0}^{m} u_i^{j+1} Y_j \qquad (8.6\text{-}1)$$

We define

$$Z_j(x_i) = u_i^{j+1} Y_j(x_i) \qquad Z_0(x_i) = u_i \qquad (8.6\text{-}2)$$

Using (8.4-10) we may show $\{10\}$

$$(j + 1)Z_j = jZ_{j-1} - u_i Z_{j-1}' \qquad (8.6\text{-}3)$$

Now consider the Taylor-series expansion of $Z_j(x_i)$ about α.   Since $Z_j(\alpha) = 0$ (why?), we have

$$Z_j(x_i) = \sum_{k=1}^{\infty} c_{jk} \epsilon_i^k \qquad (8.6\text{-}4)$$

From (8.6-1), (8.6-2), and (8.6-4) $\{31\}$

$$\epsilon_{i+1} = \epsilon_i \left(1 + \sum_{j=0}^{m} c_{j1}\right) + O(\epsilon_i^2) \qquad (8.6\text{-}5)$$

We suppose that α is a root of multiplicity r.   Then $\{31\}$

$$u_i = -(\epsilon_i/r) + O(\epsilon_i^2) \qquad (8.6\text{-}6)$$

Substituting (8.6-4) into (8.6-3) and using (8.6-6) we get {31}

$$(j + 1)c_{j1} = jc_{j-1,1} - (1/r)c_{j-1,1} \tag{8.6-7}$$

or

$$c_{j1} = \frac{j - 1/r}{j + 1} c_{j-1,1} \qquad c_{01} = -\frac{1}{r} \tag{8.6-8}$$

Therefore,

$$c_{j1} = (-1)^{j+1}(1/r)_{j+1} \tag{8.6-9}$$

where $(1/r)_{j+1}$ is a binomial coefficient.   Substituting (8.6-9) into (8.6-5) we get

$$
\begin{aligned}
\epsilon_{i+1} &= \epsilon_i \left[1 + \sum_{j=0}^{m} (-1)^{j+1} \left(\frac{1}{r}\right)_{j+1} \right] + O(\epsilon_i^2) \\
&= \epsilon_i \left[\sum_{j=0}^{m+1} (-1)^{j} \left(\frac{1}{r}\right)_{j} \right] + O(\epsilon_i^2) \\
&= (-1)^{m+1} \epsilon_i \left(\frac{1}{r} - 1\right)_{m+1} + O(\epsilon_i^2)
\end{aligned} \tag{8.6-10}
$$

since {31}

$$\sum_{j=0}^{m+1} (-1)^{j} \left(\frac{1}{r}\right)_{j} = (-1)^{m+1} \left(\frac{1}{r} - 1\right)_{m+1} \tag{8.6-11}$$

Finally we have from (8.6-10) that, when the iteration converges

$$\lim_{i \to \infty} \left| \frac{\epsilon_{i+1}}{\epsilon_i} \right| = (-1)^{m+1} \left(\frac{1}{r} - 1\right)_{m+1} \neq 0 \tag{8.6-12}$$

if $r \neq 1$ which proves that the order of (8.4-9) is 1 if α is not a simple root. But note that, since $(1/r - 1)_{m+1}$ has magnitude less than 1, the methods of this class do converge in the neighborhood of a multiple root.

If the multiplicity of the root at α is known, then the class of methods (8.4-9) may be modified so that they retain their order of convergence of $m + 2$. In particular, the Newton-Raphson method (8.4-18) may be modified so that it still has quadratic convergence for a root of multiplicity r if we write

$$x_{i+1} = x_i - r \frac{f(x_i)}{f'(x_i)} \tag{8.6-13}$$

We have

$$\alpha - x_{i+1} = \alpha - x_i + r \frac{f(x_i)}{f'(x_i)} \tag{8.6-14}$$

so that

$$(\alpha - x_{i+1})f'(x_i) = G(x_i) \tag{8.6-15}$$

where we have defined

$$G(x) = (\alpha - x)f'(x) + rf(x) \tag{8.6-16}$$

Differentiating we have

$$G^{(j)}(x) = rf^{(j)}(x) + (\alpha - x)f^{(j+1)}(x) - jf^{(j)}(x) \tag{8.6-17}$$

and, since α is a root of multiplicity r

$$G^{(j)}(\alpha) = 0 \qquad j = 0, \ldots, r \qquad G^{(r+1)}(\alpha) \neq 0 \tag{8.6-18}$$

Therefore,

$$G(x) = \frac{(x - \alpha)^{r+1}}{(r + 1)!} G^{(r+1)}(\xi_1) \tag{8.6-19}$$

Since

$$f'(x) = \frac{(x - \alpha)^{r-1}}{(r - 1)!} f^{(r)}(\xi_2) \tag{8.6-20}$$

because α is a root of multiplicity r, we have, using (8.6-19) and (8.6-20) in (8.6-15),

$$\epsilon_{i+1} = \frac{1}{(r)(r + 1)} \frac{G^{(r+1)}(\xi_1)}{f^{(r)}(\xi_2)} \epsilon_i^2 \tag{8.6-21}$$

Therefore, the order is 2 since $f^{(r)}(\xi_2)$ is bounded away from zero in a neighborhood of $x = \alpha$ and $G^{(r+1)}(\alpha) \neq 0$.

Generally, however, the multiplicity of the root is not known a priori. Thus it would be very desirable to have iteration methods whose order of convergence is independent of the multiplicity. Such methods can indeed be found; the key to finding them is to note that $u(x)$ has a zero of multiplicity 1 at $x = \alpha$ no matter what the multiplicity of the zero of $f(x)$ (why?). Therefore, if, instead of (8.1-1), we consider the equation

$$u(x) = 0 \tag{8.6-22}$$

the roots of this equation are identical with those of (8.1-1) and they are all simple. We need then only replace $f(x)$ by $u(x)$ in any iteration formula we have developed thus far to get a formula whose order of convergence is independent of the multiplicity of the root. For example, the secant method (8.3-11) and the Newton-Raphson method (8.4-18) become

$$x_{i+1} = \frac{u(x_i)}{u(x_i) - u(x_{i-1})} x_{i-1} + \frac{u(x_{i-1})}{u(x_{i-1}) - u(x_i)} x_i \tag{8.6-23}$$

and

$$x_{i+1} = x_i - [u(x_i)/u'(x_i)] \tag{8.6-24}$$

The efficiency of each of these methods is, however, less than that of the secant and Newton-Raphson methods, respectively, because of the need to calculate one higher derivative in each case.

Example 8.5   Find the positive root of $(\sin x - x/2)^2 = 0$ using (1) the Newton-Raphson method (8.4-18); (2) the modified Newton-Raphson method (8.6-13) with $r = 2$; (3) the modified Newton-Raphson method (8.6-24). This equation is, of course, identical with that of Example 8.1, but here we use the above form for illustrative purposes.

We have

$$f(x) = (\sin x - x/2)^2$$
$$f'(x) = 2(\sin x - x/2)(\cos x - \tfrac{1}{2})$$
$$f''(x) = 2[(\cos x - \tfrac{1}{2})^2 - \sin x(\sin x - x/2)]$$
$$u(x) = \frac{f(x)}{f'(x)}$$
$$u'(x) = 1 - \frac{f(x)f''(x)}{[f'(x)]^2}$$

Using $x_1 = \pi/2$ in all cases, we may calculate the following results:

	Method		
	(1)	(2)	(3)
x_2	1.78540	2.00000	1.80175
x_3	1.84456	1.90100	1.88963
x_4	1.87083	1.89551	1.89547
x_5	1.88335	1.89549	1.89549
x_6	1.88946		
x_7	1.89249		
x_8	1.89399		
x_9	1.89475		
x_{10}	1.89512		
x_{11}	1.89531		
x_{12}	1.89540		
x_{13}	1.89545		
x_{14}	1.89547		
x_{15}	1.89548		
x_{16}	1.89549		

As we expect, methods 2 and 3 converge rapidly and much faster than method 1. Note that each successive iterate for method 1 has about one-half the error of the previous iterate {32}.

8.7 SOME COMPUTATIONAL ASPECTS OF FUNCTIONAL ITERATION

Each method of functional iteration that we have discussed has the property that, if the initial approximation is sufficiently close to the root α, then the method will converge if α is a simple root. For a one-point iteration method, this is true even if the root is not simple although, as we have seen, the convergence will be slower in this case. In general, however, it is not possible to prove that a multipoint iteration function will always converge to a multiple root even if the initial approximations are arbitrarily close to the root. For the secant method it is easy to see that the iteration may not converge to a double root by considering the case in which x_1 and x_2 are on opposite sides of the root and are such that $f(x_1) = f(x_2)$ {34}.

If the initial error is not small enough to guarantee decreasing errors in every subsequent iteration, then the iteration may (1) diverge or (2) converge anyhow because a small initial error is a sufficient but not a necessary condition for convergence. The two examples below illustrate these two types of behavior.

Example 8.6   Use the Newton-Raphson method to try to find the root of $xe^{-x} = 0$ starting with $x_1 = 2$.

The graph of the function is shown in Fig. 8.4. Since x_{i+1} in the Newton-Raphson method is the intersection of the x axis with the tangent to the curve at $f(x_i)$, the divergence of the method in this case is clear. On the other hand, if $0 < x_1 \leqq 1$ the iteration would converge {35}.

Example 8.7   Use the Newton-Raphson method to find the positive root of $x^{20} - 1 = 0$ starting with $x_1 = \frac{1}{2}$.

For $f(x) = x^{20} - 1$ Eq. (8.4-18) becomes

$$x_{i+1} = x_i - \frac{x_i^{20} - 1}{20x_i^{19}}$$

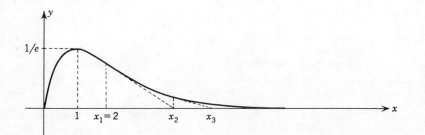

Fig. 8.4   Graph of $f(x) = xe^{-x}$.

so that

$$x_2 = \frac{1}{2} - \frac{(\frac{1}{2})^{20} - 1}{20/2^{19}} \approx \frac{1}{20} 2^{19} = 26,214.4$$

Thus, because $\frac{1}{2}$ was not close enough to the root $x = 1$, the first iterate leads to a far worse result. But

$$x_3 = x_2 - \frac{x_2^{20} - 1}{20x_2^{19}} \approx \frac{19}{20} x_2$$

and thus lies closer to $x = 1$ than x_2. In fact, it is not hard to see that successive iterates do in fact converge to 1, albeit very slowly {37}.

The slow convergence in Example 8.7 illustrates one of the computational problems associated with the use of functional iteration on a digital computer. It is important that the computer be programmed to recognize this slow convergence and take appropriate action. For example, if $|x_{i+1}/x_i|$ is greater than some specified constant k, then, instead of the computed x_{i+1}, the program would set $x_{i+1} = \pm Kx_i$ where K is another specified constant (e.g., $K = k/2$) and the sign agrees with that of x_{i+1}/x_i {37}.

It is clearly also important that divergence be recognized. When it is, a new starting value should be tried or an always-convergent method such as the method of false position should be used. Sometimes successive iterates may oscillate in such a way that it is not clear whether they are converging or not. In this case, it is often more efficient to err on the safe side and take action similar to that in the case of divergence.

8.7-1 The δ^2 process

When an iteration is converging linearly, it is possible to use a technique similar to Richardson extrapolation (see Sec. 4.12-1) in order to accelerate the convergence. If the iteration is converging we have

$$\alpha - x_{i+1} = C_i(\alpha - x_i) \qquad |C_i| < 1 \tag{8.7-1}$$

where $|C_i| \to C$, the asymptotic error constant. Near convergence then C_i will remain nearly constant and we may write

$$\alpha - x_{i+1} \approx \bar{C}(\alpha - x_i) \qquad |\bar{C}| = C \tag{8.7-2}$$

Writing (8.7-2) with i replaced by $i + 1$ and eliminating $\bar{C}$ we have

$$\frac{\alpha - x_{i+2}}{\alpha - x_{i+1}} \approx \frac{\alpha - x_{i+1}}{\alpha - x_i} \tag{8.7-3}$$

Solving for α we obtain

$$\alpha \approx \frac{x_i x_{i+2} - x_{i+1}^2}{x_{i+2} - 2x_{i+1} + x_i} = x_{i+2} - \frac{(\Delta x_{i+1})^2}{\Delta^2 x_i} \tag{8.7-4}$$

where Δ is the forward-difference operator of Chap. 3. This extrapolation procedure is associated with the name of Aitken. Because of the second difference in (8.7-4) (which could be expressed as a central difference), this procedure is called *Aitken's δ^2 process.*

As an example of the use of this technique, we may use the data of Example 8.1. Using x_5, x_6, and x_7 in (8.7-4), we obtain as the new approximation 1.89554, which is a substantial improvement over any of the values used. Because of the simplicity of this procedure, it should always be used to accelerate the convergence of linear iterations. Another application of this procedure is in the determination of the multiplicity of a multiple root {38}.

For iterations whose order of convergence is greater than 1, (8.7-4) should not be used. For such iterations it is sometimes possible to speed up the convergence using so-called *self-acceleration* procedures. A discussion of these is beyond our scope here; see Traub (1964, pp. 185–187).

8.8   SYSTEMS OF NONLINEAR EQUATIONS

The system of nonlinear equations

$$f_j[x^{(1)},x^{(2)}, \ldots ,x^{(N)}] = 0 \qquad j = 1, \ldots , N \tag{8.8-1}$$

may be rewritten in vector notation as†

$$\mathbf{f(x)} = 0 \tag{8.8-2}$$

where

$$\mathbf{f} = (f_1,f_2, \ldots ,f_N) \qquad \mathbf{x} = [x^{(1)}, \ldots ,x^{(N)}] \tag{8.8-3}$$

Using the form (8.8-2) we may then derive functional iteration methods as in Sec. 8.4. The general form of the functional iteration equation for stationary iterations is

$$\mathbf{x}_{i+1} = \mathbf{F}(\mathbf{x}_i,\mathbf{x}_{i-1}, \ldots ,\mathbf{x}_{i-n}) \tag{8.8-4}$$

where

$$\mathbf{F} = (F_1,F_2, \ldots ,F_N) \tag{8.8-5}$$

We suppose that in some neighborhood of the solution $\boldsymbol{\alpha} = (\alpha_1, \ldots ,\alpha_N)$ of (8.8-2) the vector function $\mathbf{f}$ has an inverse

$$\mathbf{g} = (g_1,g_2, \ldots ,g_N) \tag{8.8-6}$$

† For convenience and because it causes no confusion, we shall not distinguish between row and column vectors in this section.

Then using the notation $\mathbf{y} = [y^{(1)}, \ldots , y^{(N)}]$ for the point inverse to $\mathbf{x}$, we expand $\mathbf{g}(\mathbf{y})$ in a Taylor series about $\mathbf{y}_i$ [see Apostol (1957), pp. 123–124].

$$\mathbf{x} = \mathbf{g}(\mathbf{y}) = \mathbf{g}(\mathbf{y}_i) + \sum_{j=1}^{m+1} \frac{1}{j!} \, d^j\mathbf{g}(\mathbf{y}_i, \mathbf{y} - \mathbf{y}_i)$$

$$+ \frac{1}{(m+2)!} \, d^{m+2}\mathbf{g}(\xi, \mathbf{y} - \mathbf{y}_i) \quad (8.8\text{-}7)$$

where ξ lies on the line segment joining $\mathbf{y}$ and $\mathbf{y}_i$ and the jth-order differential is defined by

$$d^j h(\mathbf{x};\mathbf{s}) = \sum_{i_1=1}^{N} \sum_{i_2=1}^{N} \cdots \sum_{i_j=1}^{N} D_{i_1,i_2,\ldots,i_j} h(\mathbf{x}) s^{(i_1)} s^{(i_2)} \cdots s^{(i_j)} \quad (8.8\text{-}8)$$

where $D_{i_1,\ldots,i_j} h(\mathbf{x})$ is the partial derivative of h with respect to the variables $x_{i_1}, \ldots , x_{i_j}$ at the point $\mathbf{x}$ and $s^{(i_1)}, \ldots , s^{(i_j)}$ are components of $\mathbf{s}$. We assume, of course, that all needed partial derivatives exist. Then, since $\boldsymbol{\alpha} = \mathbf{g}(\mathbf{0})$, setting $\mathbf{y} = \mathbf{0}$ in (8.8-7) and dropping the remainder term we get the equation analogous to (8.4-9). For example, with $m = 0$ we get the N-dimensional analog of the Newton-Raphson method

$$\mathbf{x}_{i+1} = \mathbf{x}_i + d\mathbf{g}(\mathbf{y}_i, -\mathbf{y}_i) = \mathbf{x}_i + \sum_{j=1}^{N} \frac{\partial}{\partial y^{(j)}} \, \mathbf{g}(\mathbf{y}_i) y_i^{(j)} \quad (8.8\text{-}9)$$

In particular, if $N = 2$, we may use the implicit function theorem to express the derivatives of $\mathbf{g}$ in terms of derivatives of $\mathbf{f}$ and so may write {39}

$$\mathbf{x}_{i+1} = \mathbf{x}_i - \left\{ \frac{1}{J} \begin{bmatrix} \dfrac{\partial f_2}{\partial x^{(2)}} & -\dfrac{\partial f_1}{\partial x^{(2)}} \\ -\dfrac{\partial f_2}{\partial x^{(1)}} & \dfrac{\partial f_1}{\partial x^{(1)}} \end{bmatrix} \begin{bmatrix} f_1 \\ f_2 \end{bmatrix} \right\}_{\mathbf{x}=\mathbf{x}_i} \quad (8.8\text{-}10)$$

where

$$J = \begin{vmatrix} \dfrac{\partial f_1}{\partial x^{(1)}} & \dfrac{\partial f_1}{\partial x^{(2)}} \\ \dfrac{\partial f_2}{\partial x^{(1)}} & \dfrac{\partial f_2}{\partial x^{(2)}} \end{vmatrix} \quad (8.8\text{-}11)$$

As in the one-dimensional case, the order of convergence is 2 {39}. Here, however, we must note that the problems in the use of functional iteration methods with systems of equations are quite different from those for single equations. For single equations we have noted that good a priori information on the location of the root is often available; when it is not then we may use an always-convergent method to obtain a good approximation to the root.   In this case we were therefore mainly interested in the efficiency of methods and comparatively little worried about whether or not a method converged.   But with systems of equations convergence itself is such a serious problem that usually we shall be satisfied with any order of convergence if only the method will converge.   Any reader who doubts this should try using the Newton-Raphson method to solve two simultaneous polynomial equations of degree 2 in two variables.   Often, if the initial approximation is not quite close to the solution, the iteration will not converge {41}.   The form of the error in (8.8-10), which we leave to a problem {39}, would make the reason for this clearer.

The extensions of most methods of functional iteration to systems of equations are subject to the same type of convergence limitations as the Newton-Raphson method.   In searching for a method for systems of equations whose convergence is assured or whose convergence properties are at least reasonably good, an obvious idea is to try to generalize the method of false position to systems, but since we cannot talk about the sign of $f(x)$, no always-convergent generalization is possible.   However, generalizations of the secant method are possible and a number have been proposed {42, 43}.   But all are subject to convergence limitations similar to those above.   Our conclusions are that the solution of simultaneous nonlinear equations is usually a very difficult problem and that no very satisfactory methods of functional iteration for this problem are known.

Another approach to the problem of solving (8.8-1) is to solve a related minimum problem.   Let

$$\phi[x^{(1)}, \ldots ,x^{(n)}] = \sum_{i=1}^{n} \{f_i[x^{(1)}, \ldots ,x^{(n)}]\}^2 \tag{8.8-12}$$

The function ϕ takes on its absolute minimum, zero, at a solution of (8.8-1). Therefore, if we can find an absolute minimum for ϕ, we shall have solved (8.8-1).   One method for doing this, called the method of steepest descent, is discussed in some detail in the next chapter.   The reader will probably not be surprised to learn that the problem in minimizing ϕ is not so much to find *a* minimum as to find *the* absolute minimum which gives us the solution to (8.8-1).

8.9   THE ZEROS OF POLYNOMIALS—THE PROBLEM

In the remainder of this chapter, we shall be concerned with finding the complex and real roots of

$$f(z) \equiv a_n z^n + a_{n-1} z^{n-1} + \cdots + a_1 z + a_0 = 0 \tag{8.9-1}$$

where the coefficients a_i, $i = 0, \ldots, n$ are real numbers† and z is a complex variable. The methods of functional iteration discussed previously in this chapter may all be applied to finding the real roots of (8.9-1) and generally, with simple modifications, they may be applied to complex roots. However, the problem of finding the roots of (8.9-1) arises with such frequency that this alone justifies looking for methods particularly adapted to this problem. The particularly simple form of $f(z)$ in fact greatly aids us in finding such special methods. Also the need to find complex as well as real roots and, often, the need to find *all* the roots of (8.9-1) adds another dimension to the problem which merits special attention.

The need to find all the roots of (8.9-1) commonly arises, as we have seen, for example, in Sec. 5.4 in the consideration of stability problems. Generally in such cases there is not good a priori information about the location of all or, sometimes, any of the roots. This implies the need to emphasize, more than we have done previously, methods which are always convergent, particularly for high-degree polynomials. We note that the method of false position is not applicable to the case of complex roots. Our approach then will be to consider carefully methods which, while they may converge slowly, at least converge surely, and then to consider methods which will converge rapidly if the starting point is sufficiently close to the root.

But before considering directly methods for the solution of (8.9-1), it is important to note that there is a large literature on the *location* of the zeros of a polynomial as a function of its coefficients. The problem of solving (8.9-1) cannot be properly attacked without some knowledge of the theorems on the location of the zeros of polynomials. A general discussion of these theorems is beyond our scope here; see Marden (1949), Wall (1948), and Wilf (1962). One aspect of the location of real roots is so important both for the problems of this chapter and in other areas (see Sec. 10.4-2) that we shall discuss it in some detail here.

8.9-1 Sturm sequences

Definition 8.1   Let

$$f_1(x), f_2(x), \ldots, f_m(x) \tag{8.9-2}$$

be a sequence of polynomials. Such a sequence is called a *Sturm sequence* on an interval (a,b), where either a or b may be infinite, if (1) $f_m(x)$ does not vanish in (a,b); (2) at any zero of $f_k(x)$, $k = 2, \ldots$,

---

† Many of the methods to be discussed are also applicable when the a_i's are allowed to be complex, but the case of real coefficients is by far the most important.

$m - 1$ the two adjacent functions are nonzero and have opposite signs; that is,

$$f_{k-1}(x)f_{k+1}(x) < 0 \qquad (8.9\text{-}3)$$

Definition 8.2   Let $\{f_i(x)\}$, $i = 1, \ldots, m$ be a Sturm sequence on (a,b) and let x_0 be a point of (a,b) at which $f_1(x) \neq 0$. We define $V(x_0)$ to be the number of changes of sign of $\{f_i(x_0)\}$, zero values being ignored. If a is finite, then $V(a)$ is defined as $V(a + \epsilon)$ where ϵ is such that no $f_i(x)$ vanishes in $(a, a + \epsilon)$ and similarly for b when b is finite. If $a = -\infty$, then $V(a)$ is defined to be the number of changes of sign of $\{ \lim_{x \to -\infty} f_i(x) \}$ and similarly for $V(b)$ when $b = +\infty$.

Definition 8.3   Let $R(x)$ be any rational function. We define the *Cauchy index* of $R(x)$ on (a,b), denoted by $I_a^b R(x)$, to be the difference between the number of jumps of $R(x)$ from $-\infty$ to $+\infty$ and the number of jumps from $+\infty$ to $-\infty$ as x goes from a to b, excluding the end points. That is, at every real pole of $R(x)$ in (a,b) add 1 to the Cauchy index if $R(x) \to -\infty$ on the left of the pole and $R(x) \to +\infty$ on the right of the pole and subtract 1 if vice versa.

With these three definitions, we may prove

Theorem 8.2 (Sturm)   If $f_i(x)$, $i = 1, \ldots, m$ is a Sturm sequence on an interval (a,b), then, if neither $f_1(a)$ nor $f_1(b)$ equals zero

$$I_a^b \frac{f_2(x)}{f_1(x)} = V(a) - V(b) \qquad (8.9\text{-}4)$$

Proof   The value of $V(x)$ does not change when x passes through a zero of $f_k(x)$, $k = 2, \ldots, m$ because of (8.9-3). Thus $V(x)$ can change only when $f_1(x)$ goes through zero. If x_0 is a zero of $f_1(x)$, it is not a zero of $f_2(x)$ because of property 2 of Sturm sequences. Therefore, $f_2(x)$ has the same sign on both sides of x_0. If x_0 is a zero of $f_1(x)$ of even multiplicity, then $V(x)$ does not change as x increases through x_0, and there is no contribution to the Cauchy index. If the zero is of odd multiplicity, then $V(x)$ will increase by 1 if $f_1(x)$ and $f_2(x)$ have the same sign to the left of x_0 and will decrease by 1 if the signs to the left are different. Correspondingly for zeros of odd multiplicity, there is a -1 contribution to the Cauchy index if the signs of $f_1(x)$ and $f_2(x)$ are the same to the left of x_0 and a $+1$ contribution if they are different. This establishes the theorem.

Our chief interest here is in applying this theorem to find the real roots of (8.9-1) in an interval (a,b). Consider the sequence of functions $f_i(x)$,

$i = 1, \ldots, m$ where

$$f_1(x) = f(x) \qquad f_2(x) = f'(x)$$
$$f_{j-1}(x) = q_{j-1}(x)f_j(x) - f_{j+1}(x) \qquad j = 2, \ldots, m-1 \qquad (8.9\text{-}5)$$
$$f_{m-1}(x) = q_{m-1}(x)f_m(x)$$

where $q_{j-1}(x)$ is the quotient and $f_{j+1}(x)$ is the negative of the remainder when $f_{j-1}(x)$ is divided by $f_j(x)$. Thus $\{f_i(x)\}$ is a sequence of polynomials of decreasing degree which eventually must terminate in a polynomial $f_m(x)$, $m \le n+1$ which divides $f_{m-1}(x)$ (why?). The polynomial $f_m(x)$ is the greatest common divisor of $f_1(x)$ and $f_2(x)$ and also of every other member of the sequence (8.9-5). Now suppose $f_m(x)$ does not vanish in (a,b) so that the first condition of Definition 8.1 is satisfied. But in this case, the second condition is also satisfied since, if $f_j(x) = 0, j = 2, \ldots,$ $m - 1$, then $f_{j-1}(x) = -f_{j+1}(x)$. Moreover, when $f_j(x) = 0, f_{j+1}(x) \ne 0$ since, if it were, $f_m(x)$ would also be zero (why?). Thus the sequence $\{f_i(x)\}$ is a Sturm sequence when $f_m(x)$ does not vanish in (a,b).

If $f_m(x)$ is not of constant sign in (a,b), then, in place of (8.9-5), we use the sequence $\{f_i(x)/f_m(x)\}$, $i = 1, \ldots, m$. Not only is this a Sturm sequence but also both sides of (8.9-4) are the same for this sequence and for the sequence (8.9-5) (why?). Therefore, we may use these two sequences interchangeably in applying Sturm's theorem.

Now for the sequence (8.9-5) we may write

$$\frac{f_2(x)}{f_1(x)} = \frac{f'(x)}{f(x)} = \sum_{j=1}^{p} \frac{n_j}{x - a_j} + R_1(x) \qquad (8.9\text{-}6)$$

where the a_j, $j = 1, \ldots, p$ are the distinct real zeros of $f(x)$, n_j is the multiplicity of the zero a_j, and $R_1(x)$ has no poles on the real axis $\{45\}$. Since the n_j are all positive, $I_a^b[f'(x)/f(x)]$ is equal to the number of distinct real zeros of $f(x)$ in the interval (a,b). Therefore, we have the

Theorem 8.3   The number of distinct real zeros of the polynomial $f(x)$ in the interval $[a,b]$ is equal to $V(a) - V(b)$ if neither $f(a)$ nor $f(b)$ is equal to zero. Moreover, if $f(a)$ or $f(b)$ or both is equal to zero and the root is simple, the result holds on $[a,b]$ if we define $V(x)$ to be the number of changes of sign in $f_2(x), \ldots, f_m(x)$ when $f_1(x) = 0$ $\{46\}$.

This result can be extremely useful in locating the roots of (8.9-1). If, for example, we are interested only in the real roots of (8.9-1), this theorem enables us to determine exactly how many such roots there are. In fact, by making use of $f_m(x)$, we may use this theorem to help find the multiplicity of these roots $\{46\}$.

Example 8.8   Apply Sturm's theorem to finding the number of real roots of

$$f(x) = x^6 + 4x^5 + 4x^4 - x^2 - 4x - 4 = (x^2 + 1)(x^2 - 1)(x + 2)^2$$

Using (8.9-5) we calculate

$$f_1(x) = x^6 + 4x^5 + 4x^4 - x^2 - 4x - 4$$
$$f_2(x) = 6x^5 + 20x^4 + 16x^3 - 2x - 4$$
$$f_3(x) = 4x^4 + 8x^3 + 3x^2 + 14x + 16$$
$$f_4(x) = x^3 + 6x^2 + 12x + 8$$
$$f_5(x) = -17x^2 - 58x - 48$$
$$f_6(x) = -x - 2 = f_5(x)/(17x + 24)$$

where the coefficients have been made integers by multiplying by a suitable positive constant. For some sample values of x the signs of the $f_i(x)$ are

	$-\infty$	∞	0	-1	$+1$	$-24\frac{7}{17}$
$f_1(x)$	$+$	$+$	$-$	0	0	$+$
$f_2(x)$	$-$	$+$	$-$	$-$	$+$	$-$
$f_3(x)$	$+$	$+$	$+$	$+$	$+$	$-$
$f_4(x)$	$-$	$+$	$+$	$+$	$+$	$+$
$f_5(x)$	$-$	$-$	$-$	$-$	$-$	0
$f_6(x)$	$+$	$-$	$-$	$-$	$-$	$-$
Number of sign changes	4	1	2	2	1	3

Thus we have three distinct real zeros, two negative real zeros, and one positive real zero. Although -1 and $+1$ are zeros, the rule above shows that there are two distinct zeros in $(-\infty, -1]$ and three in $(-\infty, +1]$. The point $-24\frac{7}{17}$ illustrates the case when an $f_i(x) = 0$. For example, in $(-\infty, -24\frac{7}{17}]$, there is one distinct root. Since $f_6(x) = -x - 2$, the root at -2 is a double root {46}.

8.10   ALWAYS–CONVERGENT METHODS

The first three methods to be described in this section, namely, the Lehmer-Schur method, Graeffe's root-squaring method, and Bernoulli's method, are guaranteed to converge to a root of (8.9-1) if certain special cases (e.g., roots of multiplicity greater than 1) are specially taken care of. In the Lehmer-Schur method only one special case can arise, and this is so easily taken care of that the method, which is quite new, should prove very valuable for use on digital computers. In Graeffe's method, roots of equal magnitude cause difficulties, but these can be taken care of by careful programming of a computer. Therefore, this method is also a candidate for general-purpose use on a digital computer. Roots of equal magnitude are, however, quite difficult to take care of in Bernoulli's method, so that it is not a serious rival to the first two for general use.   Nevertheless, Bernoulli's method is useful for certain problems as well as being of theoretical and historical interest.

The fourth method of this section—Laguerre's method—is analyzed only in the case of a polynomial whose zeros are all real and simple, although it also converges to multiple zeros when all the zeros are real.   Little is known analytically about this method when there are complex zeros, but there is empirical evidence that it also performs very well in this case. It is therefore also a candidate for general-purpose use on a digital computer.

8.10-1   The Lehmer-Schur method

In Prob. 18 of Chap. 5 a criterion due to Schur is considered which may be used to determine whether or not all the zeros of a polynomial lie within the unit circle.   Here a related criterion, also due to Schur, which may be used to determine whether *any* zero of a polynomial lies within the unit circle, will be used as the basis of a method to find the roots of (8.9-1).

With $f(z)$ given by (8.9-1) define

$$f^*(z) = z^n \bar{f}(\bar{z}^{-1}) = \bar{a}_n + \bar{a}_{n-1}z + \cdots + \bar{a}_0 z^n \tag{8.10-1}$$

where bars denoted conjugates.†   Now define

$$T[f(z)] = \bar{a}_0 f(z) - a_n f^*(z) \tag{8.10-2}$$

so that, in particular

$$T[f(0)] = \bar{a}_0 a_0 - a_n \bar{a}_n = |a_0|^2 - |a_n|^2 \tag{8.10-3}$$

is real.   Note also that $T[f(z)]$ has no term in z^n so that if we define

$$T^j[f(z)] = T\{T^{j-1}[f(z)]\} \tag{8.10-4}$$

we get a sequence of polynomials of decreasing degree.   Let k be the smallest integer for which $T^k[f(0)] = 0$.   The basic theorem that we use is

> **Theorem 8.4**   Suppose $f(0) \neq 0$.   If for some h such that $0 < h < k$, $T^h[f(0)] < 0$, then $f(z)$ has at least one zero inside the unit circle.   If instead $T^i[f(0)] > 0$ for $1 \leq i < k$ and $T^{k-1}[f(z)]$ is a constant, then no zero of $f(z)$ lies inside the unit circle.

The proof of this theorem, which we leave to a problem {49}, requires various elementary results from complex-variable theory.   To use this theorem to determine whether or not $f(z)$ has a zero inside the unit circle,

† This method is applicable to the case of complex as well as real coefficients.

we proceed as follows:

1. Is $f(0) = 0$? If so we have a zero $z = 0$; if not, do step 2.
2. Calculate $T[f(z)]$. Is $T[f(0)] < 0$? If so, there is a root inside the unit circle; if not, go to step 3.
3. Calculate $T^j[f(z)]$, $j = 1, 2, \ldots$ until $T^j[f(0)] < 0$, $j < k$ or $T^k[f(0)] = 0$. If the former occurs, there is a root inside the unit circle. If the latter occurs and if $T^{k-1}[f(z)]$ is a constant, then there is no root inside the unit circle.

Note that the theorem does not cover one possibility; if $T^k[f(0)] = 0$ but $T^{k-1}[f(z)]$ is not a constant, the theorem tells us nothing. We shall close this loophole a little later.

To apply this theorem to find the roots of (8.9-1), we note first that if $f(z)$ has a zero inside the circle $|z| = \rho$, then

$$g(z) = f(\rho z) \tag{8.10-5a}$$

has a zero inside the unit circle. More generally, if $f(z)$ has a zero inside the circle $|z - c| = \rho$

$$g(z) = f(\rho z + c) \tag{8.10-5b}$$

has a zero inside the unit circle.† Thus we proceed as follows, using Theorem 8.4 at each step:

1. Does $f(z)$ have a zero inside the unit circle? If not, consider $g(z) = f(2z)$ and ask whether $g(z)$ has a zero inside the unit circle. If not, consider $f(2^2 z)$. Continuing in this way, sooner or later we find an annulus

$$R = 2^j \leq |z| < 2^{j+1} = 2R \tag{8.10-6}$$

such that $f(z)$ contains a zero in this annulus and none inside the circle $|z| = R$. [If $f(z)$ does have a zero inside the unit circle, we halve the radius until we find a circle inside which there is no zero. Again we get an inequality of the form (8.10-6) for the annulus that contains the zero.]
2. This annulus can be completely covered by eight overlapping circles each of radius $4R/5$ with centers at {50}

$$\frac{3R}{2 \cos (\pi/8)} e^{2\pi i k/8} \qquad k = 0, 1, \ldots, 7 \qquad i = \sqrt{-1} \tag{8.10-7}$$

Testing each of these circles in turn (using Theorem 8.4), we shall find at least one containing a root of (8.9-1). If the coefficients of

† Even if $f(z)$ has real coefficients, $g(z)$ may have complex coefficients, but Theorem 8.4 is still valid.

the polynomial are real, there must be a root in a circle for $k = 0$, 1, 2, 3, or 4 (why?).

3. Calling the center of this circle C_1 and starting with the radius $\frac{4}{5}R$, we proceed as in step 1 except that now we halve the radius at each stage. Finally we find an annulus

$$R_1 = (4R/5) \times 2^{-j_1} \leqq |z - C_1| < (4R/5) \times 2^{-(j_1-1)} = 2R_1 \tag{8.10-8}$$

for some positive integer j_1 which contains a zero of $f(z)$. As in step 2 we cover this annulus with eight circles and repeat steps 2 and 3 as long as desired.

The method is illustrated graphically in Fig. 8.5. Note that the method need not converge to the root α_1 which determined the annulus (8.10-6). In fact the end of any stage may be determined by a root other

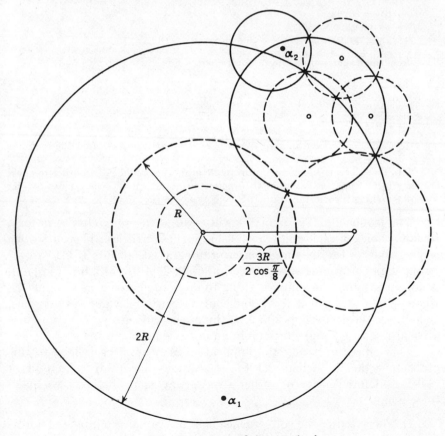

Fig. 8.5 The Lehmer-Schur method.

than that which determined the end of the previous stage.   But if R is the radius of (8.10-6), we may show that the magnitude of the root to which the process converges does not exceed $5R/2 \cos (\pi/8)$ {50}.

Since j_1 in step 3 is positive $2R_1 \leq \frac{4}{5}R$, $2R_2 \leq \frac{4}{5}R_1 \leq \frac{8}{25}R$ and in general after k steps the root lies within a circle of radius $2R_k$ such that

$$R_k \leq (\tfrac{2}{5})^k R \tag{8.10-9}$$

and probably R_k is much smaller than this bound (why?).

Example 8.9   Apply the Lehmer-Schur algorithm to the polynomial $f(z) = 4z^3 - 8z^2 + 9z - 18$.

We have

$$f^*(z) = -18z^3 + 9z^2 - 8z + 4$$
$$f_1(z) = T[f(z)] = -18f(z) - 4f^*(z) = 108z^2 - 130z + 308$$
$$T[f(0)] = 308$$
$$f_1^*(z) = 308z^2 - 130z + 108$$
$$f_2(z) = T[f_1(z)] = T^2[f(z)] = 308f_1(z) - 108f_1^*(z) = 400(-65z + 208)$$
$$T^2[f(0)] = 83{,}200$$
$$f_2^*(z) = 400(208z - 65)$$
$$T[f_2(z)] = T^3[f(z)] = [(208)^2 - (65)^2](400)^2$$

Therefore, there is no root inside the unit circle.   For $g(z) = f(2z)$ we find

$$T[g(z)] = 700z - 700$$

so that $T[g(0)] = -700$ and $f(z)$ has a root in

$$1 \leq z < 2$$

and we could then proceed to steps 2 and 3 of the algorithm.   In fact the roots are $+2, -3i/2, +3i/2$.

Note that the coefficients in this example grow very rapidly.   In order to avoid this rapid growth, it is desirable in practice to normalize the coefficients by, for example, making the constant term 1 in magnitude in each $T^j[f(z)]$.

The loophole in Theorem 8.4 will occur with probability zero for a random choice of coefficients in (8.9-1), but, nevertheless, it occurs when $a_0 = a_n$ and for certain simple cases of integral coefficients {51}.   If, for example, in performing step 1 for a radius R, $T^k[g(0)] = 0$, but $T^{k-1}[g(z)]$ is not a constant, the simplest thing to do is to choose a new radius βR where $\frac{1}{2} < \beta < 1$, say $\beta = \frac{3}{4}$, and continue with this value of the radius, choosing as the next radius $2\beta R$.   If this case occurs in step 3, then we use a value $1 < \beta < 2$ and continue in an obvious fashion.

This procedure then—the application of Schur's basic idea to this problem is due to Lehmer (1961)—converges inevitably to a root of (8.9-1).   Before considering other always-convergent methods, we make these points:

1. The speed of the convergence is in no way affected by the multiplicity of the roots or by whether the roots are clustered in any

way.   These considerations will be important in the next two methods we shall discuss.

2. At any stage we may switch over to a more rapidly convergent method (e.g., a method of functional iteration applied to the polynomials; see Secs. 8.11 and 8.12).   Whether this more rapidly convergent method does indeed converge will depend on how close we are to the root.   If it does not converge, we may switch back to the Lehmer-Schur method (see Sec. 8.14).

3. Having found one root we may remove it from (8.9-1) by synthetic division (see Sec. 8.11) and proceed to find the others, remembering to make $2R$ the starting radius for the next root (why?).

The algorithm of this section provides a convenient technique for determining the interval $[\alpha,\beta]$ over which a numerical integration scheme (5.2-5) is relatively stable according to Definition 5.2 (page 176).   To find β we would consider a sequence of positive values of hK starting at $hK = 0$.   For such a sequence, it is not hard to "follow" the root r_0 since we know $r_0 = 1$ when $hK = 0$.   Simple methods of functional iteration like the secant method or the Newton-Raphson method may be used for this purpose.   Having found r_0 we then make the change of variable $r = 1/s$ in (5.4-5) and use the Lehmer-Schur algorithm to determine if any of the other roots of (5.4-5) have magnitude greater than r_0.

8.10-2   Graeffe's root-squaring method

The essence of Graeffe's method is to replace (8.9-1) by an equation, still of degree n, whose roots are the squares of the roots of (8.9-1).   By iterating this procedure, roots of (8.9-1) which are unequal in magnitude become more widely separated in magnitude.   By separating the roots sufficiently we can, as we shall see, calculate the roots directly from the coefficients.   When there are roots of equal magnitude, this process runs into difficulties, but these can be overcome.

Let the roots of (8.9-1) be α_i, $i = 1, \ldots, n$.   We assume in the remainder of this section that $a_n = 1$.   Then, writing $f_0(z)$ for $f(z)$, we have

$$f_0(z) = (z - \alpha_1)(z - \alpha_2) \cdots (z - \alpha_n) \qquad (8.10\text{-}10)$$

Using this we may write

$$f_1(w) = (-1)^n f_0(z) f_0(-z) = (w - \alpha_1^2)(w - \alpha_2^2) \cdots (w - \alpha_n^2)$$
$$w = z^2 \quad (8.10\text{-}11)$$

so that the zeros of $f_1(w)$ are the squares of those of $f_0(z)$.   Therefore, the sequence

$$f_{r+1}(w) = (-1)^n f_r(z) f_r(-z) \qquad r = 0, 1, \ldots \qquad (8.10\text{-}12)$$

is such that the zeros of each polynomial are the squares of the zeros of the previous polynomial. If we denote the coefficients of $f_r(z)$ by $a_j^{(r)}$, $j = 0$, . . . , n then we may show that $\{53\}$

$$a_j^{(r+1)} = (-1)^{n-j}\{[a_j^{(r)}]^2 + 2 \sum_{k=1}^{\min(n-j,j)} (-1)^k a_{j-k}^{(r)} a_{j+k}^{(r)}\} \qquad (8.10\text{-}13)$$

To use the sequence of polynomials $\{f_r(z)\}$, we need the well-known relationship between the coefficients of a polynomial and its zeros. This relationship is expressed by the equation

$$a_j^{(r)} = (-1)^{n-j} S_{n-j}(\alpha_1^{2^r}, \alpha_2^{2^r}, \ldots, \alpha_n^{2^r}) \qquad j = 0, \ldots, n-1 \qquad (8.10\text{-}14)$$

where $S_k(x_1, \ldots, x_n)$ is the kth symmetric function of $x_1, \ldots, x_n$. This function is defined by the equation

$$S_k(x_1, \ldots, x_n) = \sum_{1}^{n} x_{r_1} x_{r_2} \cdots x_{r_k} \qquad (8.10\text{-}15)$$

where the notation $\sum_{1}^{n}{}_c$ denotes that the sum is over all *combinations* of the digits 1 to n in the subscripts. Thus, for example,

$$a_{n-1}^{(r)} = -S_1(\alpha_1^{2^r}, \ldots, \alpha_n^{2^r}) = -\sum_{k=1}^{n} \alpha_k^{2^r} \qquad (8.10\text{-}16)$$

Let

$$\alpha_k = \rho_k e^{i\phi_k} \qquad k = 1, \ldots, n \qquad (8.10\text{-}17)$$

Suppose first that all the roots are distinct in magnitude and ordered so that

$$\rho_1 > \rho_2 > \cdots > \rho_n \qquad (8.10\text{-}18)$$

We write (8.10-16) as

$$a_{n-1}^{(r)} = -\alpha_1^{2^r}\left[1 + \sum_{k=2}^{n} \left(\frac{\alpha_k}{\alpha_1}\right)^{2^r}\right] \qquad (8.10\text{-}19)$$

Then using (8.10-18)

$$\lim_{r \to \infty} |-a_{n-1}^{(r)}|^{1/2^r} = |\alpha_1| \qquad (8.10\text{-}20)$$

Therefore, for sufficiently large r

$$\rho_1 \approx |-a_{n-1}^{(r)}|^{1/2^r} \qquad (8.10\text{-}21)$$

Similarly, we have

$$a_{n-2}^{(r)} = \sum_{1}^{n}{}_{c} \alpha_{r_1}^{2^r}\alpha_{r_2}^{2^r} = \alpha_1^{2^r}\alpha_2^{2^r}\left[1 + \sum_{\substack{1 \\ (r_1,r_2)\,\neq\,(1,2)}}^{n}{}_{c} \left(\frac{\alpha_{r_1}\alpha_{r_2}}{\alpha_1\alpha_2}\right)^{2^r}\right] \qquad (8.10\text{-}22)$$

and, therefore, for sufficiently large r

$$\rho_2 \approx \frac{1}{\rho_1}\,|a_{n-2}^{(r)}|^{1/2^r} \approx \left|\frac{a_{n-2}^{(r)}}{a_{n-1}^{(r)}}\right|^{1/2^r} \qquad (8.10\text{-}23)$$

Continuing in this way we have in general

$$\rho_k \approx \left|\frac{a_{n-k}^{(r)}}{a_{n-k+1}^{(r)}}\right|^{1/2^r} \qquad k = 3, \ldots, n \qquad (8.10\text{-}24)$$

In practice "sufficiently large r" means only that we must continue the root-squaring process until the approximations to the magnitudes have stabilized to the number of decimal places that we desire.

When the roots are all separated, then once we have the magnitudes, determining the sign is easily accomplished by inserting the magnitude into (8.9-1).

Example 8.10   Use the root-squaring method to find the zeros of $z^3 - 5z^2 - 17z + 21$.

Using (8.10-13) we calculate

r	$a_3^{(r)}$	$a_2^{(r)}$	$a_1^{(r)}$	$a_0^{(r)}$
1	1	-59	499	-441
2	1	-2483	196963	-194481
3	1	-5771363	37,828,630,723	$-37,822,859,361$

and from these we may estimate at each stage

r	ρ_1	ρ_2	ρ_3
1	7.68	2.91	.94
2	7.06	2.98	.997
3	7.001	2.999	.99998

Insertion of these three magnitudes into the polynomial leads easily to the result that α_1 and α_3 are positive and α_2 is negative.   The true roots are 7, -3, 1.

The difficulties in the use of the root-squaring procedure arise when some of the roots have equal magnitudes.   These difficulties are of two kinds: (1) The relations (8.10-21), (8.10-23), and (8.10-24) no longer are correct in general. Therefore, determining the magnitudes of the roots is more difficult. (2) Since some roots may be complex, it is no longer simple to determine the root given the magnitude.

Both these difficulties are, in fact, not hard to overcome. Let (8.9-1) have ν_i roots of magnitude ρ_i such that

$$\nu_1 + \nu_2 + \cdots + \nu_N = n \qquad \rho_1 > \rho_2 > \cdots > \rho_N \qquad (8.10\text{-}25)$$

Let $\mu_0 = 0$ and $\mu_j = \nu_1 + \cdots + \nu_j$, $j = 1, \ldots, N - 1$. From (8.10-14) the dominant term in magnitude in $a_{n-\mu_j}^{(r)}$ is

$$(-1)^{\mu_j}(\rho_1^{\nu_1}\rho_2^{\nu_2} \cdots \rho_j^{\nu_j})^{2^r} \qquad (8.10\text{-}26)$$

since the product of the argument terms is 1 (why?). Therefore,

$$\left|a_{n-\mu_j}^{(r)}\right| = (\rho_1^{\nu_1}\rho_2^{\nu_2} \cdots \rho_j^{\nu_j})^{2^r}[1 + \delta_j^{(r)}] \qquad (8.10\text{-}27)$$

where $\lim_{r \to \infty} \delta_j^{(r)} = 0$. Then, analogously to (8.10-24), we obtain

$$\lim_{r \to \infty} \left|\frac{a_{n-\mu_{j+1}}^{(r)}}{a_{n-\mu_j}^{(r)}}\right|^{1/2^r} = \rho_{j+1}^{\nu_{j+1}} \qquad (8.10\text{-}28)$$

The coefficients $a_{n-\mu_j}^{(r)}$ are called *pivotal* coefficients. In general then to use the root-squaring process we must search for the pivotal coefficients and use them to determine $\rho_1, \ldots, \rho_N$. Suffice it to say here that, using a good deal of ingenuity, this can be programmed for a computer.

Assume then that we have the magnitudes $\rho_1, \ldots, \rho_N$ and with them their multiplicities, since the determination of the pivotal coefficients has as a by-product the numbers $\nu_1, \ldots, \nu_N$. If any magnitude has an odd multiplicity we know that it corresponds to at least one real root which can be found as above. For magnitudes of even multiplicity there exist real factors of (8.9-1) of the form $z^2 + pz + q$, where q is the square of the magnitude or its negative (why?). In what follows we assume $q = \rho_k^2$. If the procedure below to find p leads to $\nu_k - 2$ roots of magnitude ρ_k, then the remaining factor is $z^2 - \rho_k^2$.

We proceed as follows: Write (8.9-1) (with $a_n = 1$) as

$$z^n + a_{n-1}z^{n-1} + \cdots + a_1z + a_0$$
$$= (z^2 + pz + q)(z^{n-2} + b_{n-3}z^{n-3} + \cdots + b_1z + b_0) \qquad (8.10\text{-}29)$$

Equating coefficients of like powers, we have

$$a_k = b_{k-2} + pb_{k-1} + qb_k \qquad k = 0, \ldots, n - 1$$
$$b_{n-2} = 1, b_{n-1} = b_{-1} = b_{-2} = 0$$
$$(8.10\text{-}30)$$

We may write this as a recurrence relation for the b_k's

$$b_k = a_{k+2} - pb_{k+1} - qb_{k+2} \qquad k = n - 3, \ldots, 0$$
$$b_{n-2} = 1, b_{n-1} = 0 \qquad \text{(8.10-31)}$$

In particular

$$
\begin{aligned}
b_{n-3} &= a_{n-1} - p \\
b_{n-4} &= a_{n-2} - pb_{n-3} - q = a_{n-2} - p(a_{n-1} - p) - q \\
b_{n-5} &= a_{n-3} - pb_{n-4} - qb_{n-3} \\
&= a_{n-3} - p[a_{n-2} - p(a_{n-1} - p) - q] - q(a_{n-1} - p)
\end{aligned}
\qquad \text{(8.10-32)}
$$

The point we wish to elucidate is that b_{n-k} is a polynomial of degree $k - 2$ in p where all the coefficients are known. Therefore, b_0 is a polynomial of degree $n - 2$ in p. From (8.10-29) we have

$$a_0 = qb_0 \qquad \text{(8.10-33)}$$

This is a polynomial equation of degree $n - 2$ in p all of whose coefficients can be calculated (see below). *Some* real root of this equation is the value of p in (8.10-29). If $q = \rho_k^2$ then $p = -2\rho_k \cos \theta_k$ so that

$$p^2 \leqq 4q \qquad \text{(8.10-34)}$$

We leave to a problem $\{54\}$ the result that *every* real solution of (8.10-33) which satisfies (8.10-34) corresponds to a quadratic factor of (8.9-1) which is the product of two roots of magnitude ρ_k.

Our only remaining problem is the calculation of the coefficients of p in the polynomial (8.10-33). We write

$$b_{n-k} = \sum_{j=0}^{k-2} c_{kj} p^j \qquad k = 3, 4, \ldots, n \qquad \text{(8.10-35)}$$

For example, from (8.10-32) we have $c_{30} = a_{n-1}$, $c_{31} = -1$. Then from (8.10-31) we may derive recurrence relations for the c_{kj}'s $\{54\}$

$$
\left.
\begin{aligned}
c_{kj} &= -c_{k-1,j-1} - qc_{k-2,j} \qquad j = 1, \ldots, k - 2 \\
c_{kj} &= 0, j > k - 2, \quad c_{20} = 1 \\
c_{k0} &= a_{n-k+2} - qc_{k-2,0} \qquad c_{10} = 0
\end{aligned}
\right\}
\begin{aligned}
k = 3, \ldots, n \\
\text{(8.10-36)}
\end{aligned}
$$

Equation (8.10-33) then may be written

$$a_0 = q \sum_{j=0}^{n-2} c_{nj} p^j \qquad \text{(8.10-37)}$$

with the c_{nj}'s given by (8.10-36). To solve this polynomial equation, we may again use root squaring, but since we are interested only in the real roots with magnitude constrained by (8.10-34), this problem can be solved without recourse to further equations of the type (8.10-37) (why?).

Example 8.11   Use root squaring to find the zeros of $z^4 - 3z^3 - 54z^2 - 150z - 100$.

Using (8.10-13) we calculate

r	$a_4^{(r)}$	$a_3^{(r)}$	$a_2^{(r)}$	$a_1^{(r)}$	$a_0^{(r)}$
1	1	-117	1,816	$-11,700$	10,000
2	1	$-10,057$	580,056	$-10,057 \times 10^4$	10^8
3	1	$-99,983,137$	$-1,686,200,016,864$	$-99,983,137 \times 10^8$	10^{16}

The $1/2^r$ roots of $-a_3^{(r)}/a_4^{(r)}$ give 10.82, 10.014, 9.9998 as approximations to the true magnitude of 10.   The corresponding roots of $-a_2^{(r)}/a_3^{(r)}$ show no such convergence. However, the $1/2^r$ roots of $a_1^{(r)}/a_3^{(r)}$ are all 10, which is in fact the square of the magnitude of the root of second greatest magnitude.   Finally, the roots of $a_0^{(r)}/a_1^{(r)}$ give .92, .9986, 1.00002 as approximations to the true value of 1.

Let us suppose then that we have carried the root-squaring process far enough to get as good approximations as we desire to $\rho_1 = 10$, $\rho_2 = \sqrt{10}$, $\rho_3 = 1$.   Since $\nu_1 = \nu_3 = 1$ we may easily find that $\alpha_1 = 10$, $\alpha_3 = -1$.   For ρ_2, $q = 10$ and (8.10-29) becomes

$$z^4 - 3z^3 - 54z^2 - 150z - 100 = (z^2 + pz + 10)(z^2 + b_1 z + b_0)$$

Using (8.10-36) we may then calculate for (8.10-37)

$$-100 = 10(p^2 + 3p - 64)$$

whose roots are $p = 6$, $p = -9$.   Only $p = 6$ satisfies (8.10-34); thus we find the other two roots to be $-3 \pm i$.

The reader may think that we have brushed too quickly past the computational details of the root-squaring method.   For example, the large coefficients in Examples 8.10 and 8.11 might cause trouble, particularly if a large number of root squarings are required.   Also how do we know when we have performed a sufficient number of root squarings to separate adequately the roots of different magnitudes?   We shall not go into these details here, but in fact these difficulties can and have been overcome by a computer program.   Although a program for the root-squaring method is substantially more complicated than that for the Lehmer-Schur method, root squaring appears to be a more efficient (i.e., faster) method. A comparison of the speeds of the two methods is in fact quite difficult. This is particularly true because in practice the Lehmer-Schur method would be coupled with a more rapidly convergent method (see Sec. 8.12) which would be used when a good approximation to a root had been found.

8.10-3   Bernoulli's method

Consider the difference equation

$$a_n u_k + a_{n-1} u_{k-1} + \cdots + a_0 u_{k-n} = 0 \qquad (8.10\text{-}38)$$

where the coefficients a_i, $i = 0, \ldots, n$ are those of (8.9-1). If the roots α_i of (8.9-1) are distinct then the solution of this equation is given by {57}

$$u_k = \sum_{i=1}^{n} c_i \alpha_i^k \qquad (8.10\text{-}39)$$

where the c_i's depend on the initial conditions used to solve (8.10-38). If the roots are ordered in magnitude as in (8.10-18) then by rewriting (8.10-39) as

$$u_k = c_1 \alpha_1^k \left[1 + \sum_{i=2}^{n} \frac{c_i}{c_1} \left(\frac{\alpha_i}{\alpha_1} \right)^k \right] \qquad (8.10\text{-}40)$$

we have, if $c_1 \neq 0$

$$\lim_{k \to \infty} \frac{u_k}{u_{k-1}} = \alpha_1 \qquad (8.10\text{-}41)$$

The essence of Bernoulli's method is to use (8.10-38) to compute successive values of u_k and then to compute the ratio of successive values of u_k until these ratios converge to α_1.

For this method to work at all, it is necessary that $c_1 \neq 0$. The c_i's depend, as we said, on the n initial conditions required by (8.10-38). If we generate these initial values using the equation

$$a_n u_m + a_{n-1} u_{m-1} + \cdots + a_{n-m+1} u_1 + m a_{n-m} = 0$$
$$m = 1, \ldots, n \qquad (8.10\text{-}42)$$

then it can be shown {56} that all c_i's are unity and thus

$$u_k = \sum_{i=1}^{n} \alpha_i^k \qquad (8.10\text{-}43)$$

Therefore, (8.10-41) always holds for this choice of initial conditions.

The above was predicated on the assumption that α_1, the root of largest magnitude, is real and distinct. Nevertheless, (8.10-41) also holds if α_1 is multiple but real {57}. But when the root of largest magnitude is complex or when there is some combination of real and complex roots of largest magnitude, (8.10-41) no longer holds. The number of possible special cases is therefore very large. Each such special case can be taken care of by a suitable modification of (8.10-41). For example, if there is a single pair of complex conjugate roots of largest magnitude, then writing

$$\alpha_1 = \beta_1 e^{i\phi_1} \qquad \alpha_2 = \beta_1 e^{-i\phi_1} \qquad (8.10\text{-}44)$$

we may write (8.10-43) as

$$u_k = 2\beta_1^k \cos k\phi_1 \left(1 + \sum_{i=3}^{n} \frac{\alpha_i^k}{\alpha_1^k + \alpha_2^k} \right) \qquad (8.10\text{-}45)$$

Using (8.10-45) it is not hard to show that {57}

$$\beta_1^2 = \lim_{k \to \infty} \frac{u_k^2 - u_{k+1}u_{k-1}}{u_{k-1}^2 - u_k u_{k-2}} \tag{8.10-46}$$

and

$$2\beta_1 \cos \phi_1 = \lim_{k \to \infty} \frac{u_k u_{k-1} - u_{k+1}u_{k-2}}{u_{k-1}^2 - u_k u_{k-2}} \tag{8.10-47}$$

Other special cases such as repeated complex roots and combinations of real and complex roots of equal magnitude can also be handled separately but especially for automatic computation, it is extremely tedious to have to provide for all these cases. Moreover, if α_2 has nearly the same magnitude as α_1, the convergence of the process is extremely slow (why?). Thus, as a general-purpose method, Bernoulli's method is inferior to the Lehmer-Schur and root-squaring methods. However, a scheme known as the quotient-difference algorithm may be used in conjunction with Bernoulli's method to obtain all the zeros of a polynomial simultaneously even when there are zeros of equal magnitude. This algorithm generally converges quite slowly and should, like the Lehmer-Schur method, be used in conjunction with a more rapidly convergent method (see Sec. 8.12). We shall not consider the quotient-difference algorithm here; for details of its application to polynomials see Henrici (1964, pp. 162–168). The quotient-difference algorithm has, however, many other applications besides the calculation of the zeros of polynomials. In Sec. 10.6-1 we shall discuss one of these.

When the root of largest or smallest magnitude [by considering $f(1/z)$] is the only one that is desired and is distinct, Bernoulli's method can be very useful. When a root has been found and removed from (8.9-1) by synthetic division, Bernoulli's method can then be used to find an approximation to the root of next greatest magnitude.

Example 8.12   Use Bernoulli's method to find the zero of greatest magnitude of the polynomial $z^3 - 5z^2 - 17z + 21$ of Example 8.10.

Using (8.10-42) we have

$$u_1 - 5 = 0 \to u_1 = 5$$
$$u_2 - 5u_1 - 34 = 0 \to u_2 = 59$$
$$u_3 - 5u_2 - 17u_1 + 63 = 0 \to u_3 = 317$$

Then using (8.10-38) in the form

$$u_k = 5u_{k-1} + 17u_{k-2} - 21u_{k-3}$$

we calculate

$u_4 = 2483$		$u_4/u_3 = 7.83$	
$u_5 = 16{,}565$		$u_5/u_4 = 6.67$	
$u_6 = 118{,}379$		$u_6/u_5 = 7.15$	
$u_7 = 821{,}357$		$u_7/u_6 = 6.94$	
$u_8 = 5{,}771{,}363$		$u_8/u_7 = 7.03$	
$u_9 = 40{,}333{,}925$		$u_9/u_8 = 6.989$	

This example illustrates two characteristic features of Bernoulli's method. First, it generally converges more slowly than the root-squaring method. However, because of the linear convergence of the method [note (8.10-41)], the δ^2 process may be used to accelerate the convergence. For example, using the first three approximations to the zero in the table above (7.83, 6.67, 7.15), Eq. (8.7-4) gives 6.998 as the improved approximation. The second characteristic feature of Bernoulli's method is that, like the root-squaring method, the numbers involved grow very rapidly for roots of magnitude greater than 1. This latter problem can be avoided as follows: We assume $a_n \neq 0$ and rewrite (8.10-38) as

$$u_k = -b_{n-1}u_{k-1} - b_{n-2}u_{k-2} - \cdots - b_0 u_{k-n} \qquad (8.10\text{-}48)$$

where $b_i = a_i/a_n$, $i = 0, \ldots, n-1$. Then

$$\frac{u_k}{u_{k-1}} = -b_{n-1} - b_{n-2}\frac{u_{k-2}}{u_{k-1}} - b_{n-3}\frac{u_{k-3}}{u_{k-2}}\frac{u_{k-2}}{u_{k-1}} - \cdots$$
$$- b_0\left(\frac{u_{k-n}}{u_{k-n+1}}\frac{u_{k-n+1}}{u_{k-n+2}} \cdots \frac{u_{k-2}}{u_{k-1}}\right) \qquad (8.10\text{-}49)$$

Now defining

$$\lambda_k = u_{k-1}/u_k \qquad (8.10\text{-}50)$$

we have

$$-(1/\lambda_k) = b_{n-1} + b_{n-2}\lambda_{k-1} + b_{n-3}\lambda_{k-2}\lambda_{k-1} + \cdots$$
$$+ b_0(\lambda_{k-n+1} \cdots \lambda_{k-1}) \qquad (8.10\text{-}51)$$

The right-hand side of (8.10-51) is conveniently calculated using the recurrence relation {58}

$$\gamma_{k0} = b_0$$
$$\gamma_{kr} = \gamma_{k,r-1}\lambda_{k-n+r} + b_r \qquad r = 1, \ldots, n-1 \qquad k > n \qquad (8.10\text{-}52)$$
$$\lambda_k = -1/\gamma_{k,n-1}$$

When $k \leq n$, Eq. (8.10-42) is also easily expressed in terms of the λ_i's. Using the above, (8.10-41) may be written

$$\lim_{k \to \infty} \frac{1}{\lambda_k} = \alpha_1$$

and (8.10-46) and (8.10-47) are also easily modifiable {58}. Since the calculations in terms of the λ_i's involve only ratios of the u_i's, the numbers do not get large.

With slowly convergent methods like the Lehmer-Schur or Bernoulli methods, it is desirable to use them only to get a good approximation to a root. Then a more rapidly convergent method—but one whose convergence depends on a good initial approximation—may be used. In Sec.

8.12 we shall consider the adaptation of rapidly convergent methods of functional iteration to the problem of finding zeros of polynomials.

8.10-4   Laguerre's method

Suppose all the zeros of $f(z)$ are real, distinct, and ordered such that

$$x^{(1)} < x^{(2)} < \cdots < x^{(n-1)} < x^{(n)} \qquad (8.10\text{-}53)$$

We define

$$I_i = [x^{(i)}, x^{(i+1)}] \qquad i = 0, \ldots, n$$
$$x^{(0)} = -\infty, \; x^{(n+1)} = \infty \qquad (8.10\text{-}54)$$

Let x be an approximation to a zero of $f(z)$. This approximation lies in some interval I_i. The essence of Laguerre's method is to construct a parabola with two real zeros in I_i, one of which will be closer to a zero of $f(z)$ than x. In what follows we assume that $n > 2$.

The desired parabola has the form

$$\Phi(X) = \left[S(\lambda) - \left(\frac{\lambda - X}{x - X} \right)^2 \right] (x - X)^2$$
$$= (x - X)^2 S(\lambda) - (\lambda - X)^2 \quad (8.10\text{-}55)$$

where λ is a real parameter to be chosen later and

$$S(\lambda) = \sum_{i=1}^{n} \left(\frac{\lambda - x^{(i)}}{x - x^{(i)}} \right)^2 \qquad (8.10\text{-}56)$$

To know this parabola as a function of λ seems to require a knowledge of the zeros of $f(z)$. But we shall show [cf. (8.10-59)] that in fact the seeming dependence on the zeros may be eliminated.

Now suppose that $\lambda \neq x$. Then, if x is not a zero of $f(z)$, it follows from (8.10-55) and (8.10-56) that $\Phi(x) < 0$ and $\Phi[x^{(i)}] > 0, i = 0, \ldots, n + 1$. Therefore, $\Phi(X)$ does have the desired property of having two real zeros in $I_i, i = 1, \ldots, n - 1$, and for $i = 0$ or n, there is one real zero between x and $x^{(1)}$ or $x^{(n)}$ and x, respectively. Our problem now is to choose λ so that one of these zeros is as near as possible to a zero of $f(x)$. This means that, if X is a zero of $\Phi(X)$, we wish to maximize $|x - X|$ as a function of λ or, alternatively, as a function of $y = \lambda - x$ (why?).

From (8.9-1) we may easily calculate $\{60\}$

$$\frac{f'(x)}{f(x)} = \sum_{i=1}^{n} \frac{1}{x - x^{(i)}}$$

$$\frac{[f'(x)]^2 - f(x)f''(x)}{[f(x)]^2} = \sum_{i=1}^{n} \frac{1}{[x - x^{(i)}]^2}$$

$$(8.10\text{-}57)$$

Also

$$\left[\frac{\lambda - x^{(i)}}{x - x^{(i)}}\right]^2 = \left[\frac{\lambda - x}{x - x^{(i)}}\right]^2 + \frac{2(\lambda - x)}{x - x^{(i)}} + 1 \tag{8.10-58}$$

Using (8.10-56) to (8.10-58) in (8.10-55) we may calculate {60}

$$[f(x)]^2 \Phi(X) = y^2((x - X)^2\{[f'(x)]^2 - f(x)f''(x)\} - [f(x)]^2)$$
$$+ 2y(x - X)f(x)[(x - X)f'(x) - f(x)]$$
$$+ (n - 1)(x - X)^2[f(x)]^2 \tag{8.10-59}$$

Equation (8.10-59) is a verification of our previous assertion that $\Phi(X)$ may be evaluated without a knowledge of the zeros of $f(z)$. Setting $\Phi(X) = 0$ in (8.10-59) results in a quadratic equation for y whose roots are continuous functions of the parameter $x - X$. Our object is to find the maximum value of $|x - X|$ such that y is real. Since this implies that greater values of $|x - X|$ will result in complex roots, the desired value must be such that the discriminant D of the quadratic equation in y is zero (why?). This means that it is only necessary to determine the values of $x - X$ which make $D = 0$. Thus λ need not be determined explicitly at all.

A tedious calculation {60} leads to the result that

$$D = -4(x - X)^2[f(x)]^2(\{(n - 1)f(x)f''(x)$$
$$- (n - 2)[f'(x)]^2\}(x - X)^2$$
$$+ n[f(x)]^2 - 2(x - X)f'(x)f(x)) \tag{8.10-60}$$

Setting $D = 0$ and ignoring the uninteresting case $x = X$, we get by solving the resulting quadratic equation for $x - X$ {60}

$$X = x - \frac{nf(x)}{f'(x) \pm \sqrt{H(x)}} \tag{8.10-61}$$

where

$$H(x) = (n - 1)\{(n - 1)[f'(x)]^2 - nf(x)f''(x)\} \tag{8.10-62}$$

When all the zeros are real we may show that H is always nonnegative {60}. Equation (8.10-61) suggests the iteration

$$x_{i+1} = x_i - \frac{nf(x_i)}{f'(x_i) \pm \sqrt{H(x_i)}} \tag{8.10-63}$$

In order to determine which sign to use in the denominator of (8.10-63), let us use Theorem 8.1 to determine the order of this iteration. We have, with α any of the zeros of (8.10-53) $\{60\}$

$$F(x) = x - \frac{nf(x)}{f'(x) \pm \sqrt{H(x)}}$$

$$F'(\alpha) = 1 - \frac{nf'(\alpha)}{f'(\alpha) \pm \sqrt{H(\alpha)}}$$

$$= 1 - \frac{nf'(\alpha)}{f'(\alpha) \pm (n-1)|f'(\alpha)|} \qquad (8.10\text{-}64)$$

$$F''(\alpha) = \frac{-nf''(\alpha)}{f'(\alpha) \pm (n-1)|f'(\alpha)|}$$

$$\times \left\{ 1 - \frac{2f'(\alpha)}{f'(\alpha) \pm (n-1)|f'(\alpha)|} \left[1 \pm \frac{n-2}{2} \frac{f'(\alpha)}{|f'(\alpha)|} \right] \right\}$$

From (8.10-64) it is easy to see that, if the sign is chosen to agree with the sign of $f'(\alpha)$, then both $F'(\alpha)$ and $F''(\alpha)$ are zero. Therefore, in practice we should choose the sign in (8.10-63) to agree with $f'(x_i)$. In particular we may then show that, if the initial approximation $x_1 < x^{(1)}$, then $x_i < x_{i+1} < x^{(1)}$ and, similarly, if $x^{(n)} < x_1$, then $x^{(n)} < x_{i+1} < x_i$ $\{60\}$. Since it can be shown that $F'''(\alpha) \neq 0$, Laguerre's method is a third-order method for simple real zeros. This is obtained at the expense of calculating $f(x)$, $f'(x)$, and $f''(x)$ at every stage of the iteration.

The great advantage of Laguerre's method is that the method is sure to converge independent of the initial approximation x_1. From our construction, this is obvious if $x_1 \, \varepsilon \, [x^{(1)}, \, x^{(n)}]$, and from the comments above, it is also true if x_1 is outside this interval. This method is then a powerful, rapidly converging method for a polynomial all of whose zeros are real and simple. If all the zeros are real but some are not simple, the method still converges but is first-order in the neighborhood of a multiple zero. For polynomials, some of whose zeros are complex, little is known about the overall convergence properties of the method. However, when the method converges to a simple complex zero, the convergence is third order [Parlett (1964)]. Empirical evidence suggests that lack of convergence is extremely unusual. Laguerre's method is therefore a candidate for use as a general-purpose method for finding the zeros of polynomials, either by itself or in conjunction with one of the methods to be described in Sec. 8.12. Note that a real initial approximation may nevertheless converge to a complex zero, since $H(x)$ can be negative in this case.

Example 8.13   Use Laguerre's method to find the largest positive zero of the polynomial of Example 8.10.

To illustrate the power of this method, we choose a very bad initial approximation $x_1 = 10^6$. We have

$$f(x) = x^3 - 5x^2 - 17x + 21$$
$$f'(x) = 3x^2 - 10x - 17$$
$$f''(x) = 6x - 10$$

Then using (8.10-62) and (8.10-63), we calculate

i	x_i
2	7.4785207
3	7.0001011
4	7.0000000

and the true zero is 7. We note that if the magnitude of x_1 is large, then the arithmetic at the first iteration must be done to high precision or substantial loss of significance results.

8.11 SYNTHETIC–DIVISION ALGORITHMS

In our previous discussion of functional iteration, we considered only real roots of (8.1-1). Now that we wish to consider complex roots as well we must either (1) use complex arithmetic in our calculations or (2) look directly for quadratic factors of the polynomial $f(z)$.

In this and the next section we shall consider both these approaches. Our basic computational tool in both cases will be synthetic division. In this section we consider some algorithms for synthetic division.

8.11-1 Linear factors

When the polynomial $f(z)$ is divided by $(z - z_j)$ the remainder R_j is $f(z_j)$. That is

$$f(z) = (z - z_j)(b_{n-1}z^{n-1} + b_{n-2}z^{n-2} + \cdots + b_0) + R_j \qquad (8.11\text{-}1)$$

To derive the recurrence relations of synthetic division we equate like powers in (8.9-1) and (8.11-1) and obtain

$$\begin{aligned}
a_n &= b_{n-1} \\
a_{n-1} &= b_{n-2} - z_j b_{n-1} \\
&\cdots\cdots\cdots\cdots \\
a_k &= b_{k-1} - z_j b_k \\
&\cdots\cdots\cdots\cdots \\
a_0 &= R_j - z_j b_0
\end{aligned} \qquad (8.11\text{-}2)$$

so that the b_k's may be calculated from the recurrence relation [cf. (7.2-4)]

$$b_k = a_{k+1} + z_j b_{k+1} \qquad k = n-1, \ldots, 0 \qquad b_n = 0 \qquad (8.11\text{-}3)$$

From the last relation in (8.11-2) we have

$$R_j = a_0 + z_j b_0 \equiv b_{-1} \tag{8.11-4}$$

the definition of b_{-1} following naturally from (8.11-3).

If the quotient in (8.11-1) is again divided by $(z - z_j)$ we get

$$f(z) = (z - z_j)^2(c_{n-2}z^{n-2} + c_{n-3}z^{n-3} + \cdots + c_0) \\ + (z - z_j)R_j' + R_j \tag{8.11-5}$$

where $R_j' = f'(z_j)$. Since the c_k's are related to the b_k's as the b_k's are to the a_k's, we get corresponding to (8.11-3) and (8.11-4)

$$c_k = b_{k+1} + z_j c_{k+1} \qquad k = n - 2, \ldots, 0 \qquad c_{n-1} = 0 \tag{8.11-6}$$
$$R_j' = b_0 + z_j c_0 \equiv c_{-1} \tag{8.11-7}$$

8.11-2   Quadratic factors

If instead of dividing $f(z)$ by $(z - z_j)$, we use the quadratic factor $(z^2 + p_j z + q_j)$ then we may write

$$f(z) = (z^2 + p_j z + q_j)(b_{n-2}z^{n-2} + b_{n-3}z^{n-3} + \cdots + b_0) \\ + R_j z + S_j \tag{8.11-8}$$

Analogously to (8.10-31) we have then

$$b_k = a_{k+2} - p_j b_{k+1} - q_j b_{k+2} \qquad k = n - 2, \ldots, 0 \\ b_{n-1} = b_n = 0 \tag{8.11-9}$$

For R_j and S_j we get

$$R_j = a_1 - p_j b_0 - q_j b_1 \equiv b_{-1} \qquad S_j = a_0 - q_j b_0 \equiv b_{-2} + p_j b_{-1} \tag{8.11-10}$$

with the definitions of b_{-1} and b_{-2} following naturally from (8.11-9).

8.12   ZEROS OF POLYNOMIALS USING ITERATED SYNTHETIC DIVISION

In this section we shall apply the two algorithms of the previous section to the problem of finding the zeros of polynomials.

8.12-1   Linear factors

If $\{z_k\}$ $k = 1, \ldots, j$ is a sequence of approximations to a *real* root of (8.9-1) then any of the functional iteration formulas discussed previously may be used to generate z_{j+1}. In particular, using the notation of the previous section we have (1) The secant method:

$$z_{j+1} = z_j - \frac{R_j(z_j - z_{j-1})}{R_j - R_{j-1}} \tag{8.12-1}$$

(2) The Newton-Raphson method:

$$z_{j+1} = z_j - R_j/R_j' \tag{8.12-2}$$

A variation of (8.12-2) known as Lin's iteration uses the formula

$$z_{j+1} = z_j - R_j/b_0 \tag{8.12-3}$$

with b_0 given by (8.11-3).   The justification for this formula is found by setting $R_j = 0$ in (8.11-4) (as it would be if z_j were a root) and getting the next approximation by solving for z_j and calling it z_{j+1}.   Thus

$$z_{j+1} = -a_0/b_0 = z_j - z_j - a_0/b_0 = z_j - (b_0 z_j + a_0)/b_0 = z_j - R_j/b_0 \tag{8.12-4}$$

Not surprisingly the convergence of Lin's iteration is only linear {62}. It requires less computation than the Newton-Raphson method (since the c_k's need not be calculated), but along with its relatively slow convergence, it has the further disadvantage that, even with a very good initial approximation, it may not converge.   The theoretical reason for this is considered in {62}.

Example 8.14   Use (8.12-1), (8.12-2), and (8.12-3) to find the real root of $z^3 - z - 1$ starting with the initial approximation $z_1 = 1.30$ for the Lin and Newton-Raphson iterations and $z_1 = 1.20$, $z_2 = 1.30$ for the secant method.

For the Lin iteration and the secant method, it is natural to arrange the synthetic division calculations of (8.11-3) and (8.11-4) as follows:

	z_j	z_{j+1}
a_n	b_{n-1}	b_{n-1}
a_{n-1}	b_{n-2}	b_{n-2}
.	.	.
.	.	.
.	.	.
.	b_0	b_0
a_0	$b_{-1} = R_j$	R_{j+1}

while for the Newton-Raphson method, we add an extra column for (8.11-6) and (8.11-7)

	z_j		z_{j+1}	
a_n	b_{n-1}	c_{n-2}	b_{n-1}	c_{n-2}
a_{n-1}	.		.	.
'	.	.	.	.
.	.	c_0	.	c_0
.	b_0	R_j'	b_0	R_{j+1}'
a_0	R_j		R_{j+1}	

Using this layout, the calculations for the secant method are

	$z_1 = 1.20$	$z_2 = 1.30$	$z_3 = 1.328$	$z_4 = 1.3246$
1	1	1	1	1
0	1.20	1.30	1.328	1.3246
-1	.44	.69	.7636	.754565
-1	$-.472$	$-.103$	.0141	$-.000503$

and finally $z_5 = 1.324717$. For the Newton-Raphson method the calculations are

	$z_1 = 1.30$		$z_2 = 1.325$	
1	1	1	1	1
0	1.3	2.6	1.325	2.65
-1	.69	4.07	.755625	4.267
-1	$-.103$		.001203	

and $z_3 = 1.324718$. For the Lin iteration we get

	$z_1 = 1.30$	$z_2 = 1.45$	$z_3 = 0.91$
1	1	1	1
0	1.3	1.45	.91
-1	.69	1.102	$-.172$
-1	$-.103$	.598	-1.157

and $z_4 = -5.8$ so that the iteration is not converging even though the initial approximation is quite near the true root 1.324718. In fact no matter how close to the true solution the initial approximation is, Lin's iteration does not converge for this problem {62}.

When the root we are seeking is complex, then the computations of (8.12-1) to (8.12-3) may still all be carried through using complex arithmetic. We note that our derivations of rates of convergence all depended on the use of real variables and so are no longer applicable. But, for example, it is known [see Ostrowski (1960), pp. 43–50] that for the Newton-Raphson method, if the initial approximation is sufficiently close to the root, the method still converges for all roots and converges quadratically for simple complex roots. For the secant method it is also known that the secant method converges with order $(1 + \sqrt{5})/2$ to simple complex roots if the initial approximations are sufficiently good. Although the secant method is more efficient than the Newton-Raphson method for polynomials, the equations for the Newton-Raphson method are somewhat simpler to present and more commonly used. Therefore, we shall consider the Newton-Raphson method here and leave the secant method to a problem {63}.

Except for the a_k's all the quantities in Sec. 8.11-1 can be complex if z_j is complex. Let

$$\begin{aligned} z_j &= x_j + iy_j \\ b_k &= \gamma_k + i\delta_k \qquad i = \sqrt{-1} \\ c_k &= \epsilon_k + i\eta_k \end{aligned} \qquad (8.12\text{-}5)$$

Then (8.11-3) and (8.11-6) become

$$\gamma_k = a_{k+1} + x_j\gamma_{k+1} - y_j\delta_{k+1} \qquad k = n - 1, \ldots, 0,$$
$$\gamma_n = \delta_n = 0$$

$$\left.\begin{array}{l} \delta_k = x_j\delta_{k+1} + y_j\gamma_{k+1} \\ \epsilon_k = \gamma_{k+1} + x_j\epsilon_{k+1} - y_j\eta_{k+1} \end{array}\right\} \qquad \begin{array}{l} k = n - 2, \ldots, 0, \\ \delta_{n-1} = \epsilon_{n-1} = \eta_{n-1} = 0 \end{array} \qquad (8.12\text{-}6)$$

$$\eta_k = \delta_{k+1} + x_j\eta_{k+1} + y_j\epsilon_{k+1} \qquad k = n - 3, \ldots, 0,$$
$$\eta_{n-2} = 0$$

and (8.11-4) and (8.11-7) become

$$R_j = b_{-1} = \gamma_{-1} + i\delta_{-1} \qquad R'_j = c_{-1} = \epsilon_{-1} + i\eta_{-1} \qquad (8.12\text{-}7)$$

Thus (8.12-2) becomes

$$x_{j+1} = x_j - \frac{\epsilon_{-1}\gamma_{-1} + \eta_{-1}\delta_{-1}}{\epsilon_{-1}^2 + \eta_{-1}^2} \qquad y_{j+1} = y_j - \frac{\delta_{-1}\epsilon_{-1} - \gamma_{-1}\eta_{-1}}{\epsilon_{-1}^2 + \eta_{-1}^2}$$

$$(8.12\text{-}8)$$

Example 8.15   Use the Newton-Raphson method to find the complex zeros of $z^3 - z - 1$ (assuming, of course, the real zero is not known) starting from an initial approximation $z_1 = -1 + i$. (Note that in looking for a complex root, the initial approximation must be complex.)

We use a computational layout similar to that of Example 8.14.

		z_j		
a_n	γ_{n-1}	δ_{n-1}	ϵ_{n-2}	η_{n-2}
.	.	.	.	.
.	.	.	.	.
.	.	.	.	.
a_1	γ_0	δ_0	ϵ_{-1}	η_{-1}
a_0	γ_{-1}	δ_{-1}		

For this problem we have

	$z_1 = -1 + i$				$z_2 = -.78 + .70i$			
1	1	0	1	0	1	0	1	0
0	-1	1	-2	2	$-.78$	.70	-1.56	1.40
-1	-1	-2	-1	-6	$-.88$	-1.09	$-.64$	-2.18
-1	2	1			.45	.23		

	$z_3 = -.69 + .58i$			
1	1	0	1	0
0	$-.69$	.58	-1.38	1.16
-1	$-.860$	$-.800$	$-.581$	-2.401
-1	.057	.053		

and finally $z_4 = -.664 + .563i$, whereas the true value is $-.662359 + .562279i$.

Equations (8.12-6) to (8.12-8) are cumbersome for hand computation but are readily mechanized for a digital computer. Nevertheless, in order to avoid complex arithmetic entirely, the idea of looking directly for real quadratic factors of $f(z)$ suggests itself.

8.12-2   Quadratic factors

Looking for quadratic factors is a departure from the basic ideas of functional iteration, but as we shall see, functional iteration plays an important part in the method we are about to consider.

Lin's iteration may be applied to this problem by setting R_j and S_j in (8.11-10) equal to zero, solving for p_j and q_j, respectively, and calling the new values p_{j+1} and q_{j+1}.   Thus

$$p_{j+1} = \frac{a_1 - q_j b_1}{b_0} \qquad q_{j+1} = \frac{a_0}{b_0} \tag{8.12-9}$$

However, as with the Lin iteration discussed previously, this method again has the disadvantage that it may not converge even when the initial approximation is very good.

A more sophisticated use of (8.11-10) is the iteration of *Bairstow*. Using p and q instead of p_j and q_j Eqs. (8.11-10) may be written

$$R(p,q) = 0 \qquad S(p,q) = 0 \tag{8.12-10}$$

where b_1 and b_0 are also functions of p and q.   In the Bairstow iteration, these two simultaneous equations for the two unknowns p and q are solved using the Newton-Raphson method for simultaneous equations (8.8-10).   Let p_i and q_i and p_{i+1} and q_{i+1} denote, respectively, the results of the ith and $(i + 1)$st steps in the iteration.   Then from (8.8-10) we have

$$
\begin{aligned}
p_{i+1} &= p_i - \frac{1}{J}\left[R\frac{\partial S}{\partial q} - S\frac{\partial R}{\partial q} \right]_{\substack{p=p_i \\ q=q_i}} \\
q_{i+1} &= q_i - \frac{1}{J}\left[S\frac{\partial R}{\partial p} - R\frac{\partial S}{\partial p} \right]_{\substack{p=p_i \\ q=q_i}}
\end{aligned}
\tag{8.12-11}
$$

where

$$
J = \begin{vmatrix} \dfrac{\partial R}{\partial p} & \dfrac{\partial S}{\partial p} \\[2mm] \dfrac{\partial R}{\partial q} & \dfrac{\partial S}{\partial q} \end{vmatrix}_{\substack{p=p_i \\ q=q_i}}
\tag{8.12-12}
$$

Now using (8.11-10) we may write

$$
\begin{aligned}
\frac{\partial R}{\partial p} &= -p\frac{\partial b_0}{\partial p} - q\frac{\partial b_1}{\partial p} - b_0 & \frac{\partial R}{\partial q} &= -p\frac{\partial b_0}{\partial q} - q\frac{\partial b_1}{\partial q} - b_1 \\
\frac{\partial S}{\partial p} &= -q\frac{\partial b_0}{\partial p} & \frac{\partial S}{\partial q} &= \frac{\partial b_{-2}}{\partial q} + p\frac{\partial b_{-1}}{\partial q}
\end{aligned}
\tag{8.12-13}
$$

From (8.11-9)

$$\frac{\partial b_k}{\partial p} = -b_{k+1} - p\frac{\partial b_{k+1}}{\partial p} - q\frac{\partial b_{k+2}}{\partial p} \qquad k = n - 3, \ldots, 0$$

$$\frac{\partial b_{n-2}}{\partial p} = \frac{\partial b_{n-1}}{\partial p} = 0 \quad (8.12\text{-}14)$$

$$\frac{\partial b_k}{\partial q} = -b_{k+2} - p\frac{\partial b_{k+1}}{\partial q} - q\frac{\partial b_{k+2}}{\partial q} \qquad k = n - 3, \ldots, 0$$

$$\frac{\partial b_{n-2}}{\partial q} = \frac{\partial b_{n-1}}{\partial q} = 0 \quad (8.12\text{-}15)$$

If we define d_k by the recurrence relation

$$d_k = -b_{k+1} - pd_{k+1} - qd_{k+2} \qquad k = n - 3, \ldots, 0, -1$$

$$d_{n-2} = d_{n-1} = 0 \quad (8.12\text{-}16)$$

then it follows from (8.12-14) and (8.12-15) that

$$\partial b_k/\partial p = d_k \qquad \partial b_{k-1}/\partial q = d_k \qquad k = n - 3, \ldots, 0, -1$$
$$(8.12\text{-}17)$$

and finally that

$$\begin{aligned}
\partial R/\partial p &= d_{-1} & \partial R/\partial q &= d_0 \\
\partial S/\partial p &= -qd_0 & \partial S/\partial q &= d_{-1} + pd_0
\end{aligned} \qquad (8.12\text{-}18)$$

Therefore, (8.12-11) and (8.12-12) become

$$\begin{aligned}
p_{i+1} &= p_i - (1/J)[b_{-1}(d_{-1} + p_id_0) - (b_{-2} + p_ib_{-1})d_0] \\
q_{i+1} &= q_i - (1/J)[(b_{-2} + p_ib_{-1})d_{-1} + d_0b_{-1}q_i]
\end{aligned} \qquad (8.12\text{-}19)$$

where

$$J = d_{-1}^2 + p_id_0d_{-1} + q_id_0^2 \qquad (8.12\text{-}20)$$

Example 8.16   Use the Bairstow iteration to find a quadratic factor of $z^3 - z - 1$ starting with $p_1 = q_1 = 1$.

We arrange the calculation in the form

	(p_i, q_i)	
a_n	b_{n-2}	d_{n-3}
a_{n-1}	$\cdot$	$\cdot$
$\cdot$	$\cdot$	$\cdot$
$\cdot$	$\cdot$	d_0
$\cdot$	b_0	d_{-1}
$\cdot$	b_{-1}	
a_0	b_{-2}	

with (8.11-9) and (8.12-16) used to calculate the last two columns. For this problem we have, using (8.12-19) and (8.12-20):

	$(p_1, q_1) = (1,1)$		$(p_2, q_2) = (\frac{4}{3}, \frac{2}{3})$	
1	1	-1	1	-1
0	-1	2	$-\frac{4}{3}$	$\frac{8}{3}$
-1	-1		$\frac{1}{9}$	
-1	1		$-\frac{7}{27}$	

and finally $p_3 = 1.3246$, $q_3 = .7544$ whereas the true values are $p = 1.3247$, $q = .7549$.

When it converges, Bairstow's method has the characteristic rapid convergence of the Newton-Raphson method. But, as is usually the case in solving simultaneous nonlinear equations, convergence requires a quite good initial approximation {64}.

8.13 THE EFFECT OF COEFFICIENT ERRORS ON THE ROOTS. ILL–CONDITIONED POLYNOMIALS

The coefficients of the polynomial whose zeros we actually compute are seldom the true coefficients of the polynomial whose zeros we desire. The coefficients we use may arise from empirical data, in which case we shall not know the true coefficients. More often we know the true coefficients but must round them when inserting them into the computer. How then do these coefficient errors affect the accuracy of the calculated zeros?

Let the true polynomial be

$$F(z) = A_n z^n + A_{n-1} z^{n-1} + \cdots + A_1 z + A_0 \tag{8.13-1}$$

and define

$$\delta_i = A_i - a_i \qquad i = 0, 1, \ldots, n \tag{8.13-2}$$

If the computed zero is z_0 and the true zero is

$$Z_0 = z_0 + \epsilon \tag{8.13-3}$$

where ϵ may be real or complex, we wish to find an estimate of the magnitude of ϵ. Assume for now that ϵ and the δ_i's are sufficiently small so that all products of the errors can be neglected. Then substituting (8.13-2) and (8.13-3) into (8.13-1) and using the fact that z_0 is a root of (8.9-1), we get {68}

$$\sum_{i=0}^{n} \delta_i z_0^i + \epsilon f'(z_0) \approx 0 \tag{8.13-4}$$

Therefore,

$$|\epsilon| \approx \frac{\left| \sum_{i=0}^{n} \delta_i z_0^i \right|}{|f'(z_0)|} \tag{8.13-5}$$

One obvious limitation of this estimate occurs when $f'(z_0)$ is zero or small, in which case the previous assumption that products of errors could be neglected was unfounded {68}.   We might expect, however, that, when $f'(z_0)$ is not small and when the δ_i's are the result only of roundoff in entering the coefficients into the computer, then $|\epsilon|$ would indeed be small and (8.13-5) would give a good estimate.   The following example due to Wilkinson (1959) indicates that this need not be so for polynomials of high degree.

Consider the polynomial

$$f(z) = (z + 1)(z + 2) \cdots (z + 20) \tag{8.13-6}$$

with zeros $-1, -2, \ldots, -20$. If $z_0 = -20$, then $|f'(z_0)| = 19!$
Suppose that $\delta_i = 0$, $i = 0, 1, 2, \ldots, 17, 18, 20$, but that $\delta_{19} = 2^{-23} \approx 10^{-7}$.   Then (8.13-5) becomes

$$|\epsilon| \approx \frac{10^{-7}(20)^{19}}{19!} \approx 4.4 \tag{8.13-7}$$

which is not small.   In fact, correct to nine decimal places, the zeros of $f(z) + 2^{-23}z^{19}$ are

-1.000000000	-10.095266145
-2.000000000	$\pm 0.643500904i$
-3.000000000	-11.793633881
-4.000000000	$\pm 1.652329728i$
-4.999999928	-13.992358137
-6.000006944	$\pm 2.518830070i$
-6.999697234	-16.730737466
-8.007267603	$\pm 2.812624894i$
-8.917250249	-19.502439400
-20.846908101	$\pm 1.940330347i$

For example, the zero corresponding to -19 in $f(z)$ has not only changed substantially but has become complex.   It is therefore no surprise that (8.13-7) gives a poor result.   The small changes in the zeros of small magnitude suggest that (8.13-5) would give accurate estimates for these errors, and in fact this is correct {68}.

A polynomial such as (8.13-6) in which a small change in a coefficient may cause a large change in one or more zeros is called ill-conditioned (cf.

Sec. 9.5). If the coefficients are in fact known exactly so that the coefficient error is the result of roundoff in entering the coefficients into the computer, then, by using multiple-precision arithmetic (see Sec. 1.5-3), we may decrease this roundoff and increase the accuracy of the zeros. In fact, it is generally true that the solution of high-degree polynomial equations requires the use of multiple-precision floating-point arithmetic in order to achieve high accuracy.

8.14 AN INTEGRATED PROCEDURE FOR CALCULATING THE ZEROS OF POLYNOMIALS

To conclude this chapter, we present a procedure to calculate all the zeros of a polynomial, for use on automatic computing machinery, which combines two of the techniques we have considered here. It is by no means the only such procedure possible, and indeed it is probably quite a bit slower for most polynomials than other possible procedures. However, it is extremely simple to program and use.

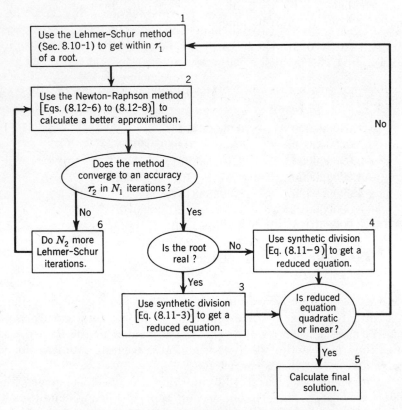

Fig. 8.6 Integrated procedure for the zeros of a polynomial.

This procedure is illustrated by the flow chart of Fig. 8.6.   Starting with the Lehmer-Schur method, we calculate an approximation (the center of the circle of step 2) in error by no more than τ_1.   Then this approximation is used as the initial approximation of the Newton-Raphson method.   If, after N_1 iterations of the Newton-Raphson method, convergence to an accuracy of τ_2 (judged by the magnitude of the difference between two successive iterates) has not been obtained, the Lehmer-Schur method picks up from where it left off in box 1, and N_2 more iterations are computed (box 6).   Then control is switched back to the Newton-Raphson method, and so on.   This process is sure to converge (why?).   After convergence, the real root or complex conjugate roots are removed from the polynomial by synthetic division (box 3 or 4), and the process continues until a linear or quadratic polynomial is left.

The tolerance τ_2 is determined by the accuracy desired.   The choices of τ_1, N_1, and N_2 will depend upon the particular polynomial equation being solved; the experience of the user with similar equations should be an important guide in these choices.

The synthetic division in boxes 3 and 4 introduces a roundoff problem which relates to the discussion of the previous section.   For ill-conditioned polynomials or even quite well-conditioned polynomials of high degree, the roundoff so introduced may cause serious errors in the zeros computed subsequently.   This loss of accuracy is most pronounced if the zeros of greatest magnitude are computed first and then divided out.   The loss is usually less pronounced if, as in the Lehmer-Schur method, the zeros are computed in order of increasing magnitude.   The problem discussed in this paragraph may be avoided, at the cost of increased computation, by continuing to use the original polynomial throughout or at least in the final stages of the Newton-Raphson part of the computation.   But now the process is no longer absolutely sure to converge (why?).

BIBLIOGRAPHIC NOTES

8.1–8.7   The basis of much of these sections is the book by Traub (1964), which will not be referred to explicitly below.   This book contains the best and most complete treatment available on functional iteration including much that can be found nowhere else.   It also contains an excellent bibliography.   In some instances, our terminology differs somewhat from that of Traub.   Another excellent book that we have used extensively is that by Ostrowski (1960).   A third excellent general reference for these sections and for the remainder of the chapter is Durand (1960–1961).

8.3   The secant method and the method of false position are discussed in detail and with insight by Ostrowski (1960).   Most standard texts in numerical analysis consider one or both of these methods.

8.4   Much of this section may be found in the papers by Traub (1961a, b). Ostrowski (1960) discusses the Newton-Raphson method in detail.

8.5   A widely used multipoint iteration method which is not discussed in this section is that of Muller (1956) (see Prob. 28).

8.7   Ostrowski (1960) has an interesting discussion of convergence. Wilkinson (1959) discusses the problems that arise in Example 8.7. The δ^2 process is due to Aitken (1926) and is discussed in a number of numerical analysis texts. For other acceleration procedures, see Ostrowski (1960).

8.8   Chapter 11 of Traub (1964) discusses the extension of methods of functional iteration to systems of equations. The methods discussed in Probs. 42 to 44 are due, respectively, to Ostrowski (1960), Wolfe (1959), and Kincaid (1961).

8.9   Marden (1949) is the most complete reference on the location of the zeros of polynomials. Wall (1948) contains a number of results in this area; Wilf (1962) contains some selected results. The material on Sturm sequences is mainly from Gantmacher (1959). Wilf (1960) discusses the general problem of computing the zeros of polynomials.

8.10   The application of Schur's theorem is due to Lehmer (1961). Graeffe's and Bernoulli's methods are discussed in many numerical analysis texts; see, for example, Hildebrand (1956) and Householder (1953). Many authors have discussed these two methods. Hildebrand (1956) contains a number of references to these papers. The mechanization of Graeffe's method for digital computation is due to Bareiss (1960). Durand (1960–1961) contains a good exposition of Laguerre's method.

8.11–8.12   Hildebrand (1956) has good discussions of both Lin's and Bairstow's methods. The source of the former is Lin (1943). A method very similar to Bairstow's is discussed by McAuley (1962). The convergence of the Newton-Raphson method in the complex case is given by Ostrowski (1960); for the secant method an unpublished proof has been given by a student of the author's, T. L. Ray.

8.13   Wilkinson (1964) contains an excellent discussion of the computational problems that arise in the solution of high-degree polynomial equations when the polynomials are ill-conditioned. McCracken and Dorn (1964) give a discussion, similar to ours, of the estimation of errors.

BIBLIOGRAPHY

Aitken, A. C. (1926): On Bernoulli's Numerical Solution of Algebraic Equations, *Proc. Roy. Soc. Edinburgh*, vol. 46, pp. 289–305.

Apostol, T. M. (1957): *Mathematical Analysis*, Addison-Wesley Publishing Company, Inc., Reading, Mass.

Bareiss, E. H. (1960): Resultant Procedure and the Mechanization of the Graeffe Process, *J. Assoc. Comput. Mach.*, vol. 7, pp. 346–386.

Durand, E. (1960–1961): *Solutions Numériques des Equations Algebriques*, vols. 1, 2, Masson et Cie, Paris.

Gantmacher, F. R. (1959): *Theory of Matrices*, vol. II, Chelsea Publishing Company, New York.

Henrici, P. (1964): *Elements of Numerical Analysis*, John Wiley & Sons, Inc., New York.

Hildebrand, F. B. (1956): *Introduction to Numerical Analysis*, McGraw-Hill Book Company, New York.

Householder, A. S. (1953): *Principles of Numerical Analysis*, McGraw-Hill Book Company, New York.

Kincaid, W. M. (1961): A Two-point Method for the Numerical Solution of Systems of Simultaneous Equations, *Quart. Appl. Math.*, vol. 18, pp. 305–324.

Lehmer, D. H. (1961): A Machine Method for Solving Polynomial Equations, *J. Assoc. Comput. Mach.*, vol. 2, pp. 151–162.

Lin, S. (1943): A Method of Finding Roots of Algebraic Equations, *J. Math. and Phys.*, vol. 22, pp. 60–77.

McAuley, V. A. (1962): A Method for the Real and Complex Roots of a Polynomial, *J. Soc. Indust. Appl. Math.*, vol. 10, pp. 657–667.

McCracken, D. D., and W. S. Dorn (1964): *Numerical Methods and FORTRAN Programming*, John Wiley & Sons, Inc., New York.

Marden, M. (1949): *The Geometry of the Zeros of a Polynomial*, American Mathematical Society, Providence, R.I.

Muller, D. E. (1956): A Method for Solving Algebraic Equations Using an Automatic Computer, *MTAC*, vol. 10, pp. 208–215.

Ostrowski, A. M. (1960): *Solution of Equations and Systems of Equations*, Academic Press Inc., New York.

Parlett, B. (1964): Laguerre's Method Applied to the Matrix Eigenvalue Problem, *Math. Comput.*, vol. 18, pp. 464–485.

Traub, J. F. (1961a): Comparison of Iterative Methods for the Calculation of Nth Roots, *Comm. ACM*, vol. 4, pp. 143–145.

Traub, J. F. (1961b): On a Class of Iteration Formulas and Some Historical Notes, *Comm. ACM*, vol. 4, pp. 276–278.

Traub, J. F. (1964): *Iterative Methods for the Solution of Equations*, Prentice-Hall, Inc., Englewood Cliffs, N.J.

Wall, H. S. (1948): *Analytic Theory of Continued Fractions*, D. Van Nostrand Company, Inc., Princeton, N.J.

Wilf, H. S. (1960): The Numerical Solution of Polynomial Equations in *Mathematical Methods for Digital Computers* (A. Ralston and H. S. Wilf, eds.), John Wiley & Sons, Inc., New York.

Wilf, H. S. (1962): *Mathematics for the Physical Sciences*, John Wiley & Sons, Inc., New York.

Wilkinson, J. H. (1959): The Evaluation of Zeros of Ill-conditioned Polynomials, *Numer. Math.*, vol. 1, pp. 150–166, 167–180.

Wilkinson, J. H. (1964): *Rounding Errors in Algebraic Processes*, Prentice-Hall, Inc., Englewood Cliffs, N.J.

Wolfe, P. (1959): The Secant Method for Simultaneous Non-linear Equations, *Comm. ACM*, vol. 2, pp. 12–13 (Dec.).

PROBLEMS

Section 8.2

1. Let $x = g(y)$ be the function inverse to $y = f(x)$.

(a) By using induction, show that we may write

$$g^{(k)}(y) = X_k/(y')^{2k-1} \qquad k = 1, 2, \ldots$$

where X_k is a polynomial in y', y'', $\ldots$, $y^{(k)}$ which satisfies the recurrence relation

$$X_{n+1} = (dX_n/dx)y' - (2n - 1)X_n y'' \qquad X_1 = 1 \qquad n = 1, 2, \ldots$$

(b) Use this result to find explicit expressions for $g^{(k)}(y)$ for $k = 1, 2, 3$. [Ref.: Ostrowski (1960), pp. 9–11.]

2. (a) Show that the convergence of a functional iteration method of order 1 implies that the asymptotic error constant is less than or equal to 1 but that, for methods of order greater than 1, this need not be so. Why is the "or equal" part needed above?

(b) May functional iteration methods have order less than 1 and still converge? Why?

3. Solve the difference equations (8.2-11) and then use (8.2-12) to derive (8.2-13).

4. (a) On a digital computer, let the time required (i.e., the cost) to compute a multiplication or division be 1, a square root be 3, and any elementary function be 6. Ignoring the cost of additions and subtractions, what are the costs of evaluating $f(x)$ and $f'(x)$ when $f(x) = e^x \cos^2 x + \ln x \tan x$? Use this result to explain why it is generally quite inexpensive to compute $f'(x)$ once $f(x)$ has been computed.

(b) If $f(x)$ is a polynomial, what are the relative costs of computing $f(x)$ and $f'(x)$ if the algorithm (7.2-4) is used to evaluate a polynomial?

Section 8.3

5. (a) Prove that the sequence of iterates in the method of false position approaches a limit and that this limit is a solution of (8.1-1).

(b) Show that, if the conditions (i) $f''(x) \neq 0$ in $[x_1, x_2]$; (ii) $f(x_1)f''(x_1) > 0$ are satisfied, then x_1 always remains one of the points in the false-position iteration. These conditions are called *Fourier's conditions*.

(c) Therefore, deduce that a sufficient condition for the method of false position to be a one-point iteration method is for $f(x)$ to be convex between $f(x_1)$ and $f(x_2)$.

6. Bisection. If $f(x_1)$ and $f(x_2)$ have opposite signs, show that a method which will always converge to a root of $f(x) = 0$ is obtained by considering the sequence of points which lie halfway between the previous two points of opposite sign. What are the first six iterates if this method is applied to the equation of Example 8.1 with $x_1 = \pi/2$, $x_2 = \pi$?

7. (a) Solve the difference equation (8.3-18) to get the solution (8.3-20).

(b) Thus deduce the plausibility of (8.3-23).

8. (a) Calculate the smallest positive root of $\cos x - xe^x = 0$ using (i) the secant method, (ii) the method of false position with $x_1 = 0$, $x_2 = 1$.

(b) Calculate the smallest positive root of $\tan x - \cos x = \frac{1}{2}$ using the secant method.

(c) Use the secant method to find the root of

$$e^z = z \qquad z = x + iy$$

with smallest positive imaginary part by eliminating x between the two equations for the real and imaginary parts of $e^z = z$.

Section 8.4

9. (a) Derive (8.4-10) and (8.4-12) and use these to calculate (8.4-13).

(b) Prove that Y_j is a polynomial in $D_2, D_3, \ldots, D_{j+1}$. [Ref.: Traub (1961b).]

10. Define $Z_j(x_i) = u_i^{j+1} Y_j(x_i)$.

(a) Use (8.4-10) to derive the recurrence relation

$$(j + 1)Z_j = jZ_{j-1} - u_i Z'_{j-1} \qquad Z_0(x_i) = u_i$$

(b) Use (8.4-21) and the definition of Z_j to show that $I_{m+1,0}(x_i) = I_{m,0}(x_i) - Z_{m+1}(x_i)$ and $I'_{m,0}(x_i) = 1 - \sum_{j=0}^{m} Z'_j(x_i)$.

(c) Use parts a and b to derive the relation $I_{m+1,0}(x_i) = I_{m,0}(x_i) - [u_i/(m + 2)]I'_{m,0}(x_i)$. [Ref.: Traub (1964), pp. 85–88.]

*11. (a) With x_{i+1} defined by (8.4-9) show that for a convergent iteration

$$\lim_{i \to \infty} \frac{\alpha - x_{i+1}}{(\alpha - x_i)^{m+2}} = (-1)^{m+1} Y_{m+1}(\alpha)$$

and thus deduce that

$$\epsilon_{i+1} = (-1)^{m+1} Y_{m+1}(\alpha)\epsilon_i^{m+2} + 0(\epsilon_i^{m+3})$$

(b) Defining

$$u_i = \sum_{j=1}^{\infty} \nu_j \epsilon_i^j$$

derive the recurrence relation

$$\nu_j = (-1)^j A_j - \sum_{k=1}^{j-1} (-1)^{j-k}(j + 1 - k)\nu_k A_{j+1-k} \qquad j = 2, 3, \ldots \qquad \nu_1 = -1$$

where

$$A_j = D_j/j!$$

(c) Use part b to calculate ν_2, ν_3, and ν_4. [Ref.: Traub (1964), pp. 100–101; note that Traub uses $x_i - \alpha$ instead of $\alpha - x_i$.]

*12. Define the *complete error series* for $I_{m0}(x_i)$ to be the series

$$I_{m0}(x_i) = \sum_{j=0}^{\infty} \tau_{jm}\epsilon_i^j$$

(a) Use induction and the results of the previous problem to show that

$$\tau_{0m} = \alpha \qquad \tau_{jm} = 0 \qquad j = 1, \ldots, m + 1$$

Why would we expect this result?

(b) Use Probs. 10c and 11b to derive the recurrence relation

$$(m + 2)\tau_{j,m+1} = (m - j + 2)\tau_{jm} + \sum_{r=1}^{j-1} r\nu_{j+1-r}\tau_{rm} = 0$$

(c) Use (8.4-9) with $m = -1$ to show that the proper initial conditions for this recurrence relation are $\tau_{0,-1} = \alpha$, $\tau_{1,-1} = -1$, $\tau_{j,-1} = 0, j > 1$.

(d) Calculate $\tau_{jm}, j = 1, 2, 3, 4; m = 0, 1, 2$. [Ref.: Traub (1964), pp. 102–104.]

13. (a) Derive the Newton-Raphson method by expanding $f(x_{i+1})$ in a Taylor series about x_i and ignoring all but the first two terms.

(b) Use the Taylor-series expansion of $f(\alpha)$ about x_i to derive (8.4-20) directly.

14. (a) Use (8.3-23) and (8.4-20) to show that, if the two iteration functions in (8.2-9) are the secant method and the Newton-Raphson method, respectively, then $C_1 = C_2^{(\sqrt{5}-1)/2}$.

(b) Use this result in (8.2-13) to show that the Newton-Raphson method has a lower computational efficiency than the secant method unless the cost of evaluating $f'(x)$ is less than .44 times the cost of evaluating $f(x)$. Is this the same result that would have been obtained using (8.2-15)?

15. (a) Derive the formulas (8.4-28).

(b) For Halley's method $[x_{i+1} = I_{01}(x_i)]$, show that the order is 3 by direct use of Theorem 8.1.

(c) Derive Eqs. (8.4-31).

16. (a) Derive (8.4-33).

(b) Explain why all three methods in Example 8.3 give the same result to seven decimals for x_3.

(c) Compare I_{10} and I_{01} as in Example 8.3. Use two iterations of each method to approximate $\sqrt{2}$ starting with $x_1 = 2$.

17. (a) Find the smallest positive root of the equation of part a of Prob. 8 using (i) I_{00} (Newton's method); (ii) I_{10}; (iii) I_{01} (Halley's method). Use $x_1 = 0$; compare the results with each other and with those of Prob. 8a for speed of convergence.

(b) Repeat the calculations of Prob. 8b using the three methods of part a with $x_1 = 0$.

18. (a) Use Newton's and Halley's methods to compute $(10)^{1/3}$ starting with $x_1 = 10$.

(b) Some computers do not have the operation of division built into them. Newton's method may be used to find the reciprocal of a number without doing any divisions. Use this technique to calculate $\frac{1}{10}$ starting with $x_1 = .001$. Can Halley's method be used similarly to find a reciprocal? Why?

(c) Try to use the Newton-Raphson method to compute $\frac{1}{10}$ starting with $x_1 = 1.0$. Explain the behavior.

19. Calculate (a) $\pi^{1/3}$, and (b) $(.0004371)^{1/7}$ using (i) I_{20}, (ii) I_{11}, (iii) I_{02}, all with $x_1 = 1$, to get a result with an error of less than 5×10^{-8}. Is the conclusion of Example 8.3 that I_{11} is generally the best of these three methods borne out?

20. (a) If $F(x_i)$ is an iteration function of order p, under what conditions on the function $U(x_i)$ will

$$G(x_i) = F(x_i) + U(x_i)u_i^r \qquad r \geqq p$$

be an iteration function of order p?

(b) Use this result to deduce that (8.4-34) gives the form of the most general one-point iteration function of order $m + 2$.

21. Consider the iteration formula

$$x_{i+1} = x_i - cf(x_i)$$

where c may depend on f and x_i. Deduce that this method has linear convergence unless $c = 1/f'(x_i)$.

22. Consider the iteration

$$y_i = x_i - \frac{f(x_i)}{f'(x_i)} \qquad x_{i+1} = y_i - \frac{f(y_i)}{f'(x_i)}$$

This is the Newton-Raphson iteration with the derivative computed only every second step.

(a) Show that, if the iteration converges

$$\lim_{i \to \infty} \frac{x_{i+1} - \alpha}{(y_i - \alpha)(x_i - \alpha)} = \frac{f''(\alpha)}{f'(\alpha)}$$

(b) Thus deduce that

$$\lim_{i \to \infty} \frac{x_{i+1} - \alpha}{(x_i - \alpha)^3} = \frac{1}{2}\left[\frac{f''(\alpha)}{f'(\alpha)}\right]^2$$

(c) If the cost of computing $f(x)$ is 1 and $f'(x)$ is θ_1, for what values of θ_1 is this method more efficient than (i) the Newton-Raphson method; (ii) the secant method?

(d) Use this method to repeat the calculation of Prob. 8a with $x_1 = 0$.

*23. Kiss's method: Let

$$x_{i+1} = x_i - u_i \frac{1 - \frac{1}{2} u_i D_2}{1 - u_i D_2 + \frac{1}{6} u_i^2 D_3}$$

with D_2 and D_3 given by (8.4-11).

(a) Show that this method is of order 4 by calculating $\alpha - x_{i+1}$.

(b) Derive this method from I_{02} by multiplying the numerator and denominator of I_{02} by $1 - \frac{1}{2} u_i D_2$ and neglecting terms in u_i^3.

(c) Use Prob. 20 to deduce that this method has order 4.

Section 8.5

24. (a) Derive (8.5-9).

(b) Find the order of an iteration function derived from (8.5-2) with $n = 3$ and $r_j = 0$ for all j.

(c) Repeat part b with $n = 2$ and $r_1 = r_2 = 1$.

25. (a) Derive the form of the three-point iteration function whose order was calculated in part b of the previous problem.

(b) Similarly, derive the two-point iteration function whose order was calculated in part c of the previous problem.

(c) Use the methods of parts a and b to repeat the calculation of Prob. 8a using suitable starting values.

*26. Iteration functions by direct interpolation: Let $y(x)$ be the interpolation polynomial of (8.5-1). If the equation $y(x_{i+1}) = 0$ can be solved for x_{i+1}, then this defines an iteration function.

(a) Suppose all the points $x_{i-j}, j = 0, \ldots, n$ lie in an interval J which contains the root α and in which $f'(x) \neq 0$. If there is at least one x_{i-j} on each side of α, show that $y(x_{i+1}) = 0$ has a real solution in J. Need this solution be unique? (Even when all the points lie on one side of α, there is such a real solution in general.)

(b) Derive the following formula for the error

$$\epsilon_{i+1} = \frac{-f^{(\beta+1)}(\xi)}{(\beta + 1)! y'(\eta)} \prod_{j=1}^{n} \epsilon_{i+1-j}^{r_{j+1}}$$

where η lies in the interval determined by x_{i+1} and α. [Ref.: Traub (1964), pp. 67–75.]

27. (a) Derive the secant method using direct interpolation.

(b) Derive the Newton-Raphson method using direct interpolation. Show that this derivation leads directly to (8.4-20) for the error.

*28. Muller's method:

(a) Use a three-point Lagrangian interpolation formula and direct interpolation to derive the iteration formula

$$x_{i+1} = x_i + (x_i - x_{i-1}) \frac{-2f_i \delta_i}{c_i \pm [c_i^2 - 4f_i \delta_i \lambda_i (f_{i-2}\lambda_i - f_{i-1}\delta_i + f_i)]^{1/2}}$$

where $\lambda_i = (x_i - x_{i-1})/(x_{i-1} - x_{i-2})$, $\delta_i = 1 + \lambda_i$, $c_i = f_{i-2}\lambda_i^2 - f_{i-1}\delta_i^2 + f_i(\lambda_i + \delta_i)$. Why should the sign in the denominator be chosen to give the denominator the greatest magnitude?

(b) Use part b of Prob. 26 to deduce that $\epsilon_{i+1} = -\epsilon_i \epsilon_{i-1} \epsilon_{i-2} [f'''(\xi)/y'(\eta)]$.

(c) Proceed as in Sec. 8.3 to deduce the order of Muller's method.

(d) Use this method to repeat the calculation of Prob. 8a.   [Ref.: Muller (1956).]

29. (a) Verify that substitution of (8.5-13) into the Newton-Raphson method gives the secant method.

(b) Verify Eqs. (8.5-15) and (8.5-16).

(c) Show that the order of (8.5-17) is given by the result of Prob. 24c.

***30.** (a) Derive a new iteration method from the Newton-Raphson method by replacing $f'(x_i)$ by its approximation found by differentiating a three-point Lagrangian interpolation formula based on x_i, x_{i-1}, and x_{i-2}.

(b) Use reasoning similar to that in Sec. 8.5-2 to show that the order of this method is 1.84.

(c) Repeat the calculation of Prob. 8a using this method.   What advantage does this method have over Muller's method (Prob. 28)?   Any disadvantages?

Section 8.6

31. (a) Verify (8.6-5) and (8.6-6).   (b) Then derive (8.6-7) and (8.6-9). (c) Derive (8.6-11) and from this deduce (8.6-10).   (d) Finally deduce that the order of (8.4-9) is 1 if α is not a simple root.

32. (a) Approximately how fast will the error in the Newton-Raphson method decrease from one iterate to the next in the neighborhood of a root of multiplicity $r > 1$?

(b) Test this conclusion on the equation $(\cos x - xe^x)^3 = 0$ and compare with the results of Prob. 8a.   Use $x_1 = 0$.

33. Apply the iterations of (a) Eq. (8.6-23) with $x_1 = 0$, $x_2 = 1$ and (b) Eq. (8.6-24) with $x_1 = 0$ to the equation of part b of the previous problem, and compare with the previous results.

Section 8.7

34. (a) Why can't the method of false position be used to find a root of even multiplicity?

(b) If α is a root of even multiplicity, show that the secant method may diverge no matter how close to α the initial approximations x_1 and x_2 are.

35. Prove that the iteration of Example 8.6 would have converged if $0 < x_1 < 1$.

36. (a) Why is it reasonable to test the convergence of an iteration by considering $|x_{i+1} - x_i|$?

(b) If the relative rather than the absolute error in the result is of interest, what would be a good quantity to use instead of $|x_{i+1} - x_i|$ to test for convergence?

37. (a) Show that the iteration in Example 8.7 eventually converges.

(b) Calculate the positive root of $x^{20} - 1 = 0$ using the Newton-Raphson method with $x_1 = \frac{1}{2}$ and the rule that, if $|x_{i+1}/x_i| > 3$, then, in place of the computed x_{i+1}, use $x_{i+1} = \pm \frac{3}{2} x_i$, where the sign is chosen to agree with x_{i+1}/x_i.

38. Suppose the Newton-Raphson method is converging slowly, thereby indicating the presence of a multiple root.

(a) Show how (8.7-4) may be used in conjunction with (8.6-10) to get an estimate of the multiplicity.   [Since the multiplicity is an integer, this estimate amounts to a determination of the multiplicity.   Having found the multiplicity, (8.6-13) may then be used to get rapid convergence.]

(b) Apply this technique to the equation of Prob. 32b.

Section 8.8

*39. (a) Use the implicit-function theorem to derive (8.8-10).

(b) Derive (8.8-10) by expanding $f_1[x^{(1)}, x^{(2)}]$ and $f_2[x^{(1)}, x^{(2)}]$ in two Taylor series about the root $[\alpha^{(1)}, \alpha^{(2)}]$, setting $f_1[\alpha^{(1)}, \alpha^{(2)}] = f_2[\alpha^{(1)}, \alpha^{(2)}] = 0$ and dropping all derivative terms of order higher than 1.

(c) Derive the error term in (8.8-10) by using Eq. (8.8-7).

(d) By analogy with (8.2-8), how would you define order for iteration methods for simultaneous equations? Use this definition to show that (8.8-10) has order 2 at a simple root.

40. Find a root of the equation of Prob. 8c by solving the two equations for the real and imaginary parts using (8.8-10). Use $x_1^{(1)} = .2$, $x_1^{(2)} = 1.1$.

41. Consider the two simultaneous equations

$$42.25x^2 + 27.885x - .749y^2 - 2.54y - 2.466 = 0$$
$$-.052x - .0192 + .00359y^2 + .00356y = 0$$

(a) Attempt to solve these two equations using (8.8-10) with $x_1 = -.01$, $y_1 = .01$. Carry out 15 iterations.

(b) Now use $x_1 = .3$, $y_1 = 2.5$ in (8.8-10).

*42. (a) Given three approximations (x_i, y_i), (x_{i-1}, y_{i-1}), (x_{i-2}, y_{i-2}) to the solution of $f_1(x,y) = 0$, $f_2(x,y) = 0$, find the equations of two planes $z = L_1(x,y)$ and $z = L_2(x,y)$ such that $L_j(x_{i-k}, y_{i-k}) = f_j(x_{i-k}, y_{i-k})$, $j = 1, 2$; $i = 0, 1, 2$.

(b) Calculate the next approximation (x_{i+1}, y_{i+1}) to be the intersection of $z = L_1(x,y)$, $z = L_2(x,y)$ and $z = 0$. When will this procedure fail?

(c) Use this method to solve the equation of Prob. 8c by considering the two equations for the real and imaginary parts. Use as initial points $(.4, 1.4)$, $(.2, 1.4)$, and $(.3, 1.1)$, and do three iterations. Will this method always converge? Is there a two-dimensional analog of the method of false position which will always converge? [Ref.: Ostrowski (1960), pp. 146–147.]

*43. Let $\mathbf{x}_i$, $\mathbf{x}_{i-1}$, . . . , $\mathbf{x}_{i-n}$ be $n + 1$ approximations to the solution of (8.8-2) and let π_0, . . . , π_n be such that

$$\sum_{j=0}^{n} \pi_j = 1 \quad \text{and} \quad \sum_{j=0}^{n} \pi_j f_k(\mathbf{x}_{i-j}) = 0 \quad k = 1, \ldots, n$$

Define

$$\mathbf{x}_{i+1} = \sum_{j=0}^{n} \pi_j \mathbf{x}_{i-j}$$

(a) Show that when $n = 1$ this iteration method is the secant method.

(b) Let α be the solution of (8.8-2) and $G_k(\mathbf{x})$ and $2Q_k(\mathbf{x})$, respectively, the vector of first partial derivatives of $f_k(\mathbf{x})$ and the matrix of second partial derivatives of $f_k(\mathbf{x})$. Use the first two nonzero terms of the Taylor-series expansion of $f_k(\mathbf{x}_{i+1})$ about α to get the approximation

$$f_k(\mathbf{x}_{i+1}) \approx \sum_{j=0}^{n} \pi_j (G_k(\alpha), \mathbf{x}_{i-j} - \alpha) + (\mathbf{x}_{i+1} - \alpha)^T Q_k(\alpha)(\mathbf{x}_{i+1} - \alpha)$$

where T denotes the transpose.

(c) Use the first two nonzero terms of the Taylor-series expansion of $f_k(\mathbf{x}_{i-j})$ to eliminate $G_k(\alpha)$ in the above approximation and thereby derive

$$f_k(\mathbf{x}_{i+1}) \approx - \sum_{j=0}^{n} \pi_j(\mathbf{x}_{i+1} - \mathbf{x}_{i-j})^T Q_k(\alpha)(\mathbf{x}_{i+1} - \mathbf{x}_{i-j})$$

Can you infer from this that this method has quadratic convergence? Why?

(d) Use this method to repeat the calculation of Prob. 8c. Use the starting values of Prob. 42. At every step replace that $\mathbf{x}_{i-j}$ with $\mathbf{x}_{i+1}$ for which

$$\sum_{k=1}^{n} |f_k(\mathbf{x}_{i-j})|^2$$

is maximal. Why is this latter a reasonable rule? [Ref.: Wolfe (1959).]

*44. Consider the same two equations as in Prob. 42. Let $f_3(x,y) = -f_1(x,y) -f_2(x,y)$.

(a) Let R_1, S_1, and T_1 be three points in the xy plane which are the initial approximations to the solution of the pair of equations. Let

$$S_1' = R_1 f_1 S_1$$

where $R_1 f_1 S_1$ denotes the intersection with the xy plane of the line joining $f_1(R_1)$ and $f_1(S_1)$. Similarly, let

$$\begin{aligned} T_1' &= R_1 f_1 T_1 & R_1' &= S_1' f_2 R_1 \\ T_2 &= S_1' f_2 T_1' & R_2 &= T_2 f_3 R_1' & S_2 &= T_2 f_3 S_1' \end{aligned}$$

Show that, if this process leads to a solution of the system, then the points R_i, S_i, T_i form a sequence of nearly similar triangles of decreasing size.

(b) Use this method to repeat the computation of Prob. 8c. Use the starting values of Prob. 42. [Ref.: Kincaid (1961).]

Section 8.9

45. Derive (8.9-6).

46. (a) If a zero of $f(x)$ in $[a,b]$ has been found, how can the Sturm sequence (8.9-5) be used to find the multiplicity of the zero?

(b) Prove that part of Theorem 8.3 relating to the case where $f(a)$ or $f(b)$ or both is zero. What happens when the zero is not simple?

47. If $\{f_i(x)\}$, $i = 1, \ldots, m$ is a Sturm sequence, a *generalized Sturm sequence* is any sequence $\{p(x)f_i(x)\}$ where $p(x)$ is an arbitrary polynomial.

(a) Does Theorem 8.2 also hold for generalized Sturm sequences?

(b) If $f(x)$ and $g(x)$ are two polynomials, use the Euclidean algorithm in a fashion analogous to (8.9-5) to generate a sequence of polynomials using $f_1(x) = f(x)$ and $f_2(x) = g(x)$. Show that this sequence is either a Sturm sequence or a generalized Sturm sequence. Thus deduce a method for finding the Cauchy index of any rational function.

48. (a) Determine the number of positive and negative real zeros of $z^4 - 3z^3 - 54z^2 - 150z - 100$.

(b) Determine the number of real zeros greater than one of $z^4 - 10z^3 + 34z^2 - 50z + 25$.

Section 8.10

*49. The Lehmer-Schur method: Let $f(z)$ be a polynomial of degree n with no zero on the unit circle Γ and with m roots inside Γ, and let $f^*(z)$ be defined as in (8.10-1).

(a) Show that on Γ, f and f^* have the same magnitude.

(b) Define T as in (8.10-2). Show that, if $T[f(0)] \neq 0$, then $T[f(z)] \neq 0$ on Γ.

(c) If $T[f(0)] > 0$ show that $T[f(z)]$ and $f(z)$ have the same number of zeros inside Γ. (*Hint:* Use Rouche's theorem.)

(d) If $T[f(0)] < 0$ show that $T[f(z)]$ and $f^*(z)$ have the same number of zeros inside Γ.

(e) Thus deduce that, if $T[f(z)] \neq 0$ on Γ, then $T[f(z)]$ has m zeros inside Γ if $T[f(0)] > 0$ and $n - m$ zeros inside Γ if $T[f(0)] < 0$.

(f) By repeated application of part e to the sequence $\{T^j[f(z)]\}$, deduce the conclusions of Theorem 8.4 in the case where $f(z)$ has no zeros on Γ. [When $f(z)$ does have a zero on Γ, the theorem is also true.] [Ref.: Lehmer (1961).]

50. (a) Show that the annulus $R \leq |z| < 2R$ may be covered by eight overlapping circles of radius $4R/5$ with centers at $[3R/2 \cos (\pi/8)]e^{2\pi ik/8}$, $k = 0, 1, \ldots, 7$. (This result is an improvement over Lehmer's result and is due to G. R. Hagen.)

(b) Show that, if the Lehmer-Schur method indicates there is a root inside a circle of radius $2R$, then the root the process converges to will be less than $5R/2 \cos (\pi/8)$ in magnitude.

51. (a) Apply step 2 of the Lehmer-Schur algorithm to the polynomial of Example 8.9 using $R = 1$. Is the zero which terminates this step the same one that terminated step 1 in Example 8.9?

(b) Apply the Lehmer-Schur algorithm to the polynomial $f(z) = 6 - 35z + 62z^2 - 35z^3 + 6z^4$. What does the result indicate about whether or not there is a zero of $f(z)$ inside the unit circle? What can be done about this result?

52. Use the Lehmer-Schur method to find the roots of $z^4 + 2z^3 + 3z^2 + 4z + 5 = 0$ with an error of less than .1 in the real and imaginary parts.

53. (a) Verify (8.10-13).

(b) Use (8.10-14), (8.10-15), and (8.10-17) to show that

$$a_{n-j}^{(r)} = (-1)^j a_n^{(r)} \sum_{1}^{n} {}_c (\rho_{k_1}\rho_{k_2} \cdots \rho_{k_j})^{2^r} \exp [i2^r(\phi_{k_1} + \cdots + \phi_{k_j})]$$

(c) Use this to deduce (8.10-24) when (8.10-18) holds and to deduce (8.10-28) in the general case.

54. (a) Let $f(z)$ be a polynomial with a zero of magnitude ρ. Show that $f(z)$ has a factor $z^2 + pz + q$ with $q = \rho^2$, which is the product of two roots of magnitude ρ, if and only if p satisfies (8.10-33) and (8.10-34).

(b) Derive (8.10-36).

55. Use root squaring to calculate all the zeros of $z^4 - 5z^3 + 9\frac{1}{2}z^2 - 7z + \frac{5}{2}$.

56. Let the polynomial $f(z)$ of degree n have zeros z_i, $i = 1, \ldots, n$.

(a) Show that, if z is sufficiently large, then

$$(z - z_i)^{-1} = z^{-1} + z_i z^{-2} + z_i^2 z^{-3} + \cdots$$

and, thus,

$$\sum_{i=1}^{n} (z - z_i)^{-1} = nz^{-1} + s_1 z^{-2} + s_2 z^{-3} + \cdots$$

where $s_j = \sum_{i=1}^{n} z_i^j$.

(b) Show that

$$f(z) \sum_{i=1}^{n} {}' (z - z_i)^{-1} = f'(z)$$

(c) Thus deduce *Newton's identities*

$$a_n s_m + a_{n-1} s_{m-1} + \cdots + a_{n-m+1} s_1 + m a_{n-m} = 0 \qquad m = 1, \ldots, n$$
$$a_n s_{n+j} + a_{n-1} s_{n+j-1} + \cdots + a_0 s_j = 0 \qquad j = 1, 2, \ldots$$

(d) From this deduce that, if (8.10-42) is used to generate the starting values in Bernoulli's method, then all the c_i's are unity.

57. (a) How must (8.10-39) be modified when some of the roots of (8.9-1) are multiple?

(b) Nevertheless, show that, if α_1 is multiple but real, then (8.10-41) still holds.

(c) Verify (8.10-46) and (8.10-47).

58. (a) Verify the recurrence relations (8.10-52).

(b) Use these to derive relations analogous to (8.10-46) and (8.10-47) in terms of λ_k. [Ref.: Wilf (1960), p. 237.]

59. Use Bernoulli's method to find the zero of maximum magnitude of (a) the polynomial of Prob. 55; (b) the polynomial of Prob. 52. Use the result of Prob. 52 to explain the slow convergence in part b (you will need to calculate at least to u_{70} in order to stabilize the first decimal of β_1). Then calculate the remaining zeros of the polynomial.

*60. (a) Verify (8.10-57) to (8.10-62).

(b) Show that, if all the zeros of $f(z)$ are real, then H is always nonnegative.

(c) Verify (8.10-64).

(d) Show that, if the sign is chosen in (8.10-63) to agree with $f'(x_i)$, then, if $x_1 < x^{(1)}$, $x_i < x_{i+1} < x^{(1)}$ and, if $x^{(n)} < x_1$, $x^{(n)} < x_{i+1} < x_i$.

(e) Use Laguerre's method with $x_1 = 10^6$ to find a zero of (i) $z^4 + 8.1z^3 - 19.8z^2 - 5.9z + 21$; (ii) $z^4 + 2z^3 + 3z^2 + 4z + 5$.

Section 8.11

61. (a) Derive a synthetic division algorithm analogous to those in Sec. 8.11 for the division of a polynomial of degree n by a polynomial of degree $j < n$.

(b) Use this algorithm to determine if $z^5 - z^4 - 2z^3 + 2z^2 + z - 1$ has a triple zero at (i) $z = 1$; (ii) $z = -1$. Find all the zeros of this polynomial.

Section 8.12

62. (a) Show that Lin's method can be written in the form

$$z_{j+1} = -\frac{a_0 z_j}{f(z_j) - a_0}$$

(b) Use this result to deduce that

$$\alpha - z_{j+1} = \frac{a_0 + \alpha f'(\xi)}{a_0 - f(z_j)} (\alpha - z_j)$$

with ξ between α and z_j. Thus deduce that, when the method converges, it has order 1.

(c) Thus deduce that a necessary condition for convergence is that $|1 + (\alpha/a_0)f'(\alpha)| \leq 1$.

(d) Show finally that in Example 8.14, no matter how close to the real root the initial approximation is, Lin's method will not converge.

63. Derive the equations analogous to (8.12-5) to (8.12-8) for the secant method.

64. Do the calculation of Example 8.16 with an initial approximation $p_1 = -1$, $q_1 = -1$. Would you expect the convergence of the Bairstow iteration to be very sensitive to the initial approximation? Why?

65. (a) Use (8.12-5) to (8.12-8) to find the zero of maximum magnitude of $z^4 + 2z^3 + 3z^2 + 4z + 5$. Use the result of Prob. 52 as the initial approximation.

(b) Repeat this calculation using the equations derived in Prob. 52.

66. Use any method or combination of methods to find the roots of (a) $z^3 - 2z - 5 = 0$; (b) $z^3 - 16z^2 + 3 = 0$; (c) $z^4 - 3z^2 + 2z - 1 = 0$; (d) $z^4 + 4z^2 - 3z - 1 = 0$; (e) $z^6 + 5z^3 + 7z^2 + 1 = 0$.

67. Use any method to find the root of largest magnitude of (a) $z^3 - 20z^2 - 3z + 18 = 0$; (b) $z^4 - 3z^3 - 60z^2 + 150z + 300 = 0$; (c) $10z^3 - 21z^2 - 40z + 84 = 0$.

Section 8.13

68. (a) Derive (8.13-4) under the assumption that products of errors can be neglected.

(b) Why is the assumption that products of errors can be neglected generally unfounded when $f'(z_0)$ is small?

(c) Apply (8.13-5) to $f(z)$ of (8.13-6) with $\delta_i = 0$, $i \neq 19$ and $\delta_{19} = 2^{-23}$ for $z_0 = -1, -5, -8$, and -15.

chapter 9

THE SOLUTION OF SIMULTANEOUS LINEAR EQUATIONS

9.1 THE BASIC THEOREM AND THE PROBLEM

Our concern in this chapter is with the solution of n simultaneous linear equations in n unknowns

$$\sum_{j=1}^{n} a_{ij}x_j = b_i \qquad i = 1, \ldots, n \tag{9.1-1}$$

Equation (9.1-1) is conveniently written in the matrix form

$$A\mathbf{x} = \mathbf{b} \tag{9.1-2}$$

where $A = [a_{ij}]$ is the $n \times n$ matrix of coefficients $\mathbf{x}^T = (x_1, \ldots, x_n)$ and $\mathbf{b}^T = (b_1, \ldots, b_n)$ with T denoting the transpose.† We shall use matrix algebra and matrix notation extensively but not exclusively in this chapter. We assume everywhere in this chapter that A and $\mathbf{b}$ are real.

We denote by A_b the $n \times n + 1$ matrix which has the column vector $\mathbf{b}$ appended as an $(n + 1)$st column to A. We denote the rank of any matrix A by $r(A)$. The basic theorem on the existence of solutions of (9.1-2) is

† In this and the next chapter column vectors will be in boldface and row vectors will be in boldface with a superscript T.

394

Theorem 9.1   1. The system of equations (9.1-2) has a solution if and only if

$$r(A) = r(A_b)$$

2. If $r(A) = r(A_b) = k < n$ then, if $x_{i_1}, x_{i_2}, \ldots, x_{i_k}$ are k variables whose corresponding columns are linearly independent in A, the remaining $n - k$ variables may be arbitrarily assigned [i.e., since there must be some set of k linearly independent columns of A (why?), there is an $n - k$ parameter family of solutions].

3. If $r(A) = r(A_b) = n$, there is a unique solution.

Corollary 9.1   From 2 and 3 it follows that in the homogeneous case ($\mathbf{b} = 0$), there is a nontrivial solution if and only if $r(A) < n$.

This familiar theorem and its corollary may be proved using Gaussian elimination, which will be discussed in Sec. 9.3-1; the proofs themselves we leave to a problem {1}.

In contrast to the equations of Chaps. 5 and 8, there is no problem in finding an analytic solution of (9.1-1). Cramer's rule gives us such a solution. Instead the problem is in *computing* the solution. Even for quite low order systems, the large amount of computation required to evaluate determinants makes the use of Cramer's rule impractical. Therefore, our major aim in this chapter will be to develop more efficient computational algorithms for the solution of (9.1-1).

The efficiency of an algorithm will be judged by two main criteria: (1) How fast is it (i.e., how many operations are involved)? (2) How accurate is the computed solution?

These two criteria are aimed at the evaluation of algorithms for the solution of high-order systems (up to 100 equations or more) on a digital computer. Because of the formidable amount of computation required to solve (9.1-1) for large systems, the need to answer the first question is clear. The need to answer the second question arises because small roundoff errors may cause errors in the computed solution out of all proportion to their size. In Sec. 6.3-1 we had a glimpse of how such roundoff errors could cause substantial loss of accuracy.

We shall consider briefly the solution of low-order systems on desk calculators. For very low order systems the main computational problem is not efficiency as defined above but rather the avoidance of blunders. But for larger systems (say of order 6 to 10) efficiency is important. Systems of more than 10 equations are almost always solved on digital computers.

Before getting into the details of solving (9.1-1), we shall, in the next section, consider the problem in rather general terms in order to get an intuitive feeling for the difficulties that will be encountered.

9.2   GENERAL REMARKS

1. Sources and types of problems.   The matrices of coefficients that occur in practice generally fall into one of two categories:
    (i) Filled but not large.   By filled we mean that there are few zero elements and by not large we mean matrices of order, say, less than 30.   Such matrices occur in a wide variety of problems in statistics, mathematical physics, engineering, etc.
    (ii) Sparse and perhaps very large.   In contrast to the above a sparse matrix has few nonzero elements.   In most cases, these elements lie on or near the main diagonal.   Very large may mean of order 100 or more.   Such matrices arise commonly in the numerical solution of partial differential equations {2}.

It should not be surprising that different approaches are commonly used for matrices in these two categories.   One cause of this is that the size of the matrices in the second category often makes memory space a problem even on the largest computers.   But, basically, it is the different characters—sparse and filled—of the matrices that make the direct methods to be described in Secs. 9.3 to 9.5 generally superior for the first category, while the iterative methods of Secs. 9.6 to 9.8 are most often used for problems in the second category.   It should be emphasized that there are no hard-and-fast rules in this, however, and indeed there is some controversy.   Almost no one would recommend iterative methods for filled, low-order matrices, but there is substantial opinion in favor of direct methods even for large, sparse matrices.

2. Ill condition.   Assuming that A is nonsingular, as we shall throughout this chapter, the solution of (9.1-2) may be written

$$\mathbf{x} = A^{-1}\mathbf{b} \tag{9.2-1}$$

Suppose that the elements of A have been normalized so that the largest in magnitude has order of magnitude unity.   Suppose also that A^{-1} has some very large elements, one of which is

$$a_{ji}^{-1} = A_{ij}/|A| \tag{9.2-2}$$

where $|A|$ denotes the determinant of A and A_{ij} is the cofactor of a_{ij} and is therefore unaffected by a change in a_{ij}.   The assumption that a_{ji}^{-1} is large means that A_{ij} must be large relative to $|A|$.   Since one of the terms in the expansion of $|A|$ about the ith row or jth column is $a_{ij}A_{ij}$, a small error in a_{ij} (relative to unity; that is, relative to the normalization of A) may cause a large relative error in $|A|$ and therefore a large relative error in a_{ji}^{-1}.   This in turn can cause a large relative error in $\mathbf{x}$.   Similarly, a small change in an element of $\mathbf{b}$ could cause a large change in $\mathbf{x}$.   This effect can also be produced by roundoff errors in the course of the computation (cf. Sec. 6.3-1) because a roundoff error introduced during the computation is equivalent in effect to an initial error in the elements of A (why?—see Sec. 9.4).

An alternative way of looking at this problem is to consider the residual vector

$$\mathbf{r} = \mathbf{b} - A\mathbf{x}_c \qquad (9.2\text{-}3)$$

where $\mathbf{x}_c$ is the computed solution. If A^{-1} has some large elements, then $\mathbf{r}$ may be very small even if $\mathbf{x}_c$ is substantially different from the true solution. For let $\mathbf{x}_t$ be the true solution of (9.1-2) so that $A\mathbf{x}_t = \mathbf{b}$. Then (9.2-3) may be written

$$\mathbf{r} = A(\mathbf{x}_t - \mathbf{x}_c) \qquad (9.2\text{-}4)$$

or

$$\mathbf{x}_t - \mathbf{x}_c = A^{-1}\mathbf{r} \qquad (9.2\text{-}5)$$

Therefore, if some elements of A^{-1} are large, a small component of $\mathbf{r}$ can still mean a large difference between $\mathbf{x}_t$ and $\mathbf{x}_c$, or conversely, $\mathbf{x}_c$ may be far from $\mathbf{x}_t$ but $\mathbf{r}$ can nevertheless still be small. This implies that we cannot test the correctness of a computed solution of (9.1-2) merely by substituting the result into the equations and calculating the residuals. Or to put it another way, an accurate solution (i.e., a small difference between $\mathbf{x}_c$ and $\mathbf{x}_t$; see Sec. 9.4) will always produce small residuals, but small residuals do not guarantee an accurate solution.

If the matrix A is normalized as described above and is such that A^{-1} contains some very large elements, then we say the matrix and, therefore, the system of equations is *ill-conditioned*. (Conversely, if the largest element in magnitude of A^{-1} has order of magnitude unity, the matrix may be said to be well-conditioned.) The following simple example will illustrate the dangers inherent in solving ill-conditioned systems. Consider the system

$$2x + 6y = 8 \qquad 2x + 6.00001y = 8.00001 \qquad (9.2\text{-}6)$$

which has the solution $x = 1$, $y = 1$, and the system

$$2x + 6y = 8 \qquad 2x + 5.99999y = 8.00002 \qquad (9.2\text{-}7)$$

which has the solution $x = 10$, $y = -2$. Here a change of $.00002$ in a_{22} and $.00001$ in b_2 has caused a gross change in the solution. The inverse of the matrix of coefficients in (9.2-6) has elements whose order of magnitude is 10^5, which indicates the ill condition of A. The necessity in the preceding discussion of the requirement that A be normalized can be seen by considering the systems (9.2-6) and (9.2-7) both multiplied by 10^5.

Now a small *relative* change in a_{22} and b_2 causes the same gross change in the solution as above although the elements of A^{-1} are all of order magnitude unity.

The coefficients in (9.2-7) might, for example, be empirical values of those in (9.2-6). If empirical values of the coefficients accurate to more than five decimal places cannot be obtained, then the solution of (9.2-7), *no matter how accurately it is calculated*, may be grossly in error. How to calculate solutions of (9.1-2), *as accurate as the data warrant*, when the system is ill-conditioned is probably the single most difficult problem encountered in the solution of simultaneous linear equations. In Sec. 9.5 we shall consider the solution of ill-conditioned systems in some detail.

3. Sources of error. There are three sources of error in the solution of systems of linear equations, two of which were mentioned above. The first is caused by errors in the coefficients and the elements of **b**. When such errors occur because these quantities are empirical, we must live with them. If a bound on the empirical errors is known, then we can do no more than use this to get bounds on the errors in the solution (see Sec. 9.4). When the coefficients and the vector **b** are known exactly (as they are, for example, when a partial differential equation is approximated by differences) but must be rounded when they are inserted into the computer, we can control this source of error by using double-precision arithmetic, if necessary.

The second source of error is the roundoff error introduced in calculating the solution. The third source is truncation error. In direct methods (e.g., Cramer's rule or Gaussian elimination), which would lead to an exact solution in the absence of roundoff, there is no truncation error. But the iterative methods to be discussed in Secs. 9.6 to 9.8 generally converge only as the number of iterations goes to infinity. They are therefore subject to truncation error. One of the determining factors in deciding to use an iterative instead of a direct method is whether the truncation error can be made extremely small with an amount of computation comparable with or less than that required for a direct method. Truncation error is therefore almost always a minor source of error in the computed solution of (9.1-1).

9.3   DIRECT METHODS

As we indicated above, a direct method for the solution of (9.1-1) is one which, if all computations were carried out without roundoff, would lead to the true solution of the *given* system. All direct methods involve some variation of the elimination procedure associated with the name of Gauss which we shall now consider in detail.

9.3-1   Gaussian elimination

We write out the system (9.1-1) in the form

$$
\begin{aligned}
a_{11}x_1 + a_{12}x_2 + \cdots + a_{1n}x_n &= a_{1,n+1} \\
a_{21}x_1 + a_{22}x_2 + \cdots + a_{2n}x_n &= a_{2,n+1} \\
\cdots\cdots\cdots\cdots\cdots\cdots\cdots\cdots\cdots \\
a_{n1}x_1 + a_{n2}x_2 + \cdots + a_{nn}x_n &= a_{n,n+1}
\end{aligned}
\tag{9.3-1}
$$

where for notational simplicity we have written $b_j = a_{j,n+1}$. We assume, of course, that the matrix of coefficients is nonsingular. Suppose $a_{11} \neq 0$. We subtract the multiple a_{i1}/a_{11} of the first equation from the ith equation, $i = 2, \ldots , n$, to get the *first derived system*

$$
\begin{aligned}
a_{11}x_1 + a_{12}x_2 + \cdots + a_{1n}x_n &= a_{1,n+1} \\
a_{22}^{(1)}x_2 + \cdots + a_{2n}^{(1)}x_n &= a_{2,n+1}^{(1)} \\
\cdots\cdots\cdots\cdots\cdots\cdots\cdots \\
a_{n2}^{(1)}x_2 + \cdots + a_{nn}^{(1)}x_n &= a_{n,n+1}^{(1)}
\end{aligned}
\tag{9.3-2}
$$

The new coefficients $a_{ij}^{(1)}$ are given by

$$
a_{ij}^{(1)} = a_{ij} - \frac{a_{i1}}{a_{11}} a_{1j} \qquad
\begin{aligned}
i &= 2, \ldots , n \\
j &= 2, \ldots , n + 1
\end{aligned}
\tag{9.3-3}
$$

If $a_{11} = 0$ then, because A is nonsingular, we may, by interchanging two rows or columns of (9.3-1), get a nonzero element in the upper left-hand corner (why?).

Now, if $a_{22}^{(1)}$ in (9.3-2) is nonzero, we subtract $a_{i2}^{(1)}/a_{22}^{(1)}$ times the second equation from the ith equation in (9.3-2), $i = 3, \ldots , n$ and get the second derived system

$$
\begin{aligned}
a_{11}x_1 + a_{12}x_2 + \cdots\cdots\cdots\cdots + a_{1n}x_n &= a_{1,n+1} \\
a_{22}^{(1)}x_2 + \cdots\cdots\cdots\cdots + a_{2n}^{(1)}x_n &= a_{2,n+1}^{(1)} \\
a_{33}^{(2)}x_3 + \cdots + a_{3n}^{(2)}x_n &= a_{3,n+1}^{(2)} \\
\cdots\cdots\cdots\cdots\cdots\cdots \\
a_{n3}^{(2)}x_3 + \cdots + a_{nn}^{(2)}x_n &= a_{n,n+1}^{(2)}
\end{aligned}
\tag{9.3-4}
$$

where

$$
a_{ij}^{(2)} = a_{ij}^{(1)} - \frac{a_{i2}^{(1)}}{a_{22}^{(1)}} a_{2j}^{(1)} \qquad
\begin{aligned}
i &= 3, \ldots , n \\
j &= 3, \ldots , n + 1
\end{aligned}
\tag{9.3-5}
$$

Again, if $a_{22}^{(1)} = 0$ we may interchange two rows or columns to get a non-zero element in the (2,2) position. Continuing with this process through

$n - 1$ steps we arrive at the final system

$$
\begin{aligned}
a_{11}x_1 + a_{12}x_2 + \cdots\cdots\cdots + a_{1n}x_n &= a_{1,n+1} \\
a_{22}^{(1)}x_2 + \cdots\cdots\cdots + a_{2n}^{(1)}x_n &= a_{2,n+1}^{(1)} \\
a_{33}^{(2)}x_3 + \cdots + a_{3n}^{(2)}x_n &= a_{3,n+1}^{(2)}
\end{aligned}
$$

$$(9.3\text{-}6)$$

$$
a_{nn}^{(n-1)}x_n = a_{n,n+1}^{(n-1)}
$$

with the diagonal elements all nonzero and where

$$
a_{ij}^{(k)} = a_{ij}^{(k-1)} - \frac{a_{ik}^{(k-1)}}{a_{kk}^{(k-1)}}\, a_{kj}^{(k-1)} \qquad
\begin{aligned}
& k = 1, \ldots, n-1 \\
& j = k+1, \ldots, n+1 \\
& i = k+1, \ldots, n \\
& a_{ij}^{(0)} = a_{ij}
\end{aligned}
\qquad (9.3\text{-}7)
$$

Given (9.3-6) the solution is easily calculated as

$$
x_i = \frac{1}{a_{ii}^{(i-1)}}\left[a_{i,n+1}^{(i-1)} - \sum_{j=i+1}^{n} a_{ij}^{(i-1)}x_j \right] \qquad i = n, \ldots, 1 \qquad (9.3\text{-}8)
$$

The process leading to (9.3-6) is called *Gaussian elimination;* the calculation of the solution by (9.3-8) is called the *back substitution.* Using Gaussian elimination, it is easy to prove Theorem 9.1 {1}.

A variant of the above process, which it is convenient to consider here, is the *Gauss-Jordan reduction.* In this technique we proceed as before to get (9.3-2), but in place of (9.3-4) we derive the system

$$
\begin{aligned}
a_{11}x_1 + \qquad\quad a_{13}^{(2)}x_3 + \cdots + a_{1n}^{(2)}x_n &= a_{1,n+1}^{(2)} \\
a_{22}^{(1)}x_2 + a_{23}^{(1)}x_3 + \cdots + a_{2n}^{(1)}x_n &= a_{2,n+1}^{(1)} \\
a_{33}^{(2)}x_3 + \cdots + a_{3n}^{(2)}x_n &= a_{3,n+1}^{(2)} \\
& \cdots\cdots\cdots\cdots\cdots \\
a_{n3}^{(2)}x_3 + \cdots + a_{nn}^{(2)}x_n &= a_{n,n+1}^{(2)}
\end{aligned}
$$

$$(9.3\text{-}9)$$

in which the element in the first row and second column has also been reduced to zero, the remaining elements in the first row are given by (9.3-5) with $i = 1$ and $a_{2,n+1}^{(2)} = a_{2,n+1}^{(1)}$. Continuing in this way, so that at each stage all the elements in a column except the diagonal element are reduced to zero, we get finally

$$
\begin{aligned}
a_{11}x_1 \qquad\qquad\qquad\qquad\qquad &= a_{1,n+1}^{(n-1)} \\
a_{22}^{(1)}x_2 \qquad\qquad\qquad\qquad &= a_{2,n+1}^{(n-1)}
\end{aligned}
$$

$$(9.3\text{-}10)$$

$$
a_{nn}^{(n-1)}x_n = a_{n,n+1}^{(n-1)}
$$

with the $a_{ii}^{(i-1)}$ given by (9.3-7) and with

$$a_{i,n+1}^{(k)} = \begin{cases} a_{i,n+1}^{(k-1)} - \dfrac{a_{ik}^{(k-1)}}{a_{kk}^{(k-1)}} a_{k,n+1}^{(k-1)} & \begin{aligned} i &= 1, \ldots, k-1, \\ & k+1, \ldots, n \end{aligned} \\ a_{i,n+1}^{(k-1)} & i = k \end{cases}$$
$$k = 1, \ldots, n-1 \quad (9.3\text{-}11)$$

The solution of (9.3-10) is then simply given by

$$x_i = \frac{a_{i,n+1}^{(n-1)}}{a_{ii}^{(i-1)}} \qquad i = 1, \ldots, n \tag{9.3-12}$$

At first glance it might seem that the Gauss-Jordan reduction is to be preferred to Gaussian elimination, but we shall show now that in fact Gaussian elimination is the more efficient of the two.

As usual in determining the number of operations required, we shall consider only multiplications and divisions. To estimate the number of operations in Gaussian elimination, we use (9.3-7). For each k we need $n - k$ divisions† $[a_{ik}^{(k-1)}/a_{kk}^{(k-1)}]$ and $(n - k)(n - k + 1)$ multiplications. The total number of multiplications and divisions is then {4}

$$M = \sum_{k=1}^{n-1} [(n - k)(n - k + 1) + (n - k)] = \tfrac{1}{3}n^3 + O(n^2) \ddagger$$
$$(9.3\text{-}13)$$

We single out the n^3 term since it is only for large n that we are interested in M. The back substitution adds to M a factor $n(n + 1)/2$ and so does not affect the n^3 term.

For the Gauss-Jordan reduction, we again use (9.3-7), but this time with i running from 1 to $k - 1$ as well as from $k + 1$ to n. The calculation corresponding to (9.3-13) results in {4}

$$M = \tfrac{1}{2}n^3 + O(n^2) \tag{9.3-14}$$

For large n, therefore, the Gauss-Jordan reduction requires about 50 percent more operations than Gaussian elimination. For this reason we shall, in the remainder of this section, consider only Gaussian elimination.

9.3-2   A method for desk calculators

When the number of equations is small (say five or fewer) then it may be quicker to solve the system on a desk calculator than to prepare the data

† Or one division $[1/a_{kk}^{(k-1)}]$ and $n - k$ multiplications $[1/a_{kk}^{(k-1)}]a_{ik}^{(k-1)}$.

‡ In this chapter, in contrast to Chap. 5, the notation $O(n^k)$ will always refer to the situation as $n \to \infty$.

for and run the problem on a digital computer. When a digital computer is just not available, somewhat higher-order systems (say up to order 10) may be done on a desk calculator. Efficiency and the avoidance of blunders are of paramount importance here. In this section we adapt the method of Gaussian elimination to desk calculators to achieve the above aims and to give the reader some of the flavor of desk computation which has been somewhat neglected in this book thus far. The essence of this method is also applicable, as we shall see, to digital computers.

9.3-2-1 *Elimination without positioning—the Gauss-Doolittle process*

The essence of this method is to use Gaussian elimination but to avoid having to record the derived systems (9.3-2), (9.3-4), etc. To see how this can be done, we note first that the values in the second row in the final matrix (9.3-6) are given by (9.3-3) with $i = 2$:

$$a_{2j}^{(1)} = a_{2j} - (a_{21}/a_{11})a_{1j} = a_{2j} + m_{12}a_{1j} \qquad j = 2, \ldots, n + 1$$
$$(9.3\text{-}15)$$

where m_{12} satisfies the equation

$$m_{12}a_{11} + a_{21} = 0 \qquad\qquad (9.3\text{-}16)$$

The values of the third row of (9.3-6) are given by (9.3-5) with $i = 3$:

$$a_{3j}^{(2)} = a_{3j}^{(1)} - [a_{32}^{(1)}/a_{22}^{(1)}]a_{2j}^{(1)} \qquad j = 3, \ldots, n + 1 \qquad (9.3\text{-}17)$$

Now $a_{3j}^{(1)}$ is given by (9.3-3) as

$$a_{3j}^{(1)} = a_{3j} - (a_{31}/a_{11})a_{1j} \qquad\qquad (9.3\text{-}18)$$

which, when substituted in (9.3-17), gives

$$a_{3j}^{(2)} = a_{3j} - \frac{a_{31}}{a_{11}}a_{1j} - \frac{a_{32} - (a_{31}/a_{11})a_{12}}{a_{22}^{(1)}}a_{2j}^{(1)}$$
$$= a_{3j} + m_{13}a_{1j} + m_{23}a_{2j}^{(1)} \qquad j = 3, \ldots, n + 1 \qquad (9.3\text{-}19)$$

where m_{13} and m_{23} satisfy the equations

$$m_{13}a_{11} + a_{31} = 0 \qquad m_{13}a_{12} + m_{23}a_{22}^{(1)} + a_{32} = 0 \qquad (9.3\text{-}20)$$

Thus, having calculated the second row using (9.3-15) and (9.3-16), we may then use (9.3-20) to get m_{13} and m_{23}. Then (9.3-19) may be used to get $a_{3j}^{(2)}, j = 3, \ldots, n + 1$. We can therefore avoid explicit calculation of $a_{3j}^{(1)}$, although implicitly this is included in (9.3-19) and (9.3-20).

Study of (9.3-15) and (9.3-16) on the one hand and (9.3-19) and (9.3-20) on the other implies the general procedure by which each row of (9.3-6) may be calculated without explicitly calculating any of the elements of the derived systems. The general equations for the coefficients in the ith row of (9.3-6) are

$$a_{ij}^{(i-1)} = a_{ij} + m_{1i}a_{1j} + m_{2i}a_{2j}^{(1)} + \cdots + m_{i-1,i}a_{i-1,j}^{(i-2)}$$
$$i = 2, \ldots, n \qquad j = i, \ldots, n+1 \qquad (9.3\text{-}21)$$

with the m_{ki} defined by the equations

$$\begin{aligned} &m_{1i}a_{11} + a_{i1} = 0 \\ &m_{1i}a_{12} + m_{2i}a_{22}^{(1)} + a_{i2} = 0 \\ &\cdots\cdots\cdots\cdots\cdots\cdots \\ &m_{1i}a_{1k} + m_{2i}a_{2k}^{(1)} + \cdots + m_{ki}a_{kk}^{(k-1)} + a_{ik} = 0 \\ &\cdots\cdots\cdots\cdots\cdots\cdots\cdots\cdots\cdots \\ &m_{1i}a_{1,i-1} + m_{2i}a_{2,i-1}^{(1)} + \cdots + m_{i-1,i}a_{i-1,i-1}^{(i-2)} + a_{i,i-1} = 0 \end{aligned} \qquad (9.3\text{-}22)$$

That these equations do indeed lead to (9.3-6) may be proved by induction {5}. Note that (9.3-21) and (9.3-22) involve only values $a_{ij}^{(k)}$ which have been calculated at a previous stage.

What we have done so far will also be the basis of the use of Gaussian elimination on a digital computer. We shall indicate now, using Fig. 9.1, how the calculations outlined above can be most easily organized for hand computation. We first record the augmented matrix A_b. Then we

1. Record the first row again.
2. Compute m_{12} from (9.3-16).
3. Compute $a_{2j}^{(1)}$, $j = 2, \ldots, n+1$ from (9.3-15).
4. Compute m_{13} and m_{23} from (9.3-20).
5. Compute $a_{8j}^{(2)}$, $j = 3, \ldots, n+1$ from (9.3-19).
6. Continue as above computing a column m_{ki} followed by a row $a_{ij}^{(i-1)}$, etc., using (9.3-22) and (9.3-21).

$$\begin{array}{cccc|ccccc}
 & & & & a_{11} & a_{12} \cdots\cdots & a_{1n} & a_{1,n+1} & s_1 \\
 & & & & a_{21} & \cdots\cdots & a_{2n} & \cdot & \cdot \\
 & & & & \vdots & & \vdots & \vdots & \vdots \\
 & & & & a_{n1} & \cdots\cdots & a_{nn} & a_{n,n+1} & s_n \\
\hline
m_{12} & m_{13} & \cdots & m_{1n} & a_{11} & \cdots\cdots & a_{1n} & a_{1,n+1} & s_1 \\
 & m_{23} & \cdots & m_{2n} & a_{22}^{(1)} & \cdots\cdots & a_{2n}^{(1)} & a_{2,n+1}^{(1)} & s_2^{(1)} \\
 & & \ddots & \vdots & \ddots & & \vdots & \vdots & \vdots \\
 & & & m_{n-1,n} & & a_{n-1,n-1}^{(n-2)} & a_{n-1,n}^{(n-2)} & \cdot & \cdot \\
 & & & & & & a_{nn}^{(n-1)} & a_{n,n+1}^{(n-1)} & s_n^{(n-1)}
\end{array}$$

Fig. 9.1 The Gauss-Doolittle process—desk calculator layout.

Figure 9.1, therefore, contains all the quantities that need to be recorded. Moreover, with the arrangement shown, the factors in all products in (9.3-21) and (9.3-22) lie in the same row, which is convenient and reduces blunders.

In order to catch almost all blunders, we have appended a column to the augmented matrix. Define

$$s_i = \sum_{j=1}^{n+1} a_{ij} \tag{9.3-23}$$

so that s_i is the sum of the elements in the ith row. We then compute the $s_i^{(i-1)}$, $i = 2, \ldots, n$ in precisely the same way that we compute $a_{ij}^{(i-1)}$. That is, we treat the sum column as if it were the $n + 2$ column of the original array. Therefore,

$$s_i^{(i-1)} = s_i + m_{1i}s_1 + m_{2i}s_2^{(1)} + \cdots + m_{i-1,i}s_{i-1}^{(i-2)} \tag{9.3-24}$$

We should like to show that $s_i^{(i-1)}$ is the sum of the ith row in the final array. For if so, this will serve as an excellent check on the calculation. We do this by induction. For the first row this is certainly true. Suppose it is true for all rows through the $i - 1$ row. Summing (9.3-21) from $j = i$ to $n + 1$ and using (9.3-23) and (9.3-24), we get

$$\sum_{j=i}^{n+1} a_{ij}^{(i-1)} = \sum_{j=i}^{n+1} a_{ij} + m_{1i} \sum_{j=i}^{n+1} a_{1j} + \cdots + m_{i-1,i} \sum_{j=i}^{n+1} a_{i-1,j}^{(i-2)}$$
$$= s_i + m_{1i}s_1 + m_{2i}s_2^{(1)} + \cdots + m_{i-1,i}s_{i-1}^{(i-2)}$$
$$= s_i^{(i-1)} \tag{9.3-25}$$

which completes the induction. If at any stage of the calculation an element in check column is not the sum of the other elements in its row, then there is an error somewhere in that row (perhaps in the check element itself). To find the error, each element in the row must be recomputed until the error is found.

The back substitution is easily accomplished using (9.3-8) once the array in Fig. 9.1 has been calculated. One final check that may be performed is to add together all the equations (9.1-1) and insert the solution in this sum equation. Except for roundoff, the result should, of course, be equality.

Example 9.1   Use the technique of this section to solve the system

$$4.6237x_1 + 2.6914x_2 - 3.7517x_3 = 1.4023$$
$$-2.4037x_1 + 1.0432x_2 + .7589x_3 = .3724$$
$$1.0462x_1 + 2.0495x_2 + 6.3524x_3 = -2.4728$$

The array in Fig. 9.1 becomes

		4.6237	2.6914	−3.7517	1.4023	4.9657
		−2.4037	1.0432	.7589	.3724	−.2292
		1.0462	2.0495	6.3524	−2.4728	6.9753
.5199	−.2263	4.6237	2.6914	−3.7517	1.4023	4.9657
	−.5897		2.4425	−1.1916	1.1015	2.3525
			7.9041	−3.4397	4.4643

The back substitution then gives

$$x_3 = -.4352 \qquad x_2 = .2387 \qquad x_1 = -.1888$$

The final check of summing the three equations and substituting in the results checks exactly to four decimal places. The discrepancy between the sum check column and the row sums is due to roundoff error.

When A is symmetric, it can be shown {7} that in place of (9.3-22) we may write

$$m_{ij} = -a_{ij}^{(i-1)}/a_{ii}^{(i-1)} \qquad (9.3\text{-}26)$$

which simplifies the computation considerably.

9.3-2-2 Positioning for size

When the elements of A and the successive derived systems do not vary much in magnitude, the above procedure is quite satisfactory. But, when any of the divisors $a_{ii}^{(i-1)}$ is small in magnitude compared with the elements $a_{ki}^{(i-1)}$, $k > i$, then a serious roundoff error may be incurred. We shall discuss roundoff errors in detail in Sec. 9.4. Here we only need recall the fact mentioned in Sec. 1.3-1 that the percentage error in the reciprocal of a number varies inversely with the magnitude of the number. Thus, if four decimal places are being carried in the computation, a round-off error in a small value of one of the $a_{ii}^{(i-1)}$ will cause a serious error in the reciprocal and, thus, in the calculation of the m_{ik} by (9.3-22).†

To avoid division by numbers small in comparison with other elements, we use a technique called *positioning for size* (or, sometimes, *using pivotal elements*). This technique consists of the following:

1. At the ith stage of the calculation (i.e., when the ith row is being calculated), we locate that element $a_{p,i-1}^{(i-2)}$, $p \geq i - 1$ of greatest magnitude and interchange rows $i - 1$ and p.
2. Then the elements in the ith row are calculated as before.

Unfortunately, using this technique, it is not possible in any reasonable way to avoid recording the successive derived systems, although the

† Since $a_{ii}^{(i-1)}$ is computed as the difference of two quantities, the use of floating-point arithmetic would not alleviate this loss of significance.

physical interchange of the rows can be avoided as indicated in the example below.

Example 9.2   Find the solution of the system

$$2.4759x_1 + 1.6235x_2 + 4.6231x_3 = .0647$$
$$1.4725x_1 + .9589x_2 - 1.3253x_3 = 1.0475$$
$$2.6951x_1 + 2.8965x_2 - 1.4794x_3 = -.6789$$

first as in Example 9.1 and then using positioning for size, carrying four decimal places in all computations.

The array in Fig. 9.1 becomes

		2.4759	1.6235	4.6231	.0647	8.7872
		1.4725	.9589	-1.3253	1.0475	2.1536
		2.6951	2.8965	-1.4794	-.6789	3.4333
-.5947	1.0885	2.4759	1.6235	4.6231	.0647	8.7872
	171.1091		-.0066	-4.0747	1.0090	-3.0721
				-703.7299	171.8998	-531.7958

The back substitution gives

$$x_3 = -.2443 \qquad x_2 = -2.0532 \qquad x_1 = 1.8286$$

Summing the equations and substituting in these values gives .4548 on the left-hand side and .4333 on the right-hand side. This large discrepancy as well as the sizable discrepancy between the third row sum and the sum column is the result of the large percentage error incurred in taking the reciprocal of $-.0066$.

If we use positioning for size, the first stage of the computation then is

		-1.0375	5.9822	.6884	5.6330
First derived		-.6237	-.5170	1.4185	.2776
system	2.6951	2.8965	-1.4794	-.6789	3.4333

since 2.6951 is the element of greatest magnitude in the first column. At the next stage, -1.0375 is the element of greatest magnitude in the two remaining rows. Therefore, as the final system we get

		-1.0375	5.9822	.6884	5.6330
Final system		-4.1135	1.0046	-3.1090	
	2.6951	2.8965	-1.4794	-.6789	3.4333

from which, by back substitution

$$x_3 = -.2442 \qquad x_2 = -2.0716 \qquad x_1 = 1.8405$$

which gives .4339 when substituted into the sum equation. The improvement of this result over the previous one is due to the avoidance of $-.0066$ as a divisor in calculating the final system. Note that the check column plays the same role with positioning for size as it does without positioning. When using positioning for size it is also possible to carry a check row as well as a check column {8}. Any incorrectly computed element will then show up in an incorrect row check and column check. In this way the incorrect element is isolated immediately.

The method we have described above is more precisely called *partial* positioning for size. Complete positioning for size, in which we interchange both rows and columns to get the element $a_{pq}^{(i-2)}$, p, $q \geq i - 1$ of greatest magnitude into the $(i - 1, i - 1)$ position, is seldom worthwhile for matrices of the order that can reasonably be solved on a desk calculator. However, for large-order systems solved on a digital computer, complete positioning for size can be useful {11}, but because of the intricacies of the manipulations involved in complete positioning, we shall not consider algorithms to implement it.

9.3-3 Solution on digital computers

The most important computational differences between solving linear equations on desk calculators and digital computers are:

1. Roundoff error. We have noted that for large systems the control of roundoff is vital. Positioning for size is one way of achieving this control. Another important area where proper computational technique is important is in the accumulation of sums which are in the form of inner products such as those in (9.3-21) and (9.3-22). In Sec. 1.3-1 we noted the importance of forming double-precision products, summing, and then rounding instead of rounding and then summing. Doing this on a digital computer is extremely important; see Sec. 9.4. Moreover, it is also important (and possible in most computers) to use a double-length dividend when computing m_{ik} using (9.3-22).

2. Storage and matrix manipulations. We noted the difficulty in arranging the computation in a compact form when using positioning for size. But on a digital computer, it is important—particularly for very large matrices—to minimize the amount of storage required for intermediate calculations. Moreover, we wish to avoid physically interchanging rows and columns since this can be quite time-consuming even on a very fast computer. We shall therefore in what follows develop a method which achieves the aims of minimizing intermediate storage and minimizing manipulation of the elements of the matrix.

3. Size of numbers. Using fixed-point arithmetic (see Sec. 1.5-2) it is important to control the magnitude of the numbers as carefully as possible so that overflow and, therefore, scaling can be avoided. This is usually not a severe problem in the solution of linear equations. Although it is possible to do double-precision floating-point operations on many computers, we shall for simplicity consider only the use of fixed-point arithmetic in what follows.

In order to deal with these computational problems, it is convenient to reformulate the computational scheme of Sec. 9.3-2-1 in matrix terms.

9.3-3-1 *Matrix formulation*

Denote by A_1 the matrix of coefficients in (9.3-2). Then

$$A_1 = L_1 A \qquad (9.3\text{-}27)$$

where

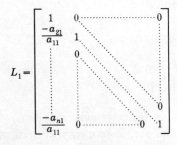

$$(9.3\text{-}28)$$

In general, if we denote the matrix of coefficients in the $i + 1$ derived system by A_{i+1} then {9}

$$A_{i+1} = L_{i+1} A_i \qquad i = 0, \ldots, n - 2 \qquad (9.3\text{-}29)$$

where

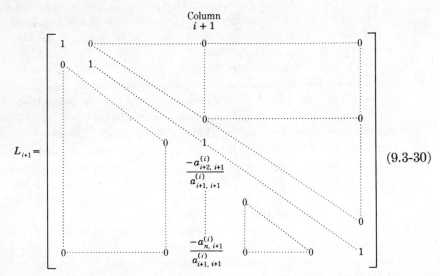

$$(9.3\text{-}30)$$

Finally, denoting the upper triangular matrix of coefficients in the final system (9.3-6) by $U = [u_{ij}]$ we have

$$U = L_{n-1}L_{n-2}L_{n-3} \cdots L_1 A = \bar{L}A \qquad (9.3\text{-}31)$$

where $\bar{L}$ is lower triangular with 1's on the diagonal, since the product of two lower triangular matrices with 1's on the diagonal is a matrix of the same form {9}. Since, further, the inverse of a matrix of the form $\bar{L}$ is again a matrix of this form {9}, we may write $\bar{L}^{-1} = L$ where

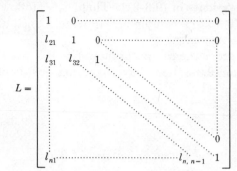

$$L = \qquad\qquad\qquad\qquad\qquad\qquad\qquad\qquad (9.3\text{-}32)$$

and from (9.3-31)

$$A = LU \qquad\qquad\qquad\qquad\qquad\qquad (9.3\text{-}33)$$

Because this approach results in the decomposition of A into the product of a lower triangular and upper triangular matrix, this technique is often called *triangular decomposition*.

Now when the matrix A has been decomposed into the product LU by a method we shall describe below, then the solution of (9.1-2) is found by first solving the system

$$Ly = b \qquad\qquad\qquad\qquad\qquad\qquad (9.3\text{-}34)$$

and then solving

$$Ux = y \qquad\qquad\qquad\qquad\qquad\qquad (9.3\text{-}35)$$

since

$$Ax = LUx = Ly = b \qquad\qquad\qquad\qquad\qquad (9.3\text{-}36)$$

But the solution of the systems (9.3-34) and (9.3-35) is, of course, simple since L and U are both triangular.

From the construction above, it is clear that $u_{ij} = a_{ij}^{(i-1)}$, $i,j = 1, \ldots , n$. From (9.3-33) we have

$$a_{ij} = \sum_{k=1}^{\min(i,j)} l_{ik} u_{kj} = \sum_{k=1}^{\min(i,j)} l_{ik} a_{kj}^{(k-1)} \qquad\qquad (9.3\text{-}37)$$

Recalling that $l_{ii} = 1$ and comparing (9.3-37) with (9.3-21) when $i < j$, we get

$$l_{ik} = -m_{ki} \qquad k = 1, \ldots , i - 1 \qquad\qquad\qquad (9.3\text{-}38)$$

Finally, we see that the solution of (9.3-34) is

$$y_j = a_{j,n+1}^{(j-1)} \qquad j = 1, \ldots, n \tag{9.3-39}$$

Since the solution of (9.3-35) is precisely the back substitution, this matrix formulation involving the decomposition of A into the product LU followed by the solution of (9.3-34) and (9.3-35) is completely equivalent to Gaussian elimination with back substitution.

On a digital computer, we order the computation differently than in the desk-calculator case. From (9.3-37) we have, ignoring positioning for size,

$$\begin{aligned}
a_{11} &= u_{11} \\
a_{i1} &= l_{i1}u_{11} \qquad i = 2, \ldots, n
\end{aligned} \tag{9.3-40}$$

which gives us the first column of the U and L matrices. Then

$$\begin{aligned}
a_{12} &= u_{12} \\
a_{22} &= l_{21}u_{12} + u_{22} \\
a_{i2} &= l_{i1}u_{12} + l_{i2}u_{22} \qquad i = 3, \ldots, n
\end{aligned} \tag{9.3-41}$$

which gives us the second column of U and L. Continuing in this way, we compute successive columns of U and L. For the rth column the equations are

$$\begin{aligned}
a_{1r} &= u_{1r} \\
a_{2r} &= l_{21}u_{1r} + u_{2r} \\
&\cdots \cdots \cdots \cdots \\
a_{rr} &= l_{r1}u_{1r} + l_{r2}u_{2r} + \cdots + l_{r,r-1}u_{r-1,r} + u_{rr} \\
a_{ir} &= l_{i1}u_{1r} + \cdots + l_{ir}u_{rr} \qquad i = r + 1, \ldots, n
\end{aligned} \tag{9.3-42}$$

The contrast between this and the previous case in which we computed successively rows of U and L should be noted. The solutions of (9.3-34) and (9.3-35) are then calculated using equations analogous to (9.3-8) (see Sec. 9.3-3-2).

When A is symmetric then the calculation above can be greatly simplified by noting that A may be written

$$A = LL^T \tag{9.3-43}$$

if we modify the decomposition into two triangular matrices to make the diagonal elements of L and U the same (even though some of the diagonal elements may then be imaginary). This variation of the Gauss-Doolittle process is called *Choleski's method*. We leave to a problem {13} the derivation of the particular equations for the symmetric case.

Thus far we have ignored positioning for size and scaling. In the following section we indicate how the calculations of this section can be performed on a digital computer so that we can take care of these matters and the control of roundoff error.

9.3-3-2 The computer algorithm

In the desk-computer case we saw that, using partial positioning for size, no actual interchanges of rows were necessary as long as it was clear at each stage which rows were in their final state and which were not.   On a digital computer we achieve this by the simple device of keeping track at every stage of which row has the largest element in the relevant column.

The use of partial positioning for size simplifies the scaling problem considerably (complete positioning for size would still further lessen the problem).   This is because the use of the largest element in the column as divisor is assurance that all quotients will be less than 1.   Of course, some growth in the numbers as the computation proceeds is possible because of the need to calculate the scalar products in (9.3-21) and (9.3-22).   Since we are considering fixed-point computation, we assume that all numbers must be less than 1 in magnitude.   It is necessary, therefore, to test for overflow whenever any quantity could be greater than 1 and to rescale (i.e., decrease the magnitude of all elements) when this happens.   Without going into the details of this here, we note that this is not a serious programming problem.   The only place where scaling can be a difficult problem is in the back substitution because the magnitude of a component of the solution may be large compared with the matrix elements.   We shall say more about this problem in Sec. 9.4.

We are now ready to describe the computer algorithm.   In Fig. 9.2 we have illustrated some relevant parts of the process.   We start with the array A as shown in panel 1.   At the first stage we adjoin to A the column d_1 whose elements d_{i1}, $i = 1, \ldots, n$ are merely a_{i1} expressed in double-length form (see Sec. 1.5-3).   The appended $n + 1$ row is initially all zeros. The number p_1 denotes the row containing the element d_{i1} which has the largest magnitude and is therefore the record of the positioning for size. The largest (in magnitude) of the d_{i1} is then rounded to single length[†] and set equal to u_{11}.   Then a_{11} is overwritten with u_{11} (i.e., the location in memory originally containing a_{11} now contains u_{11}) and $d_{p_1,1}$ is overwritten with d_{11}.   Finally, l_{i1} is computed by dividing d_{i1} by u_{11}, $i = 2, \ldots, n$ and a_{i1} is overwritten with l_{i1}, this last step corresponding to Eq. (9.3-40). The use of the double-length dividend is important in error control; see Sec. 9.4.   The quantities stored at the end of stage 1 are shown in panel 2 of Fig. 9.2.   Note that overwriting $d_{p_1,1}$ with d_{11} means that $l_{p_1,1}$ is the original a_{11}/u_{11}.   Therefore, in the first column we have in effect inter-

---

† At the first stage, the expansion to double length followed by the rounding to single length is clearly wasted effort, but as will be seen, this procedure is needed in later stages and so is included here to make the algorithm consistent.

changed rows 1 and p_1.   The other elements in the p_1 row are still the original ones, however.

The second stage now proceeds as follows:

Step 1: For $i = 1, \ldots, n$ replace d_{i1} by d_{i2}, the double-length equivalent of a_{i2}.

Step 2: Calculate u_{12} by taking $d_{p_1,2}$, rounded to single length, and overwriting a_{12}.   (Note that choosing $d_{p_1,2}$ means that we use that element of column 2 corresponding to the largest element of column 1.)   Overwrite $d_{p_1,2}$ with d_{12}.

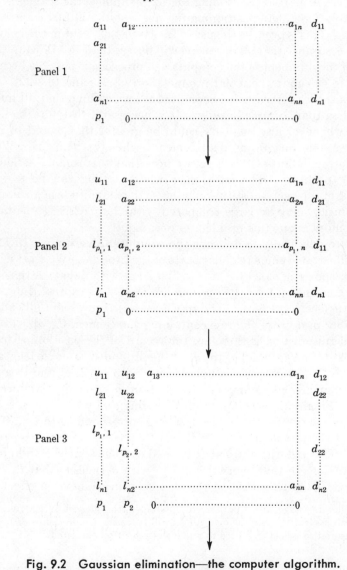

Fig. 9.2   Gaussian elimination—the computer algorithm.

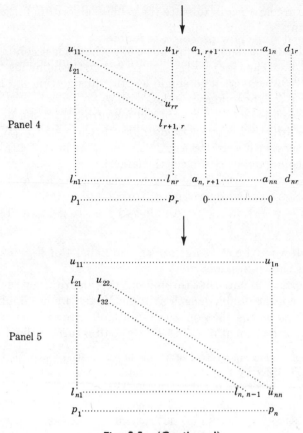

Panel 4

Panel 5

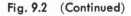

Fig. 9.2   (Continued)

Step 3: Subtract $l_{i1}u_{12}$ from d_{i2}, $i = 2, \ldots, n$, using double-precision arithmetic.   Leave the result in the location that previously held d_{i2}.   [This corresponds to subtracting the first term on the right-hand side of the second and third equations of (9.3-41) from the left-hand side.]

Step 4: Positioning for size.   Select the largest of d_{i2}, $i = 2, \ldots, n$, call it $d_{p_2,2}$, round it to single length, thus getting u_{22}, and overwrite a_{22}.   Then store p_2 and overwrite $d_{p_2,2}$ with d_{22}.   This is the correct point to apply positioning for size since the result of step 3 gives the d_{i2} column in the form of the second column of the first derived system (9.3-2).

Step 5: Compute l_{i2}, $i = 3, \ldots, n$ by dividing the current value of d_{i2} by u_{22}, convert this to single length, and overwrite a_{i2}, $i = 3, \ldots, n$.   [This completes the calculation in the last equation of (9.3-41).]

The contents of memory at the end of this step are shown in panel 3 of

Fig. 9.2.   We are now ready to state the general algorithm for generating the rth column:

Step 1: Put the double-length equivalent of a_{kr} in the last column, $k = 1$, . . . , n.   Then for $j = 1$, . . . , $r - 1$ do the following two steps:

Step 2: Take $d_{p_j,r}$, convert it to single length, thus getting u_{jr}, and overwrite a_{jr}.   Then overwrite $d_{p_j,r}$ with d_{jr}.

Step 3: For $i = j + 1$, . . . , n subtract $l_{ij}u_{jr}$ from d_{ir} using double-precision arithmetic, overwriting d_{ir} with the result.   [With these two steps we determine u_{1r}, . . . , $u_{r-1,r}$ as in (9.3-42).]

Step 4: Positioning for size.   Select the largest of d_{ir}, $i = r$, . . . , n, call it $d_{p_r,r}$, round it to single length, thus getting u_{rr}, and overwrite a_{rr}.   Store p_r and overwrite $d_{p_r,r}$ with d_{rr}.

Step 5: For $i = r + 1$, . . . , n, divide d_{ir} by u_{rr} to get l_{ir} and overwrite a_{ir}.

The result after the rth stage appears in panel 4 of Fig. 9.2, and the final matrix is shown in panel 5.

It is important to note that throughout this algorithm we accumulate scalar products using double-length arithmetic, and we use double-length dividends.   This means that only one roundoff error is incurred in the calculation of each element of L and U; we shall return to this in Sec. 9.4.

Example 9.3   For the system of Example 9.2, indicate how the sequence of calculations proceeds for the computer algorithm.

For this system the array in panel 1 of Fig. 9.2 is

.24759	.16235	.46231	.2475900000
.14725	.09589	−.13253	.1472500000
.26951	.28965	−.14794	.2695100000
3	0	0	

We have assumed a computer with a five-digit word length and have scaled all numbers to be less than 1 in magnitude.   We have $p_1 = 3$ since .26951 is the largest element in column 1.   For panel 2 we have

.26951	.16235	.46231	.2475900000
.54636	.09589	−.13253	.1472500000
.91867	.28965	−.14794	.2475900000
3	0	0	

with u_{11}, l_{21}, and l_{31} now in column 1.   To get the array equivalent to panel 3, we replace the last column by the double-length equivalent of the second column and, using the fact that $p_1 = 3$ to get $u_{12} = .28965$, overwrite .2896500000 with .1623500000. We then perform steps 3, 4, and 5 of the algorithm to get

.26951	.28965	.46231	.1623500000
.54636	−.10374	−.13253	−.0623631740
.91867	.60115	−.14794	−.0623631740
3	3	0	

Note that p_1 and p_2 are both equal to 3, but that p_1 refers to the original row 3 while p_2 refers to the original row 1 which was in effect exchanged with row 3 in the first stage. The next stage leads to the final array

.26951	.28965	−.14794
.54636	−.10374	.59822
.91867	.60115	−.41132
3	3	3

The portion of the matrix on the main diagonal and above is identical (except for roundoff and the interchange of rows) with the matrix in Example 9.2 which is labeled "Final system."

When the above process is finished, the *matrix U is that which would result if the original equations had been such that positioning for size would have required no interchange of rows at any stage* (i.e., for Example 9.3 if the original order were third, first, second equation). The matrix L which would have resulted if no interchanges had been needed is not the matrix in panel 5 of Fig. 9.2, but can be obtained from it by using the p_i's.

When A is symmetric, the above algorithm may be modified to give substantial savings in memory usage and computation time {13}.

After the computation resulting in panel 5 of Fig. 9.2 has been completed, we can solve (9.3-34). Because the interchanges of rows also interchange the right-hand sides, we must use care in solving for **y**. The algorithm is as follows:

Step 1: Put the double-length equivalent of b_i, $i = 1, \ldots, n$ in the double-length locations used in the elimination procedure. We shall refer to these double-length locations as b_i below. Then for $i = 1, \ldots, n$ do steps 2 and 3:

Step 2: Round b_{p_i} to single length, thus getting y_i, and overwrite b_{p_i} with b_i.

Step 3: For $j = i + 1, \ldots, n$ subtract $l_{ji}y_i$ from b_j and overwrite b_j using double-precision arithmetic.

After calculation of the y_i's, the calculation of the x_i's from (9.3-35) is straightforward and uses equations analogous to (9.3-8).

Example 9.3 (*continued*)   In order to calculate the y_i's we start with the column of double-length scaled b_i's:

```
 .0064700000
 .1047500000
−.0678900000
```

Since $p_1 = 3$ we have $y_1 = −.06789$ and after step 3 above we have

```
.0064700000
.1418423804
.0688385063
```

Since $p_2 = 3$ we have $y_2 = .06884$.   We then get the array

.0064700000
.1418423804
.1004592144

and finally $y_3 = .10046$.   Then the back substitution yields (using double-precision arithmetic)

$$x_3 = -.24424 \qquad x_2 = -2.07200 \qquad x_1 = 1.84087$$

Substitution of these values into the sum equation gives .43341.   This substantial improvement over the result in Example 9.2 occurs because we have carried one extra decimal place in parts of this computation and because of the double-precision arithmetic.   Note that, since the results are unaffected by the original scaling, in actual computer computation some further scaling would have to be done since two of the three values of x_i have magnitude greater than 1.

9.4   ERROR ANALYSIS

Let A and $\mathbf{b}$ be the actual matrix and vector in the computer.   Denote by $\mathbf{x}_t$ and $\mathbf{x}_c$ the true and computed solutions, respectively, of $A\mathbf{x} = \mathbf{b}$.   One possible measure of the error in the computed solution would be the magnitude of the residual vector

$$\mathbf{r} = A\mathbf{x}_c - \mathbf{b} \tag{9.4-1}$$

But we have already pointed out (see Sec. 9.2) that $|\mathbf{r}|$† can be quite small even though $\mathbf{x}_c$ is a very poor solution.   A more reasonable measure of the error is given by

$$E = |\mathbf{x}_c - \mathbf{x}_t| \tag{9.4-2}$$

It is this error that we shall try to estimate in this section.

Any bound on E will depend on the magnitude of the roundoff errors incurred, the order of the matrix A (because this determines the number of computations), and the size of A^{-1} (because this determines how important each roundoff is).   One approach to finding such a bound would be to consider the worst possible case of roundoff at each stage of the procedure and to derive a bound based on the accumulation of these errors.   Such bounds can be calculated, but because the roundoff at one stage is a quite complicated function of the roundoff at previous stages, such bounds are difficult to calculate and, more importantly, are quite pessimistic.   Instead our approach here will be to estimate the perturbed system of equations whose *true* solution is the calculated solution $\mathbf{x}_c$.   That is, the

---

† If $\mathbf{r}^T = (r_1, r_2, \ldots, r_n)$ then $|\mathbf{r}| = \left(\sum_{i=1}^{n} r_i^2 \right)^{\frac{1}{2}}$.

computed solution $\mathbf{x}_c$ is the true solution of *some* system which we write as

$$(A + \delta A)\mathbf{x} = \mathbf{b} + \delta\mathbf{b} \tag{9.4-3}$$

We cannot hope to find δA and $\delta\mathbf{b}$ precisely; our object is to find bounds on their elements.

One advantage of this approach is that it gives us an indication of the *system that was actually solved*. This enables us to judge the relative importance of the roundoff error in the calculation and the inherent coefficient error (why?).

Perhaps a more important advantage of this approach is that the analysis is substantially simpler than that for the other approach mentioned above. The result of this is a much less conservative bound in general.

Our immediate object, before we consider how to bound the elements of δA and $\delta\mathbf{b}$, is to see how a knowledge of these bounds together with a knowledge of the size of A^{-1} can be used to bound E. We have

$$\begin{aligned}
\mathbf{x}_c - \mathbf{x}_t &= (A + \delta A)^{-1}(\mathbf{b} + \delta\mathbf{b}) - A^{-1}\mathbf{b} \\
&= [(A + \delta A)^{-1} - A^{-1}]\mathbf{b} + (A + \delta A)^{-1}\delta\mathbf{b} \\
&= [(A + \delta A)^{-1} - A^{-1}]\mathbf{b} + (I + A^{-1}\delta A)^{-1}A^{-1}\delta\mathbf{b} \tag{9.4-4}
\end{aligned}$$

In order to use (9.4-4) to bound E, we must first discuss matrix and vector norms, a topic which we shall use again later in this chapter.

9.4-1 Norms

The norm of a matrix is a number assigned to the matrix which is in some sense a measure of the magnitude of the matrix. It is natural, therefore, to wish the norm of A, denoted by $\|A\|$, to have the following properties

(1) $\|A\| \geqq 0$, $\|A\| = 0$ if and only if $A = 0$
(2) $\|cA\| = |c|\,\|A\|$ where c is any real number
(3) $\|A + B\| \leq \|A\| + \|B\|$
(4) $\|AB\| \leq \|A\|\,\|B\|$

$$\tag{9.4-5}$$

The third condition is the triangle inequality, and the last is the Schwarz inequality. From (4) it follows in particular that

$$\|A^m\| \leqq (\|A\|)^m \tag{9.4-6}$$

Among the many possible ways of defining $\|A\|$ which satisfy (9.4-5), we shall consider two {18}

(1) $\|A\|_E = \left(\displaystyle\sum_{i=1}^{m} \sum_{j=1}^{n} a_{ij}^2\right)^{1/2}$ the Euclidean norm

(2) $\|A\|_S = \max_{i} [\lambda_i(A^T A)]^{1/2}$ the spectral norm

$$\tag{9.4-7}$$

both of which are defined for any $m \times n$ matrix. In the definition of the spectral norm the notation $\lambda_i(AA^T)$ denotes an eigenvalue of AA^T.† For vectors we define the norm in the Euclidean sense as

$$\|\mathbf{x}\| = (\mathbf{x}^T\mathbf{x})^{1/2} = |\mathbf{x}| \qquad (9.4\text{-}8)$$

The Euclidean norm may also be expressed as {20}

$$\|A\|_E = [\text{tr }(AA^T)]^{1/2} \qquad (9.4\text{-}9)$$

where tr denotes the trace. Since the trace of a matrix is the sum of its eigenvalues {20}

$$\|A\|_E^2 = \sum_{i=1}^{n} \lambda_i(AA^T) \qquad (9.4\text{-}10)$$

where n is the order of AA^T. Thus we have the important result

$$\|A\|_S \leqq \|A\|_E \qquad (9.4\text{-}11)$$

We note for later reference that this result implies that, if $\|A^{-1}\|_S$ is large, then A^{-1} must have some large elements.

For our purposes the spectral norm is much the more useful of the two norms. We shall hereafter drop the subscript S on the spectral norm. We shall also have need to use the *spectral radius*, which is defined as

$$\rho(A) = \max_i |\lambda_i(A)| \qquad (9.4\text{-}12)$$

Thus

$$\|A\| = [\rho(AA^T)]^{1/2} \qquad (9.4\text{-}13)$$

and, when A is symmetric,

$$\|A\| = \rho(A) \qquad (9.4\text{-}14)$$

The following theorem will be important in both this and the following sections:

Theorem 9.2   Let A be a square matrix and $\mathbf{x}$ any vector. Then

$$\max_{\mathbf{x}} \frac{\|A\mathbf{x}\|}{\|\mathbf{x}\|} = \|A\| \qquad (9.4\text{-}15)$$

Proof   Let λ_1 be the largest eigenvalue in magnitude of AA^T. For any $\mathbf{x}$

$$\frac{\|A\mathbf{x}\|^2}{\|\mathbf{x}\|^2} - \|A\|^2 = \frac{\mathbf{x}^T A^T A \mathbf{x}}{\mathbf{x}^T \mathbf{x}} - \lambda_1 = \frac{\mathbf{x}^T(A^T A - \lambda_1 I)\mathbf{x}}{\mathbf{x}^T \mathbf{x}} \leqq 0 \qquad (9.4\text{-}16)$$

† Note that for any real matrix A the matrix AA^T is symmetric and nonnegative definite.

since the eigenvalues of $A^T A - \lambda_1 I$ are nonpositive and, therefore, the numerator is negative semidefinite. Since we get equality in (9.4-16) when $\mathbf{x}$ is an eigenvector of $A^T A$ corresponding to λ_1, the theorem is proved. From this theorem we get the following corollaries:

Corollary 9.1 $\|A\| \geq \rho(A)$

Proof   This result follows by letting $\mathbf{x}$ be the eigenvector corresponding to any eigenvalue of A.

Corollary 9.2   If $\|A\| < 1$, then $I + A$ is nonsingular.

Proof $\lambda_i(I + A) = 1 + \lambda_i(A)$. Thus

$$|\lambda_i(I + A)| \geq 1 - |\lambda_i(A)| \geq 1 - \|A\| > 0$$

Corollary 9.3   If $\|A\| < 1$, then

$$\|(I + A)^{-1}\| \leq \frac{1}{1 - \|A\|} \quad \text{and}$$

$$\|(I + A)^{-1} - I\| \leq \frac{\|A\|}{1 - \|A\|} \tag{9.4-17}$$

Proof   Since $I + A$ is nonsingular by Corollary 9.2, we have

$$I = (I + A)^{-1}(I + A) = R + RA \tag{9.4-18}$$

where $R = (I + A)^{-1}$. Therefore $\{19\}$,

$$1 = \|I\| \geq \|R\| - \|RA\| \geq \|R\| - \|R\|\,\|A\|$$

from which the first part of (9.4-17) follows. Using this result the second part follows easily $\{19\}$.

Corollary 9.4   If A is nonsingular and $\|A^{-1}B\| < 1$, then $A + B$ is nonsingular and

$$\|(A + B)^{-1} - A^{-1}\| \leq k\|A^{-1}\| \tag{9.4-19}$$

where $k = \|A^{-1}B\|/(1 - \|A^{-1}B\|)$.

Proof   Using Corollary 9.2 the nonsingularity of both $A + B$ and $I + A^{-1}B$ follows since

$$A + B = A(I + A^{-1}B)$$

We have

$$(A + B)^{-1} = (I + A^{-1}B)^{-1}A^{-1}$$

Thus

$$(A + B)^{-1} - A^{-1} = [(I + A^{-1}B)^{-1} - I]A^{-1}$$

Using Corollary 9.3, the result follows.

9.4-2   Error bounds

From our definition of vector norm in the previous section, we see that E in (9.4-2) is just $\|\mathbf{x}_c - \mathbf{x}_t\|$. Using Corollaries 9.3 and 9.4, we have from (9.4-4)

$$
\begin{aligned}
\|\mathbf{x}_c - \mathbf{x}_t\| &\leqq \|(A + \delta A)^{-1} - A^{-1}\| \, \|\mathbf{b}\| \\
&\quad + \|(I + A^{-1}\delta A)^{-1}\| \, \|A^{-1}\| \, \|\delta\mathbf{b}\| \\
&\leqq \frac{\|A^{-1}\|}{1 - \|A^{-1}\| \, \|\delta A\|} \, [\|\delta A\| \, \|A^{-1}\| \, \|\mathbf{b}\| + \|\delta\mathbf{b}\|]
\end{aligned}
\qquad (9.4\text{-}20)
$$

where we have assumed that $\|A^{-1}\| \, \|\delta A\| < 1$. If this condition is not satisfied—that is, if A^{-1} has elements so large that, even though δA is small, the product of the norms is not small—then the matrix A is so ill-conditioned that an accurate solution $\mathbf{x}$ cannot be obtained unless by some means δA can be made still smaller (see Sec. 9.5).

Even if we have bounds on $\|\delta A\|$ and $\|\delta\mathbf{b}\|$, the use of (9.4-20) depends upon our being able to estimate or bound $\|A^{-1}\|$, a problem we can never avoid in getting bounds for the solution of (9.1-1). In the remainder of this section, our object is to find bounds for $\|\delta A\|$ and $\|\delta\mathbf{b}\|$.

We shall assume that the original data have been scaled so that all elements of L, U, and $\mathbf{y}$ in (9.3-36) are less than 1 in magnitude. If we use partial positioning for size, then, on a decimal computer, it will usually be sufficient to scale A and $\mathbf{b}$ so that the leading digit is zero (i.e., all elements less than .1 in magnitude). The loss of significance thereby incurred is seldom important.

The triangular decomposition of A together with the solution of (9.3-34) results in an equation which without roundoff would be

$$
(A,\mathbf{b}) = L(U,\mathbf{y}) \qquad (9.4\text{-}21)
$$

where $(A,\mathbf{b})$ and $(U,\mathbf{y})$ are both $n \times n + 1$ matrices. But, because of roundoff, the *computed* matrices L and $(U,\mathbf{y})$ are the *true* results of operating not on A and $\mathbf{b}$ but rather on perturbations $A + \Delta A$ and $\mathbf{b} + \Delta\mathbf{b}$. Therefore, the correct equation is

$$
(A + \Delta A, \, \mathbf{b} + \Delta\mathbf{b}) = L(U,\mathbf{y}) \qquad (9.4\text{-}22)
$$

We now wish to estimate the elements Δa_{ij} of ΔA and Δb_i of $\Delta\mathbf{b}$.

From (9.3-42) the theoretical equation for the element l_{ij} of L is

$$
l_{ij} = (1/u_{jj})(a_{ij} - l_{i1}u_{1j} - l_{i2}u_{2j} - \cdots - l_{i,j-1}u_{j-1,j}) \qquad i > j
\qquad (9.4\text{-}23)
$$

but because of roundoff the *calculation* equation is

$$
l_{ij} = (1/u_{jj})(a_{ij} - l_{i1}u_{1j} - \cdots - l_{i,j-1}u_{j-1,j}) + \eta_{ij} \qquad i > j
\qquad (9.4\text{-}24)
$$

where η_{ij} is the roundoff error incurred. If we accumulate double-length scalar products and then use a double-length dividend, the only roundoff is incurred in rounding the quotient to single length (i.e., d decimals). Thus†

$$|\eta_{ij}| \leq \tfrac{1}{2} \times 10^{-d} \tag{9.4-25}$$

Rewriting (9.4-24) we have

$$l_{i1}u_{1j} + l_{i2}u_{2j} + \cdots + l_{ij}u_{jj} = a_{ij} + \Delta a_{ij} \qquad i > j \tag{9.4-26}$$

where

$$|\Delta a_{ij}| = |\eta_{ij}u_{jj}| \leq \tfrac{1}{2} \times 10^{-d} \qquad i > j \tag{9.4-27}$$

since we have assumed that $|u_{jj}| \leq 1$. Again using (9.3-42) the theoretical equation for u_{ij} is

$$u_{ij} = a_{ij} - l_{i1}u_{1j} - l_{i2}u_{2j} - \cdots - l_{i,i-1}u_{i-1,j} \qquad i \leq j \tag{9.4-28}$$

and the calculation equation is

$$u_{ij} = a_{ij} - l_{i1}u_{1j} - \cdots - l_{i,i-1}u_{i-1,j} + \Delta a_{ij} \qquad i \leq j \tag{9.4-29}$$

with the only roundoff occurring when the double-length scalar product is rounded to single length. Thus

$$|\Delta a_{ij}| \leq \tfrac{1}{2} \times 10^{-d} \qquad i \leq j \tag{9.4-30}$$

By an argument precisely similar to the above, the calculation of the y_i using (9.3-34) leads to the equation

$$l_{i1}y_1 + \cdots + l_{i,i-1}y_{i-1} + y_i = b_i + \Delta b_i \tag{9.4-31}$$

with

$$|\Delta b_i| \leq \tfrac{1}{2} \times 10^{-d} \tag{9.4-32}$$

Thus, from (9.4-27), (9.4-30), and (9.4-32), we get the result that all elements of ΔA and $\Delta \mathbf{b}$ are less than $\tfrac{1}{2} \times 10^{-d}$ in magnitude. This is in an important sense the "best possible" result. For it says that the result of the triangular decomposition and the solution of (9.3-34) corresponds to an original matrix and vector which differ from A and $\mathbf{b}$ by no more than the roundoff required to insert A and $\mathbf{b}$ into the computer.

Now we are ready to consider the back substitution, that is, the solution of

$$U\mathbf{x} = \mathbf{y} \tag{9.4-33}$$

---

† We shall assume here that we are dealing with a computer which is decimal internally. The argument for a binary computer is precisely analogous.

This set of equations is the result of applying the elimination procedure to

$$(A + \Delta A)\mathbf{x} = \mathbf{b} + \Delta\mathbf{b} \tag{9.4-34}$$

The solution of (9.4-33) is given by (9.3-8). But now we must consider the scaling problem in some detail since the x_i's are not affected by the previous scaling. Suppose that we know that the largest x_i in magnitude lies between 10^k and 10^{k-1}, $k \geq 1$ in magnitude. Before computing x_i by the back-substitution equations (9.3-8) we would then scale all $a_{ij}^{(i-1)}$ in the numerator by k digits (i.e., multiply the numerators by 10^{-k}) so that the quotient would be less than 1 in magnitude. If the computed quotient were then rounded to d *digits*, we would have (hereafter dropping the subscript c on the computed solution)

$$x_i = \frac{y_i - (u_{i,i+1}x_{i+1} + \cdots + u_{in}x_n)}{u_{ii}} + \epsilon_i \tag{9.4-35}$$

with

$$|\epsilon_i| \leq \tfrac{1}{2} \times 10^{k-d} \tag{9.4-36}$$

since we again assume the numerator of (9.4-35) is computed using double-precision arithmetic.† From (9.4-35) we have

$$u_{ii}x_i + \cdots + u_{in}x_n = y_i + \Delta c_i \tag{9.4-37}$$

where

$$|\Delta c_i| = |u_{ii}|\,|\epsilon_i| \leq \tfrac{1}{2} \times 10^{k-d} \tag{9.4-38}$$

Therefore, the computed solution $\mathbf{x}$ is really the solution of

$$U\mathbf{x} = \mathbf{y} + \Delta\mathbf{c} \tag{9.4-39}$$

with elements of $\Delta\mathbf{c}$ bounded as in (9.4-38). We are interested, though, in the effect of $\Delta\mathbf{c}$ on the perturbation of the original equation.

We define a vector $\Delta\mathbf{s}$ with components

$$\Delta s_i = \Delta c_i + l_{i,i-1}\Delta c_{i-1} + \cdots + l_{i1}\Delta c_1 \tag{9.4-40}$$

We now consider in place of (9.4-34) the equation

$$(A + \Delta A)\mathbf{x} = \mathbf{b} + \Delta\mathbf{b} + \Delta\mathbf{s} \tag{9.4-41}$$

Then we may show {22} that, if U and L are the result of an exact triangular decomposition of $A + \Delta A$, the vector $\mathbf{y} + \Delta\mathbf{c}$ is the result of exact solution of (9.3-34) with a right-hand side $\mathbf{b} + \Delta\mathbf{b} + \Delta\mathbf{s}$. Since

---

† Of course, a priori we do not know k. But if we assume a k which we expect is too large and then perform the back substitution, we can determine the true k. Then we can go back and do the back substitution again. Since the back substitution is not a major part of the computation, this does not add seriously to the computation time.

$|l_{ij}| \leqq 1$ we have, using (9.4-38) in (9.4-40),

$$|\Delta s_i| \leqq (i/2) \times 10^{k-d} \tag{9.4-42}$$

Thus our result is that the computed solution $\mathbf{x}$ is the solution of (9.4-41) with the elements of ΔA, $\Delta \mathbf{b}$, and $\Delta \mathbf{s}$ bounded as above.   In the notation of (9.4-3), $\delta A = \Delta A$ and $\delta \mathbf{b} = \Delta \mathbf{b} + \Delta \mathbf{s}$.

Our "best possible" result now seems to have vanished because of the 10^k factor in (9.4-42).   But in fact we shall now show that things are not so bad as they seem.   Let x_j be the largest element of $\mathbf{x}$ so that

$$10^{k-1} < |x_j| \leqq 10^k \tag{9.4-43}$$

Let B be a matrix with elements

$$\begin{aligned} B_{ik} &= 0 \qquad k \neq j \\ B_{ij} &= -\Delta s_i / x_j \end{aligned} \tag{9.4-44}$$

Then $\{22\}$

$$B\mathbf{x} = -\Delta \mathbf{s} \tag{9.4-45}$$

and using (9.4-42) to (9.4-44)

$$|B_{ij}| \leqq (i/2) \times 10^{k-d}/10^{k-1} = (i/2)10^{1-d} \tag{9.4-46}$$

Now using (9.4-45) we may rewrite (9.4-41) as

$$(A + \Delta A + B)\mathbf{x} = \mathbf{b} + \Delta \mathbf{b} \tag{9.4-47}$$

Therefore, we may consider $\mathbf{x}_c$ to be the solution of (9.4-47).   Now only B has elements larger than $\frac{1}{2} \times 10^{-d}$, and even these elements no longer have the 10^k factor.   Often in fact the inherent errors in the elements of A and $\mathbf{b}$ are such that these elements are known only to $t < d$ decimals. If $d - t > 1 + \log_{10} n$, then the elements of ΔA, B, and $\Delta \mathbf{b}$ are all less than the inherent error in the elements of A and $\mathbf{b}$.   Therefore, in this case the computation would not have added substantially to the error. This enables us to judge whether the computed solution is as *accurate as the data warrant*.

In any case our computational procedure has kept the accumulation of roundoff error to a minimum.   Since we have derived *bounds* on the elements of ΔA, B, and $\Delta \mathbf{b}$ and since we expect the roundoff errors to combine in some statistical fashion, the computed $\mathbf{x}$ will generally be the solution of a system (9.4-47) in which the elements of the error matrices are considerably smaller than these bounds.   In fact, the probable error we expect is the order of the square root of the maximum error [cf. Eq. (1.4-5)].   We note finally that, if double-precision arithmetic is not used where possible, the bounds on the size of the elements of ΔA, B, and $\Delta \mathbf{b}$ are substantially greater than those we have obtained here $\{23\}$.

Given the bounds on ΔA, B, and $\Delta \mathbf{b}$ and an estimate of $\|A^{-1}\|$, we may then use (9.4-20) to estimate $\|\mathbf{x}_c - \mathbf{x}_t\|$ using $\delta A = \Delta A + B$ and $\delta \mathbf{b} = \Delta \mathbf{b}$. To find bounds on $\|\delta A\|$ and $\|\delta \mathbf{b}\|$, it is most convenient to calculate $\|\delta A\|_E$ and $\|\delta \mathbf{b}\|_E$ by virtue of (9.4-11).

When A is symmetric, the above analysis may be simplified. In particular, if A is also positive definite, no initial scaling is necessary (other than to get all elements less than 1 in magnitude) because, in this case, it can be shown {14} that even without positioning for size no element in L, U, or $\mathbf{y}$ exceeds the maximum element of A or $\mathbf{b}$ in magnitude.

Example 9.4   Use the results of this section to bound the error in the system of Example 9.3. Bounds on the matrices ΔA, B, and $\Delta \mathbf{b}$ are given by, respectively,

$$\begin{bmatrix} \frac{1}{2} \times 10^{-5} & \frac{1}{2} \times 10^{-5} & \frac{1}{2} \times 10^{-5} \\ \frac{1}{2} \times 10^{-5} & \frac{1}{2} \times 10^{-5} & \frac{1}{2} \times 10^{-5} \\ \frac{1}{2} \times 10^{-5} & \frac{1}{2} \times 10^{-5} & \frac{1}{2} \times 10^{-5} \end{bmatrix} \begin{bmatrix} 0 & \frac{1}{2} \times 10^{-4} & 0 \\ 0 & 10^{-4} & 0 \\ 0 & \frac{3}{4} \times 10^{-4} & 0 \end{bmatrix} \begin{bmatrix} \frac{1}{2} \times 10^{-5} \\ \frac{1}{2} \times 10^{-5} \\ \frac{1}{2} \times 10^{-5} \end{bmatrix}$$

where, in the bound on B, we have made use of the fact that x_2 is the largest element of the solution. We have

$$\|\delta A\|_E = \|\Delta A + B\|_E \leqq 2 \times 10^{-4} \qquad \|\delta \mathbf{b}\| = \|\Delta \mathbf{b}\| \leqq (\sqrt{3}/2) \times 10^{-5}$$

For purposes of illustration here, we assume we know that

$$A^{-1} = \begin{bmatrix} 2.1044 & 13.7325 & -5.7257 \\ -1.2116 & -14.0196 & 8.7728 \\ 1.4615 & -2.4312 & -.0143 \end{bmatrix}$$

Then

$$\|A^{-1}\|_E \approx 22.5570$$

Since $\|\mathbf{b}\| \approx .1250$, we have using (9.4-20)

$$\|\mathbf{x}_c - \mathbf{x}_t\| \leqq \frac{(22.5570)}{1 - (22.5570)(2 \times 10^{-4})} [(2 \times 10^{-4})(22.5570)(.1250) + (\sqrt{3}/2) \times 10^{-5}] \approx .0128$$

Very conservatively estimated we have, therefore, an accuracy of two decimals in the result of Example 9.3.

In this and the previous section, we concentrated on the use of fixed-point arithmetic. Floating-point arithmetic, however, can be and often is used in practice to solve simultaneous linear equations. The errors in direct methods using floating-point arithmetic can be analyzed using techniques similar to those in this section. We have used fixed-point arithmetic here because the analysis is straightforward and instructive and because the scaling problems that arise in the fixed-point solution of (9.1-1) on computers are usually not very serious. As we noted previously, fixed-point arithmetic does have the advantage that double-precision arithmetic can be used where desirable whereas double-precision floating-point arithmetic is not available on some computers.

9.5   ILL–CONDITIONED EQUATIONS

Our assumption that all the elements of A and $\mathbf{b}$ have been scaled so that their magnitudes are all less than 1 (but such that the element of greatest magnitude is not much less than 1) constitutes a normalization of the matrix A similar to that considered in Sec. 9.2.   There we defined a matrix to be ill-conditioned if, after such a normalization, some element or elements of A^{-1} are large.   Therefore, an alternative definition of ill condition is that $\|A^{-1}\|_E$ is large.   This does not justify using the spectral norm as a measure of ill condition, since from (9.4-11) we know only that $\|A^{-1}\| \leqq \|A^{-1}\|_E$ but not how much less it may be.   But the sum of the eigenvalues of a matrix is the trace of the matrix.   Therefore, from (9.4-7) and (9.4-10),

$$\|A\|^2 = \max_i \, [\lambda_i(AA^T)] \geqq (1/n) \, \|A\|_E^2 \tag{9.5-1}$$

From (9.5-1) and (9.4-11) then

$$(1/\sqrt{n})\|A\|_E \leqq \|A\| \leqq \|A\|_E \tag{9.5-2}$$

This justifies using the magnitude of the spectral norm as a measure of ill condition.

The assumption that A is normalized is equivalent to assuming that $\|A\|$ has order of magnitude 1 {26}.   A more convenient measure of the *condition* of a matrix is therefore the product of the norms of A and A^{-1}. From the definition of the spectral norm, we have

$$\|A\| \, \|A^{-1}\| = [|\lambda(AA^T)|_{\max}/|\lambda(AA^T)|_{\min}]^{\frac{1}{2}} \tag{9.5-3}$$

When A is symmetric, we have the simpler relation

$$\|A\| \, \|A^{-1}\| = |\lambda(A)|_{\max}/|\lambda(A)|_{\min} = \rho(A)\rho(A^{-1}) \tag{9.5-4}$$

It is possible to calculate bounds on both $\rho(A)$ and $\rho(A^{-1})$ using the elements of A (see Sec. 10.1-3).   But such bounds are often very conservative.   Therefore, to recognize that a system is ill-conditioned may be quite difficult.   Equation (9.4-20) assures us of the fact that we adduced in Sec. 9.2; namely, that, if the system is ill-conditioned (i.e., if $\|A^{-1}\|$ is large), then the error in the computed solution may be large even if the computations are carried out as described in Sec. 9.3-3-2.   In particular, if the coefficients of an ill-conditioned system† have an inherent empirical error, then there is a large inherent uncertainty in the solution which we

---

† The reader will search in vain for a definition of when a system is ill-conditioned and when it is not.   There is no boundary between the two.   Equation (9.4-20) indicates that as the measure of the condition (i.e., $\|A^{-1}\|$) gets larger the norm of the error vector is increased approximately proportionally.

are helpless to do anything about.   In this section we shall concern ourselves with trying to improve the accuracy of the solution of an ill-conditioned system, assuming that A and $\mathbf{b}$ *as they appear in the computer are
exact.*

Before considering how to do this, let us consider the residual vector
which, as we noted in Sec. 9.2, can be very small even though the error
vector is not small.   From (9.4-41)

$$\mathbf{r} = \mathbf{b} - A\mathbf{x}_c = -\Delta\mathbf{b} - \Delta\mathbf{s} + \Delta A\mathbf{x}_c \tag{9.5-5}$$

Using the derived bounds for the quantities on the right-hand side, we
have (with ΔA_i the ith row of ΔA)

$$\begin{aligned}
|r_i| &\leq |\Delta b_i| + |\Delta s_i| + |\Delta A_i \mathbf{x}_c| \\
&\leq \tfrac{1}{2} \times 10^{-d} + (i/2) \times 10^{k-d} + n \times \tfrac{1}{2} \times 10^{-d} \times 10^k \\
&= \tfrac{1}{2} \times 10^{-d} + \tfrac{1}{2}(n + i)\,10^{k-d} \\
&\leq n \times 10^{k-d} + \tfrac{1}{2} \times 10^{-d} \qquad \text{for all } i
\end{aligned} \tag{9.5-6}$$

Now denote by $\mathbf{x}_{\text{tr}}$ the true solution rounded to $d - k$ decimals.   We have

$$|r_i|_{\text{tr}} = |\mathbf{b} - A\mathbf{x}_{\text{tr}}|_i = |A(\mathbf{x}_t - \mathbf{x}_{\text{tr}})|_i \leq (n/2) \times 10^{k-d} \tag{9.5-7}$$

A comparison of (9.5-6) and (9.5-7) indicates that the magnitude of the
residuals calculated from $\mathbf{x}_c$ should not exceed about twice the residuals of
the exact rounded solution *even though* $\mathbf{x}_c$ *itself may be highly inaccurate.*

Suppose we have solved the system (9.1-2) by the method of Sec.
9.3-3-2 and have calculated the residuals using double-precision arithmetic
(so that the error in calculating the residuals is small compared with the
magnitude of the residuals themselves).   If we suspect or (from knowledge of A^{-1}) know that the system is ill-conditioned, we may improve
upon the calculated solution using the following procedure.   We now
denote the computed solution by $\mathbf{x}^{(1)}$ and the residual by

$$\mathbf{r}^{(1)} = \mathbf{b} - A\mathbf{x}^{(1)} \tag{9.5-8}$$

Let the largest element of $\mathbf{r}^{(1)}$ lie between $10^{-k^{(1)}}$ and $10^{-[k^{(1)}+1]}$ where
$k^{(1)} \geq 0$.   We shall assume that the elements of $\mathbf{r}^{(1)}$ are no larger than
those of $\mathbf{x}$; in all but the most pathological cases they will be smaller.
Now we multiply each component of $\mathbf{r}^{(1)}$ by $10^{k^{(1)}}$ and round each element
to single precision, calling the resulting vector $10^{k^{(1)}}\mathbf{v}^{(1)}$.   Then we solve

$$A\mathbf{w} = 10^{k^{(1)}}\mathbf{v}^{(1)} \tag{9.5-9}$$

as in Sec. 9.3-3-2 and call the result $\mathbf{w}^{(1)}$.   Since the coefficient matrix is
the same as in the original solution, solving (9.5-9) requires only the solution of the equations corresponding to (9.3-34) and (9.3-35).   Defining

$$\mathbf{x}^{(2)} = \mathbf{x}^{(1)} + 10^{-k^{(1)}}\mathbf{w}^{(1)} \tag{9.5-10}$$

we have

$$\mathbf{r}^{(2)} = \mathbf{b} - A\mathbf{x}^{(2)} = \mathbf{r}^{(1)} - \mathbf{v}^{(1)} \tag{9.5-11}$$

Since the elements of $\mathbf{v}^{(1)}$ are just rounded values of those of $\mathbf{r}^{(1)}$, $\mathbf{r}^{(2)}$ should be substantially smaller than $\mathbf{r}^{(1)}$. Therefore, $\mathbf{x}^{(2)}$ should be an improved solution.† We may continue this process as long as the residuals decrease by defining in a natural way

$$\mathbf{x}^{(i+1)} = \mathbf{x}^{(i)} + 10^{-k^{(i)}}\mathbf{w}^{(i)} \tag{9.5-12}$$

Since each system analogous to (9.5-9) requires only the solution of the equations corresponding to (9.3-34) and (9.3-35), this approach will usually be more efficient than using double-precision arithmetic *throughout* the computation in the first place.

Equation (9.5-12), which defines an *iterative* method for finding the solution of $A\mathbf{x} = \mathbf{b}$, naturally concludes our discussion of direct methods for the solution of simultaneous linear equations and brings us to a discussion of iterative methods.

9.6 MATRIX ITERATIVE METHODS

The methods we shall consider in the remainder of this chapter are analogous to the methods of functional iteration of the last chapter. Starting with an initial vector $\mathbf{x}_1$, we shall generate a sequence of vectors

$$\mathbf{x}_{i+1} = F_i(\mathbf{x}_i, \mathbf{x}_{i-1}, \ldots, \mathbf{x}_{i-k}) \tag{9.6-1}$$

where the i subscript on F denotes that the iteration function itself may change from one iteration to the next. Analogously to Chap. 8, if the iteration function is not dependent on i, we say that the iteration is *stationary*.

For most matrices A iterative methods require more computation to achieve a desired degree of convergence than the direct methods we have discussed. Why consider them then? We noted the basic answer to this question in Sec. 9.2. This is that for sparse matrices—which arise commonly in solving partial differential equations by difference techniques—iterative techniques may indeed compare favorably with direct methods in terms of total amount of computation. Furthermore, because they are economical in their use of the computer memory, iterative methods are particularly advantageous for the very large matrices that often occur in the numerical solution of partial differential equations.‡

† The reader should not lose sight of the fact that, although a small residual may still mean a large error, generally the *smaller* the residual the better the solution.

‡ Computer programs to handle systems of up to order 108,000 have been written!

We shall restrict ourselves to linear iterative processes, that is, iterations in which F_i is a linear function of x_i, x_{i-1}, . . . , x_{i-k}. The primary reason for this is not that we are dealing with linear equations but rather that nonlinear iterations are much more difficult to analyze in general. Moreover, they tend to be computationally inefficient because of the number of matrix-vector products which must be calculated. As in Chap. 8 our interest will be focused on one-point iteration functions. A *linear one-point matrix iteration* has the form

$$\mathbf{x}_{i+1} = B_i\mathbf{x}_i + \mathbf{c}_i \tag{9.6-2}$$

where the matrix B_i and vector $\mathbf{c}_i$ are independent of i in a stationary iteration.

To motivate considering iterations of the type (9.6-2) to solve

$$A\mathbf{x} = \mathbf{b} \tag{9.6-3}$$

let us write (9.6-3) in the form

$$(I + A)\mathbf{x} = \mathbf{x} + \mathbf{b} \tag{9.6-4}$$

or

$$\mathbf{x} = (I + A)\mathbf{x} - \mathbf{b} \tag{9.6-5}$$

Equation (9.6-5) suggests the iteration

$$\mathbf{x}_{i+1} = (I + A)\mathbf{x}_i - \mathbf{b} \tag{9.6-6}$$

Equation (9.6-2) is then just a generalization of (9.6-6).

As in Chap. 8 we require that the true solution $\mathbf{x}_t$ of (9.6-3) be a fixed point of (9.6-2). Therefore, analogously to (9.6-5) we must have

$$\mathbf{x}_t = B_i\mathbf{x}_t + \mathbf{c}_i \tag{9.6-7}$$

for all i. Since $\mathbf{x}_t = A^{-1}\mathbf{b}$ we have

$$A^{-1}\mathbf{b} = B_iA^{-1}\mathbf{b} + \mathbf{c}_i \tag{9.6-8}$$

or

$$\mathbf{c}_i = (I - B_i)A^{-1}\mathbf{b} = C_i\mathbf{b} \tag{9.6-9}$$

We assume that B_i and C_i are independent of $\mathbf{b}$. Therefore, we must have

$$(I - B_i)A^{-1} = C_i \tag{9.6-10}$$

or

$$B_i + C_iA = I \tag{9.6-11}$$

This is called the *condition of consistency* for B_i and C_i.

Because of (9.6-9) we may rewrite (9.6-2) in its more usual form

$$\mathbf{x}_{i+1} = B_i\mathbf{x}_i + C_i\mathbf{b} \tag{9.6-12}$$

In order to consider the convergence of (9.6-12), we define

$$\epsilon_i = \mathbf{x}_i - \mathbf{x}_t \tag{9.6-13}$$

Using (9.6-10) and (9.6-12) we have

$$\epsilon_{i+1} = B_i\mathbf{x}_i + C_i\mathbf{b} - \mathbf{x}_t = B_i\mathbf{x}_i + C_i\mathbf{b} - A^{-1}\mathbf{b} = B_i\mathbf{x}_i - B_iA^{-1}\mathbf{b}$$
$$= B_i\mathbf{x}_i - B_i\mathbf{x}_t = B_i\epsilon_i \tag{9.6-14}$$

If $\mathbf{x}_1$ is the initial approximation to the solution of (9.6-3), then

$$\epsilon_{i+1} = K_i\epsilon_1 \tag{9.6-15}$$

where

$$K_i = B_iB_{i-1} \cdots B_1 \tag{9.6-16}$$

Therefore, a necessary and sufficient condition for the convergence of the sequence $\{\mathbf{x}_i\}$ to $\mathbf{x}_t$ *for arbitrary* $\mathbf{x}_1$ is that

$$\lim_{i \to \infty} K_i\mathbf{y} = 0 \qquad \text{for all } \mathbf{y} \tag{9.6-17}$$

while a sufficient condition for convergence is that

$$\lim_{i \to \infty} \|\epsilon_i\| = 0 \tag{9.6-18}$$

Using Theorem 9.2 we have

$$\max_{\epsilon_1} \frac{\|\epsilon_{i+1}\|}{\|\epsilon_1\|} = \max_{\epsilon_1} \frac{\|K_i\epsilon_1\|}{\|\epsilon_1\|} = \|K_i\| \tag{9.6-19}$$

Therefore,

$$\lim_{i \to \infty} \|K_i\| = 0 \tag{9.6-20}$$

is also a sufficient condition for the convergence of (9.6-2).   For stationary processes still another sufficient condition for convergence is

$$\lim_{i \to \infty} \rho(K_i) = 0 \tag{9.6-21}$$

9.7   STATIONARY ITERATIVE PROCESSES AND RELATED MATTERS

Because they are easier to analyze and computationally more desirable, most matrix iterative methods are stationary.   Our main concern in this section will be with stationary iterations.   In Sec. 9.7-5, however, we shall consider briefly the use of nonstationary iterations to accelerate the convergence of stationary iterative processes.

When an iteration is stationary, then $B_i = B$, $C_i = C$, and from (9.6-16)

$$K_i = B^i \tag{9.7-1}$$

The eigenvalues of B^i are the ith powers of the eigenvalues of B. Therefor, the condition (9.6-21) is equivalent to requiring that all eigenvalues of B lie within the unit circle (why?). In fact, this is a necessary as well as sufficient condition for the convergence of stationary iterations [see Varga (1962), pp. 13–15]. A somewhat stronger sufficient condition which follows from the inequality (9.4-11) is

$$\|B\|_E < 1 \tag{9.7-2}$$

If the iteration converges, the rate at which it does so is of interest. From (9.6-15)

$$\|\epsilon_{i+1}\| \leq \|K_i\| \, \|\epsilon_i\| \leq \|B\|^i \|\epsilon_i\| \tag{9.7-3}$$

Therefore, the smaller the spectral norm of B, the more rapidly we expect the iteration to converge. If B is symmetric, the spectral norm and spectral radius are equal and the latter can then be used as a measure of the rate of convergence. If, as is more usual, B is not symmetric then, although we know that $\rho(B) \leq \|B\|$, it is not obvious that the spectral radius can be used to measure the rate of convergence. However, it can be shown, although it is beyond our scope here [see Varga (1962), pp. 61–68], that, even in the nonsymmetric case, the spectral radius does measure the rate of convergence. Although it is usually impractical actually to calculate the spectral radius, the effect of the spectral radius on the rate of convergence has important ramifications; see, for example, Sec. 9.7-5.

9.7-1   The Jacobi iteration

We write the matrix A in the form

$$A = D + L + U \tag{9.7-4}$$

where D is a diagonal matrix and L and U are, respectively, lower and upper triangular matrices with zeros on the diagonal. Then (9.6-3) may be written

$$Dx = -(L + U)x + b \tag{9.7-5}$$

which suggests the iteration

$$x_{i+1} = -D^{-1}(L + U)x_i + D^{-1}b \tag{9.7-6}$$

We assume here naturally that the diagonal of A contains no zero elements. If it does have zero terms but A is nonsingular, then by permuting rows and columns it is always possible to get a nonsingular matrix D. It is in fact desirable to have the diagonal elements as large as possible in relation to the off-diagonal elements. For suppose we set $x_1 = 0$. Then $x_2 = D^{-1}b$, and if the diagonal terms are dominant, this is already a good approximation to the solution.

The iteration (9.7-6) is known by many names, but the most usual are the *Jacobi iteration* or the method of simultaneous displacements. The latter name follows from the fact that every element of the solution vector is changed before any of the new elements are used in the iteration (cf. Sec. 9.7-2). For this method the matrix B is

$$B = -D^{-1}(L + U) \tag{9.7-7}$$

It may be quite difficult to determine whether B is such that the iteration converges. Of course, from (9.7-2) if $\|D^{-1}(L + U)\|_E < 1$, the iteration does converge.

The Jacobi method as we have presented it here is seldom used in practice for the solution of (9.6-3). This is largely because the Gauss-Seidel method to be considered below almost always converges when the Jacobi method does, may converge when the Jacobi method does not, and generally converges faster than the Jacobi method.

9.7-2 The Gauss-Seidel method

The difference between the Jacobi and Gauss-Seidel methods is that in the latter, as each component of x_{i+1} is computed, we use it immediately in the iteration. For this reason the Gauss-Seidel method is sometimes called the method of successive displacements.

Denote the jth component of x_i by $x_i^{(j)}$. Consider the system of equations written in the form (9.1-1). To compute $x_{i+1}^{(1)}$ we use the first equation in the form

$$x_{i+1}^{(1)} = -(1/a_{11}) \left[\sum_{j=2}^{n} a_{1j}x_i^{(j)} - b_1 \right] \tag{9.7-8}$$

(We assume here as before that D is nonsingular.) To get $x_{i+1}^{(2)}$ we use the second equation, but with $x_i^{(1)}$ replaced by the result of (9.7-8)

$$x_{i+1}^{(2)} = -\frac{1}{a_{22}} \left[a_{21}x_{i+1}^{(1)} + \sum_{j=3}^{n} a_{2j}x_i^{(j)} - b_2 \right] \tag{9.7-9}$$

In general

$$x_{i+1}^{(r)} = -\frac{1}{a_{rr}} \left[\sum_{j=1}^{r-1} a_{rj}x_{i+1}^{(j)} + \sum_{j=r+1}^{n} a_{rj}x_i^{(j)} - b_r \right]$$
$$r = 1, \ldots, n \tag{9.7-10}$$

With A written in the form (9.7-4), this method becomes {31}

$$\mathbf{x}_{i+1} = -D^{-1}[L\mathbf{x}_{i+1} + U\mathbf{x}_i] + D^{-1}\mathbf{b} \qquad (9.7\text{-}11)$$

which can be solved for $\mathbf{x}_{i+1}$ to give

$$\mathbf{x}_{i+1} = -(D + L)^{-1}U\mathbf{x}_i + (D + L)^{-1}\mathbf{b} \qquad (9.7\text{-}12)$$

Since $B = -(D + L)^{-1}U$, a sufficient condition for convergence is then that $\|(D + L)^{-1}U\|_E < 1$, but this is not very useful in practice (why?). In the important case, however, in which A is positive definite, we can prove that the Gauss-Seidel method converges.

Theorem 9.3   If the matrix A is positive definite, the Gauss-Seidel iteration (9.7-12) converges independently of the initial vector.

Proof   We write A as

$$A = L + D + L^T \qquad (9.7\text{-}13)$$

since A is symmetric.   The matrix B is then

$$B = -(D + L)^{-1}L^T \qquad (9.7\text{-}14)$$

Let $-\lambda$ and $\mathbf{v}$ be, respectively, an eigenvalue and eigenvector of B.   Then

$$(D + L)^{-1}L^T\mathbf{v} = \lambda\mathbf{v} \qquad (9.7\text{-}15)$$

or

$$L^T\mathbf{v} = \lambda(D + L)\mathbf{v} \qquad (9.7\text{-}16)$$

Even though A is positive definite, the eigenvalues of B may still be complex.   We have†

$$\mathbf{v}^*L^T\mathbf{v} = \mathbf{v}^*\lambda(D + L)\mathbf{v} \qquad (9.7\text{-}17)$$

Adding $\mathbf{v}^*(D + L)\mathbf{v}$ to both sides of (9.7-17) we get

$$\mathbf{v}^*A\mathbf{v} = (1 + \lambda)\mathbf{v}^*(D + L)\mathbf{v} \qquad (9.7\text{-}18)$$

Since A is real and symmetric, the conjugate transpose of the left-hand side of (9.7-18) leaves this quantity unchanged.   Therefore,

$$(1 + \bar{\lambda})\mathbf{v}^*(D + L)^T\mathbf{v} = (1 + \lambda)\mathbf{v}^*(D + L)\mathbf{v} = (1 + \lambda)(\mathbf{v}^*D\mathbf{v}$$
$$+ \mathbf{v}^*L\mathbf{v}) = (1 + \lambda)[\mathbf{v}^*D\mathbf{v} + \bar{\lambda}\mathbf{v}^*(D + L)^T\mathbf{v}] \quad (9.7\text{-}19)$$

the last line following from use of the conjugate transpose of (9.7-16). Canceling like terms in (9.7-19) and rearranging the remaining terms, we have

$$(1 - |\lambda|^2)\mathbf{v}^*(D + L)^T\mathbf{v} = (1 + \lambda)\mathbf{v}^*D\mathbf{v} \qquad (9.7\text{-}20)$$

† $\mathbf{v}^*$ denotes the conjugate transpose of $\mathbf{v}$.

Multiplying both sides of (9.7-20) by $(1 + \bar{\lambda})$ and then using the conjugate transpose of (9.7-18), we get

$$(1 - |\lambda|^2)\mathbf{v}^*A\mathbf{v} = |1 + \lambda|^2\mathbf{v}^*D\mathbf{v} \tag{9.7-21}$$

Since A is positive definite so is D; moreover, no eigenvalue $-\lambda$ of B can equal 1 (why?). Therefore, we must have $(1 - |\lambda|^2) > 0$, which means that the eigenvalues of B lie within the unit circle. This completes the proof. A partial converse of this theorem will be found in a problem {32}.

We have noted that much of the application of iterative methods such as the Jacobi and Gauss-Seidel methods is in the numerical solution of partial differential equations. The coefficient matrices that arise in the numerical solution of partial differential equations are often such that the iteration matrix B in (9.7-1) is nonnegative (i.e., all the elements of B are nonnegative). The Perron-Frobenius theory of nonnegative matrices—a subject which is beyond the scope of this book [see Varga (1962), pp. 26–33]—provides the basis for analysis of iterative methods when B is nonnegative. We content ourselves here with stating the Stein-Rosenberg theorem, which follows from the Perron-Frobenius theory. Suppose that by dividing each equation by its diagonal element we make D in (9.7-4) the identity matrix. Suppose further that $B_J = -(L + U)$ in (9.7-7) is nonnegative. Then it follows {33} that $B_G = -(I + L)^{-1}U$ in (9.7-12) is also nonnegative. Let ρ_J and ρ_G be the spectral radii, respectively, of B_J and B_G. Then this theorem states that one of the following conditions holds:

(1) $\rho_J = \rho_G = 0$
(2) $\rho_J = \rho_G = 1$
(3) $0 < \rho_G < \rho_J < 1$
(4) $1 < \rho_J < \rho_G$

Thus the Jacobi and Gauss-Seidel iterations both converge or both diverge, and when they both converge, the Gauss-Seidel method converges faster [except for the trivial case (1)]. This theorem is the basis for our previous statement that the Jacobi iteration is seldom used in preference to the Gauss-Seidel iteration.

Equation (9.6-14) implies that matrix iterative methods converge linearly. They are therefore candidates for the δ^2 process (see Sec. 8.7-1). Analogous to Eq. (8.7-4) we may write

$$x_i^{(r)} \approx x_{i+2}^{(r)} - \frac{(\Delta x_{i+1}^{(r)})^2}{\Delta^2 x_i^{(r)}} \qquad r = 1, \ldots, n \tag{9.7-22}$$

where the superscripts denote components of the relevant vectors.

Example 9.5   For the system

$$
\begin{aligned}
4x^{(1)} - \; x^{(2)} \qquad\quad &= 2 \\
-x^{(1)} + 4x^{(2)} - \; x^{(3)} &= 6 \\
- \; x^{(2)} + 4x^{(3)} &= 2
\end{aligned}
$$

do four iterations of the Jacobi and Gauss-Seidel methods and then use (9.7-22) to get an improved solution. (Although of too low an order to arise in a practical problem the form of the coefficient matrix is typical of those which arise in the numerical solution of partial differential equations.) Use $x_1 = 0$ for both methods.

For the Jacobi iteration

$$
\begin{aligned}
B &= -D^{-1}(L + U) \\
&= -\begin{bmatrix} \tfrac14 & 0 & 0 \\ 0 & \tfrac14 & 0 \\ 0 & 0 & \tfrac14 \end{bmatrix}\begin{bmatrix} 0 & -1 & 0 \\ -1 & 0 & -1 \\ 0 & -1 & 0 \end{bmatrix} = \begin{bmatrix} 0 & \tfrac14 & 0 \\ \tfrac14 & 0 & \tfrac14 \\ 0 & \tfrac14 & 0 \end{bmatrix}
\end{aligned}
$$

From (9.7-6) we calculate

$$
\begin{aligned}
\mathbf{x}_2^T &= (\tfrac12, \tfrac32, \tfrac12) \\
\mathbf{x}_3^T &= (\tfrac78, \tfrac74, \tfrac78) \\
\mathbf{x}_4^T &= (\tfrac{15}{16}, \tfrac{31}{16}, \tfrac{15}{16}) \\
\mathbf{x}_5^T &= (\tfrac{63}{64}, \tfrac{63}{32}, \tfrac{63}{64})
\end{aligned}
$$

For the Gauss-Seidel iteration, using (9.7-10) we calculate

$$
\begin{aligned}
\mathbf{x}_2^T &= (\tfrac12, \tfrac{13}{8}, \tfrac{29}{32}) \\
\mathbf{x}_3^T &= (\tfrac{29}{32}, \tfrac{125}{64}, \tfrac{253}{256}) \\
\mathbf{x}_4^T &= (\tfrac{253}{256}, \tfrac{1021}{512}, \tfrac{2045}{2048}) \\
\mathbf{x}_5^T &= (\tfrac{2045}{2048}, \tfrac{8189}{4096}, \tfrac{16381}{16384})
\end{aligned}
$$

and, since the true solution is $\mathbf{x}_t^T = (1,2,1)$, it is clear that both iterations are converging and that the Gauss-Seidel is converging more rapidly. Calculation of the spectral radii of the B matrices for the two iterations would indicate just how fast each is converging {34}.

If we apply (9.7-22) with $i = 2$ to the Gauss-Seidel results, we have

$$
\begin{aligned}
\Delta x_3^{(1)} &= \tfrac{21}{256} & \Delta^2 x_2^{(1)} &= -\tfrac{85}{256} \\
\Delta x_3^{(2)} &= \tfrac{21}{512} & \Delta^2 x_2^{(2)} &= -\tfrac{147}{512} \\
\Delta x_3^{(3)} &= \tfrac{21}{2048} & \Delta^2 x_2^{(3)} &= -\tfrac{147}{2048}
\end{aligned}
$$

which gives as the new approximation

$$(\tfrac{335}{332}, 2, 1)$$

which is an improved result in all components and a perfect result in two of them. However, it is important that the δ^2 process not be used too early in the computation in which case it may give poorer results than the last iteration {34}.

9.7-3   Roundoff error in iterative methods

The roundoff error incurred in an iterative method is only that which is incurred in the last iteration. This is because we always use the original coefficient matrix and, so to speak, start from scratch at each iteration using the last iterate as the initial vector. It is perhaps natural to expect then that roundoff error is a much less severe problem in iterative methods than it is in direct methods.   However, not only can roundoff be a serious source of error in iterative methods, but also it may be very nearly as serious as in direct methods.   In this section we shall consider roundoff error in the Gauss-Seidel iteration.   In analogy with the error analysis of Sec. 9.4, we ask the question: What are the perturbations of the matrix A and vector $\mathbf{b}$ such that, starting from $\mathbf{x}_i$ as computed, the result of using these perturbations in (9.7-12) would have been the computed value $\mathbf{x}_{i+1}$ if no roundoff error were incurred?

In the calculation of $x_{i+1}^{(r)}$ using (9.7-10), we assume that scalar products are computed using double-precision arithmetic and that a double-length dividend is used.   Moreover, we assume that before dividing we scale the numerator by 10^{-k} where the maximum component of $\mathbf{x}_t$ is assumed to lie between 10^k and 10^{k-1} in magnitude.   Then the actual calculation equation corresponding to (9.7-10) is

$$x_{i+1}^{(r)} = -\frac{1}{a_{rr}} \left[\sum_{j=1}^{r-1} a_{rj} x_{i+1}^{(j)} + \sum_{j=r+1}^{n} a_{rj} x_i^{(j)} - b_r \right] + \eta_r \tag{9.7-23}$$

where

$$|\eta_r| \leqq \tfrac{1}{2} \times 10^{k-d} \tag{9.7-24}$$

Multiplying through by a_{rr} we have

$$a_{rr} x_{i+1}^{(r)} = - \left[\sum_{j=1}^{r-1} a_{rj} x_{i+1}^{(j)} + \sum_{j=r+1}^{n} a_{rj} x_i^{(j)} \right] + b_r + \delta b_r \tag{9.7-25}$$

where

$$|\delta b_r| = |a_{rr}|\, |\eta_r| \leqq \tfrac{1}{2} \times 10^{k-d} \tag{9.7-26}$$

since as before we assume $a_{rr} < 1$.   In matrix terms we have

$$D\mathbf{x}_{i+1} = -L\mathbf{x}_{i+1} - U\mathbf{x}_i + \mathbf{b} + \delta\mathbf{b} \tag{9.7-27}$$

with $\delta\mathbf{b}$ the vector of the δb_r's.   Thus at any stage of the iteration we may consider the computed vector $\mathbf{x}_{i+1}$ to be the result of using the true matrix A and a perturbed right-hand side $\mathbf{b} + \delta\mathbf{b}$ with the elements of $\delta\mathbf{b}$ bounded as in (9.7-26).   In the case of the direct method, the dominant term in the error was $\Delta\mathbf{s}$ in (9.4-41) whose elements were bounded as in (9.4-42). The difference in the two bounds (9.4-42) and (9.7-26) is just the factor i in (9.4-42).   Our conclusion, then, is that, while roundoff is generally less serious in the Gauss-Seidel iteration (and for iterative methods in general) than it is for direct methods, it can be a serious problem when the system is ill-conditioned.   In {35} a simple example illustrating this is considered.

9.7-4   Relaxation

The Gauss-Seidel method is an example of a class of methods known as *relaxation* methods.   Relaxation methods are, for reasons that will appear, quite convenient for hand computation.   The basis of all relaxation methods is to take the residual vector

$$\mathbf{r} = \mathbf{b} - A\mathbf{x} \tag{9.7-28}$$

and to modify (or *relax*) one or more components of the approximate solution $\mathbf{x}$ in order to reduce to zero one or more components of $\mathbf{r}$.   In the Gauss-Seidel method at each stage we modify $x^{(j)}$ in order to reduce $r^{(j)}$ to zero.

Methods of this type are convenient for hand computation because they enable the computor to, for example, reduce the largest component of $\mathbf{r}$ to zero at every stage and, moreover, to do this by making the least possible change in $\mathbf{x}$.   Such an algorithm for hand computation might go as follows:

1. Choose an initial vector $\mathbf{x}_1$.
2. Calculate $\mathbf{r}_1 = \mathbf{b} - A\mathbf{x}_1$.
3. Choose the largest component in magnitude of $\mathbf{r}_1$, say $r_1^{(L)}$, and that value in the Lth row of A which is largest in magnitude, say a_{LJ}.
4. Let $\mathbf{x}_2$ have all its components the same as $\mathbf{x}_1$ except for $x_2^{(J)}$ which is given by

$$x_2^{(J)} = x_1^{(J)} + r_1^{(L)}/a_{LJ} \tag{9.7-29}$$

   (By choosing J as in step 3 we assure the smallest possible change in a component.)
5. Repeat steps 2 to 4 for as long as is desired.

Note that, after the first iteration, step 2 requires only the calculation

$$\mathbf{r}_2 = \mathbf{r}_1 + [x_1^{(J)} - x_2^{(J)}]A_L = \mathbf{r}_1 - [r_1^{(L)}/a_{LJ}]A_L \tag{9.7-30}$$

where A_L is the Lth column of A.   Also, if the equations can be rearranged so that the largest element in each row is on the diagonal, then, to change the Lth component of $\mathbf{r}$ to zero, we modify the Lth component of the solution vector.

Example 9.6   Use the above technique to solve the system of Example 9.5. With $\mathbf{x}_1 = 0$ we have $\mathbf{r}_1^T = (2,6,2)$.   To set $r_1^{(2)} = 0$, we use (9.7-29) to calculate

$$x_2^{(2)} = 0 + \tfrac{6}{4} = \tfrac{3}{2}$$

Then from (9.7-30)

$$
\mathbf{r}_2 = \begin{bmatrix} 2 \\ 6 \\ 2 \end{bmatrix} - \frac{3}{2} \begin{bmatrix} -1 \\ 4 \\ -1 \end{bmatrix} = \begin{bmatrix} \frac{7}{2} \\ 0 \\ \frac{7}{2} \end{bmatrix}
$$

Next we set $r_2^{(1)} = 0$ by letting $x_3^{(1)} = \frac{7}{8}$, from which $\mathbf{r}_3^T = (0, \frac{7}{8}, \frac{7}{2})$. Then setting the third component equal to $\frac{7}{8}$ we get $\mathbf{r}_4^T = (0, \frac{7}{4}, 0)$ with the approximate solution now $(\frac{7}{8}, \frac{3}{2}, \frac{7}{8})$. These three steps are an equivalent amount of computation to one Jacobi or Gauss-Seidel iteration. This approximation is about as good as the first Gauss-Seidel iteration in Example 9.5 if we use $\|\mathbf{r}\|$ as a criterion {36}.

An important advantage of the relaxation procedure for hand computation is that the (human) computor may vary the algorithm whenever he thinks some other action (e.g., changing a component of $\mathbf{x}$ other than that indicated above or making some component of $\mathbf{r}$ other than the largest zero) might be more desirable. Further, since a component of the residual which is made zero at one stage generally becomes nonzero at the next stage, it is not necessary to carry more than a few decimals early in the computation. Later, when the process is converging, more and more decimals may be carried.

The algorithm outlined above is not very satisfactory on a computer because of the need to search the components of $\mathbf{r}$ at each stage to find the largest. While this is trivial for the human computor, it is time-consuming on a digital computer. Thus methods such as the Gauss-Seidel iteration are better on a computer.

The algorithm presented in this section is not a stationary iterative process (why?) but is still a linear iterative process (why?), and so the results of Sec. 9.6 are applicable.

Important variations of the iterative procedures we have considered thus far are found in so-called "block" or "group" iterations in which not one component of $\mathbf{r}$ but rather a group of components are reduced to zero at each step. If k components of $\mathbf{r}$ are reduced to zero at each step, then k simultaneous linear equations must be solved at each step {37}. Although at first glance this might not appear to be a very profitable procedure, for certain types of sparse matrices it can be a very useful procedure {37}, but a discussion of this topic is beyond the scope of this book [see Varga (1962), pp. 79-80].

9.7-5 Acceleration of stationary iterative processes

Since the rate of convergence of a stationary iterative process depends on the spectral radius of B, any modification of the matrix B that will reduce the spectral radius will increase the rate of convergence. We consider briefly here a method of accelerating the convergence of an iterative process called the method of *successive overrelaxation*.   First we rearrange the system (9.6-3) so that each diagonal element of A is 1.   This can be done by arranging the system so that no diagonal term is zero and then dividing each equation by its diagonal element.   For positive definite matrices, we preserve symmetry by pre- and postmultiplying A by $D^{-\frac{1}{2}}$.   Having done this, Eq. (9.7-10) for the Gauss-Seidel iteration becomes

$$
\begin{aligned}
x_{i+1}^{(r)} &= -\sum_{j=1}^{r-1} a_{rj}x_{i+1}^{(j)} - \sum_{j=r+1}^{n} a_{rj}x_i^{(j)} + b_r \\
&= x_i^{(r)} - \sum_{j=1}^{r-1} a_{rj}x_{i+1}^{(j)} - \sum_{j=r}^{n} a_{rj}x_i^{(j)} + b_r
\end{aligned}
\tag{9.7-31}
$$

since $a_{rr} = 1$.   Consider replacing (9.7-31) by

$$
x_{i+1}^{(r)} = x_i^{(r)} - \omega \left[\sum_{j=1}^{r-1} a_{rj}x_{i+1}^{(j)} + \sum_{j=r}^{n} a_{rj}x_i^{(j)} - b_r \right]
\tag{9.7-32}
$$

where ω is the overrelaxation factor.   Using (9.7-32) we may write this iteration in matrix form as {38}

$$
\mathbf{x}_{i+1} = B_\omega \mathbf{x}_i + C_\omega \mathbf{b}
\tag{9.7-33}
$$

where

$$
B_\omega = (I + \omega L)^{-1}[(1 - \omega)I - \omega U] \qquad C_\omega = \omega(I + \omega L)^{-1}
\tag{9.7-34}
$$

with L and U as in (9.7-4).   The crux of the matter now, of course, is to choose ω so as to minimize $\rho(B_\omega)$.   The reader will probably not be surprised to find that this is a problem of some difficulty.   It is in fact the subject of a large literature.   We content ourselves here with stating that for a large class of matrices that arise in the numerical solution of partial differential equations, there is a simple relationship between the optimum value of ω and $\rho(L + U)$.   This does not get rid of the problem, but finding the eigenvalues or, at least, estimates of the eigenvalues of $L + U$ may be reasonably simple.   Moreover, the insight gained from the relationship between ω and $\rho(L + U)$ is useful, for example, in indicating that it is preferable to overestimate ω than underestimate it.

Successive overrelaxation is only one of a large class of methods that have been developed to accelerate the convergence of iterative processes. Some of these accelerations lead to nonstationary iterations; for example,

$$
\mathbf{x}_{i+1} = [(1 + \omega_i)B - \omega_i I]\mathbf{x}_i + (1 + \omega_i)C\mathbf{b}
\tag{9.7-35}
$$

where the relaxation factor ω_i changes from step to step.   The proper use of such acceleration procedures lies at the heart of much of the utilization of high-speed computing equipment for the solution of partial differential equations.

9.8   ITERATIVE METHODS BASED ON THE MINIMIZATION OF A QUADRATIC FORM

In this section we shall formulate some iterative methods in terms of minimizing a quadratic form whose unique minimum is the solution of $A\mathbf{x} = \mathbf{b}$. The Gauss-Seidel method can in fact be formulated in these terms {42}. If the matrix A is not symmetric and positive definite, it is appropriate to consider the form

$$R = \mathbf{r}^T\mathbf{r} = (\mathbf{b} - A\mathbf{x})^T(\mathbf{b} - A\mathbf{x}) \tag{9.8-1}$$

This quadratic form is positive definite and has a unique minimum when $\mathbf{x}$ is the solution of the linear system (9.6-3) {43}. But methods to minimize (9.8-1) typically require a formidable amount of computation {46}. Therefore, what application the methods of this section do find is generally restricted to positive definite matrices. In the remainder of this section we assume that A is symmetric and positive definite.

When A is positive definite we may use the form

$$Q = \tfrac{1}{2}\mathbf{x}^T A\mathbf{x} - \mathbf{x}^T\mathbf{b} \tag{9.8-2}$$

This form also has a unique minimum at the solution of (9.6-3). For consider

$$
\begin{aligned}
Q(\mathbf{x} + \Delta\mathbf{x}) - Q(\mathbf{x}) &= \tfrac{1}{2}(\mathbf{x} + \Delta\mathbf{x})^T A(\mathbf{x} + \Delta\mathbf{x}) - (\mathbf{x} + \Delta\mathbf{x})^T\mathbf{b} \\
&\qquad - \tfrac{1}{2}\mathbf{x}^T A\mathbf{x} + \mathbf{x}^T\mathbf{b} \\
&= \Delta\mathbf{x}^T A\mathbf{x} - \Delta\mathbf{x}^T\mathbf{b} + \tfrac{1}{2}\Delta\mathbf{x}^T A\,\Delta\mathbf{x} \\
&= \tfrac{1}{2}\Delta\mathbf{x}^T A\,\Delta\mathbf{x}
\end{aligned}
\tag{9.8-3}
$$

if $\mathbf{x}$ is the solution of (9.6-3). Since the final right-hand side is positive for any nonzero $\Delta\mathbf{x}$, we have a minimum at $\mathbf{x}$. Again we leave the proof of the uniqueness of this minimum to a problem {43}. Our approach in this section will be to seek a sequence of vectors $\{\mathbf{x}_i\}$ such that an x_{i+1} can always be found for which $Q(\mathbf{x}_{i+1}) < Q(\mathbf{x}_i)$ if $Q(\mathbf{x}_i) \neq 0$ for, since the minimum of Q is unique, such a sequence must lead to the solution of (9.6-3) (why?).

9.8-1   Geometrical considerations

Let $\mathbf{x}_t = [x_t^{(1)}, \ldots, x_t^{(n)}]$ be the true solution of $A\mathbf{x} = \mathbf{b}$ and let

$$\mathbf{x} = \mathbf{x}_t + \boldsymbol{\epsilon} \qquad \boldsymbol{\epsilon} = (\epsilon_1, \ldots, \epsilon_n) \tag{9.8-4}$$

For this $\mathbf{x}$

$$Q = \tfrac{1}{2}(\mathbf{x}_t + \boldsymbol{\epsilon})^T A(\mathbf{x}_t + \boldsymbol{\epsilon}) - (\mathbf{x}_t + \boldsymbol{\epsilon})^T\mathbf{b} = \tfrac{1}{2}\boldsymbol{\epsilon}^T A\boldsymbol{\epsilon} - \tfrac{1}{2}\mathbf{x}_t^T\mathbf{b} \tag{9.8-5}$$

so that

$$Q + \frac{1}{2}\mathbf{x}_t^T\mathbf{b} = \frac{1}{2}\boldsymbol{\epsilon}^T A\boldsymbol{\epsilon} = \frac{1}{2}\sum_{i=1}^{n}\sum_{j=1}^{n}a_{ij}\epsilon_i\epsilon_j \tag{9.8-6}$$

The surface

$$S = Q + \tfrac{1}{2}\mathbf{x}_t^T\mathbf{b} = \text{const} \tag{9.8-7}$$

is therefore a hyperellipsoid in the variables $\epsilon_1', \ldots, \epsilon_n$ with center at $\boldsymbol{\epsilon} = 0$ (i.e., at the solution of $A\mathbf{x} = \mathbf{b}$ in the $x_1, \ldots, x_n$ coordinate system). Now, because A is symmetric, there exists an orthogonal matrix P such that

$$P^T A P = D \tag{9.8-8}$$

where D is a diagonal matrix with the eigenvalues of A on the diagonal (see Sec. 10.1-4). Therefore, if we make the change of variable

$$\boldsymbol{\xi} = P^T\boldsymbol{\epsilon} \qquad \boldsymbol{\xi}^T = (\xi_1, \ldots, \xi_n) \tag{9.8-9}$$

then

$$\frac{1}{2}\sum_{i=1}^{n}\sum_{j=1}^{n}a_{ij}\epsilon_i\epsilon_j = \frac{1}{2}\sum_{i=1}^{n}\lambda_i\xi_i^2 \tag{9.8-10}$$

where the λ_i's are the eigenvalues of A.

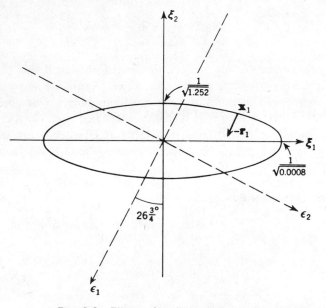

Fig. 9.3   Ellipse for the value $c = .50$.

From (9.8-10) it follows that the hyperellipsoid (9.8-7) has axes in the directions ξ_i of lengths proportional to $1/\sqrt{\lambda_i}$, $i = 1, \ldots, n$. Using (9.5-4) we have as a geometrical interpretation of the condition of a matrix that the better a matrix is conditioned the more nearly the hyperellipsoid will approach a hypersphere. Conversely, the more ill-conditioned a matrix, the more "elongated" the hyperellipsoid will be.

Example 9.7   Calculate the ellipse (9.8-7) for the system

$$x^{(1)} + .5x^{(2)} = 1.5$$
$$.5x^{(1)} + .26x^{(2)} = .76$$

for which the true solution is $x^{(1)} = 1$, $x^{(2)} = 1$.

The eigenvalues of the coefficient matrix are given by

$$\tfrac{1}{2}(1.26 \pm \sqrt{1.5476}) \approx 1.252, .008$$

so that the system is quite ill-conditioned. The equation of the ellipse is

$$\tfrac{1}{2}(.008\xi_1^2 + 1.252\xi_2^2) = c$$

In Fig. 9.3 this ellipse is plotted for $c = .50$ with the scale of ξ_2 expanded in relation to that of ξ_1. Therefore, the true ellipse is even more elongated than shown. The change of variable (9.8-9) is equivalent to a rotation of axes through an angle of $\tfrac{1}{2} \cot^{-1} .74 \approx 116\tfrac{3}{4}°$.

Our general technique in attempting to minimize Q will be to choose an initial vector $\mathbf{x}_1$ and then to choose a *direction* $\mathbf{v}_1$ and a *distance* α_1 in the direction $\mathbf{v}_1$ to get $\mathbf{x}_2$. In general

$$\mathbf{x}_{i+1} = \mathbf{x}_i + \alpha_i\mathbf{v}_i \qquad i = 1, 2, \ldots \tag{9.8-11}$$

An infinite number of procedures of the type (9.8-11) are possible. In the next two sections, we shall consider two techniques of choosing the distance and direction at each stage.

9.8-2   The method of steepest descent

The basis of this method is the natural idea of choosing $\mathbf{v}_i$ to be in the direction of the greatest rate of change of Q, namely, the direction of the gradient and, also naturally, to choose α_i so that Q is minimized. From (9.8-2) the gradient of Q when $\mathbf{x} = \mathbf{x}_i$ is

$$\nabla Q = A\mathbf{x}_i - \mathbf{b} = -\mathbf{r}_i \tag{9.8-12}$$

so that $\mathbf{v}_i = -\mathbf{r}_i$. Now to find α_i we calculate

$$Q(\mathbf{x}_i - \alpha_i\mathbf{r}_i) = -\tfrac{1}{2}\mathbf{x}_i^T\mathbf{r}_i + \alpha_i\mathbf{r}_i^T\mathbf{r}_i + \tfrac{1}{2}\alpha_i^2\mathbf{r}_i^T A\mathbf{r}_i - \tfrac{1}{2}\mathbf{x}_i^T\mathbf{b} \tag{9.8-13}$$

Thus

$$\partial Q/\partial\alpha_i = \mathbf{r}_i^T\mathbf{r}_i + \alpha_i\mathbf{r}_i^T A\mathbf{r}_i \tag{9.8-14}$$

Setting $\partial Q/\partial\alpha_i$ equal to zero we get

$$\alpha_i = -\mathbf{r}_i^T\mathbf{r}_i/\mathbf{r}_i^TA\mathbf{r}_i \tag{9.8-15}$$

The steepest-descent algorithm then is

$$\mathbf{x}_{i+1} = \mathbf{x}_i + (\mathbf{r}_i^T\mathbf{r}_i/\mathbf{r}_i^TA\mathbf{r}_i)\mathbf{r}_i \tag{9.8-16}$$

It is easily proved that $Q(\mathbf{x}_{i+1}) < Q(\mathbf{x}_i)$ {49} so that the convergence is assured. For ill-conditioned systems, however, the convergence may be very slow {47}. This may be seen by noting that $\nabla Q = \nabla S$ since $\mathbf{x}_t$ is a constant. Therefore, when a system is ill-conditioned so that the hyperellipsoid (9.8-7) is elongated, the gradient will point in a direction very different from the direction of the center of the hyperellipsoid. This is illustrated in Fig. 9.3 for the case $n = 2$. The point labeled $\mathbf{x}_1$ is actually the position of the initial error vector in the coordinate system shown.

Example 9.8   Find an approximate solution of the system of Example 9.5 using the method of steepest descent with $\mathbf{x}_1 = 0$.

We have $\mathbf{r}_1^T = (2,6,2)$. Therefore, from (9.8-16) we may calculate

$$\mathbf{x}_2 = \begin{pmatrix} 0 \\ 0 \\ 0 \end{pmatrix} + \frac{11}{32}\begin{pmatrix} 2 \\ 6 \\ 2 \end{pmatrix} = \frac{1}{16}\begin{pmatrix} 11 \\ 33 \\ 11 \end{pmatrix}$$

Then $\mathbf{r}_2^T = \frac{1}{16}(21,-14,21)$ and

$$\mathbf{x}_3 = \frac{1}{16}\begin{pmatrix} 11 \\ 33 \\ 11 \end{pmatrix} + \frac{11}{56\times 16}\begin{pmatrix} 21 \\ -14 \\ 21 \end{pmatrix} = \frac{1}{128}\begin{pmatrix} 121 \\ 242 \\ 121 \end{pmatrix}$$

From this we get $\mathbf{r}_3^T = \frac{1}{64}(7,21,7)$ and

$$\mathbf{x}_4 = \frac{1}{128}\begin{pmatrix} 121 \\ 242 \\ 121 \end{pmatrix} + \frac{11}{32\times 64}\begin{pmatrix} 7 \\ 21 \\ 7 \end{pmatrix} = \frac{1}{2048}\begin{pmatrix} 2013 \\ 4103 \\ 2013 \end{pmatrix}$$

9.8-3   The conjugate gradient method

Proceeding in the direction of the gradient of Q seems a very logical thing to do, but as we shall see in this section, if we choose our direction more carefully we can theoretically guarantee convergence in a *finite* number of steps. In practice roundoff prevents us from achieving this theoretical convergence.

Let $\mathbf{v}_1, \ldots, \mathbf{v}_n$ be a basis for Euclidean n space and, as before, let $\mathbf{x}_t$ be the true solution of (9.6-3). Then, if $\mathbf{x}_1$ is our initial approximation to the solution, we may write

$$\mathbf{x}_t - \mathbf{x}_1 = \sum_{j=1}^{n} \alpha_j\mathbf{v}_j \tag{9.8-17}$$

If, for example, the $\mathbf{v}_j$'s are orthogonal then

$$\alpha_j = \frac{\mathbf{v}_j^T(\mathbf{x}_t - \mathbf{x}_1)}{\mathbf{v}_j^T\mathbf{v}_j} \qquad j = 1, \ldots, n \tag{9.8-18}$$

but this is of little help since it is $\mathbf{x}_t$ for which we are looking. On the other hand, suppose that

$$\mathbf{v}_j^T A \mathbf{v}_i = 0 \qquad i \neq j \tag{9.8-19}$$

In this case the $\mathbf{v}_j$'s are called A-orthogonal or A-conjugate. Then

$$\alpha_j = \frac{\mathbf{v}_j^T A(\mathbf{x}_t - \mathbf{x}_1)}{\mathbf{v}_j^T A \mathbf{v}_j} = \frac{\mathbf{v}_j^T \mathbf{r}_1}{\mathbf{v}_j^T A \mathbf{v}_j} \qquad j = 1, \ldots, n \tag{9.8-20}$$

from which the α_j's are easily calculable. (Note that $\mathbf{v}_j^T A \mathbf{v}_j \neq 0$ if A is positive definite.) The basic idea of the *conjugate gradient method* is to generate a sequence $\{\mathbf{v}_j\}$ of A-orthogonal vectors, calculate the α_j's as in (9.8-20), and thus get $\mathbf{x}_t$.

In order to generate an A-orthogonal set of vectors, we assume that we have some set of vectors $\mathbf{u}_1, \ldots, \mathbf{u}_n$ which are a basis. Then we use the Gram-Schmidt orthogonalization procedure to calculate

$$\begin{aligned}\mathbf{v}_1 &= \mathbf{u}_1 \\ \mathbf{v}_{i+1} &= \mathbf{u}_{i+1} + \sum_{k=1}^{i} \beta_{i+1,k}\mathbf{v}_k \qquad i = 1, \ldots, n-1 \end{aligned} \tag{9.8-21}$$

where

$$\beta_{i+1,k} = -(\mathbf{v}_k^T A \mathbf{u}_{i+1}/\mathbf{v}_k^T A \mathbf{v}_k) \tag{9.8-22}$$

Since the $\mathbf{u}_i$'s are linearly independent so are the $\mathbf{v}_i$'s (why?). It remains then to choose the sequence $\{\mathbf{u}_j\}$. One possibility would be to use the n coordinate vectors. If we do so the resulting procedure can be shown to be functionally equivalent to Gaussian elimination $\{50\}$. A choice leading to a more convenient algorithm, however, is the following. We define

$$\mathbf{x}_i = \mathbf{x}_1 + \sum_{j=1}^{i-1} \alpha_j\mathbf{v}_j \qquad i = 1, \ldots, n \tag{9.8-23}$$

with the α_j's given by (9.8-20). Thus,

$$\mathbf{x}_{i+1} = \mathbf{x}_i + \alpha_i\mathbf{v}_i \qquad i = 1, \ldots, n \tag{9.8-24}$$

in accordance with (9.8-11). The ith residual is given by

$$\mathbf{r}_i = \mathbf{b} - A\mathbf{x}_i \qquad i = 1, \ldots, n \tag{9.8-25}$$

The basis of the conjugate gradient method is to choose $\mathbf{u}_i = \mathbf{r}_i$, $i = 1$, $\ldots, n$. We leave to a problem $\{52\}$ the proof of the fact that either the sequence $\{r_i\}$ terminates (i.e., some $r_i = 0$) before $i = n + 1$, in which case we have a solution, or the sequence forms an orthogonal basis for n space. We also leave to a problem $\{54\}$ the proof that $Q(x_{i+1}) < Q(x_i)$. A priori we do not know the sequence $\{r_i\}$, but as we shall now indicate, we can determine the v_i's and r_i's by an interlocking iterative process.

From the initial approximation we have

$$r_1 = b - Ax_1 \tag{9.8-26}$$

From (9.8-21)

$$v_1 = r_1 \tag{9.8-27}$$

Then from (9.8-20) and (9.8-24)

$$\alpha_1 = v_1^T r_1 / v_1^T A v_1 \tag{9.8-28}$$

and

$$x_2 = x_1 + \alpha_1 v_1 \tag{9.8-29}$$

Then

$$r_2 = b - Ax_2 = r_1 - \alpha_1 A v_1 \tag{9.8-30}$$

and

$$v_2 = r_2 + \beta_{21} v_1 \tag{9.8-31}$$

where

$$\beta_{21} = -v_1^T A r_2 / v_1^T A v_1 \tag{9.8-32}$$

The equations of the general algorithm are

$$\left.\begin{aligned}
\alpha_i &= v_i^T r_i / v_i^T A v_i \\
x_{i+1} &= x_i + \alpha_i v_i \\
r_{i+1} &= r_i - \alpha_i A v_i \\
\beta_i &= -v_i^T A r_{i+1} / v_i^T A v_i \\
v_{i+1} &= r_{i+1} + \beta_i v_i
\end{aligned}\right\} \quad \begin{aligned} i &= 1, \ldots, n \\ v_1 &= r_1 = b - Ax_1 \end{aligned} \tag{9.8-33}$$

Note that α_i as given above differs from α_i as given by (9.8-20). However, using the A orthogonality of the v_i's the two forms can be shown to be identical $\{51\}$. Also v_{i+1} in (9.8-33) involves only a single β_i in contrast to (9.8-21). But, again using the A orthogonality of the v_i's, it can be shown that all the other β_{ik}'s vanish $\{52\}$. From (9.8-17) and (9.8-33) it follows that

$$x_{n+1} = x_t \tag{9.8-34}$$

The conjugate gradient method is therefore not an infinite but a finite (i.e., n-step) iterative method. In this sense it is directly analogous to direct methods, a statement which is borne out by the above-mentioned connection between Gaussian elimination and the conjugate gradient method.   Using (9.8-33) it is not hard to show {55} that each iteration requires $n^2 + O(n)$ multiplications and divisions so that the solution requires $n^3 + O(n^2)$ operations, which compares unfavorably with the result for Gaussian elimination.   For sparse matrices the number of operations can be reduced considerably because the original matrix A is used at each stage.   However, for such matrices the methods of Sec. 9.7 are more easily organized for a digital computer.

In actual computation using the conjugate gradient method n iterations do not lead to the *exact* solution because of accumulated roundoff. A useful feature of the method is that, if the iteration (9.8-33) is carried on for values of $i > n$, then

$$\|\epsilon_{i+1}\| < \|\epsilon_i\| \qquad \text{for all } i \text{ where } \epsilon_i = \mathbf{x}_t - \mathbf{x}_i \tag{9.8-35}$$

until the roundoff *at each iteration* prevents further improvement {56}.

Example 9.9   Use the conjugate gradient method to find the solution of the system of Example 9.5.

Again we choose $\mathbf{x}_1 = 0$ so that

$$\mathbf{r}_1^T = (2,6,2) = \mathbf{v}_1^T$$

Then using (9.8-33) we calculate

$$
\begin{aligned}
&\alpha_1 = {}^{11}\!/_{32} & &\mathbf{x}_2^T = {}^{11}\!/_{16}(1,3,1) & &\mathbf{r}_2^T = {}^{7}\!/_{16}(3,-2,3) \\
&\beta_1 = {}^{49}\!/_{512} & &\mathbf{v}_2^T = {}^{77}\!/_{256}(5,-1,5) & & \\
&\alpha_2 = {}^{16}\!/_{77} & &\mathbf{x}_3^T = (1,2,1) & &
\end{aligned}
$$

Therefore, although (9.8-34) would lead us to expect that the true solution would be given by $\mathbf{x}_4$, $\mathbf{x}_3$ is in fact the true solution.   This example then illustrates one other advantage of the conjugate gradient method, namely, that it may converge or very nearly converge to the true solution in less than n iterations, thereby reducing the total computation.

Despite the elegance of the methods of this section and the advantages we noted above for the conjugate gradient method, these methods are seldom used on digital computers for the solution of simultaneous linear equations.   The main reason for this was noted above, namely, that direct methods require less computation while for large, sparse matrices, the methods of the previous section are more easily applied on digital computers.

9.9 MATRIX INVERSION

The solution of simultaneous linear equations can certainly be accomplished by inverting the matrix A.   In fact, if the system (9.1-1) is to be solved for many different right-hand sides, it may be most efficient to first invert A and then calculate $A^{-1}\mathbf{b}$ for each right-hand side. One very efficient way to invert A in general is a simple extension of the algorithm of Sec. 9.3-3. It will be discussed below. We shall also consider briefly matrix inversion by partitioning, which may be necessary if the order of A is very large.

9.9-1   Inversion by triangular decomposition

We suppose that the matrix A which we wish to invert has been decomposed into a product LU by the techniques of Sec. 9.3-3 where L has the form (9.3-32) and U the form

$$
U = \begin{bmatrix}
u_{11} & \cdots\cdots & u_{1n} \\
0 & u_{22} & & \cdot \\
\cdot & \cdot & \cdot & \cdot \\
\cdot & & \cdot & \cdot \\
\cdot & & & \cdot \\
0 & \cdots\cdots & 0 & u_{nn}
\end{bmatrix}
\tag{9.9-1}
$$

Then since

$$
A^{-1} = U^{-1}L^{-1}
\tag{9.9-2}
$$

our problem is to invert the triangular matrices L and U. We leave to a problem {9} the derivation of the result that the inverse of a lower (upper) triangular matrix is lower (upper) triangular.

Let $L^{-1} = [r_{ij}]$ with $r_{ij} = 0$, $i < j$ and let L_i and L_j^{-1} be, respectively, the ith column of L and the jth row of L^{-1}. Then for $1 \leqq k \leqq n$

$$
\begin{aligned}
L_k^{-1}L_k &= 1 = r_{kk} \\
L_k^{-1}L_j &= 0 = \sum_{i=j}^{k} r_{ki}l_{ij} \qquad j = k-1, \ldots, 1
\end{aligned}
\tag{9.9-3}
$$

from which we may calculate r_{ki}, $i = k, k-1, \ldots, 1$ for any k, thereby obtaining all the elements of L^{-1}.

Similarly we may calculate U^{-1}, the only difference being the fact that the diagonal elements of U are not 1's {59}. The calculation of L^{-1} and U^{-1} followed by the matrix multiplication $U^{-1}L^{-1}$ requires $\frac{2}{3}n^3 + O(n^2)$ multiplications and divisions {59} so that $n^3 + O(n^2)$ are required for the complete inversion. Some variants of the procedure of this section and other methods of matrix inversion are considered in the problems {60 to 66}.

9.9-2 Inversion by partitioning

We write

$$A = \begin{bmatrix} P & Q \\ R & S \end{bmatrix} \tag{9.9-4}$$

where P and S are square matrices of order p and s, respectively, and Q is $p \times s$ and R is $s \times p$. Similarly we write

$$A^{-1} = \begin{bmatrix} K & L \\ M & N \end{bmatrix} \tag{9.9-5}$$

with K, L, M, and N the same size as, respectively, P, Q, R, and S. Since $AA^{-1} = I$ we may write

$$\begin{aligned} PK + QM &= I_{pp} \\ PL + QN &= O_{ps} \\ RK + SM &= O_{sp} \\ RL + SN &= I_{qq} \end{aligned} \tag{9.9-6}$$

where the subscripts denote the orders of the identity and zero matrices. Eliminating M between the first and third equations of (9.9-6) we get

$$(P - QS^{-1}R)K = I_{pp} \tag{9.9-7}$$

from which

$$K = (P - QS^{-1}R)^{-1} \tag{9.9-8}$$

and

$$M = -S^{-1}RK \tag{9.9-9}$$

Similarly we calculate

$$N = (S - RP^{-1}Q)^{-1} \tag{9.9-10}$$
$$L = -P^{-1}QN \tag{9.9-11}$$

We assume, of course, in the above that all the matrices requiring inversion are nonsingular.

Equations (9.9-8) to (9.9-11) require the inversion of four matrices—P, S, $(P - QS^{-1}R)$, and $(S - RP^{-1}Q)$—to obtain A^{-1}. By manipulating these equations, however, we may write in place of (9.9-8) and (9.9-9) {67}

$$M = -NRP^{-1} \tag{9.9-12}$$
$$K = P^{-1} - P^{-1}QM \tag{9.9-13}$$

so that (9.9-10) to (9.9-13) require the inversion of only P and $(S - RP^{-1}Q)$. Computationally we would first invert P, invert $(S - RP^{-1}Q)$

to obtain N, and then calculate L, M, and K.   The largest matrix required in the computer memory at any time is the size of the largest of P, Q, R, and S.   Generally there will be some flexibility in choosing P, Q, R, and S, and when this is so, they should be chosen so that the matrices to be inverted are of the simplest possible form.

BIBLIOGRAPHIC NOTES

The literature on the solution of simultaneous linear equations is vast.   Householder (1964) gives a very extensive bibliography; for partial bibliographies, see Forsythe (1953), Newman (1962), and Varga (1962).   For the material of this chapter on direct methods, we have drawn heavily on the work of Wilkinson (1960, 1961, 1964). For the use of iterative techniques in the solution of partial differential equations, the most up-to-date source is Varga (1962).   Other good general sources for the material of this chapter are Bodewig (1959) and Fadeeva (1959).   Householder (1964) presents an extensive survey of the theoretical aspects of the solution of linear systems.

9.1   The material in this section is classical; see, for example, Birkhoff and MacLane (1953).

9.2   Discussion of some of the matters considered here can be found in Bodewig (1959), Newman (1962), Forsythe (1953), and also in *Modern Computing Methods* (1961).

9.3   Gaussian elimination and the Gauss-Jordan reduction are discussed in any source that considers direct methods; see, for example, Bodewig (1959) or Hildebrand (1956).   The desk-calculator algorithm may be found in *Modern Computing Methods* (1961); an earlier and perhaps more widely known method is that of Crout (1941), which is discussed in Hildebrand (1956).   The Gauss-Doolittle algorithm is discussed in *Modern Computing Methods* (1961) and by Bodewig (1959).   The digital computer algorithm is drawn mainly from *Modern Computing Methods* (1961), where positioning for size (there called pivoting) is also discussed.   Bodewig (1959) discusses the number of operations required for various methods.

9.4   Matrix and vector norms are discussed by many authors; see Householder (1953, 1964), Bodewig (1959), Varga (1962), and Wilkinson (1961).   The approach to error analysis based on bounding the roundoff accumulation from stage to stage is exhaustively discussed in the now classical papers of Von Neumann and Goldstine (1947) and Goldstine and Von Neumann (1951).   Our approach here is due to Wilkinson (1964), which is a mine of information and Wilkinson (1960).   Wilkinson (1961) discusses the errors in a number of direct methods in terms of both fixed- and floating-point arithmetic.   Bodewig (1959) discusses errors at some length.

9.5   Our approach to finding improved solutions of ill-conditioned equations may be found in *Modern Computing Methods* (1961); Bodewig (1959) also discusses ill-conditioned equations.

9.6   Iterative methods are discussed by many authors; see Varga (1962), Bodewig (1959), Fadeeva (1959), Booth (1957), Newman (1962), and Sheldon (1960). The paper by Martin and Tee (1961) contains a useful survey of iterative methods which emphasizes recent developments.

9.7   The Jacobi and Gauss-Seidel iterations have been widely analyzed. Varga (1962) considers both; the Gauss-Seidel method is discussed by Van Norton (1960).   Relaxation techniques were originally due to Southwell (1946) and are discussed by Bodewig (1959), and Varga (1962), who both also discuss theorems on the convergence of iterative processes. There is no better source on the acceleration of stationary iterative processes and their use in partial differential equations than Varga (1962); see also Sheldon (1960).

9.8   The method of steepest descent is due to Stiefel (1952) and is well presented by Booth (1957). The conjugate gradient method is due to Hestenes and Stiefel (1952) and is discussed by Beckman (1960). Bodewig (1959) also discusses the methods of this section.

9.9   Thorough discussions of matrix inversion are given by Bodewig (1959). For other techniques than we have presented here, see Wilf (1960) and Householder (1953).

BIBLIOGRAPHY

Beckman, F. (1960): The Solution of Linear Equations by the Conjugate Gradient Method in *Mathematical Methods for Digital Computers* (A. Ralston and H. S. Wilf, eds.), John Wiley & Sons, Inc., New York.

Birkhoff, G., and S. MacLane (1953): *A Survey of Modern Algebra*, rev. ed., The Macmillan Company, New York.

Bodewig, E. (1959): *Matrix Calculus*, 2d ed., Interscience Publishers, Inc., New York.

Booth, A. D. (1957): *Numerical Methods*, 2d ed., Butterworth Scientific Publications, London.

Crout, P. D. (1941): A Short Method for Evaluating Determinants and Solving Systems of Linear Equations with Real or Complex Coefficients, *Trans. AIEE*, vol. 60, pp. 1235–1240.

Faddeeva, V. N. (1959): *Computational Methods of Linear Algebra* (translated by C. D. Benster), Dover Publications, Inc., New York.

Forsythe, G. E. (1953): Solving Linear Algebraic Equations Can Be Interesting, *Bull. Amer. Math. Soc.*, vol. 59, pp. 299–329.

Goldstine, H. H., and J. Von Neumann (1951): Numerical Inverting of Matrices of High Order, II, *Proc. Amer. Math. Soc.*, vol. 2, pp. 188–202.

Hestenes, M. R., and E. Stiefel (1952): Method of Conjugate Gradients for Solving Linear Systems, *J. Res. Nat. Bur. Standards*, vol. 49, pp. 409–436.

Hildebrand, F. B. (1956): *Introduction to Numerical Analysis*, McGraw-Hill Book Company, New York.

Householder, A. S. (1953): *Principles of Numerical Analysis*, McGraw-Hill Book Company, New York.

Householder, A. S. (1958): Unitary Triangularization of a Nonsymmetric Matrix, *J. Assoc. Comput. Mach.*, vol. 5, pp. 339–342.

Householder, A. S. (1964): *The Theory of Matrices in Numerical Analysis*, Blaisdell Publishing Company, New York.

Martin, D. W., and G. J. Tee (1961): Iterative Methods for Linear Equations with Symmetric Positive Definite Matrix, *Comput. J.*, vol. 4, pp. 242–254.

Miles, E. P. (1960): Generalized Fibonacci Numbers and Associated Matrices, *Amer. Math. Monthly*, vol. 67, pp. 745–752.

Modern Computing Methods (1961): Philosophical Library, New York.

Newman, M. (1962): Matrix Computations in *Survey of Numerical Analysis* (J. Todd, ed.), McGraw-Hill Book Company, New York.

Sheldon, J. W. (1960): Iterative Methods for the Solution of Partial Differential

Equations in *Mathematical Methods for Digital Computers* (A. Ralston and H. S. Wilf, eds.), John Wiley & Sons, Inc., New York.

Southwell, R. V. (1946): *Relaxation Methods in Theoretical Physics*, Oxford University Press, Fair Lawn, N.J.

Stiefel, E. (1952): Uber einige Methoden der Relaxationrechnung, *Z. Angew. Math. Phys.*, vol. 3, pp. 1–33.

Van Norton, R. (1960): The Solution of Linear Equations by the Gauss-Seidel Method in *Mathematical Methods for Digital Computers* (A. Ralston and H. S. Wilf, eds.), John Wiley & Sons, Inc., New York.

Varga, R. (1962): *Matrix Iterative Analysis*, Prentice-Hall, Inc., Englewood Cliffs, N.J.

Von Neumann, J., and H. H. Goldstine (1947): Numerical Inverting of Matrices of High Order, *Bull. Amer. Math. Soc.*, vol. 53, pp. 1021–1099.

Wilf, H. S. (1960): Matrix Inversion by the Method of Rank Annihilation in *Mathematical Methods for Digital Computers* (A. Ralston and H. S. Wilf, eds.), John Wiley & Sons, Inc., New York.

Wilkinson, J. H. (1960): Rounding Errors in Algebraic Processes in *Information Processing*, UNESCO, Paris.

Wilkinson, J. H. (1961): Error Analysis of Direct Methods of Matrix Inversion, *J. Assoc. Comput. Mach.*, vol. 8, pp. 281–330.

Wilkinson, J. H. (1964): *Rounding Errors in Algebraic Processes*, Prentice-Hall, Inc., Englewood Cliffs, N.J.

PROBLEMS

Section 9.1

1. Use Gaussian elimination to prove Theorem 9.1 and its corollary.

Section 9.2

2. (a) Is the matrix of the coefficients in the normal equations of polynomial least-squares approximations usually filled or sparse?   Explain your answer.

(b) Use Sec. 4.3 to show why the numerical solution of partial differential equations often results in systems of equations with sparse coefficient matrices.

3. The Fibonacci sequence is generated using the difference equation

$$f_j = f_{j-1} + f_{j-2} \qquad j > 1 \qquad f_0 = 0 \qquad f_1 = 1$$

(a) Show that $f_n f_{n+2} - f_{n+1}^2 = (-1)^{n+1}$, $n = 0, 1, \ldots$
(b) Thus find the unique solution of

$$f_n x_1 + f_{n+1} x_2 = f_{n+2} \qquad f_{n+1} x_1 + f_{n+2} x_2 = f_{n+3}$$

(c) How do you know that the system in part b becomes increasingly ill-conditioned as n increases?

(d) In particular let $n = 10$ in part b and replace f_{n+2} in the second equation by $f_{n+2} + \epsilon$.   Calculate the solution for $\epsilon = .018$ and $\epsilon = .02$.   For what value of ϵ does the solution not exist?   (See also Prob. 28.)   [Ref.: Miles (1960).]

Section 9.3

4. Verify Eqs. (9.3-13) and (9.3-14).
*5. (a) Let $M_{ki} = -a_{ik}^{(k-1)}/a_{kk}^{(k-1)}$.   Use (9.3-7) to derive

$$a_{ij}^{(k-1)} = a_{ij} + M_{1i}a_{1j} + M_{2i}a_{2j}^{(1)} + \cdots + M_{k-1,i}a_{k-1,j}^{(k-2)}$$

(b) Use this result to prove that (9.3-21) and (9.3-22) do lead to the coefficients in (9.3-6).

6. Consider the system

$$.4096x_1 + .1234x_2 + .3678x_3 + .2943x_4 = .4043$$
$$.2246x_1 + .3872x_2 + .4015x_3 + .1129x_4 = .1550$$
$$.3645x_1 + .1920x_2 + .3781x_3 + .0643x_4 = .4240$$
$$.1784x_1 + .4002x_2 + .2786x_3 + .3927x_4 = -.2557$$

(a) Suppose, using the technique of Sec. 9.3-2-1 (i.e., no positioning for size), you calculate the first and the right half of the second row of the lower panel in Fig. 9.1 to be

$-.5483$	$.4096$	$.1234$	$.3678$	$.2943$	$.4043$	1.5994
		$.3195$	$.1998$	$-.0496$	$-.0667$	$.4042$

Find and correct the element or elements in error.

(b) Then complete the solution of the system, carrying four decimal places throughout.

(c) Solve the system of part a, using positioning for size, and compare the results with those of part b.

7. (a) Verify that (9.3-22) becomes (9.3-26) when A is symmetric.

(b) Use this simplification to solve the system

$$.6428x_1 + .3475x_2 - .8468x_3 = .4127$$
$$.3475x_1 + 1.8423x_2 + .4759x_3 = 1.7321$$
$$-.8468x_1 + .4759x_2 + 1.2147x_3 = -.8621$$

8. (a) Suppose an $(n + 1)$st row, which is the sum of the elements in all the other rows, is appended to the original augmented matrix with check column. If this row is treated just like every other row of the matrix, show that it will remain the sum of the other rows at each stage.

(b) Indicate then how this *check row* in conjunction with the check column can be used to isolate an error at any stage when positioning for size is used.

9. (a) Verify (9.3-29).

(b) Prove that the product of two lower triangular matrices is lower triangular.

(c) Prove that the inverse of a triangular matrix is a triangular matrix of the same form.

10. (a) Display algorithms analogous to (9.3-8) for the solution of (9.3-34) and (9.3-35).

(b) Derive Eqs. (9.3-42).

*11. Let A_n be the matrix of order n

$$a_{ii} = 1 \qquad\qquad i \neq n$$
$$a_{ij} = (-1)^{i+j-1} \qquad i > j \text{ and } j = n$$
$$a_{ij} = 0 \qquad\qquad i < j \text{ and } j \neq n$$

(a) Show that the elements of the inverse of this matrix are given by

$$a_{ii}^{-1} = 2^{-1} \qquad\qquad i \neq n$$
$$a_{ij}^{-1} = 0 \qquad\qquad i > j, i \neq n$$
$$a_{ij}^{-1} = (-1)^{i+j-1}2^{-(j-i+1)} \qquad i < j, j \neq n$$
$$a_{nj}^{-1} = (-1)^{n+j-1}2^{-j} \qquad j \neq n$$
$$a_{in}^{-1} = -a_{i,n-1}^{-1} \qquad i \neq n - 1$$
$$a_{nn}^{-1} = 2^{-n+1}$$

(b) Write out A_6 and A_6^{-1}.

(c) Why is A_n very well-conditioned?

(d) Consider A_{31} and let B_{31} be the matrix formed by replacing $a_{31,31}$ by $-\frac{1}{2}$. Show that $B_{31}^{-1} = A_{31}^{-1} - \frac{1}{2}$ (last column of A_{31}^{-1}) (last row of A_{31}^{-1})/$(1 - 2^{-31})$, and thus deduce that some of the elements of A_{31}^{-1} differ from those of B_{31}^{-1} in the first decimal.

(e) Show that, if partial positioning for size is used, then Gaussian elimination applied to A_{31} and B_{31} is identical until the final step (i.e., show that the 31st row never has the element with *greatest* magnitude in a column).

(f) Show that the final element in the triangle should be -2^{30} for A_{31} and $-2^{30} + \frac{1}{2}$ for B_{31}. Thus deduce that, if fewer than 30 binary digits are used in the computation, Gaussian elimination applied to A_{31} and B_{31} leads to identical L and U matrices, and thus to identical inverses [or solutions of (9.1-1)] in spite of the fact that the true inverses differ substantially.

(g) Why would complete positioning for size avoid this difficulty? [Ref.: Wilkinson (1961), pp. 327–328.]

*12. (a) Let A in (9.1-1) be symmetric and positive definite and let B be the matrix of coefficients in (9.3-2) excluding the first row. Show that

$$\sum_{i=1}^{n}\sum_{j=1}^{n} a_{ij}x_ix_j - a_{11}\left(x_1 + \sum_{i=2}^{n}\frac{a_{i1}}{a_{11}}x_i\right)^2 = \sum_{i=2}^{n}\sum_{j=2}^{n} a_{ij}^{(1)}x_ix_j$$

(b) Deduce from this that B is positive definite and, therefore, that the matrices of all the derived systems are positive definite.

(c) Further, show that

$$a_{ii}^{(1)} \leq a_{ii} \qquad i = 2, \ldots, n$$

and thus deduce that

$$\max_{2\leq i,j\leq n} |a_{ij}^{(1)}| \leq \max_{2\leq i,j\leq n} |a_{ij}|$$

(d) From parts b and c deduce that, if $|a_{ij}| < 1$, then $|a_{ij}^{(k)}| < 1$ for all k. Thus deduce that, even with *no* positioning for size, overflow will not occur at any stage.

(e) By giving a 2×2 example, show that with no positioning some of the multipliers m_{ij} may be very large. [Ref.: Wilkinson (1961), pp. 285–286.]

*13. (a) For a nonsingular symmetric matrix, show that the following algorithm (due to Choleski) leads to the decomposition of A into LL^T where L is lower triangular:

$$l_{ii} = \left(a_{ii} - \sum_{j=1}^{i-1} l_{ij}^2\right)^{\frac{1}{2}} \qquad i = 1, \ldots, n$$

$$l_{ki} = \frac{1}{l_{ii}}\left(a_{ki} - \sum_{j=1}^{i-1} l_{ij}l_{kj}\right) \qquad \begin{aligned} k &= i+1, \ldots, n \\ i &= 1, \ldots, n \end{aligned}$$

(b) Show that, even though some l_{ii} may be imaginary, all l_{ij} are either real or pure imaginary. What condition on the matrix A is necessary and sufficient for all elements of L to be real?

(c) How many operations (i.e., multiplications and divisions) are required to perform the triangular decomposition and back substitution (assume each square root requires three operations)?

(d) Why does it make no sense to try to use partial positioning for size with this algorithm? Show, however, that complete positioning for size can be used with this algorithm for positive definite matrices.

(e) Apply this algorithm with complete positioning for size to the system of Prob. 7b. How do you account for the differences between this result and that of Prob. 7b?

*14. Let L be a lower triangular matrix such that $LL^T = B$ where B is a positive definite matrix of order $n - 1$.

(a) Show that there exist a column vector $\mathbf{c}$ and a scalar l_{nn} such that

$$\begin{bmatrix} L & \mathbf{0} \\ \mathbf{c}^T & l_{nn} \end{bmatrix} \begin{bmatrix} L^T & \mathbf{c} \\ \mathbf{0} & l_{nn} \end{bmatrix} = \begin{bmatrix} B & \mathbf{a} \\ \mathbf{a}^T & a_{nn} \end{bmatrix} = A$$

where a_{nn} is a given scalar and $\mathbf{a}$ is a given column vector such that A is positive definite.

(b) If A is such that $|a_{ij}| < 1$ for all i and j, show that the components of $\mathbf{c}$ and l_{nn} are such that all are less than 1 in magnitude.

(c) Thus deduce that, if A is such that $|a_{ij}| < 1$ in magnitude, there exists a lower triangular matrix L such that $LL^T = A$ and $|l_{ij}| < 1$ for all i and j. Thus deduce that the Choleski algorithm for the decomposition of a positive definite symmetric matrix may be done in fixed-point arithmetic with no scaling. [Ref.: Wilkinson (1961), p. 287.]

15. Solve the system

$$.2641x_1 + .1735x_2 + .8642x_3 = -.7521$$
$$.9411x_1 - .0175x_2 + .1463x_3 = .6310$$
$$-.8641x_1 - .4243x_2 + .0711x_3 = .2501$$

using, (a) the algorithm of Sec. 9.3-2-1 (no positioning for size); (b) partial positioning; (c) complete positioning for size. Carry four decimals in all computations, and check your results by inserting the solution into the sum equation. Also carry the check column in your calculation. Why is it generally not significant for low-order systems like this whether or not scalar products are accumulated with double precision?

16. (a) Display the matrices L and U ($A = LU$) for the system of the previous problem when partial positioning for size was used. How would the data have to be scaled initially to avoid overflow on a computer?

(b) What are the numbers p_1, p_2, and p_3 for this system using the algorithm of Sec. 9.3-3-2?

17. Repeat the calculations of Prob. 15 for the symmetric system

$$.4721x_1 + .2352x_2 - .2613x_3 + .8421x_4 = -.2317$$
$$.2352x_1 + .7411x_2 - .0463x_3 + .1569x_4 = .3219$$
$$-.2613x_1 - .0463x_2 + .8955x_3 + .1748x_4 = .6217$$
$$.8421x_1 + .1569x_2 + .1748x_3 + .9841x_4 = .9835$$

using the algorithm of Prob. 13.

Section 9.4

*18. (a) Verify that both norms defined in (9.4-7) satisfy the conditions (9.4-5).

(b) Show that the conditions (9.4-5) are also satisfied if the norm is defined as

$$\max_i \sum_{j=1}^n |a_{ij}|$$

(c) Which of the conditions (9.4-5) is not satisfied if we define the norm as

$$\max_{i,j} |a_{ij}|?$$

Give a counterexample. [Ref.: Fadeeva (1959), pp. 54–60.]

19. (*a*) For any norm satisfying (9.4-5), show that

$$\|A + B\| \geq \|A\| - \|B\|$$

(*b*) Use (9.4-18) and the first part of Corollary 9.3 to prove the second part.

20. (*a*) Verify (9.4-9) and (9.4-10).   (*b*) Thus deduce (9.4-11).

21. Use Theorem 9.2 to derive the following properties of the spectral norm:

(*a*) If $A^{(k)}$ is any principal submatrix of A, then $\|A^{(k)}\| \leq \|A\|$.

(*b*) If **a** and **b** are vectors

$$\|\mathbf{ab}^T\| = \|\mathbf{a}\| \, \|\mathbf{b}\|$$

(*c*) $\|A\| \leq \|B\|$ where $\|B\|$ has elements $|a_{ij}|$.

(*d*) For any matrix A

$$\|AA^T\| = \|A\|^2$$

22. (*a*) Show that exact triangular decomposition of $A + \Delta A$ in (9.4-41) followed by exact solution of (9.3-34) with right-hand side $\mathbf{b} + \Delta\mathbf{b} + \Delta\mathbf{s}$ would lead to (9.4-39).

(*b*) Verify Eq. (9.4-45).

*23. Consider a system $A\mathbf{x} = \mathbf{b}$ of four equations in four unknowns solved by Gaussian elimination as in Sec. 9.3-1 (i.e., no double-precision arithmetic used).   Let $A^{(3)}\mathbf{x} = \mathbf{b}^{(3)}$ be the final triangular system and let

$$[A^{(k)} + \Delta A^{(k)}]\mathbf{x} = \mathbf{b}^{(k)} + \Delta\mathbf{b}^{(k)} \qquad k = 0, 1, 2$$

be the *perturbed derived systems* ($k = 0$ is the original system) whose *exact* solution would be the *exact* solution of the final triangular system.   Assume all $a_{ij}^{(k)}$ and $b_j^{(k)}$ are less than 1 in magnitude.

(*a*) If d decimals are carried in the computation, use the equations of Sec. 9.3-1 to derive the following bounds on $\Delta A^{(2)}$ and $\Delta\mathbf{b}^{(2)}$:

$$[|\Delta A^{(2)}|, |\Delta\mathbf{b}^{(2)}|] \leq \tfrac{1}{2} \times 10^{-d} \begin{bmatrix} 0 & 0 & 0 & 0 & \vdots & 0 \\ 0 & 0 & 0 & 0 & \vdots & 0 \\ 0 & 0 & 0 & 0 & \vdots & 0 \\ 0 & 0 & 1 & 1 & \vdots & 1 \end{bmatrix}$$

where the inequality means that each element on the right exceeds the absolute value of the element on the left.

(*b*) Carry through a similar analysis for $k = 1$ and 0 to derive the bound

$$[|\Delta A^{(0)}|, |\Delta\mathbf{b}^{(0)}|] \leq \tfrac{1}{2} \times 10^{-d} \begin{bmatrix} 0 & 0 & 0 & 0 & \vdots & 0 \\ 1 & 1 & 1 & 1 & \vdots & 1 \\ 1 & 2 & 2 & 2 & \vdots & 2 \\ 1 & 2 & 3 & 3 & \vdots & 3 \end{bmatrix}$$

(*c*) Generalize the result of part *b* to get a bound on $\Delta A^{(0)}$ and $\Delta\mathbf{b}^{(0)}$ for a system of n equations.   Compare this result with that of Sec. 9.4-2.   [Ref.: *Modern Computing Methods* (1961), pp. 41–48.]

24. (*a*) Use any means to calculate the inverse of the coefficient matrix in Prob. 15.

(*b*) Use this result to derive, as in Example 9.4, a bound on the norm of the error in a solution of the system of Prob. 15 calculated using double-precision scalar products and dividends.

25. Repeat the calculations of the previous problem for the coefficient matrix of Prob. 17.   (See Sec. 9.9-1 before calculating the inverse.)

Section 9.5

26. Explain why the assumption that A is scaled so that all its elements are less than 1 in magnitude, with the largest being nearly 1 in magnitude, generally is equivalent to the assumption that $\|A\|_S$ has order of magnitude 1.

27. Consider the system

$$.05x_1 + .07x_2 + .06x_3 + .05x_4 = .23$$
$$.07x_1 + .10x_2 + .08x_3 + .07x_4 = .32$$
$$.06x_1 + .08x_2 + .10x_3 + .09x_4 = .33$$
$$.05x_1 + .07x_2 + .09x_3 + .10x_4 = .31$$

(*a*) What is the true solution of this system?

(*b*) Solve this system using the method of Sec. 9.3-2-2 (i.e., with positioning for size). Carry four decimal places in your computation. How do you explain your result? Would complete positioning for size have given a better result?

(*c*) Do four iterations of the method of Sec. 9.5 to get an improved solution.

28. Let A_n be the coefficient matrix of Prob. 3*b*.

(*a*) Calculate the eigenvalues λ_1 and λ_2 of A_0.

(*b*) Prove that A_n has eigenvalues λ_1^{n+1} and λ_2^{n+1}.

(*c*) Thus use (9.5-4) to deduce that A_n becomes increasingly ill-conditioned as n increases.

Section 9.6

29. (*a*) Show that the matrix iteration $B_{i+1} = B_i(2I - AB_i)$, B_1 arbitrary, to find A^{-1} is the matrix analog of the Newton-Raphson method for finding the reciprocal of a number.

(*b*) Defining $C_i = I - AB_i$, show that $C_i = C_1^{2^{i-1}}$.

(*c*) Thus deduce that a sufficient condition for the convergence of the iteration of part *a* to A^{-1} is that all the eigenvalues of C_1 lie within the unit circle. (This condition is also necessary.)

(*d*) How could this iteration be used to solve systems of linear equations? Do two iterations on the system of Example 9.5 with $B_1 = \frac{1}{4}I$. What is bad about this method from the computational point of view? [Ref.: Newman (1962), pp. 223–226.]

30. (*a*) Let $\mathbf{x}_t$ be a solution of $B\mathbf{x} = 0$ where det $(B) = 0$ and let $x_t^{(i)}$ be the component of $\mathbf{x}_t$ of largest magnitude. Show that

$$|b_{ii}| \leq \sum_{\substack{k=1 \\ k \neq i}}^{n} |b_{ik}|$$

(*b*) Use this result to prove that

$$|\lambda_{\max}| \leq \max_i \sum_{k=1}^{n} |a_{ik}|$$

$$|\lambda_{\min}| \geq \min_i \left(|a_{ii}| - \sum_{\substack{k=1 \\ k \neq i}}^{n} |a_{ik}| \right)$$

where $\lambda_{\max}$ and $\lambda_{\min}$ are the eigenvalues of $A = [a_{ij}]$ of maximum and minimum magnitude, respectively.

(c) Thus deduce that the Jacobi iteration for a matrix A with diagonal terms equal to 1 converges if

$$\sum_{\substack{k=1 \\ k \neq i}}^{n} |a_{ik}| < 1 \qquad i = 1, \ldots, n$$

or if

$$\sum_{\substack{k=1 \\ k \neq i}}^{n} |a_{ki}| < 1 \qquad i = 1, \ldots, n$$

Section 9.7

31. Use (9.7-10) to derive Eqs. (9.7-11) and (9.7-12).

*32. In the Gauss-Seidel method let $x_{i+1}^{(k)}$ be the kth component of $\mathbf{x}_{i+1}$ and let

$$r_{i+1}^{(k)} = b_k - \sum_{j=1}^{k-1} a_{kj}x_{i+1}^{(j)} - \sum_{j=k}^{n} a_{kj}x_i^{(j)}$$

(a) Show that

$$x_{i+1}^{(k)} = x_i^{(k)} + r_{i+1}^{(k)}/a_{kk}$$

(b) If $\boldsymbol{\epsilon}_i = \mathbf{x}_t - \mathbf{x}_i$ show that

$$\epsilon_{i+1}^{(k)} = \epsilon_i^{(k)} - r_{i+1}^{(k)}/a_{kk}$$

and

$$r_{i+1}^{(k)} = \sum_{j=1}^{k-1} a_{kj}\,\epsilon_{i+1}^{(j)} + \sum_{j=k}^{n} a_{kj}\epsilon_i^{(j)}$$

(c) Let A be symmetric and consider the quadratic form $Q(\boldsymbol{\epsilon}_i) = \boldsymbol{\epsilon}_i^T A \boldsymbol{\epsilon}_i$. Show that

$$Q(\boldsymbol{\epsilon}_{i+1}) - Q(\boldsymbol{\epsilon}_i) = -\sum_{j=1}^{n} [r_{i+1}^{(j)}]^2/a_{jj}$$

(d) From this deduce that, if A is a nonsingular, symmetric matrix with positive diagonal elements and if the Gauss-Seidel method converges for any $\mathbf{x}_1$, then A must be positive definite. [Ref.: Van Norton (1960).]

33. (a) Let L and U be, respectively, lower and upper triangular nonnegative matrices with zeros on the main diagonal. Prove that $(I - L)^{-1}U$ is nonnegative.

(b) Thus deduce that, if A is a matrix with 1's on the main diagonal and nonpositive entries otherwise, then both B_J and B_G, the Jacobi and Gauss-Seidel iteration matrices, are nonnegative. [Ref.: Varga (1962), p. 69.]

34. (a) By calculating the spectral radius of the B matrices for the Jacobi and Gauss-Seidel iterations in Example 9.5, show that the Gauss-Seidel method would be expected to converge substantially faster than the Jacobi method.

(b) Apply the δ^2 process to the results of the Jacobi iteration in Example 9.5 with $i = 2$. How do you explain this result?

(c) Apply the δ^2 process to the Gauss-Seidel results with $i = 3$. How do you explain this result?

35. (*a*) Determine the spectral radius of the B matrix for the Gauss-Seidel iteration for the system

$$.96326x^{(1)} + .81321x^{(2)} = .88824$$
$$.81321x^{(1)} + .68654x^{(2)} = .74988$$

(*b*) Compute the exact solution of this system to five decimal places using Cramer's rule.

(*c*) Attempt to use the Gauss-Seidel method to find a solution of this system starting with $x^{(1)} = .33116$, $x^{(2)} = .70000$. How do you explain your result? [Ref.: Wilkinson (1961), pp. 328–329.]

36. (*a*) Explain why the relaxation algorithm of Sec. 9.7-4 is not a stationary iterative process.

(*b*) Using $\|\mathbf{r}\|$ as a criterion, compare the results of Examples 9.6 and 9.5. Why is $\|\mathbf{r}\|$ a reasonable criterion for this example? When would it not be?

37. (*a*) Suppose at every stage of a relaxation procedure the $i_1, i_2, \ldots, i_k$ components of the residual vector are reduced to zero by modifying the $i_1, i_2, \ldots, i_k$ components of the solution vector. Show that this requires the solution of k simultaneous linear equations at each stage. This procedure is called *block relaxation*.

(*b*) If the matrix A has the form

$$A = \begin{bmatrix} A_1 & 0 & \cdots & 0 \\ 0 & A_2 & \cdot & \cdot \\ \cdot & \cdot & \cdot & \cdot \\ \cdot & & \cdot & 0 \\ 0 & \cdots & 0 & A_k \end{bmatrix}$$

where each A_i is a square matrix, then show that, if the k residuals are chosen properly, the k equations to be solved are trivial.

(*c*) Use relaxation to find an approximate solution for the system

$$
\begin{aligned}
4x^{(1)} - \ x^{(2)} &&&= 2 \\
-x^{(1)} + 4x^{(2)} - \ x^{(3)} &&&= 5 \\
- \ x^{(2)} + 4x^{(3)} - \ x^{(4)} &= 5 \\
- \ x^{(3)} + 4x^{(4)} &= 2
\end{aligned}
$$

by using the technique of part *a* with $k = 2$ and with i_1 and i_2 the two largest components of the residual vector. Carry out four iterations and use as the initial approximation $\mathbf{x}_1 = \mathbf{0}$. What is the true solution of this system?

38. Use (9.7-32) to derive (9.7-33) and (9.7-34).

*39. Consider the nonstationary iteration

$$\mathbf{x}_{i+1} = [(1 + \omega_i)B - \omega_i I]\mathbf{x}_i + (1 + \omega_i)C\mathbf{b}$$

where B and C satisfy the consistency condition (9.6-11).

(*a*) Show that this iteration also satisfies the consistency condition and that K_i defined by (9.6-16) is

$$K_i(B) = \prod_{j=1}^{i} [(1 + \omega_j)B - \omega_j I]$$

(*b*) By letting

$$\omega_i = \gamma_i/(1 - \gamma_i)$$

Show that

$$K_i(B) = \prod_{j=1}^{i} \frac{B - \gamma_j I}{1 - \gamma_j}$$

(c) If B is symmetric, deduce that

$$\rho[K_i(B)] = \max_j |K_i(\mu_j)|$$

where $\mu_j, j = 1, \ldots, n$ are the eigenvalues of B.

(d) Suppose we know that $-1 \leq x_0 \leq \mu_j \leq x_1 < 1$ for all μ_j. Show then that, in order to minimize the magnitude of $\rho[K_i(B)]$, we should like to have

$$K_i(x) = T_i(ax + b)/T_i(a + b)$$

where $T_i(x)$ is the Chebyshev polynomial of degree i and

$$a = \frac{2}{x_1 - x_0} \qquad b = -\frac{x_1 + x_0}{x_1 - x_0}$$

(e) Thus deduce that the γ_j's should be chosen as the zeros of $T_i(ax + b)$ with the ω_i's then given by part b.

(f) Suppose these ω_i's have been used to compute $\mathbf{x}_{i+1}$. Besides requiring some knowledge of the eigenvalues of B, what disadvantage does this technique have if, having computed $\mathbf{x}_{i+1}$, we now desire $\mathbf{x}_{i+2}$? [Ref.: Sheldon (1960), pp. 146–147.]

40. Consider the system

$$
\begin{aligned}
x^{(1)} \quad & \quad - \tfrac{1}{4}x^{(3)} - \tfrac{1}{4}x^{(4)} = \tfrac{1}{2} \\
x^{(2)} & - \tfrac{1}{4}x^{(3)} - \tfrac{1}{4}x^{(4)} = \tfrac{1}{2} \\
-\tfrac{1}{4}x^{(1)} - \tfrac{1}{4}x^{(2)} + \quad x^{(3)} & \quad = \tfrac{1}{2} \\
-\tfrac{1}{4}x^{(1)} - \tfrac{1}{4}x^{(2)} & \quad + \quad x^{(4)} = \tfrac{1}{2}
\end{aligned}
$$

(a) Starting with $\mathbf{x}_1 = \mathbf{0}$ do four iterations of the Jacobi method.

(b) Using the same starting vector do four iterations of the Gauss-Seidel method.

(c) What is the true solution of the system?

41. (a) Calculate the B matrix for the Jacobi method for the system of the previous problem and find its spectral radius.

(b) Similarly, find the spectral radius of B for the Jacobi iteration.

(c) Are the results of the previous problem in accord with these results?

Section 9.8

42. (a) Let $\mathbf{x}$ be an approximation to the solution of a system of linear equations with a symmetric coefficient matrix. If all components of $\mathbf{x}$ are held constant except the jth and this is determined so that Q as defined by (9.8-2) has an extremum, show that the Gauss-Seidel method results.

(b) Thus deduce that when A is positive definite, the Gauss-Seidel method is equivalent to determining $x_i^{(j)}$ so as to minimize Q at each step.

43. (a) Prove that R has a unique minimum at the solution of $A\mathbf{x} = \mathbf{b}$.

(b) Prove that the minimum of Q at the solution of $A\mathbf{x} = \mathbf{b}$ is unique when A is positive definite.

44. (a) In the space with variables $r_1, \ldots, r_n$ show that $R = \text{const}$ is a hypersphere with center at the origin.

(b) By making the change of variable (9.8-4), show that $R = \text{const}$ is a hyper-ellipsoid with center at the solution of $A\mathbf{x} = \mathbf{b}$.

45. (a) Show that, if the matrix P in (9.8-8) were known, it could be used to transform the system $A\mathbf{x} = \mathbf{b}$, where A is symmetric, into one whose solution is immediate (see also Secs. 10.1 and 10.4).

(b) Is the Gauss-Jordan reduction equivalent to performing an orthogonal transformation? Why?

46. (a) Show that $\nabla R = -2A^T\mathbf{r}$ where the gradient is with respect to the variables $x_1, \ldots, x_n$. Thus deduce that $\mathbf{v}_i$ in the method of steepest descent for nonpositive definite matrices can be taken to be $\mathbf{v}_i = A^T\mathbf{r}_i$.

(b) Show that

$$\alpha_i = \frac{\mathbf{r}_i^T A A^T \mathbf{r}_i}{(A A^T\mathbf{r}_i)^T A A^T\mathbf{r}_i}$$

and thus derive the equation analogous to (9.8-16).

(c) Show that $R(\mathbf{x}_{i+1}) < R(\mathbf{x}_i)$. [Ref.: Booth (1957), pp. 101–102.]

47. (a) Do four iterations of the method of steepest descent (9.8-16) with a starting vector $\mathbf{x}_1^T = (.5, 1.5)$ to find an approximate solution of the system of Example 9.7. Explain the behavior of the successive iterates.

(b) Do two iterations on this system using the method of the previous problem and the same starting vector as in part a. How do these results compare with those of part a? Why?

48. (a) Use the method of steepest descent to find an approximate solution of the system

$$\begin{aligned}
x^{(1)} - 2x^{(2)} + 3x^{(3)} + x^{(4)} &= 3 \\
-2x^{(1)} + x^{(2)} - 2x^{(3)} - x^{(4)} &= -4 \\
3x^{(1)} - 2x^{(2)} + x^{(3)} + 5x^{(4)} &= 7 \\
x^{(1)} - x^{(2)} + 5x^{(3)} + 3x^{(4)} &= 8
\end{aligned}$$

Let $\mathbf{x}_1^T = (0,0,0,0)$ and carry out two iterations. How do you explain your results?

(b) Use the technique of Prob. 46 to perform three iterations on the above system using the same initial vector. How do you explain these results?

(c) Use the method of steepest descent to find a solution of the system of Prob. 40 with $\mathbf{x}_1 = 0$. How do you explain this result? [Ref.: Booth (1957), pp. 100–104.]

49. (a) In (9.8-11) if, for a given $\mathbf{v}_i$, α_i is chosen so that Q shall be minimized, show that

$$\alpha_i = \frac{\mathbf{v}_i^T\mathbf{b} - \mathbf{v}_i^T A\mathbf{x}_i}{\mathbf{v}_i^T A \mathbf{v}_i} = \frac{\mathbf{v}_i^T\mathbf{r}_i}{\mathbf{v}_i^T A \mathbf{v}_i}$$

(b) Show that for such a method

$$Q(\mathbf{x}_{i+1}) < Q(\mathbf{x}_i) \qquad \text{if } \mathbf{v}_i^T\mathbf{r}_i \neq 0$$

and

$$\mathbf{v}_i^T\mathbf{r}_{i+1} = 0$$

***50.** Let A be positive definite and let $\{\mathbf{u}_i\}$ in the conjugate gradient method be the n unit vectors in the coordinate directions.

(a) Using the notation of Sec. 9.3, show that

$$\beta_{ik} = m_{ki} \qquad i = 1, \ldots, n; k = 1, \ldots, i - 1$$

and

$$v_k^T A_j = a_{kj}^{(k-1)} \qquad k = 1, \ldots, n; j = k, \ldots, n$$

where A_j is the jth column of A.

(b) With $\mathbf{x}_1 = \mathbf{0}$ in (9.8-20) deduce that

$$\alpha_j = a_{j,n+1}^{(j-1)}/a_{jj}^{(j-1)} \qquad j = 1, \ldots, n$$

(c) Use (9.3-8) to show that the back substitution is equivalent to writing the true solution $\mathbf{x}_t$ as

$$\mathbf{x}_t = (I + D^{-1}U)^{-1}D^{-1}\mathbf{s}$$

where D is the matrix of diagonal elements in (9.3-6), U is the remainder of the coefficient matrix, and $\mathbf{s}$ is the final right-hand side vector.

(d) Use this result to deduce that (9.8-17) is equivalent to the back substitution. Therefore, deduce finally that, with this choice of $\mathbf{u}_i$'s, the conjugate gradient method results in the computation of the same quantities as Gaussian elimination and back substitution.

51. (a) Show that α_i given by (9.8-33) and by (9.8-20) are equivalent.

(b) Show that

$$\mathbf{r}_j^T A \mathbf{v}_i = 0 \qquad \text{if } j < i$$

and

$$\mathbf{r}_i^T A \mathbf{v}_i = \mathbf{v}_i^T A \mathbf{v}_i$$

Do this without assuming that all β_{ik}'s except the coefficient of $\mathbf{v}_i$ are zero in (9.8-33).

52. (a) Use the results of the previous problem to show that the $\mathbf{r}_i$'s generated by (9.8-33) are orthogonal and thus that, if $\mathbf{r}_i$, $i = 1, \ldots, n$ are all nonzero, they form an orthogonal basis for n space.

(b) Show that the equation for $\mathbf{v}_{i+1}$ in (9.8-33) is correct by showing that $\beta_{i+1,k}$ given by (9.8-22) vanishes if $k \neq i$.

53. (a) Verify the relations

$$\alpha_i = \mathbf{r}_i^T \mathbf{r}_i / \mathbf{v}_i^T A \mathbf{v}_i \qquad \beta_i = \mathbf{r}_{i+1}^T \mathbf{r}_{i+1} / \mathbf{r}_i^T \mathbf{r}_i$$

(b) Verify the identity

$$\mathbf{v}_i^T \mathbf{r}_j = \begin{cases} 0 & i < j \\ \mathbf{r}_i^T \mathbf{r}_i & i \geq j \end{cases}$$

54. For the conjugate gradient method, show that $Q(\mathbf{x}_{i+1}) < Q(\mathbf{x}_i)$.

55. Show that the number of multiplications required at each iteration of the conjugate gradient method is $n^2 + O(n)$.

*56. (a) Show that $\mathbf{v}_j^T \mathbf{v}_i > 0$ for all i and j.

(b) Using $\boldsymbol{\epsilon}_i = \mathbf{x}_t - \mathbf{x}_i$ show that

$$\boldsymbol{\epsilon}_{i+1}^T \mathbf{v}_i > 0$$

(c) Use these results to show that

$$\boldsymbol{\epsilon}_{i+1}^T \boldsymbol{\epsilon}_{i+1} < \boldsymbol{\epsilon}_i^T \boldsymbol{\epsilon}_i$$

Thus deduce that at each stage of the conjugate gradient method, the norm of the error decreases until roundoff becomes the determining factor. [Ref.: Beckman (1960), pp. 64–65.]

*57. (*a*) Display a basis for the orthogonal complement Q_k of the space V_k spanned by $v_k, v_{k+1}, \ldots, v_n$.

(*b*) Show that

$$v_k = \gamma_k r_k + \delta_k q_k$$

where γ_k and δ_k are constants and q_k is in Q_k.

(*c*) Thus deduce that v_k is a scalar multiple of the projection of r_k on V_k. Using this, give a geometrical interpretation of the conjugate gradient method. [Ref.: Beckman (1960), pp. 66–67.]

58. (*a*) For the system

$$.8573x^{(1)} + .2471x^{(2)} - .3262x^{(3)} = -.4187$$
$$.2471x^{(1)} + .6841x^{(2)} + .4213x^{(3)} = 1.0263$$
$$-.3262x^{(1)} + .4213x^{(2)} + .9372x^{(3)} = 1.9743$$

do (i) 10 iterations of the method of steepest descent; (ii) 3 iterations of the conjugate gradient method.

(*b*) For the system

$$.6841x^{(1)} - .0137x^{(2)} + .2579x^{(3)} + .2483x^{(4)} = -.1062$$
$$-.0137x^{(1)} + 1.0479x^{(2)} - .3712x^{(3)} + .2847x^{(4)} = -.4063$$
$$.2579x^{(1)} - .3712x^{(2)} + .8321x^{(3)} + .1493x^{(4)} = .9037$$
$$.2483x^{(1)} + .2847x^{(2)} + .1493x^{(3)} + .7942x^{(4)} = -.3628$$

do (i) 10 iterations of the method of steepest descent; (ii) 4 iterations of the conjugate gradient method. In both parts discuss the comparisons between the results given by the two methods.

Section 9.9

59. (*a*) Derive the algorithm for inverting the upper triangular matrix U which is analogous to (9.9-3).

(*b*) Calculate that the inversion of L and U and the computation of $U^{-1}L^{-1}$ requires $\frac{2}{3}n^3 + O(n^2)$ multiplications and divisions and thus deduce that the complete inversion of A by this method requires $n^3 + O(n^2)$ operations.

60. (*a*) Show that the inverse of a matrix A can be found by solving the n systems

$$Ax = e_i \qquad i = 1, \ldots, n$$

where e_i is the vector with a 1 in the ith position and zeros elsewhere.

*(*b*) How many operations are required to find the inverse in this manner?

(*c*) Show that the Gauss-Jordan reduction of A to I is equivalent to the premultiplication of A by a sequence of elementary matrices and thus deduce that A^{-1} may be found by applying to I the same operations required to reduce A to I by the Gauss-Jordan reduction. What is the connection of this method with that of part *a*?

61. (*a*) If $A = LU$ where L and U are as in Sec. 9.9-1 show that $A^{-1}L = U^{-1}$.

(*b*) If U^{-1} has been calculated as in Prob. 59, derive an algorithm for computing A^{-1} directly one column at a time.

(*c*) How many operations are required to calculate A^{-1} in this manner? [Ref.: Bodewig (1959), pp. 214–215.]

62. (*a*) Consider the two equations

$$UA^{-1} = L^{-1} \qquad A^{-1}L = U^{-1}$$

Show that these are $2n^2$ equations for the elements of A^{-1}, L^{-1}, and U^{-1} but that $n^2 - n$ of the equations involve only zero elements of L^{-1} and U^{-1} and n equations involve elements of L^{-1} known to be 1.

(b) Thus derive n^2 equations for the n^2 elements of A^{-1} which involve only known elements of U^{-1} or L^{-1}.

(c) Derive an algorithm for solving these equations. [Ref.: Bodewig (1959), pp. 215–216.]

63. Indicate how the matrix inversion scheme of Sec. 9.9-1 can be simplified if A is symmetric. How many operations are required for the inversion in this case?

*64. (a) Let $\mathbf{a}$ be a nonzero vector, $\mathbf{v}$ be a unit vector, and let $\alpha = \|\mathbf{a}\|$. Define

$$\mu^2 = 2\alpha(\alpha - \mathbf{v}^T\mathbf{a}) \qquad \text{and} \qquad \mathbf{u} = (1/\mu)(\mathbf{a} - \alpha\mathbf{v})$$

Show that $\mathbf{u}$ is a unit vector and that

$$(I - 2\mathbf{u}\mathbf{u}^T)\mathbf{a} = \alpha\mathbf{v}$$

(b) If $\mathbf{v}_1$ and $\mathbf{v}_2$ are vectors and σ is a constant, show that

$$\det (I - \sigma\mathbf{v}_1\mathbf{v}_2^T) = 1 - \sigma\mathbf{v}_1^T\mathbf{v}_2$$

and thus deduce that

$$\det (I - 2\mathbf{u}\mathbf{u}^T) = -1$$

(c) Let A be an arbitrary matrix and let $\mathbf{a}$ in part a be A_1, the first column of A. Let $\mathbf{v}$ be $\mathbf{e}_1$, the first column of I. Using $\mathbf{u}_1$ in place of $\mathbf{u}$ and defining

$$U_1 = I - 2\mathbf{u}_1\mathbf{u}_1^T$$

show that the first column of U_1A is $\alpha\mathbf{e}_1$.

(d) Show how this process can be continued through $n - 1$ steps to give

$$U_{n-1}U_{n-2} \cdots U_1A = UA = V$$

where V is an upper triangular matrix.

(e) Thus show how this technique may be used to invert matrices, solve linear equations, or calculate determinants. [Ref.: Householder (1958).]

65. (a) Let $\mathbf{u}$ and $\mathbf{v}$ be column vectors and A a nonsingular square matrix. Verify that

$$(A + \mathbf{u}\mathbf{v}^T)^{-1} = A^{-1} - \frac{(A^{-1}\mathbf{u})(\mathbf{v}^TA^{-1})}{1 + \mathbf{v}^TA^{-1}\mathbf{u}}$$

(b) Let

$$B = D + \sum_{i=1}^{m} \mathbf{u}_i\mathbf{v}_i^T$$

where D is a nonsingular diagonal matrix. Define

$$C_k = \Big(\sum_{i=1}^{k} \mathbf{u}_i\mathbf{v}_i^T + D \Big)^{-1}$$

Use the result of part a to prove that

$$C_{k+1} = C_k - \frac{(C_k\mathbf{u}_{k+1})(\mathbf{v}_{k+1}^T C_k)}{1 + \mathbf{v}_{k+1}^T C_k \mathbf{u}_{k+1}}$$

(c) Use the result of part b to deduce an algorithm for calculating B^{-1} with B as given in part b. [Ref.: Wilf (1960), p. 73.]

66. Let B be an $n \times n$ matrix such that $b_{11} \neq 1$ and let $A = B - I$. Define a sequence of matrices $A^{(k)} = [a_{ij}^{(k)}]$ such that

$$A^{(1)} = A$$
$$a_{ij}^{(k+1)} = a_{ij}^{(k)} - a_{ik}^{(k)} a_{kj}^{(k)} / a_{kk}^{(k)} \qquad k = 1, \ldots, n$$

(a) Prove that $a_{ij}^{(k)} = 0$ if $i < k$ or $j < k$ for $k = 1, \ldots, n$, and thus deduce that $A^{(n+1)} = 0$.

(b) Thus show that B may be expanded as in the previous problem with $D = I$, $u_i^{(j)} = a_{ji}^{(i)}/a_{ii}^{(i)}, v_i^{(j)} = a_{ij}^{(i)}$.

(c) Specialize the algorithm of part c of the previous problem for this expansion. [Ref.: Wilf (1960), p. 74.]

*67. (a) Show that (9.9-8) and (9.9-9) may be replaced by (9.9-12) and (9.9-13).

(b) Derive the equations analogous to (9.9-10) to (9.9-13) if the only matrices to be inverted are S and $P - QS^{-1}R$.

68. Invert the matrix of coefficients in Prob. 15 using (a) the method of Sec. 9.9-1; (b) the method of Prob. 60; (c) the method of Prob. 61; (d) the method of Prob. 62; (e) the method of Prob. 64; (f) the method of Probs. 65, 66; (g) partitioning with P a 2×2 matrix.

69. Repeat the calculations of the previous problem using the matrix of Prob. 17.

chapter 10

THE CALCULATION OF EIGENVALUES AND EIGENVECTORS OF MATRICES

10.1 BASIC RELATIONSHIPS

Let A be a square matrix of order n. Its eigenvalues $\lambda_1, \ldots, \lambda_n$ are the solutions of the determinantal equation, called the characteristic equation†

$$|A - \lambda I| = 0 \tag{10.1-1}$$

Corresponding to each distinct eigenvalue λ_i, there exists at least one solution (determined to within a multiplicative constant) of the system of linear equations

$$A\mathbf{x} = \lambda_i \mathbf{x} \tag{10.1-2}$$

This solution $\mathbf{x}_i^T = [x_i^{(1)}, x_i^{(2)}, \ldots, x_i^{(n)}]$ is a *right eigenvector* of A. (In what follows the term *eigenvector* will refer exclusively to right eigenvectors.) A *left eigenvector* corresponding to λ_i is a solution of

$$\mathbf{y}^T A = \lambda_i \mathbf{y}^T \tag{10.1-3}$$

Therefore, a left eigenvector of A is an eigenvector of A^T. It is easily

† Since the great majority of computational problems involve real matrices, we shall, except in Sec. 10.7, assume throughout this chapter, for simplicity, that A is real. As will generally be clear from the context, many of the theorems we shall consider are also true when A is complex or, if the real matrix is assumed symmetric, when A is Hermitian. Of course, even for real matrices, eigenvalues and eigenvectors may be complex.

shown $\{1\}$ that, if $\mathbf{y}_k$ and $\mathbf{x}_j$ are, respectively, left and right eigenvectors corresponding to distinct eigenvalues, then $\mathbf{y}_k$ and $\mathbf{x}_j$ are orthogonal.   In this chapter we shall be interested in methods for the calculation of some or all of the eigenvalues and some or all of the eigenvectors of A.   First, however, we shall review some of the basic theorems and relationships which are necessary to understand the development that follows.

10.1-1   Basic theorems

In this section we list four basic theorems concerning the eigenvalues and eigenvectors of a matrix with which the reader should be familiar. Proofs of three of them are left to a problem $\{2\}$.

Theorem 10.1   If $\lambda_1, \lambda_2, \ldots, \lambda_n$ are the eigenvalues of A, then the eigenvalues of A^k are $\lambda_1^k, \lambda_2^k, \ldots, \lambda_n^k$.   More generally, if $p(x)$ is a polynomial, the eigenvalues of $p(A)$ are $p(\lambda_1), \ldots, p(\lambda_n)$.

Theorem 10.2   If A is real and symmetric, all eigenvalues and eigenvectors are real.   Moreover, eigenvectors corresponding to distinct eigenvalues are orthogonal and the left eigenvector corresponding to the eigenvector $\mathbf{x}_i$ is $\mathbf{x}_i^T$.

Theorem 10.3   Any similarity transformation PAP^{-1} applied to A leaves the eigenvalues of the matrix unchanged.

Proof   Let λ be an eigenvalue of A and $\mathbf{x}$ the associated eigenvector. Then

$$A\mathbf{x} = \lambda\mathbf{x}$$

so that

$$PA\mathbf{x} = \lambda P\mathbf{x} \tag{10.1-4}$$

Let $\mathbf{y} = P\mathbf{x}$ so that $\mathbf{x} = P^{-1}\mathbf{y}$.   Substituting in (10.1-4) we get

$$PAP^{-1}\mathbf{y} = \lambda\mathbf{y} \tag{10.1-5}$$

Thus λ is an eigenvalue of PAP^{-1} and $\mathbf{y}$ is the associated eigenvector.

Theorem 10.4 (Cayley-Hamilton)   Let

$$f(\lambda) = |A - \lambda I| = 0 \tag{10.1-6}$$

be the characteristic equation of A.   Then $f(A) = 0$.

10.1-2   The characteristic equation

One method of determining the eigenvalues of A is to find the roots of the polynomial equation (10.1-1).   For this purpose the methods of Chap. 8

may be used.   But before we can use most of these methods to find the roots of (10.1-1) we must determine the coefficients of the characteristic equation itself.   Direct calculation of these coefficients from the definition of the determinant is never recommended except for very low order matrices, since it involves an astronomical amount of calculation.   Here we present two methods for finding the coefficients of the powers of λ in the characteristic equation without direct evaluation of the determinant.

1. *Krylov's method*   We write the characteristic equation as

$$f(\lambda) = \lambda^n + \sum_{i=0}^{n-1} b_i \lambda^i = 0 \tag{10.1-7}$$

From the Cayley-Hamilton theorem we have

$$A^n + \sum_{i=0}^{n-1} b_i A^i = 0 \tag{10.1-8}$$

Then, for any vector $\mathbf{y}$,

$$A^n \mathbf{y} + \sum_{i=0}^{n-1} b_i A^i \mathbf{y} = 0 \tag{10.1-9}$$

Equation (10.1-9) is a system of n linear equations in the n unknowns $b_0, \ldots, b_{n-1}$ which can be solved by any of the methods of the previous chapter.   Note that the calculation of $A^i \mathbf{y} = A(A^{i-1}\mathbf{y})$ requires n^2 multiplications so that about n^3 multiplications are required to establish (10.1-9) followed by about $\frac{1}{3}n^3$ to solve (10.1-9) by the method of Sec. 9.3.

2. *LeVerrier's method*   Using the property that the sum of the eigenvalues of any matrix is equal to the trace of the matrix, we may, using Theorem 10.1, write

$$\sum_{i=1}^{n} \lambda_i^k = t_k \qquad k = 1, \ldots, n \tag{10.1-10}$$

where t_k is the trace of A^k.   In Sec. 8.10-3 we noted that the sums of the powers of the roots of a polynomial could easily be computed using the coefficients of the polynomial.   This process is easily reversed; the coefficients of the polynomial are easily computed if the sums of the powers of its roots are known {3}.   Thus, using (10.1-10), we may compute the coefficients of the characteristic equation.   But LeVerrier's method is much inferior to Krylov's because of the necessity of actually computing $A^k, k = 1, \ldots, n$.

In a problem {4} we consider another technique of computing the coefficients of the characteristic polynomial.   In general, direct computation of these coefficients is inferior (i.e., less efficient) to the methods which will be discussed later in this chapter.

10.1-3   The location of and bounds on the eigenvalues

In the Lehmer-Schur method (Sec. 8.10-1) we derived a means for testing whether a given circle contained a root of a polynomial.   In this section we consider some of the more important among the many theorems which deal with the location of the eigenvalues of a matrix (i.e., the location of the zeros of the characteristic polynomial).   These theorems may be used, for example, to estimate the magnitude of the largest and smallest eigenvalues in magnitude and thus to estimate $\|A\|$ and the condition of A. Such estimates may also be used to generate initial approximations to be used in iterative methods for determining eigenvalues (see Secs. 10.2 and 10.3).

1. *Gerschgorin's theorem*   Let $A = [a_{ij}]$ and let $C_i, i = 1, \ldots, n$ be the circles with centers a_{ii} and radii

$$r_i = \sum_{\substack{k=1 \\ k \neq i}}^{n} |a_{ik}| \qquad i = 1, \ldots, n \tag{10.1-11}$$

Further let

$$D = \bigcup_{i=1}^{n} C_i \tag{10.1-12}$$

Then we may state

Theorem 10.5 (Gerschgorin)†   All the eigenvalues of A lie within the domain D.

Proof   We use the result of Prob. 30 of Chap. 9 that, if the component of largest magnitude of the solution of $B\mathbf{x} = 0$ is the ith component, then with $B = [b_{ij}]$

$$|b_{ii}| \leqq \sum_{\substack{k=1 \\ k \neq i}}^{n} |b_{ik}| \tag{10.1-13}$$

Letting $B = A - \lambda I$ where λ is an eigenvalue of A we have

$$|\lambda - a_{ii}| \leqq \sum_{\substack{k=1 \\ k \neq i}}^{n} |a_{ik}| \tag{10.1-14}$$

Equation (10.1-14) holds for any eigenvalue (although i may vary from one eigenvalue to another), and this is sufficient to prove the theorem.

† This theorem is also valid when the elements of A are complex.

As a consequence of Theorem 10.5 we get the two results of Prob. 30b of Chap. 9:

Corollary 10.1 The spectral radius of A is bounded by

$$\rho(A) \leqq \max_i \sum_{k=1}^{n} |a_{ik}| \tag{10.1-15}$$

Corollary 10.2 The spectral radius of A^{-1} is such that

$$\frac{1}{\rho(A^{-1})} \geqq \min_i \left(|a_{ii}| - \sum_{\substack{k=1 \\ k \neq i}}^{n} |a_{ik}| \right) \tag{10.1-16}$$

By making use of the result of Theorem 10.3, it may be possible to improve upon the bound for the eigenvalues given by Gerschgorin's theorem by first applying a similarity transformation to A {5}.

2. A number of theorems give information about the eigenvalues of a matrix by using related norms and analogous quantities. Theorem 9.2 on page 418 was one such theorem. The following are three other theorems of this type:

Theorem 10.6 Let A be symmetric and positive definite. Then

$$\rho(A) = \max_{\mathbf{x}} \frac{\mathbf{x}^* A \mathbf{x}}{\mathbf{x}^* \mathbf{x}}$$
$$\frac{1}{\rho(A^{-1})} = \min_{\mathbf{x}} \frac{\mathbf{x}^* A \mathbf{x}}{\mathbf{x}^* \mathbf{x}} \tag{10.1-17}$$

where $\mathbf{x}$ is an arbitrary real or complex vector and, as it will throughout this chapter, the superscript * denotes the conjugate transpose.

The proof is precisely similar to that of Theorem 9.2. If A is not positive definite the theorem is still true if $\rho(A)$ is replaced by $\lambda_{\max}$, $1/\rho(A^{-1})$ is replaced by $\lambda_{\min}$, where $\lambda_{\min} \leqq \lambda_i \leqq \lambda_{\max}$ for any eigenvalue λ_i.

Theorem 10.7 For an arbitrary nonsingular matrix A

$$\frac{1}{\rho[(A^T A)^{-1}]} \leqq |\lambda_i|^2 \leqq \rho(A^T A) \tag{10.1-18}$$

where λ_i is any eigenvalue of A.

Proof Let $\mathbf{x}_i$ be the eigenvector corresponding to λ_i. Then

$$A \mathbf{x}_i = \lambda_i \mathbf{x}_i \tag{10.1-19}$$

and

$$\mathbf{x}_i^* A^T = \bar{\lambda}_i \mathbf{x}_i^* \tag{10.1-20}$$

Therefore,

$$\mathbf{x}_i^* A^T A \mathbf{x}_i = |\lambda_i|^2 \mathbf{x}_i^* \mathbf{x}_i \tag{10.1-21}$$

Using Theorem 10.6 we have

$$\rho(A^T A) \geqq \frac{\mathbf{x}_i^* A^T A \mathbf{x}_i}{\mathbf{x}_i^* \mathbf{x}_i} \geqq \frac{1}{\rho[(A^T A)^{-1}]} \tag{10.1-22}$$

which with (10.1-21) proves the theorem.

If A is singular the theorem is true if the left-hand side of the inequality (10.1-18) is replaced by 0.

Theorem 10.8 (Schur)   Let λ_i, $i = 1, \ldots, n$ be the eigenvalues of a matrix A.   Then

$$\sum_{i=1}^{n} |\lambda_i|^2 \leqq \|A\|_E^2 \tag{10.1-23}$$

Proof   We shall use the result of Theorem 10.11 (page 471) that there exists a unitary matrix Q such that

$$Q^* A Q = T \tag{10.1-24}$$

where $T = [t_{ij}]$ is triangular (but may have complex elements).   Since T is similar to A the eigenvalues of A appear on the diagonal of T.   Therefore,

$$\sum_{i=1}^{n} |\lambda_i|^2 \leqq \sum_{i=1}^{n} \sum_{j=1}^{n} |t_{ij}|^2 \tag{10.1-25}$$

Now taking the conjugate transpose of both sides of (10.1-24), we obtain

$$Q^* A^T Q = T^* \tag{10.1-26}$$

and from (10.1-24) and (10.1-26)

$$TT^* = Q^* A A^T Q \tag{10.1-27}$$

Therefore, TT^* and AA^T are similar and thus {6}

$$\mathrm{tr}\,(TT^*) = \mathrm{tr}\,(AA^T) \tag{10.1-28}$$

But $\mathrm{tr}\,(TT^*)$ is precisely the right-hand side of (10.1-25) {6} and, from (9.4-9), $\mathrm{tr}\,(AA^T)$ is $\|A\|_E^2$.   Thus, using (10.1-25) and (10.1-28),

$$\sum_{i=1}^{n} |\lambda_i|^2 \leqq \sum_{i=1}^{n} \sum_{j=1}^{n} |t_{ij}|^2 = \mathrm{tr}\,(TT^*) = \mathrm{tr}\,(AA^T) = \|A\|_E^2 \tag{10.1-29}$$

which proves the theorem.

10.1-4   Canonical forms

One of the most important techniques in the calculation of eigenvalues and eigenvectors of matrices is to transform the given matrix into some canonical form.   Here we consider some of the theorems dealing with these canonical forms.   In particular we shall indicate the basic differences that occur in considering symmetric and nonsymmetric matrices since these have important implications on what follows in this chapter.

Theorem 10.9   Eigenvectors of an arbitrary matrix A corresponding to distinct eigenvalues are linearly independent.

Proof   By induction.   Let x_1 and x_2 be eigenvectors corresponding to λ_1 and λ_2, $\lambda_1 \neq \lambda_2$.   Then if $a_1 x_1 + a_2 x_2 = 0$ we also have

$$a_1 \lambda_1 x_1 + a_2 \lambda_2 x_2 = 0$$

which implies $a_1 = a_2 = 0$ (why?).   Now suppose $x_1, \ldots, x_k$ corresponding to distinct eigenvalues $\lambda_1, \ldots, \lambda_k$ are independent.   Then if x_{k+1} corresponds to λ_{k+1} consider

$$a_1 x_1 + \cdots + a_{k+1} x_{k+1} = 0 \tag{10.1-30}$$

Premultiplying by A we have

$$a_1 \lambda_1 x_1 + \cdots + a_{k+1} \lambda_{k+1} x_{k+1} = 0 \tag{10.1-31}$$

If $\lambda_{k+1} = 0$ it follows immediately from (10.1-31) and the induction hypothesis that $a_{k+1} = 0$.   If $\lambda_{k+1} \neq 0$ divide (10.1-31) by λ_{k+1} and subtract from (10.1-30) to obtain

$$a_1(1 - \lambda_1/\lambda_{k+1})x_1 + \cdots + a_k(1 - \lambda_k/\lambda_{k+1})x_k = 0 \tag{10.1-32}$$

Since $\lambda_1, \ldots, \lambda_{k+1}$ are all distinct, the induction hypothesis again gives $a_1 = a_2 = \cdots = a_k = 0$ and (10.1-30) then gives $a_{k+1} = 0$.   This proves the theorem.

Theorem 10.10   Let A be an arbitrary matrix whose eigenvalues are all distinct.   Then there exists a similarity transformation such that

$$P^{-1}AP = D$$

where D is a diagonal matrix whose diagonal elements are the eigenvalues of A.

Proof   Let P be the matrix whose columns are the (right) eigenvectors of A.   Since the eigenvalues are distinct, P exists (but may be complex).   Then

$$AP = PD \tag{10.1-33}$$

where D is a diagonal matrix with the eigenvalues on the diagonal. Since the eigenvectors are linearly independent by Theorem 10.9, P^{-1} exists and

$$P^{-1}AP = D \tag{10.1-34}$$

which proves the theorem.   Note that the rows of P^{-1} are the left eigenvectors of A.

The computational disadvantage of Theorem 10.10 is the need to find a matrix P and its inverse.   It would be more convenient if we could diagonalize a matrix using an orthogonal or unitary transformation.   The most general theorem we can prove in this case is

Theorem 10.11   For an arbitrary matrix A there exists a unitary transformation Q such that

$$Q^*AQ = T \tag{10.1-35}$$

where T is triangular (but may have complex elements).

Proof   By induction on the order n of the matrix.   If $n = 1$ the theorem is true since a matrix of order 1 is triangular.   Suppose the theorem is true for matrices of order $n - 1$ and let A be a matrix of order n.   Let $\mathbf{u}_1$ be an eigenvector of A of magnitude 1 corresponding to any eigenvalue, say λ_1.   Let

$$\mathbf{u}_1, \mathbf{v}_1, \ldots, \mathbf{v}_{n-1} \tag{10.1-36}$$

be an orthonormal set of vectors.†   If Q_1 is the matrix whose columns are $\mathbf{u}_1, \mathbf{v}_1, \ldots, \mathbf{v}_{n-1}$ we have

$$A_1 = Q_1^*AQ_1 = \begin{bmatrix} \lambda_1 & \mathbf{w}^T \\ \mathbf{0} & B \end{bmatrix} \tag{10.1-37}$$

By the induction hypothesis there exists a unitary matrix P of order $n - 1$ such that

$$P^*BP = T_{n-1} \tag{10.1-38}$$

Now let

$$Q_2 = \begin{bmatrix} 1 & \mathbf{0}^T \\ \mathbf{0} & P \end{bmatrix} \tag{10.1-39}$$

so that Q_2 is unitary of order n.   Then from (10.1-37) to (10.1-39)

$$Q_2^*Q_1^*AQ_1Q_2 = Q_2^* \begin{bmatrix} \lambda_1 & \mathbf{w}^T \\ \mathbf{0} & B \end{bmatrix} Q_2 = \begin{bmatrix} \lambda_1 & \mathbf{w}^TP \\ \mathbf{0} & T_{n-1} \end{bmatrix} = T_n \tag{10.1-40}$$

where T_n is triangular of order n.   Setting $Q = Q_1Q_2$ proves the theorem.

† I.e., $\mathbf{u}_1^*\mathbf{v}_i = 0$, $i = 1, \ldots, n - 1$ and $\mathbf{v}_i^*\mathbf{v}_j = \delta_{ij}$, $i, j = 1, \ldots, n - 1$.

The proof of Theorem 10.11 implies that, if all the eigenvalues of A are real, then Q is a real orthogonal matrix (why?). In particular, since the eigenvalues of a symmetric matrix are real and since the orthogonal transformation of a symmetric matrix is symmetric, we have

Corollary 10.3   If A is symmetric, then there exists an orthogonal matrix Q such that

$$Q^T A Q = D \tag{10.1-41}$$

with D as in Theorem 10.10.

For computational purposes this corollary is an improvement over Theorem 10.10 not only in that the similarity transformation is replaced by an orthogonal one but also in that there is no requirement that the eigenvalues be distinct. Since it follows from (10.4-41) and the orthogonality of Q that

$$AQ = QD \tag{10.1-42}$$

we have the result that the columns of Q are the eigenvectors of A.

Since a triangular matrix T yields its eigenvalues just as easily as a diagonal matrix, the reader may think that Theorem 10.11, except for the necessity of using complex arithmetic, will be as useful in practice as Corollary 10.3. But in practice it is much easier to diagonalize symmetric matrices than it is to triangularize nonsymmetric matrices, as we shall see in Secs. 10.4 and 10.5.

Theorem 10.10 and Corollary 10.3 take care of the diagonalization of all but nonsymmetric matrices with multiple eigenvalues. The theorem covering this case is

Theorem 10.12   Given an arbitrary matrix A, there exists a nonsingular matrix P, whose elements may be complex, such that

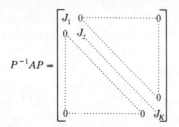

$$P^{-1}AP = \tag{10.1-43}$$

where J_k, $k = 1, \ldots, K \leqq n$ is a matrix with an eigenvalue λ_i of A on its main diagonal and 1's on the diagonal above the main diagonal.

Thus

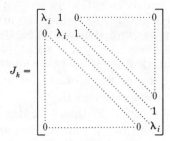

$$J_k = \begin{bmatrix} \lambda_i & 1 & 0 & \cdots\cdots\cdots\cdots & 0 \\ 0 & \lambda_i & 1 & & \\ & & & \ddots & \\ & & & & 0 \\ & & & & 1 \\ 0 & \cdots\cdots\cdots\cdots & & 0 & \lambda_i \end{bmatrix}$$ (10.1-44)

Note that a given eigenvalue may appear as the diagonal element of more than one J_k. The matrix in (10.1-43) is called the *Jordan canonical form* of A. The determinants

$$\det(J_k - \lambda I) = (\lambda_i - \lambda)^{\nu_k}$$ (10.1-45)

where ν_k is the order of J_k, are called the *elementary divisors* of A. If $\nu_k = 1$ we say the elementary divisor is linear. The proof of Theorem 10.12 is beyond the scope of this book [see, for example, Bodewig (1959), pp. 82–88].

It follows from Theorem 10.12 that, if the eigenvalues are distinct, all the elementary divisors are linear, which gives us another proof of Theorem 10.10. Theorem 10.12 together with Corollary 10.3 implies that, for a symmetric matrix, the elementary divisors are linear whether or not the eigenvalues are distinct. More important is the result that, if the elementary divisors are linear, then corresponding to an eigenvalue of multiplicity k there are k linearly independent eigenvectors. Therefore, Theorem 10.10 may be generalized to include all matrices with linear elementary divisors. If, however, there are nonlinear elementary divisors then Theorem 10.12 implies that there are eigenvalues whose multiplicity is greater than the number of independent eigenvectors corresponding to them. The simplicity of the result of Corollary 10.3 in comparison with the results of Theorems 10.11 and 10.12 is an indication that the calculation of the eigenvalues and eigenvectors of symmetric matrices will cause fewer difficulties than that of nonsymmetric matrices. The remainder of this chapter will bear out this indication.

With the theorems of this section as background, we are now ready to consider methods for the calculation of eigenvalues and eigenvectors. We begin with methods for the calculation of the largest eigenvalue in magnitude.

10.2 THE LARGEST EIGENVALUE IN MAGNITUDE BY THE POWER METHOD

The basis of our techniques for determining the largest eigenvalue in magnitude is very similar to Bernoulli's method (Sec. 8.10-3) for determining the zeros of polynomials. And this, of course, should not be surprising because of the similarity between the problems of finding the eigenvalues of a matrix and the zeros of a polynomial.

The basic assumption of this section is that all the elementary divisors of A are linear. However, the method of this section is often applicable even when A has nonlinear elementary divisors {9}. This assumption implies, as noted in the previous section, that there are n linearly independent eigenvectors of A and thus that the eigenvectors span n space. Therefore, any vector $\mathbf{v}_0$ can be expressed as a linear combination

$$\mathbf{v}_0 = \sum_{i=1}^{n} \alpha_i \mathbf{x}_i \tag{10.2-1}$$

where $\mathbf{x}_i, i = 1, \ldots, n$ are the eigenvectors of A. If λ_i is the eigenvalue corresponding to $\mathbf{x}_i$ then

$$A\mathbf{v}_0 = \sum_{i=1}^{n} \alpha_i \lambda_i \mathbf{x}_i \tag{10.2-2}$$

and in general the mth *iterated vector* is given by

$$\mathbf{v}_m = A^m \mathbf{v}_0 = \sum_{i=1}^{n} \alpha_i \lambda_i^m \mathbf{x}_i \tag{10.2-3}$$

Now we order the eigenvalues so that

$$|\lambda_1| \geq |\lambda_2| \geq |\lambda_3| \geq \cdots \geq |\lambda_n| \tag{10.2-4}$$

If then, in particular, λ_1 is dominant (i.e., $|\lambda_1| > |\lambda_2|$) and, therefore, real we have

Theorem 10.13 (Von Mises)   If the matrix A has n linearly independent eigenvectors and if the largest eigenvalue in magnitude λ_1 is dominant, then if $\mathbf{v}_0$ has a component in the direction of $\mathbf{x}_1$

$$\lim_{m \to \infty} (1/\lambda_1^m) A^m \mathbf{v}_0 = \alpha_1 \mathbf{x}_1 \tag{10.2-5}$$

The proof follows immediately from (10.2-3). The requirement that $\mathbf{v}_0$ have a component in the direction of $\mathbf{x}_1$ is assurance that $\alpha_1 \neq 0$.

As a consequence of this theorem we see that, if $\mathbf{y}$ is any vector not orthogonal to x_1, then, using (10.2-5),

$$\lambda_1 = \lim_{m \to \infty} \frac{\mathbf{y}^T \mathbf{v}_{m+1}}{\mathbf{y}^T \mathbf{v}_m} \qquad (10.2\text{-}6)$$

The numbers $\mathbf{y}^T\mathbf{v}_{m+1} = \mathbf{y}^T A \mathbf{v}_m$ are called *Schwarz constants*. A convenient choice of $\mathbf{y}$ in practice is the vector with a component of 1 in the position corresponding to the maximum component of $\mathbf{v}_m$ and zero elsewhere. This minimizes the computation in (10.2-6), and the use of the largest component minimizes the error in the division in (10.2-6). Of course, early in the computation the largest component of $\mathbf{v}_m$ may vary, but ultimately it will be the largest component of the eigenvector. In practice then, we compute successive approximations to λ_1 as the ratio of the largest component of successive $\mathbf{v}_m$'s.

Example 10.1   Find the dominant eigenvalue of the matrix

$$A = \begin{bmatrix} 1.0 & 1.0 & .5 \\ 1.0 & 1.0 & .25 \\ .5 & .25 & 2.0 \end{bmatrix}$$

using $\mathbf{v}_0^T = (1,1,1)$.

In the table below each $\mathbf{v}_m$ was calculated using (10.2-3) and then "normalized" to make its largest component 1 before doing the next iteration. The quantity λ is the normalizing factor, and thus represents the ratio of the largest components of $\mathbf{v}_m$ and $\mathbf{v}_{m-1}$ (e.g., the first entry in the λ column is the ratio of the third component of the unnormalized $\mathbf{v}_1$ to the third component of $\mathbf{v}_0$).

m	$\mathbf{v}_m^T$ (normalized)	λ
1	(.9091,.8182,1.0000)	2.7500000
5	(.7651,.6674,1.0000)	2.5587918
10	(.7494,.6508,1.0000)	2.5380029
11	(.7489,.6504,1.0000)	2.5373873
12	(.7486,.6501,1.0000)	2.5370284
13	(.7484,.6499,1.0000)	2.5368188
14	(.7484,.6498,1.0000)	2.5366969
15	(.7483,.6497,1.0000)	2.5366256
16	(.7483,.6497,1.0000)	2.5365840
17	(.7482,.6497,1.0000)	2.5365598
18	(.7482,.6497,1.0000)	2.5365456
19	(.7482,.6497,1.0000)	2.5365374
20	(.7482,.6497,1.0000)	2.5365323

The calculations were performed on a digital computer using floating-point arithmetic with an eight-digit fractional part. The values of $\mathbf{v}_m$ are rounded values. To eight figures the true value of λ is 2.5365258 and that of x_1 is (.74822116, .64966116,

1.00000000). These values were reached in 28 iterations. Although a symmetric matrix was used in this example, remember that the power method requires only that the elementary divisors be linear.

From (10.2-3)

$$\mathbf{v}_m = \lambda_1^m \left[\alpha_1 \mathbf{x}_1 + \sum_{i=2}^{n} \left(\frac{\lambda_i}{\lambda_1} \right)^m \alpha_i \mathbf{x}_i \right] \tag{10.2-7}$$

Therefore, the *rate* of convergence of the power method depends upon how fast the ratios $(\lambda_i/\lambda_1)^m$ go to zero; in particular this rate depends upon the ratio $|\lambda_2|/|\lambda_1|$. The number of iterations required to get a desired degree of convergence depends upon both the rate of convergence and on how large α_1 is compared with the other α_i, the latter depending in turn on the choice of $\mathbf{v}_0$. In Example 10.1 the convergence was quite slow. In later examples we shall see how these two factors—$|\lambda_2/\lambda_1|$ and α_1—affect the convergence. Later in this section we shall also consider means of speeding up the convergence.

If $\mathbf{v}_0$ has no component in the $\mathbf{x}_1$ direction and $|\lambda_2| > |\lambda_3|$, then the iteration should converge to λ_2 and $\mathbf{x}_2$ (why?). In practical computation, however, roundoff error will generally introduce a component in the $\mathbf{x}_1$ direction so that eventually the iteration will converge to λ_1 and $\mathbf{x}_1$. Nevertheless a good approximation to λ_2 and $\mathbf{x}_2$ may be obtained before the term in λ_1 dominates.

Example 10.2   Apply the power method to the matrix of Example 10.1 using $\mathbf{v}_0^T = (-.64966116, .74822116, 0)$ which is orthogonal to $\mathbf{x}_1$. Therefore, since A is symmetric, $\mathbf{v}_0$ has no component in the $\mathbf{x}_1$ direction.

Corresponding to the table in Example 10.1 we have

m	$\mathbf{v}_m^T$ (normalized)	λ
1	$(-.7154, -.7154, 1.0000)$	$-.1377753$
2	$(-.6360, -.8068, 1.0000)$	1.4634741
3	$(-.6369, -.8058, 1.0000)$	1.4803108
4	$(-.6369, -.8058, 1.0000)$	1.4801194
5	$(-.6369, -.8058, 1.0000)$	1.4801216
6	$(-.6369, -.8058, 1.0000)$	1.4801217
7	$(-.6369, -.8058, 1.0000)$	1.4801219
10	$(-.6369, -.8058, 1.0000)$	1.4801240
15	$(-.6368, -.8057, 1.0000)$	1.4801606
20	$(-.6356, -.8044, 1.0000)$	1.4807007
30	$(-.4008, -.5576, 1.0000)$	1.5931941
40	$(.7180, .6179, 1.0000)$	2.4976711
50	$(.7481, .6495, 1.0000)$	2.5363412
61	$(.7482, .6497, 1.0000)$	2.5365253

Initially the iteration converges to a value very nearly equal to $\lambda_2 = 1.4801215$, but although $\mathbf{v}_0$ is orthogonal to $\mathbf{x}_1$, roundoff introduces a component in the $\mathbf{x}_1$ direction and slowly, but very slowly, the term in $\mathbf{x}_1$ dominates as in Example 10.1. The reason the convergence to λ_2 is so good and so rapid is that, as we shall see in a later example, the ratio of $|\lambda_2/\lambda_3|$ is very large.

The drawbacks to this method are similar to those of Bernoulli's method. For example, if the dominant eigenvalue is complex, the iteration no longer converges and a technique similar to that in Sec. 8.10-3 must be used {10}. Similarly other special cases require special treatment. However, when the dominant eigenvalue is multiple but real, the method does converge. For, if λ_1 has multiplicity k

$$\mathbf{v}_m = A^m\mathbf{v}_0 = \lambda_1^m \sum_{i=1}^{k} \alpha_i\mathbf{x}_i + \sum_{i=k+1}^{n} \lambda_i^m\alpha_i\mathbf{x}_i \tag{10.2-8}$$

and again the term in λ_1 dominates. Further, since $\sum_{i=1}^{k} \alpha_i\mathbf{x}_i$ is an eigenvector the process converges to an eigenvector as before. A procedure to get the other eigenvectors corresponding to λ_1 is considered in a problem {11}.

10.2-1   Acceleration of convergence

Because the power method may converge slowly, means of accelerating the convergence are clearly desirable. In this section we consider four such means.

1. *The δ^2 process*   This application of the δ^2 process is similar to our previous applications. We assume that both λ_1 and λ_2 are real and that neither $-\lambda_1$ nor $-\lambda_2$ is an eigenvalue. Let $\mathbf{e}_i$ be the ith column of the identity matrix I. Then from (10.2-3) we calculate the Schwarz constant

$$\mathbf{e}_i^T\mathbf{v}_m = \sum_{i=1}^{n} a_i\lambda_i^m \tag{10.2-9}$$

where a_i depends on α_i and the ith component of $\mathbf{x}_i$. Then

$$\frac{\mathbf{e}_i^T\mathbf{v}_{m+1}}{\mathbf{e}_i^T\mathbf{v}_m} = \frac{a_1\lambda_1^{m+1} + \sum_{i=2}^{n} a_i\lambda_i^{m+1}}{a_1\lambda_1^m + \sum_{i=2}^{n} a_i\lambda_i^m} \tag{10.2-10}$$

Dividing numerator and denominator by $a_1 \lambda_1^m$ and expanding the denominator in a power series we get

$$\frac{\mathbf{e}_i^T \mathbf{v}_{m+1}}{\mathbf{e}_i^T \mathbf{v}_m} = \lambda_1 + \beta_i \left(\frac{\lambda_2}{\lambda_1}\right)^m$$

$$+ \left[\text{terms in } \left(\frac{\lambda_3}{\lambda_1}\right)^m, \ \ldots, \ \left(\frac{\lambda_n}{\lambda_1}\right)^m \text{ and higher powers} \right] \quad (10.2\text{-}11)$$

If we are near convergence the terms in parentheses are small and we have

$$\lambda_1 \approx R_m - \beta_i r^m \qquad (10.2\text{-}12)$$

with $R_m = \mathbf{e}_i^T \mathbf{v}_{m+1} / \mathbf{e}_i^T \mathbf{v}_m$ and $r = \lambda_2/\lambda_1$. Then proceeding as in Sec. 8.7 we get as a better approximation to λ_1 {16}

$$\lambda_1 \approx R_{m+2} - [(\Delta R_{m+1})^2 / \Delta^2 R_m] \qquad (10.2\text{-}13)$$

If we apply (10.2-13) with $m = 10$ and $i = 3$ in (10.2-11) to the results in Example 10.1, we get as our new approximation $\lambda_1 = 2.5365266$, which is better than that achieved after 20 iterations.

2. *Wilkinson's method*   Suppose all the eigenvalues are real but that the power method is converging slowly because there are two eigenvalues nearly equal in magnitude. Consider the matrix $A - pI$ which has eigenvalues $\lambda_i - p$. By a judicious choice of p, it may be possible to speed up the convergence markedly. We consider two cases:

(i) If the eigenvalues are all positive and λ_n is the smallest eigenvalue, then setting $p = \lambda_n$ will speed up the convergence because $(\lambda_1 - p)/(\lambda_2 - p) > \lambda_1/\lambda_2$. Of course, we need some knowledge of the eigenvalues to apply this technique, but if, for example, we know that all the eigenvalues are positive then trial values of p can be chosen to see which achieves the best rate of convergence. In fact, the optimal value of p is not λ_n but $(\lambda_2 + \lambda_n)/2$ {17}.

(ii) If the eigenvalues have both signs then p should be chosen so that, among the $\lambda_i - p$, the two subdominant ones have approximately equal magnitude and opposite signs (why?). Again, of course, we need some knowledge of the eigenvalues to apply this technique.

This method is an excellent example of one which, when used by an experienced numerical analyst, can be very powerful; but if used haphazardly—that is, if the value of p is not chosen judiciously—it will be little better than the power method. As an example of this method, if we use $p = .75$ in Example 10.1, then, in place of the table in that example, we get

m	$\mathbf{v}_m^T$ (normalized)	λ
5	(.7516,.6522,1.0000)	1.7914011
6	(.7491,.6511,1.0000)	1.7888443
7	(.7488,.6501,1.0000)	1.7873300
8	(.7484,.6499,1.0000)	1.7869152
9	(.7483,.6497,1.0000)	1.7866587
10	(.7482,.6497,1.0000)	1.7865914

which is a better result than after 15 iterations in Example 10.1.   Convergence to $\lambda_1 = 1.7865258$ was achieved in 19 iterations.   The reason why $p = .75$ was a good choice will become apparent when we calculate all the eigenvalues of the matrix A in Example 10.4.

3. *The Rayleigh quotient*   If A is symmetric then the eigenvectors are orthogonal, and if we consider them to be orthonormal

$$\mathbf{v}_m^T A \mathbf{v}_m = \mathbf{v}_m^T \mathbf{v}_{m+1} = \sum_{i=1}^n \alpha_i^2 \lambda_i^{2m+1} \tag{10.2-14}$$

and

$$\mathbf{v}_m^T \mathbf{v}_m = \sum_{i=1}^n \alpha_i^2 \lambda_i^{2m} \tag{10.2-15}$$

We may write

$$\mathbf{v}_m^T \mathbf{v}_{m+1} / \mathbf{v}_m^T \mathbf{v}_m = \lambda_1 + O[(\lambda_i/\lambda_1)^{2m}] \tag{10.2-16}$$

By comparison for an arbitrary vector $\mathbf{y}$

$$\mathbf{y}^T \mathbf{v}_{m+1} / \mathbf{y}^T \mathbf{v}_m = \lambda_1 + O[(\lambda_i/\lambda_1)^m] \tag{10.2-17}$$

Since the higher-order terms in (10.2-16) will usually be smaller than those in (10.2-17), the former will generally give a better approximation to λ_1 than the power method itself.   For example, consider Example 10.1 with $m = 11$.   The unrounded values of $\mathbf{v}_{11}^T$ and $\mathbf{v}_{12}^T$ are, respectively, (.74888011,.65035358,1.0) and (.74860561,.65006512,1.0).   For these vectors the left-hand side of (10.2-16) is 2.5365256, which is a slightly better result than that achieved using the δ^2 process, which also used data through the twelfth iteration.   It is generally true that this technique will give better results than the δ^2 process {18}.   Therefore, for symmetric matrices, it is to be preferred.   The quotient in (10.2-16) is the *Rayleigh quotient* and bears a close resemblance to the quotient in Theorem 10.6.

The use of the Rayleigh quotient is closely connected with the method of steepest descent discussed in the previous chapter {18}.

4. *Matrix powers*   If two eigenvalues are nearly equal in magnitude, then in order to separate the eigenvalues we may compute A^2, A^4, A^8, ...   This technique is directly analogous to the root-squaring procedure of Sec. 8.10-2 but is, of course, very inefficient because the computation of each power of A requires n^3 operations.   It is therefore not recommended.

10.3   THE SUBDOMINANT EIGENVALUES

Often we wish to calculate not just the dominant eigenvalue but some and perhaps all of the other eigenvalues.   In Secs. 10.4 and 10.5 we shall consider techniques for calculating all the eigenvalues of a matrix.   Here we consider techniques of calculating one or more of the subdominant eigenvalues after the power method has been used to calculate the dominant eigenvalue.

The power method itself furnishes us with some information about the other eigenvalues.   For if λ_1 is the eigenvalue found by the power method, then from (10.2-3)

$$\mathbf{w}_m = \mathbf{v}_{m+1} - \lambda_1 \mathbf{v}_m = \sum_{i=2}^{n} \alpha_i(\lambda_i - \lambda_1)\lambda_i^m \mathbf{x}_i \qquad (10.3\text{-}1)$$

Therefore, the already computed iterated vectors can be used to generate a new sequence in which the term in λ_2 is dominant if $|\lambda_2| > |\lambda_3|$.   But notice that $\mathbf{w}_m$ is the difference of two nearly equal quantities, $\mathbf{v}_{m+1}$ and $\lambda_1 \mathbf{v}_m$, so that it is generally very difficult to retain significance in $\mathbf{w}_m$. Thus this technique, which is called *vector deflation*, is not generally very useful.   In this section we shall consider techniques which make use of the known values of λ_1 and $\mathbf{x}_1$ to compute subdominant eigenvalues but which do not encounter the difficulties of (10.3-1).

10.3-1   Matrix deflation

Theorem 10.14   Let λ_1 and $\mathbf{x}_1$ be an eigenvalue and the corresponding eigenvector of A.   Let $\mathbf{v}$ be any vector such that $\mathbf{v}^T\mathbf{x}_1 = 1$. Then the matrix

$$W_1 = A - \lambda_1 \mathbf{x}_1 \mathbf{v}^T \qquad (10.3\text{-}2)$$

has the same eigenvalues as A except that λ_1 is replaced by zero. W_1 is called the *deflated matrix*.

When A is nonsingular and has no nonlinear elementary divisors, the proof of this theorem is quite simple {21}. The proof we shall give, however, while not simple, does cover the cases of singular matrices and nonlinear elementary divisors. Moreover, this proof will itself indicate a method for calculating a convenient form of the deflated matrix.

Proof   Without loss of generality, we let $x_1^{(1)}$, the first component of x_1, be 1.   Now let

$$u = x_1 - e_1 \tag{10.3-3}$$

where e_1 is the first column of I.   Further, let

$$T = I + ue_1^T \tag{10.3-4}$$

Then we shall prove first

Lemma 10.1   The matrix

$$C = T^{-1}AT \tag{10.3-5}$$

has its first column equal to $\lambda_1 e_1$.

Proof   From (10.3-4) we get {22}

$$T^{-1} = I - ue_1^T \tag{10.3-6}$$

Then, if A_{10} is the first row of A,

$$C = (I - ue_1^T)A(I + ue_1^T) = A - uA_{10} + (A - uA_{10})ue_1^T \tag{10.3-7}$$

Now

$$A_{10}u = A_{10}(x_1 - e_1) = \lambda_1 x_1^{(1)} - a_{11} = \lambda_1 - a_{11} \tag{10.3-8}$$

and

$$Au = \lambda_1 x_1 - A_{01} \tag{10.3-9}$$

where A_{01} is the first column of A.   Using (10.3-8) and (10.3-9) in (10.3-7) we get {22}

$$C = A - uA_{10} + we_1^T \tag{10.3-10}$$

where

$$w = Au - (A_{10}u)u = a_{11}u - A_{01} + \lambda_1 e_1 \tag{10.3-11}$$

The first column of C, C_{01}, is given by

$$C_{01} = Ce_1 = Ae_1 - uA_{10}e_1 + we_1^Te_1$$
$$= A_{01} - a_{11}u + a_{11}u - A_{01} + \lambda_1 e_1 = \lambda_1 e_1 \tag{10.3-12}$$

which proves the lemma.

To complete the proof of the theorem, we consider the matrix

$$D = T^{-1}\mathbf{x}_1\mathbf{v}^T T \tag{10.3-13}$$

Using the fact that $\mathbf{v}^T\mathbf{x}_1 = 1$, we may show that {22}

$$D = \mathbf{e}_1\mathbf{v}^T + [1 - v^{(1)}]\mathbf{e}_1\mathbf{e}_1^T \tag{10.3-14}$$

where $v^{(1)}$ is the first component of $\mathbf{v}$. Thus D is a matrix with zeros in every row except the first. The first row D_{10} is given by

$$D_{10} = \mathbf{v}^T + [1 - v^{(1)}]\mathbf{e}_1^T \tag{10.3-15}$$

so that its first element is 1 and the rest are the components of $\mathbf{v}$. Now since C is similar to A, C has the same eigenvalues as A. Using Lemma 10.1 and the fact that D has only its first row nonzero, $C - \lambda_1 D$ has the same eigenvalues as A except that λ_1 is replaced by zero. But

$$C - \lambda_1 D = T^{-1}(A - \lambda_1\mathbf{x}_1\mathbf{v}^T)T = T^{-1}W_1 T \tag{10.3-16}$$

Thus W_1 is similar to $C - \lambda_1 D$, and the theorem is proved.

Using the result of this theorem we can show that the eigenvectors $\mathbf{x}_i$ of A other than $\mathbf{x}_1$ are related to those $\mathbf{w}_i$ of W_1 as follows {23}:

$$\mathbf{x}_i = \begin{cases} \mathbf{w}_i & \lambda_i = \lambda_1 \text{ and } (A - \lambda_1 I)\mathbf{w}_i = 0 \\ (\lambda_i - \lambda_1)\mathbf{w}_i + \lambda_1(\mathbf{v}^T\mathbf{w}_i)\mathbf{x}_1 & \lambda_i \neq \lambda_1 \end{cases} \tag{10.3-17}$$

If A has a nonlinear elementary divisor corresponding to λ_1, then some $\mathbf{w}_i$ corresponding to λ_1 will not satisfy the first case above {23}.

The way in which we shall use this theorem is clear; since the dominant eigenvalue of W_1 is λ_2 we may use the power method applied to W_1 to find λ_2 and $\mathbf{w}_2$. This deflation process may then be repeated with

$$W_2 = W_1 - \lambda_2\mathbf{w}_2\mathbf{v}_1^T \tag{10.3-18}$$

where $\mathbf{v}_1^T\mathbf{w}_2 = 1$, to get λ_3 and so on. If λ_1 is a multiple eigenvalue of multiplicity k the first k applications will result in λ_1 but different eigenvectors if there are no nonlinear elementary divisors corresponding to λ_1. The only remaining problem is the best choice of $\mathbf{v}$. We shall now consider two possibilities for the choice of $\mathbf{v}$ and a third type of deflation which is a variation on the previous discussion.

1. *Hotelling's deflation*   Here we let $\mathbf{v} = \mathbf{y}_1$, the left eigenvector corresponding to λ_1, suitably normalized so that $\mathbf{y}_1^T\mathbf{x}_1 = 1$. The advantage of this choice is that, because of the orthogonality of left and right eigenvectors corresponding to distinct eigenvalues, the eigenvectors of

$$W_1 = A - \lambda_1\mathbf{x}_1\mathbf{y}_1^T \tag{10.3-19}$$

are the same as those of A when there are no nonlinear elementary divisors $\{24\}$. Since $\mathbf{y}_1$ will not be known in general (and in fact $\mathbf{y}_1^T \mathbf{x}_1$ may be 0 $\{24\}$), this method is best applied to symmetric matrices in which case $\mathbf{y}_1 = \mathbf{x}_1$. In general then for Hotelling's deflation applied to symmetric matrices

$$W_i = W_{i-1} - \lambda_i \mathbf{x}_i \mathbf{x}_i^T \qquad i = 1, \ldots, n-1 \qquad W_0 = A \quad (10.3\text{-}20)$$

Example 10.3   Find the first subdominant eigenvalue of A in Example 10.1 using Hotelling's deflation.

Because A is symmetric we have

$$\mathbf{y}_1^T = .50456772\,(.74822116, .64966116, 1.00000000)$$

with the multiplicative factor required so that $\mathbf{y}_1^T \mathbf{x}_1 = 1$. Then we may calculate

$$W_1 = A - \lambda_1 \mathbf{x}_1 \mathbf{y}_1^T = \begin{bmatrix} .28349586 & .37787791 & -.45761010 \\ .37787791 & .45982742 & -.58146819 \\ -.45761010 & -.58146819 & .72015100 \end{bmatrix}$$

Using the power method with $\mathbf{v}_0^T = (1.0, 1.0, 1.0)$ we get convergence after six iterations to $\lambda_2 = 1.4801214$ and $\mathbf{x}_2 = (-.63686973, -.80577478, 1.00000000)$. The rapid convergence is due to the smallness of the third eigenvalue; see Example 10.4.

2. *Wielandt's deflation*   Here we let

$$\mathbf{v}^T = [1/\lambda_1 x_1^{(j)}] A_{j0} \tag{10.3-21}$$

where $x_1^{(j)}$ is the jth component of $\mathbf{x}_1$ and A_{j0} is the jth row of A. Then

$$\mathbf{v}^T \mathbf{x}_1 = [1/\lambda_1 x_1^{(j)}] A_{j0} \mathbf{x}_1 = [1/\lambda_1 x_1^{(j)}] \lambda_1 x_1^{(j)} = 1 \tag{10.3-22}$$

and

$$W_1 = A - \lambda_1 \mathbf{x}_1 \mathbf{v}^T = A - [1/x_1^{(j)}] \mathbf{x}_1 A_{j0} \tag{10.3-23}$$

so that the jth row of W_1 is given by

$$(W_1)_{j0} = A_{j0} - [1/x_1^{(j)}] x_1^{(j)} A_{j0} = 0 \tag{10.3-24}$$

This means that all eigenvectors of W_1 corresponding to nonzero eigenvalues have their jth component zero (why?). Moreover, this means that finding the eigenvalues of W_1 is equivalent to finding the eigenvalues of B_1 where B_1 is the $n-1$ order matrix formed by canceling the jth row and column of W_1. The eigenvectors of B_1 then are the eigenvectors of W_1 with the zero jth component removed.

The advantage of this deflation is that at every stage we have a smaller matrix to deal with and thus less computation to do. We would usually choose j to correspond to the largest component of $\mathbf{x}_1$, thereby minimizing the error in the computation in (10.3-23).

Example 10.4   Find both subdominant eigenvalues of A in Example 10.1 using Wielandt's deflation.

Since the largest component of $\mathbf{x}_1$ is $x_1^{(3)} = 1.0$ we use $j = 3$. Then

$$\mathbf{v}^T = \frac{1}{2.5365258} \, (.5, .25, 2.0)$$

and

$$W_1 = \begin{bmatrix} .62588942 & .81294471 & -.99644232 \\ .67516942 & .83758471 & 1.04932232 \\ 0 & 0 & 0 \end{bmatrix}$$

Eliminating the third row and column and solving the resulting 2×2 matrix we get, accurate to seven decimal places, $\lambda_2 = 1.4801214$, $\lambda_3 = -.0166473$. We leave the calculation of the eigenvectors through the use of (10.3-17) to a problem {25}.

3. *Similarity deflation*   In this technique, we do not use the deflation equation (10.3-2) directly, but instead we use a method suggested by the proof of Theorem 10.14. The matrix C in (10.3-5) is similar to A and has as its first column $\lambda_1 \mathbf{e}_1$. Moreover, the eigenvectors $\mathbf{x}_i$ of A are related to those $\mathbf{y}_i$ of C by

$$\mathbf{x}_i = T\mathbf{y}_i = \mathbf{y}_i + (\mathbf{e}_1^T \mathbf{y}_i)(\mathbf{x}_1 - \mathbf{e}_1) \tag{10.3-25}$$

Now because the first column of C is $\lambda_1 \mathbf{e}_1$ the $n - 1 \times n - 1$ submatrix C_1, obtained by canceling the first row and column of C, has the eigenvalues $\lambda_2, \ldots, \lambda_n$. Therefore, as in Wielandt's deflation the order of the deflated matrix C_1 is reduced by 1. The eigenvectors $\mathbf{z}_i$ of C_1 are those of C except that the first component $y_i^{(1)}$ is missing. Thus

$$\mathbf{y}_i = \begin{bmatrix} y_i^{(1)} \\ \hline \mathbf{z}_i \end{bmatrix} \tag{10.3-26}$$

and

$$C\mathbf{y}_i = \begin{bmatrix} C_{10}\mathbf{y}_i \\ \hline \lambda_i \mathbf{z}_i \end{bmatrix} \tag{10.3-27}$$

where C_{10} is the first row of C. But from (10.3-10)

$$C_{10} = \mathbf{e}_1^T C = \mathbf{e}_1^T A + \mathbf{e}_1^T \mathbf{w} \mathbf{e}_1^T \tag{10.3-28}$$

since $\mathbf{e}_1^T \mathbf{u} = 0$ (why?). Using (10.3-11) then

$$C_{10} = A_{10} + (\lambda_1 - a_{11})\mathbf{e}_1^T \tag{10.3-29}$$

Thus C_{10} is identical with A_{10} except that the diagonal element is replaced by λ_1. Since $C_{10}\mathbf{y}_i = \lambda_i y_i^{(1)}$ we have, using (10.3-26) and (10.3-29),

$$\lambda_i y_i^{(1)} = \lambda_1 y_i^{(1)} + \sum_{j=2}^{n} a_{1j} z_i^{(j)} \tag{10.3-30}$$

If $\lambda_i \neq \lambda_1$ then

$$y_i^{(1)} = \frac{1}{\lambda_i - \lambda_1} \sum_{j=2}^{n} a_{1j} z_i^{(j)} \qquad (10.3\text{-}31)$$

If $\lambda_i = \lambda_1$ and the summation in (10.3-30) is zero, then $y_i^{(1)}$ is arbitrary and is most easily chosen to be zero. If the summation is not zero then no eigenvector $\mathbf{y}_i$ exists, which means that λ_1 corresponds to a nonlinear elementary divisor.

To use similarity deflation we calculate $\mathbf{w}$ from (10.3-11) and C from (10.3-10). Then we use C_1 to find the first subdominant eigenvalue. We continue as in Wielandt's deflation, reducing the order of the matrix by 1 at each stage. The eigenvectors are calculated using (10.3-25), (10.3-26), and (10.3-31).

Example 10.5 Apply similarity deflation to the matrix A of Example 10.1. We have

$$\mathbf{x}_1^T = (1.00000000, .86827424, 1.33650323)$$

so that

$$\mathbf{u}^T = (0.0, .86827424, 1.33650323)$$

Then

$$\mathbf{w} = \mathbf{u} - A_{01} + (2.5365258)\mathbf{e}_1 = \begin{pmatrix} 1.5365258 \\ -.1317258 \\ .8365032 \end{pmatrix}$$

and

$$C = A - \mathbf{u}A_{10} + \mathbf{w}\mathbf{e}_1^T = \begin{bmatrix} 2.5365258 & 1.0 & .5 \\ 0 & .13172576 & -.18413712 \\ 0 & -1.08650323 & 1.33174838 \end{bmatrix}$$

Then calculating λ_2 and λ_3 from C_1, which is the 2×2 matrix in the lower right-hand corner, we have

$$\lambda_2 = 1.4801214 \qquad \lambda_3 = -.0166473$$

The eigenvectors of C_1 are

$$\mathbf{z}_2^T = (-.1365602, 1.00000000) \qquad \mathbf{z}_3^T = (1.00000000, .8057748)$$

Using (10.3-31) we have

$$y_2^{(1)} = -.3440347 \qquad y_3^{(1)} = -.5494682$$

Finally from (10.3-25)

$$\mathbf{x}_2^T = (-.3440347, -.4352767, .5401965)$$
$$\mathbf{x}_3^T = (-.5494682, .5229109, .0714088)$$

In summary, the process of matrix deflation in any of its forms consists of the following steps:

1. Find λ_1, the dominant eigenvalue of A, and x_1, the corresponding eigenvector.
2. Deflate the matrix A to get a new matrix with dominant eigenvalue λ_2.
3. Find this dominant eigenvalue (e.g., by the power method) and the corresponding eigenvector. Then find the corresponding eigenvector of A.
4. Repeat steps 2 and 3, using the last deflated matrix at each stage, until as many eigenvalues and eigenvectors of A as desired have been found.

Even if A does not have an eigenvector corresponding to the eigenvector of the deflated matrix, because of nonlinear elementary divisors, the deflation can still be continued because it depends at each stage on the use of an eigenvector of the deflated matrix which always exists. Of course, however, at every stage of the deflation the problems with the power method discussed in the previous section may appear.

Of the three deflations we considered, the latter two are preferable for matrices of all but very low order because of the reduction in order of the matrix at each stage. Some other possible deflation procedures and techniques which can be used, for example, when complex eigenvalues are encountered, are considered in a problem {26}. The errors incurred by the successive roundoffs occurring in the calculation of each deflated matrix are an important consideration if deflation is to be used to calculate many eigenvalues, but these errors are very difficult to analyze.

10.3-2 Annihilation techniques

If v_0 is any vector and as before λ_1 and x_1 are an eigenvalue and eigenvector of A, then

$$w_0 = (A - \lambda_1 I)v_0 \tag{10.3-32}$$

has no component in the x_1 direction [cf. (10.3-1)]. If then w_0 is used in the power method, the iterated vectors w_m should converge to λ_2 and x_2. But the difficulty with this technique is that which was illustrated in Example 10.2; namely, roundoff error will ultimately introduce a component in the x_1 direction, and this will ultimately dominate. To avoid this difficulty, we may periodically *annihilate* the component in the x_1 direction by calculating

$$z_m = (A - \lambda_1 I)w_m \tag{10.3-33}$$

since z_m will have no component in the x_1 direction. Therefore, by this periodic annihilation we shall eventually get convergence to λ_2 and x_2 if the same conditions for convergence as in Sec. 10.2 are satisfied.

This procedure can be applied to find the other subdominant eigenvalues and eigenvectors.   For example, if λ_1, x_1 and λ_2, x_2 are known, then

$$w_0 = (A - \lambda_2 I)(A - \lambda_1 I)v_0 \tag{10.3-34}$$

has no components in the x_1 or x_2 directions.   Applying the power method to w_0 then, now with periodic annihilations by $(A - \lambda_2 I)(A - \lambda_1 I)$, we shall, under suitable conditions, get convergence to λ_3 and x_3.   Similarly, we can find higher eigenvalues and eigenvectors of any order.   But clearly the annihilation process becomes very tedious for all but the first few subdominant eigenvalues and eigenvectors.   In fact, even for these it has no real advantages over deflation techniques and so is seldom employed in practice.   When annihilation is used, however, the decision on how often in the iteration process to annihilate is very important in determining the efficiency of the process.   Here again is an example of a method which can be employed much more effectively by an experienced numerical analyst than by someone who is not.

10.4   THE EIGENVALUES AND EIGENVECTORS OF SYMMETRIC MATRICES

Our object here is to develop methods which will enable us to compute all the eigenvalues and eigenvectors when the matrix A is symmetric, as we shall assume it is throughout this section.   The three methods we shall consider all use as their basic tool orthogonal transformations of A.   In particular the first of these three methods has its theoretical basis in Corollary 10.3 of Sec. 10.1-4.

10.4-1   The Jacobi method

Corollary 10.3 assures us that there exists an orthogonal matrix Q such that

$$Q^T A Q = D \tag{10.4-1}$$

where D is a diagonal matrix with the eigenvalues of A on the diagonal. Our technique will be to find a sequence $\{S_k\}$ of orthogonal matrices with the property that

$$\lim_{k \to \infty} S_1 S_2 \cdots S_k = Q \tag{10.4-2}$$

We shall use the notation

$$T_k = S_k^T S_{k-1}^T \cdots S_1^T A S_1 S_2 \cdots S_k \qquad T_0 = A \tag{10.4-3}$$

We denote the elements of T_k by $t_{ij}^{(k)}$ and of S_k by $s_{ij}^{(k)}$. We define

$$v_k = \sum_{\substack{i=1 \\ i \neq j}}^{n} \sum_{j=1}^{n} [t_{ij}^{(k)}]^2 \qquad k = 0, 1, \ldots \tag{10.4-4}$$

and

$$w_k = \sum_{i=1}^{n} \sum_{j=1}^{n} [t_{ij}^{(k)}]^2 \qquad k = 0, 1, \ldots \tag{10.4-5}$$

Thus w_k is the square of the Euclidean norm of T_k and v_k is the sum of the squares of the off-diagonal elements of T_k. Our object is to choose the sequence $\{S_k\}$ so that

$$w_{k+1} = w_k \qquad v_{k+1} < v_k \qquad \text{for all } k \tag{10.4-6}$$

and

$$\lim_{k \to \infty} v_k = 0 \tag{10.4-7}$$

in which case

$$\lim_{k \to \infty} T_k = D \tag{10.4-8}$$

Let $t_{pq}^{(k-1)}$ be a nonzero off-diagonal element of T_{k-1}. We wish to choose S_k so that $t_{pq}^{(k)} = 0$. In doing so we shall show that (10.4-6) is satisfied. Let

$$\left. \begin{array}{l} s_{pp}^{(k)} = s_{qq}^{(k)} = \cos \theta_k \\ s_{pq}^{(k)} = -s_{qp}^{(k)} = \sin \theta_k \end{array} \right\} \qquad \begin{array}{ll} s_{ii}^{(k)} = 1 & i \neq p \text{ or } q \\ s_{ij}^{(k)} = 0 & \text{otherwise} \end{array} \tag{10.4-9}$$

where θ_k will be chosen below so that the pq element is annihilated; i.e., $t_{pq}^{(k)} = 0$. The orthogonal matrix defined by (10.4-9) is called a *plane rotation matrix* because the linear transformation defined by S_k consists of a rotation of the axes of the pth and qth coordinates through an angle θ_k. From (10.4-3)

$$T_k = S_k^T T_{k-1} S_k \tag{10.4-10}$$

so that we have, using (10.4-9),

$$\left. \begin{array}{l} t_{pj}^{(k)} = t_{pj}^{(k-1)} \cos \theta_k - t_{qj}^{(k-1)} \sin \theta_k \\ t_{qj}^{(k)} = t_{pj}^{(k-1)} \sin \theta_k + t_{qj}^{(k-1)} \cos \theta_k \end{array} \right\} \qquad j \neq p \text{ or } q \tag{10.4-11}$$

$$\left. \begin{array}{l} t_{ip}^{(k)} = t_{ip}^{(k-1)} \cos \theta_k - t_{iq}^{(k-1)} \sin \theta_k \\ t_{iq}^{(k)} = t_{ip}^{(k-1)} \sin \theta_k + t_{iq}^{(k-1)} \cos \theta_k \end{array} \right\} \qquad i \neq p \text{ or } q \tag{10.4-12}$$

$$\begin{array}{l} t_{pp}^{(k)} = t_{pp}^{(k-1)} \cos^2 \theta_k + t_{qq}^{(k-1)} \sin^2 \theta_k - 2t_{pq}^{(k-1)} \sin \theta_k \cos \theta_k \\ t_{qq}^{(k)} = t_{pp}^{(k-1)} \sin^2 \theta_k + t_{qq}^{(k-1)} \cos^2 \theta_k + 2t_{pq}^{(k-1)} \sin \theta_k \cos \theta_k \\ t_{pq}^{(k)} = t_{qp}^{(k)} = \frac{1}{2}[t_{pp}^{(k-1)} - t_{qq}^{(k-1)}] \sin 2\theta_k + t_{pq}^{(k-1)} \cos 2\theta_k \end{array} \tag{10.4-13}$$

$$t_{ij}^{(k)} = t_{ij}^{(k-1)} \qquad i \neq p \text{ and } j \neq q \tag{10.4-14}$$

Now we shall choose θ_k to make $t_{pq}^{(k)}$ vanish.   From the last equation of (10.4-13) we have

$$\tan 2\theta_k = \frac{-t_{pq}^{(k-1)}}{\frac{1}{2}[t_{pp}^{(k-1)} - t_{qq}^{(k-1)}]} \tag{10.4-15}$$

so that a θ_k always exists.   In practice we do not calculate θ_k itself but only $\sin \theta_k$ and $\cos \theta_k$ since these are all that are required by (10.4-11) to (10.4-13).   A convenient way to calculate $\sin \theta_k$ and $\cos \theta_k$ is as follows: Let $\lambda = -t_{pq}^{(k-1)}$, $\mu = \frac{1}{2}[t_{pp}^{(k-1)} - t_{qq}^{(k-1)}]$.   Then we may show that $\{31\}\dagger$

$$\cos \theta_k = \left(\frac{\nu + |\mu|}{2\nu}\right)^{\frac{1}{2}} \qquad \sin \theta_k = \frac{\text{sgn}\,(\mu)\,\lambda}{2\nu \cos \theta_k} \tag{10.4-16}$$

where

$$\nu = (\lambda^2 + \mu^2)^{\frac{1}{2}} \tag{10.4-17}$$

Using (10.4-11) to (10.4-13) we may easily calculate that, independent of θ_k,

$$\begin{aligned}
[t_{pj}^{(k)}]^2 + [t_{qj}^{(k)}]^2 &= [t_{pj}^{(k-1)}]^2 + [t_{qj}^{(k-1)}]^2 \qquad j \neq p \text{ or } q \\
[t_{ip}^{(k)}]^2 + [t_{iq}^{(k)}]^2 &= [t_{ip}^{(k-1)}]^2 + [t_{iq}^{(k-1)}]^2 \qquad i \neq p \text{ or } q
\end{aligned} \tag{10.4-18}$$

and

$$\begin{aligned}
[t_{pp}^{(k)}]^2 + [t_{qq}^{(k)}]^2 &+ [t_{pq}^{(k)}]^2 + [t_{qp}^{(k)}]^2 \\
&= [t_{pp}^{(k-1)}]^2 + [t_{qq}^{(k-1)}]^2 + [t_{pq}^{(k-1)}]^2 + [t_{qp}^{(k-1)}]^2 \tag{10.4-19}
\end{aligned}$$

But with θ_k chosen as in (10.4-15), $t_{pq}^{(k)} = t_{qp}^{(k)} = 0$.   Therefore, (10.4-18) and (10.4-19) together with (10.4-14) show that $w_{k-1} = w_k$ and (10.4-19) implies that $v_k < v_{k-1}$.   In fact, (10.4-19) implies that, since $t_{pq}^{(k-1)} = t_{qp}^{(k-1)}$ because all the T_k are symmetric, the off-diagonal sum of squares is reduced by $2[t_{pq}^{(k-1)}]^2$ and the sum of squares of the diagonal elements is therefore increased by a like amount.   At each stage of the Jacobi iteration then we (1) choose a *nonzero* off-diagonal element; (2) calculate $\sin \theta_k$ and $\cos \theta_k$ from (10.4-16); (3) calculate those elements in T_k which differ from those in T_{k-1} using (10.4-11) to (10.4-13).   Note that an off-diagonal element made zero at one stage will generally become nonzero at some later stage (why?).

This process may be continued for as long as is desired.   The convergence of the method may be proved for a variety of techniques, including those considered below, for choosing the nonzero off-diagonal element at each stage.   For some techniques the proof is quite difficult, but in the case where the off-diagonal element of greatest magnitude is annihilated

† Note that (10.4-16) and (10.4-17) always result in a rotation angle such that $|\theta_k| \leq \pi/4$ (why?).

at each stage, the proof is quite straightforward {32}.   The most common convergence criterion used in practice is to require that the off-diagonal norm $\sqrt{v_k}$ be less than some preset tolerance (cf. {33}).

The eigenvectors of A are also readily calculated using this iteration. We noted in Sec. 10.1-4 [cf. (10.1-41)] that the columns of the orthogonal matrix used to reduce A to diagonal form are the eigenvectors of A.   To calculate the eigenvectors then we must calculate the product of the S_k matrices in (10.4-2).   To see how this can be done simply we write (10.4-3) as

$$T_k = R_k^T A R_k \tag{10.4-20}$$

with

$$R_k = S_1 S_2 \cdots S_k \tag{10.4-21}$$

Thus

$$R_{k+1} = R_k S_{k+1} \tag{10.4-22}$$

and from (10.4-9), we may then calculate the elements of $R_{k+1} = [r_{ij}^{(k+1)}]$ in terms of those of $R_k = [r_{ij}^{(k)}]$:

$$
\begin{aligned}
r_{ip}^{(k+1)} &= r_{ip}^{(k)} \cos \theta_k - r_{iq}^{(k)} \sin \theta_k \\
r_{iq}^{(k+1)} &= r_{ip}^{(k)} \sin \theta_k + r_{iq}^{(k)} \cos \theta_k \\
r_{ij}^{(k+1)} &= r_{ij}^{(k)} \qquad j \neq p \text{ or } q
\end{aligned}
\tag{10.4-23}
$$

The one problem remaining in the use of the Jacobi method is how to choose the off-diagonal element to be annihilated at each stage.   We should like to choose that element of greatest magnitude since this would result in the greatest reduction of the off-diagonal norm $\sqrt{v_k}$ at every stage.   For hand computation this is easily done, but on a digital computer this would seem to require a search through all the off-diagonal elements (actually just through half of them since the matrix is symmetric at every stage).   To avoid this search a procedure called the *threshold Jacobi method* may be used.   The essence of this procedure is to search through the off-diagonal elements until an element of magnitude greater than some threshold value is found.   This element is then annihilated.   This method assures some minimum reduction of the off-diagonal norm at each stage.   The details of this method, in particular how to choose the threshold at every stage, are considered in a problem {33}.

Recently, however, it has been recognized that a search for the largest off-diagonal element does not require looking at all $n(n-1)/2$ off-diagonal elements above or below the diagonal.   Since each stage of the Jacobi method changes only two rows and columns of the matrix T_k, it is possible, by storing in the computer two vectors which give the magnitude and location of the largest element in each row and column, to reduce substantially the searching required [see Corbató (1963)].

Example 10.6   Apply the Jacobi method to the matrix A of Example 10.1.
The largest off-diagonal element is 1.0 in the first row and second column ($p = 1$, $q = 2$).   Using (10.4-16) and (10.4-17) we have

$$\mu = 0, \lambda = -1, \nu = 1$$
$$\sin \theta_1 = -1/\sqrt{2}$$
$$\cos \theta_1 = 1/\sqrt{2}$$

Using (10.4-11) to (10.4-13) we compute

$$T_1 = S_1^T A S_1 = \begin{bmatrix} 2 & 0 & \dfrac{3}{4\sqrt{2}} \\ 0 & 0 & \dfrac{-1}{4\sqrt{2}} \\ \dfrac{3}{4\sqrt{2}} & \dfrac{-1}{4\sqrt{2}} & 2 \end{bmatrix}$$

By continuing this process we would obtain

$$D = \begin{bmatrix} 2.5365258 & 0 & 0 \\ 0 & -.0166473 & 0 \\ 0 & 0 & 1.4801215 \end{bmatrix}$$

and, using (10.4-23),

$$Q = \begin{bmatrix} .53148338 & -.72120712 & -.44428106 \\ .46147338 & .68634928 & -.56210938 \\ .71032933 & .09372796 & .69760117 \end{bmatrix}$$

As a check on the results we may compute QDQ^T, which should equal A.

The accuracy of the results of the Jacobi method depend upon how accurately the square roots leading to $\sin \theta_k$ and $\cos \theta_k$ given by (10.4-16) are calculated and on how the roundoff error accumulates.   The error analysis of the Jacobi method is quite involved and beyond us here [see Goldstine, Murray, and Von Neumann (1959) and Wilkinson (1962)], but if the square roots are calculated with appropriate accuracy, then the method is completely stable with respect to roundoff error (i.e., no significant growth of error occurs because of roundoff).

The Jacobi method has been widely applied on digital computers to find the eigenvalues of symmetric matrices, some of very high order. Since it results in all the eigenvalues and eigenvectors, it is superior to the methods of Sec. 10.3 when all the eigenvalues and eigenvectors are desired. Its major disadvantage is that it is an infinite iterative method, and when high accuracy is desired in the eigenvalues or when the diagonal elements of A are not large compared with the off-diagonal elements, it may lead to a very lengthy computation.   In the next two sections, we consider two methods, both of which are finite iterative processes which lead not to the matrix D but instead to a new matrix whose eigenvalues are much easier to compute than those of a general symmetric matrix A.

10.4-2 Givens's method

The basis of this method is to use orthogonal matrices not to diagonalize A but rather to tridiagonalize A (i.e., reduce A to a form in which the only nonzero elements are on the main diagonal and the two diagonals directly above and below it as shown in Fig. 10.1).   We shall then consider how to find the eigenvalues of such a matrix.

The orthogonal matrices S_k used in the Jacobi method had the property that only the pth and qth rows and columns of T_{k-1} were changed in calculating $T_k = S_k^T T_{k-1} S_k$.   If then we arrange the order of the calculations carefully, we should not be surprised to find that —up to a point—we can annihilate off-diagonal elements while at the same time keeping previously annihilated elements zero.   First we note that using S_k as defined by (10.4-9) (with θ_k unspecified as yet) we can annihilate, instead of $t_{pq}^{(k-1)}$, $t_{rq}^{(k-1)}$ with $r \neq p$ or q [and by symmetry $t_{qr}^{(k-1)}$ is annihilated also].   This follows from (10.4-12) by writing

$$0 = t_{rq}^{(k)} = t_{rp}^{(k-1)} \sin \theta_k + t_{rq}^{(k-1)} \cos \theta_k \qquad (10.4\text{-}24)$$

which will be satisfied if

$$\sin \theta_k = -\alpha t_{rq}^{(k-1)} \qquad \cos \theta_k = \alpha t_{rp}^{(k-1)} \qquad (10.4\text{-}25)$$

with

$$\alpha = 1 / \{[t_{rp}^{(k-1)}]^2 + [t_{rq}^{(k-1)}]^2\}^{1/2} \qquad (10.4\text{-}26)$$

Let us denote the matrix whose elements are given by (10.4-9), with $\sin \theta_k$ and $\cos \theta_k$ given by (10.4-25) and (10.4-26), by the triplet (p,q,r), these three *distinct* integers denoting the row (and column) indices of

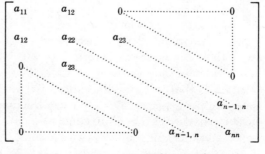

Fig. 10.1   A symmetric tridiagonal matrix.

significance in the transformation.   In particular consider the sequence of transformations

$$(p,q,r) = (2,i,1) \qquad i = 3, \ldots, n \tag{10.4-27}$$

applied in succession to the original matrix A.   That is, each triplet defines a transformation which we apply by premultiplying the current matrix by the transpose of the matrix defined by (10.4-9) and postmultiplying by the matrix itself.   Denoting this matrix now by S_{pqr} we have after the first step

$$S_{231}^T A S_{231} \tag{10.4-28}$$

Thus the transformation $(2,3,1)$ annihilates the element in the first row (column) and third column (row) with p and q in (10.4-9) being 2 and 3, respectively.   In general the $(2,i,1)$ transformation annihilates the element in the first row (column) and ith column (row).   Of equal significance, however, is the fact that *each annihilated element remains zero.* This is because the $(2,i,1)$ transformation changes only the second row (column) and the ith column (row) and therefore does not affect previously annihilated elements.   Therefore, after the sequence of transformations (10.4-27), all elements in the first row (column) except the first two (a_{11} and a_{12}) are zero.

Next we consider the sequence

$$(p,q,r) = (3,i,2) \qquad i = 4, \ldots, n \tag{10.4-29}$$

which annihilates the elements of the second row (column) from a_{24} to a_{2n}.   By reasoning similar to that in the previous paragraph and use of (10.4-12) we may show that $\{35\}$ the sequence of transformations (10.4-29) leaves *all* previously annihilated elements in the *first* and *second* rows (columns) zero.   The general algorithm is now clear.   We apply the sequence of transformations

$$(p,q,r) = (j,i,j-1) \qquad j = 2, \ldots, n-1$$
$$i = j+1, \ldots, n \tag{10.4-30}$$

and in so doing get a new symmetric matrix B with the form

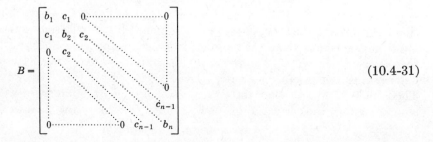

$$\tag{10.4-31}$$

From (10.4-30) the number of transformations required is $(n-2)(n-1)/2$, and we may show that the total number of operations required is of the order of $\frac{4}{3}n^3$ plus, of course, the $(n-2)(n-1)/2$ square roots required by (10.4-26) {40}.

In Sec. 10.6 we shall consider two methods particularly suited to finding the eigenvalues of tridiagonal matrices, symmetric or otherwise. Here, however, we shall show that B has a form which permits another effective way of computing its eigenvalues.   We consider the matrix

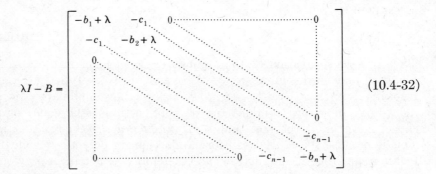

$$\lambda I - B = \qquad (10.4\text{-}32)$$

If we denote the principal minor of order i in the above matrix by $f_{n-i}(\lambda)$, then we may easily show that {36}

$$f_{n-(i+1)}(\lambda) = (\lambda - b_{i+1})f_{n-i}(\lambda) - c_i^2 f_{n-(i-1)}(\lambda)$$
$$i = 1, \ldots, n-1 \qquad (10.4\text{-}33)$$

with $f_n(\lambda) = 1$ and $f_{n-1}(\lambda) = -b_1 + \lambda$.   The characteristic equation is

$$f_0(\lambda) = 0 \qquad (10.4\text{-}34)$$

We can, of course, solve (10.4-34) by the methods of Chap. 8 [since the matrix is symmetric all roots of each $f_{n-i}(\lambda)$ are real].   But here we shall show how our results about Sturm sequences in Sec. 8.9-1 can be applied to this problem.

We assume that no c_i in (10.4-31) is zero. For if any $c_i = 0$, then the determinant of the matrix in (10.4-32) may be written as the product of two determinants of smaller tridiagonal matrices {36} and the results below will apply to each.   Under this assumption we can show that the sequence $f_0(\lambda), \ldots, f_n(\lambda)$ forms a Sturm sequence as defined in Definition 8.1; we leave the proof of this to a problem {36}.   This suggests trying to get some idea about the roots of (10.4-34) by applying Theorem 8.3, that is, by calculating $V(a)$ and $V(b)$ for various a and b and thereby determining the number of roots in various intervals $[a,b]$.   However, Theorem 8.3 requires that the Sturm sequence in question have as its second member the derivative of the first, but $f_1(\lambda)$ is not $f_0'(\lambda)$.   However, if $f_1(\lambda)$ has the same sign as $f_0'(\lambda)$ at each zero of $f_0(\lambda)$, then Theorem 8.3 is also valid if the sequence used to compute $V(a) - V(b)$ is $\{f_i(\lambda)\}$ (why?). Thus we wish to prove

Theorem 10.15   At a zero of $f_0(\lambda)$, $f_1(\lambda)$ has the same sign as $f_0'(\lambda)$. To prove this theorem we first prove

Lemma 10.2   The i zeros s_j, $j = 1, \ldots, i$ of $f_{n-i}(\lambda)$ separate those r_j, $j = 1, \ldots, i - 1$ of $f_{n-(i-1)}(\lambda)$ for $i = 2, \ldots, n$. That is

$$- \infty < s_1 < r_1 < s_2 < r_2 \cdots < r_{i-1} < s_i < \infty \qquad (10.4\text{-}35)$$

Proof   By induction. For $i = 2$ this can be proved directly using (10.4-33) $\{36\}$. Suppose (10.4-35) holds for some i. Then, using property 2 of a Sturm sequence at each s_j, the function $f_{n-(i+1)}(\lambda)$ has sign opposite to $f_{n-(i-1)}(\lambda)$. But (10.4-35) implies that the sign of $f_{n-(i-1)}(\lambda)$ alternates from one zero of $f_{n-i}(\lambda)$ to the next. Thus between s_1 and s_i, $f_{n-(i+1)}(\lambda)$ has $i - 1$ zeros lying between the zeros of $f_{n-i}(\lambda)$. At s_1, $f_{n-(i+1)}(\lambda)$ has sign opposite to $f_{n-(i-1)}(\lambda)$, but as $\lambda \to - \infty$ both $f_{n-(i-1)}(\lambda)$ and $f_{n-(i+1)}(\lambda)$ have the same sign since they differ by degree 2. Therefore, $f_{n-(i+1)}(\lambda)$ has a zero between $- \infty$ and s_1 and by a similar argument it has a zero between s_i and $+ \infty$ which proves the lemma.

The proof of Theorem 10.15 now follows easily. Since the zeros of $f_0(\lambda)$ and $f_1(\lambda)$ separate each other, the zeros of $f_0(\lambda)$ are distinct. Therefore, between each two zeros of $f_0(\lambda)$, $f_0'(\lambda)$ also has a zero. Moreover, for sufficiently large λ, $f_0'(\lambda)$ and $f_1(\lambda)$ have the same sign since both are polynomials with leading term λ^{n-1}. Therefore, they both have the same sign at the largest zero of $f_0(\lambda)$. The argument above then guarantees that they have the same sign at every zero of $f_0(\lambda)$, which proves the theorem.

To compute the value of $V(x)$ requires the evaluation of each $f_{n-i}(\lambda)$ at $\lambda = x$, but this is easily accomplished using (10.4-33). Therefore, after the reduction of the matrix to tridiagonal form, the calculation of the eigenvalues of the tridiagonal matrix can be accomplished without too much difficulty using the properties of Sturm sequences in conjunction with one of the methods of Chap. 8. In particular, the method of bisection (see Prob. 6, Chap. 8), although somewhat slow, is a very convenient method for calculating the eigenvalues. We proceed as follows: Evaluate $V(\lambda)$ (see page 352) for the set of functions (10.4-33) for a sequence of values of λ. Whenever two values, λ_1 and λ_2, are found such that $V(\lambda_1) \neq V(\lambda_2)$, then there is an eigenvalue between λ_1 and λ_2. By evaluating $V[(\lambda_1 + \lambda_2)/2]$ the interval in which λ lies may be halved, and by continuing in this way the interval may be made as small as desired.

Since the tridiagonalization is a finite iterative process, the error in generating B can be strictly controlled, and then the eigenvalues of B can be determined with arbitrary accuracy. Thus Givens's method is generally preferable to the Jacobi method. Only for matrices where the diagonal terms dominate would we expect the Jacobi method to be competitive with Givens's method (why?).

The eigenvectors of A bear the same relation to those of B as in the Jacobi method. That is, by keeping track of the successive orthogonal transformations as in (10.4-21) to (10.4-23) the eigenvectors of A may be calculated from those of B {37}. Because of the simple form of B, there exists a straightforward formal algorithm for computing the eigenvectors of B {37}. However, in practice this algorithm may result in disastrous roundoff errors [see Wilkinson (1958b)].

Example 10.7   Apply Givens's method to the matrix A of Example 10.1.

The only off-tridiagonal element is a_{13} so that there is only one transformation to perform. From (10.4-25) and (10.4-26) with $p = 2$, $q = 3$, $r = 1$

$$\alpha = 2/\sqrt{5} \qquad \sin \theta = -1/\sqrt{5} \qquad \cos \theta = 2/\sqrt{5}$$

Using these to get the matrix S of (10.4-9) we then calculate

$$B = S^T A S = \begin{bmatrix} 1 & \dfrac{\sqrt{5}}{2} & 0 \\ \dfrac{\sqrt{5}}{2} & 1.40 & .55 \\ 0 & .55 & 1.60 \end{bmatrix}$$

Then from (10.4-33) we get

$$f_3(\lambda) = 1 \qquad f_2(\lambda) = \lambda - 1$$
$$f_1(\lambda) = \lambda^2 - 2.4\lambda + .15 \qquad f_0(\lambda) = \lambda^3 - 4\lambda^2 + 3.6875\lambda + .0625$$

with $f_0(\lambda)$ the characteristic equation of A.

10.4-3   Householder's method

This method is a variation of Givens's method, which enables us to reduce A to tridiagonal form with about half as much computation as Givens's method requires. The technique is to reduce a whole row and column (except for the tridiagonal elements) to zero at a time.

Let $\mathbf{v}$ be a vector such that

$$\mathbf{v}^T \mathbf{v} = 1 \tag{10.4-36}$$

Then it is easy to show {38} that the matrix

$$P = I - 2\mathbf{v}\mathbf{v}^T \tag{10.4-37}$$

is orthogonal and symmetric. In particular we choose $\mathbf{v}_k$ to be a vector whose first $k - 1$ components are zero so that

$$\mathbf{v}_k^T = [0,0, \ldots ,0,v_k^{(k)},v_k^{(k+1)}, \ldots ,v_k^{(n)}] \tag{10.4-38}$$

Then with

$$P_k = I - 2\mathbf{v}_k\mathbf{v}_k^T \tag{10.4-39}$$

we define

$$A_k = P_k^T A_{k-1} P_k \qquad k = 2, \ldots , n - 1 \qquad A_1 = A \tag{10.4-40}$$

Now suppose that the symmetric matrix $A_{k-1} = [g_{ij}]$ has zeros in its first $k - 2$ rows and columns except for the tridiagonal elements:

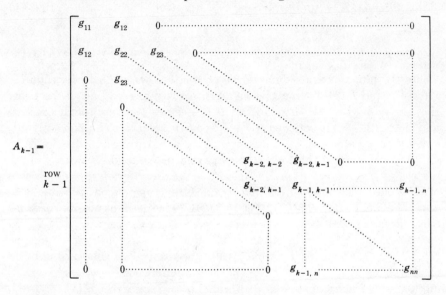

$$(10.4\text{-}41)$$

The matrix P_k has the form

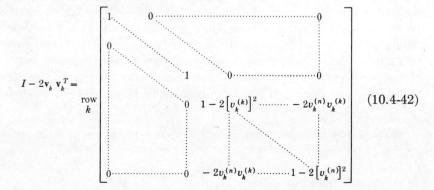

$$(10.4\text{-}42)$$

Using (10.4-40) to (10.4-42) we may verify that A_k has zeros in the positions shown as zero for A_{k-1} in (10.4-41).   Our object is to choose the $n - k + 1$ numbers $v_k^{(k)}, \ldots, v_k^{(n)}$ to satisfy (10.4-36) and so that the $n - k$ off-tridiagonal elements in row (column) $k - 1$ of A_k are zero.

We define

$$S = \sum_{j=k}^{n} g_{k-1,j}^2 \tag{10.4-43}$$

and then let

$$[v_k^{(k)}]^2 = \tfrac{1}{2}[1 \pm (g_{k-1,k}/\sqrt{S})] \tag{10.4-44}$$

and

$$v_k^{(j)} = \pm g_{k-1,j}/(2v_k^{(k)} \sqrt{S}) \qquad j = k + 1, \ldots, n \tag{10.4-45}$$

where the plus or minus sign will be chosen below.   The motivation for (10.4-44) and (10.4-45) may be found in the algebra leading to the proof that the desired $n - k$ elements in the $k - 1$ row (column) of A_k are zero and that (10.4-36) is satisfied.   We leave this algebra to a problem {38}. Proceeding as above at each step we arrive at a tridiagonal matrix A_{n-1}.

The accuracy of this method depends naturally on the accuracy of the matrices P_k, and these in turn depend upon the accuracy of the components of (10.4-38).   The key to making this accuracy as great as possible is to make the magnitude of $v_k^{(k)}$ as given by (10.4-44) as great as possible because it is a divisor in (10.4-45).   Therefore, we choose the sign in (10.4-44) so as to maximize the magnitude of $v_k^{(k)}$ and then use the same sign in (10.4-45).   We leave to a problem {40} the result that the total number of operations is of the order of $\tfrac{2}{3}n^3$ as compared with $\tfrac{4}{3}n^3$ for Givens's method.   At each stage it would appear that two square roots are required, one for $\sqrt{S}$ and one for $\{[v_k^{(k)}]^2\}^{1/2}$.   However, by arranging the calculations properly, the latter of these two need not be calculated {40}. Therefore, Householder's method requires $n - 2$ square roots compared with $(n - 2)(n - 1)/2$ for Givens's method.   For large matrices, then, Householder's method is a more efficient way than Givens's method to reduce a symmetric matrix to tridiagonal form.   The discussion in Sec. 10.4-2 on finding the eigenvalues and eigenvectors of tridiagonal matrices also applies here.   Calculation of the eigenvectors of A from the eigenvectors of the tridiagonal matrix found using Householder's method is considered in a problem {39}.

Example 10.8   Apply Householder's method to the matrix of Example 10.1. As in Example 10.7 there is only one step to perform.   We have

$$S = 1^2 + (\tfrac{1}{2})^2 = \tfrac{5}{4} \qquad \sqrt{S} \approx 1.11803$$

Since $a_{12} = 1$ we choose the $+$ sign in (10.4-44) and get

$$v_2^{(2)} \approx \left[\frac{1}{2} \left(1 + \frac{1}{1.11803} \right) \right]^{1/2} \approx .97325$$

$$v_2^{(3)} \approx \frac{1}{4 \times (1.11803) \times .97325} \approx .22975$$

[In fact the calculation of the square root required to get $v_2^{(2)}$ may be avoided as mentioned above {40}.]   The best way to proceed with the computation is to note that

$$A_{k-1}P_k = A_{k-1} - 2\mathbf{w}_k\mathbf{v}_k^T$$

with

$$\mathbf{w}_k = A_{k-1}\mathbf{v}_k$$

and then to use the result {39}

$$A_k = P_k^T A_{k-1} P_k = A_{k-1} - 2\mathbf{v}_k\mathbf{q}_k^T - 2\mathbf{q}_k\mathbf{v}_k^T$$

with

$$\mathbf{q}_k = \mathbf{w}_k - (\mathbf{v}_k^T\mathbf{w}_k)\mathbf{v}_k$$

In this example then we compute

$$\mathbf{w}_2^T = \mathbf{v}_2^T A = (1.08813, 1.03069, .70281)$$

Then

$$\mathbf{v}_2^T\mathbf{w}_2 = 1.16459$$

and

$$\mathbf{q}_2^T = (1.08813, -.10275, .43525)$$

Finally

$$A_2 = \begin{bmatrix} 1 & -1.11804 & 0 \\ -1.11804 & 1.40000 & -.55000 \\ 0 & -.55000 & 1.60000 \end{bmatrix}$$

which except for roundoff and some sign changes is the same matrix as B in Example 10.7.   Because only a single orthogonal transformation is needed in this case, we expect Givens's and Householder's methods to lead to essentially the same tridiagonal matrix.   But for higher-order matrices, this will not be the case.   Note the desirability of computing double-precision scalar products in this method in order to minimize roundoff.

10.5   METHODS FOR NONSYMMETRIC MATRICES

Our approach to nonsymmetric matrices will be similar to that of Givens's and Householder's methods in the sense that we shall perform a series of transformations on the matrix A—similarity more often than orthogonal —in order to reduce A to a matrix B with the same eigenvalues as A but whose eigenvalues are more easily calculable.   In the method to be con-

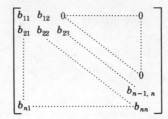

Fig. 10.2   A matrix in lower Hessenberg form.

sidered in Sec. 10.5-1 the matrix B will be tridiagonal as in the case of Givens's and Householder's methods.   In Sec. 10.5-2 we shall consider techniques for reducing A to a matrix B which has the form shown in Fig. 10.2.   Such a matrix is said to be in supertriangular or, more commonly, in lower *Hessenberg* form (whereas the transpose of such a matrix is said to be in upper Hessenberg form).   As we might expect, the methods we shall discuss may run into trouble when A has nonlinear elementary divisors or multiple eigenvalues.

A vital aspect of the calculation of the eigenvalues of nonsymmetric matrices is the stability of the calculation with respect to the growth of roundoff errors.   The details of the roundoff-error analysis of the methods we are about to consider are beyond the scope of this book.   We shall content ourselves with making some general comments on this matter in what follows; for more details the reader is referred to the references mentioned in the bibliographic notes.

10.5-1   Lanczos's method

Our object here is to construct a matrix S such that the result of the similarity transformation

$$T = S^{-1}AS \tag{10.5-1}$$

is a tridiagonal matrix T.   Our approach will be to construct a sequence of vectors $x_1, \ldots, x_n$ which, as the columns of S, achieve the desired result.   In the construction of this set of vectors, we shall also construct another set, $y_1, \ldots, y_n$, such that the sequences $\{x_i\}$ and $\{y_i\}$ are *biorthogonal;* that is

$$y_j^T x_i = 0 \qquad \text{if } i \neq j \tag{10.5-2}$$

The two sequences of vectors are generated by the following recursion

$$\begin{aligned} x_{k+1} &= Ax_k - b_k x_k - c_{k-1}x_{k-1} \\ y_{k+1} &= A^T y_k - b_k y_k - c_{k-1}y_{k-1} \end{aligned} \qquad k = 1, \ldots, n-1 \tag{10.5-3}$$

with $\mathbf{x}_0 = \mathbf{y}_0 = \mathbf{0}$, $\mathbf{x}_1$ and $\mathbf{y}_1$ arbitrary vectors and with the b_k's and c_k's defined by

$$\left.\begin{aligned} b_k &= \mathbf{y}_k^T A \mathbf{x}_k / \mathbf{y}_k^T \mathbf{x}_k \\ c_{k-1} &= \mathbf{y}_{k-1}^T A \mathbf{x}_k / \mathbf{y}_{k-1}^T \mathbf{x}_{k-1} = \mathbf{y}_k^T \mathbf{x}_k / \mathbf{y}_{k-1}^T \mathbf{x}_{k-1} \qquad c_0 = 0 \\ k &= 1, \ldots, n-1 \end{aligned}\right\} \qquad (10.5\text{-}4)$$

Now clearly this recursion requires that $\mathbf{y}_j^T \mathbf{x}_j \neq 0$, $j = 1, \ldots, n-1$. For the present let us assume this is true. We may then prove

Theorem 10.16   For the system of vectors defined by (10.5-3) and (10.5-4), Eq. (10.5-2) holds for $i, j = 1, \ldots, n$.

Proof   By induction. We have

$$\mathbf{x}_2 = A\mathbf{x}_1 - b_1\mathbf{x}_1 = A\mathbf{x}_1 - (\mathbf{y}_1^T A \mathbf{x}_1 / \mathbf{y}_1^T \mathbf{x}_1)\mathbf{x}_1$$

from which we have immediately $\mathbf{y}_1^T \mathbf{x}_2 = 0$. Similarly we get $\mathbf{x}_1^T \mathbf{y}_2 = 0$. Now suppose (10.5-2) holds for all i and j less than or equal to k. We have from (10.5-3) and (10.5-4)

$$\mathbf{y}_j^T \mathbf{x}_{k+1} = \mathbf{y}_j^T A \mathbf{x}_k - (\mathbf{y}_k^T A \mathbf{x}_k / \mathbf{y}_k^T \mathbf{x}_k)\mathbf{y}_j^T \mathbf{x}_k - (\mathbf{y}_{k-1}^T A \mathbf{x}_k / \mathbf{y}_{k-1}^T \mathbf{x}_{k-1})\mathbf{y}_j^T \mathbf{x}_{k-1} \tag{10.5-5}$$

For $j = k$ $(k-1)$ the first term on the right-hand side cancels the second (third), and the other term is zero by the induction hypothesis. For $j < k - 1$ the last two terms are zero by the induction hypothesis. The remaining term is $\mathbf{y}_j^T A \mathbf{x}_k = \mathbf{x}_k^T A^T \mathbf{y}_j$. For $j < k - 1$ this term may be shown to be zero by multiplying the second equation of (10.5-3) with $k = j$ by $\mathbf{x}_k^T$ and using the induction hypothesis. Since we may similarly show that $\mathbf{x}_j^T \mathbf{y}_{k+1} = 0$ for $j = 1, \ldots, k$ the theorem is proved. The second form of c_{k-1} in (10.5-4) follows using the second equation of (10.5-3) and the biorthogonality. From this theorem we obtain

Corollary 10.4   Under the assumption that $\mathbf{y}_j^T \mathbf{x}_j \neq 0$, $j = 1$, $\ldots, n$

1. The vectors $\mathbf{x}_i$, $i = 1, \ldots, n$ are linearly independent.
2. If (10.5-3) is used with $k = n$ to generate $\mathbf{x}_{n+1}$, then $\mathbf{x}_{n+1} = \mathbf{0}$.

Proof   If, for some $j \leqq n$, $\mathbf{x}_j$ were a linear combination of the $\mathbf{x}_k$, $k < j$ then we would have

$$\mathbf{x}_j = \sum_{k=1}^{j-1} \alpha_k \mathbf{x}_k \tag{10.5-6}$$

But this would mean that $\mathbf{y}_j^T \mathbf{x}_j = 0$ because of the biorthogonality. Since this contradicts the hypothesis, we have proved the first part of the corollary. To prove the second part we note first that the proof of Theorem 10.16 implies that, if (10.5-3) is used with $k = n$ and $\mathbf{y}_n^T \mathbf{x}_n \neq 0$, then Eq. (10.5-2) still holds if the vectors x_{n+1} and y_{n+1} are included in the sequences. But then the first part of the corollary would also hold for the vectors $x_1, \ldots, x_{n+1}$. Since $n+1$ vectors cannot be linearly independent in n space, the only way out of this impasse is to have $x_{n+1} = 0$.

Using this corollary we rewrite the first equation of (10.5-3) as

$$A x_1 = x_2 + b_1 x_1$$
$$A x_k = x_{k+1} + b_k x_k + c_{k-1} x_{k-1} \qquad k = 2, \ldots, n-1 \qquad (10.5\text{-}7)$$
$$A x_n = b_n x_n + c_{n-1} x_{n-1}$$

Thus, if S is the nonsingular matrix with columns $x_1, \ldots, x_n$, it follows from (10.5-7) that

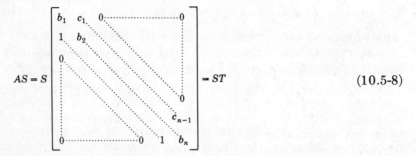

$$AS = S \qquad \qquad = ST \qquad \qquad (10.5\text{-}8)$$

Therefore, the tridiagonal matrix T of (10.5-8) is the desired matrix of (10.5-1). To find a tridiagonal matrix with the same eigenvalues as a general matrix A, we need then only calculate the b_k's and c_k's given by (10.5-4) starting from arbitrary x_1 and y_1.

We may calculate the characteristic polynomial of T in a fashion similar to that used in Givens's method. Corresponding to (10.4-33) we have

$$f_{n-(i+1)}(\lambda) = (\lambda - b_{i+1}) f_{n-i}(\lambda) - c_i f_{n-(i-1)}(\lambda) \qquad i = 1, \ldots, n-1 \qquad (10.5\text{-}9)$$

with $f_n(\lambda) = 1$ and $f_{n-1}(\lambda) = -b_1 + \lambda$ so that the characteristic equation of T is again given by

$$f_0(\lambda) = 0 \qquad \qquad (10.5\text{-}10)$$

In this case, however, the sequence of polynomials is not a Sturm sequence in general (why?). We may nevertheless use (10.5-10) to calculate the eigenvalues of A or we may use one of the techniques of Sec. 10.6 since they are particularly convenient in the case of tridiagonal matrices.

Now let us consider the situation when the method fails, that is, when $y_j^T x_j = 0$ for some $j \leq n$. We must consider two cases:

1. x_j and y_j are both nonzero (i.e., they are orthogonal). This case is of small probability but when it happens we cannot complete the process and must begin again with a new x_1 and y_1 {44}. Further, if at any stage x_j and y_j are nonzero but nearly orthogonal, then a large magnification of error will occur in the computation of b_j and c_j.

2. Either x_j or y_j or both equal zero. To see how to handle this case we use (10.5-3) to write

$$x_j = P_{j-1}(A)x_1 \qquad y_j = P_{j-1}(A^T)y_1 \qquad (10.5\text{-}11)$$

where P_{j-1} is a polynomial of degree $j-1$ in A. A comparison of (10.5-3) and (10.5-9) indicates that

$$P_k(A) = f_{n-k}(A) \qquad k = 1, \ldots, n \qquad (10.5\text{-}12)$$

Now suppose $x_j = 0$. Then there are two possibilities:

(i) $P_{j-1}(A) \equiv 0$. Then $P_{j-1}(\lambda)$ is a multiple of the minimal polynomial.† In this case we obtain all the eigenvalues from $f_{n-j+1}(\lambda)$.

(ii) $P_{j-1}(A) \not\equiv 0$. In this case we merely continue the biorthogonalization process by (a) choosing a vector x_j which is orthogonal to y_k, $k < j$; (b) setting $c_{j-1} = 0$ in the second of the equations (10.5-3) but using c_{j-1} as given by (10.5-4) in the first equation of (10.5-3); and (c) continuing the process in the usual fashion. The resulting sets of vectors may be shown {45} to be biorthogonal. If $y_j = 0$ or both x_j and y_j are zero then some straightforward modifications of the above are required {45}.

The difficulty in computing $P_{j-1}(A)$ makes it unreasonable to try to distinguish between (i) and (ii). Since the procedure for case (ii) leads to the correct characteristic equation even when case (i) has occurred, it is simplest always to assume the occurrence of case (ii).

Because of roundoff there is only a negligible possibility of obtaining a true zero x_j or y_j at any stage. But because a very small x_j or y_j will cause a large magnification of error at later stages [cf. (10.5-4)], it is necessary to have a computational criterion to decide when an x_j or y_j is sufficiently small that it should be taken as zero. The main computational problem in Lanczos's method is, however, keeping the sets {x_i} and {y_i} truly biorthogonal. Because of this difficulty, for large matrices, this method may result in a quite inaccurate T matrix. One way to overcome this problem is by periodic reorthogonalization of the two sets of vectors [see Wilkinson (1958a)]. Another technique which has worked well in some practical applications and which involves a modification of Lanczos's method is considered in a problem {49}.

---

† The minimal polynomial $g(\lambda)$ is that polynomial of lowest degree for which $g(A) = 0$. Every eigenvalue of A satisfies $g(\lambda) = 0$.

Lanczos's method is, of course, applicable to symmetric matrices also. But because of the above-mentioned inaccuracies and because Lanczos's method requires more operations than Householder's method {43}, it is not really competitive with Householder's method in the symmetric case.

The eigenvectors of T are related to those of A in a fashion similar to the relations in the Jacobi, Givens, and Householder methods (see the proof of Theorem 10.3). The actual calculation of the eigenvectors is considered in a problem {46}.

Example 10.9   Use Lanczos's method to find the eigenvalues of

$$A = \begin{bmatrix} 2 & -2 & 3 \\ 1 & 1 & 1 \\ 1 & 3 & -1 \end{bmatrix}$$

With $\mathbf{x}_1^T = \mathbf{y}_1^T = (0,0,1)$ we calculate

$(A\mathbf{x}_1)^T = (3,1,-1)$ $(A^T\mathbf{y}_1)^T = (1,3,-1)$
$b_1 = -1/1 = -1$
$\mathbf{x}_2^T = (3,1,0)$ $\mathbf{y}_2^T = (1,3,0)$
$(A\mathbf{x}_2)^T = (4,4,6)$ $(A^T\mathbf{y}_2)^T = (5,1,6)$
$b_2 = 8/3$ $c_1 = 6$
$\mathbf{x}_3^T = (-4,4/3,0)$ $\mathbf{y}_3^T = (7/3,-7,0)$
$(A\mathbf{x}_3)^T = (-32/3,-8/3,0)$ $(A^T\mathbf{y}_3)^T = (-7/3,-35/3,0)$
$b_3 = 1/3$ $c_2 = -28/9$

so that

$$T = \begin{bmatrix} -1 & 6 & 0 \\ 1 & 8/3 & -28/9 \\ 0 & 1 & 1/3 \end{bmatrix}$$

Then using (10.5-9) we calculate

$$f_0(\lambda) = \lambda^3 - 2\lambda^2 - 5\lambda + 6$$

whose three roots are $\lambda_1 = 3$, $\lambda_2 = -2$, $\lambda_3 = 1$.

If instead of $(0,0,1)$ we had chosen $\mathbf{x}_1^T = \mathbf{y}_1^T = (1,0,0)$ we would have found

$$\mathbf{x}_3 = 0$$

Since there are no multiple eigenvalues, the minimum polynomial and the characteristic polynomial are identical. Therefore, this is an example of case 2(ii) above {47}.

Lanczos's method is sometimes called the *method of minimized iterations* for reasons which are considered in {48}.

10.5-2   Supertriangularization and deflation

If Givens's or Householder's method (or a modified form of Lanczos's method; see {49}) is applied to a nonsymmetric matrix A, the result is a Hessenberg matrix as shown in Fig. 10.2 (why?). However, it is possible to reduce a general matrix A to Hessenberg form with considerably less computation than is required by the methods mentioned above. This can be achieved by using Gaussian elimination instead of orthogonal transformations. Moreover, by using positioning for size, this process can be made extremely stable with respect to roundoff error.

As in Givens's and Householder's methods, we proceed row by row to make the off-tridiagonal elements (in the upper triangle) zero. Suppose we have done this for rows $1, \ldots, k - 1$. For convenience let the elements in the matrix at this stage still be denoted by a_{ij}. Then for row k we

1. Select the largest element a_{kl} in magnitude among $a_{k,k+1}, \ldots, a_{kn}$ and interchange columns $k + 1$ and l.
2. Calculate

$$m_{kj} = -(a_{kj}/a_{k,k+1}) \qquad j = k + 2, \ldots, n \qquad (10.5\text{-}13)$$

   where, because of step 1, $|m_{kj}| \leq 1$.
3. Add m_{kj} times column $k + 1$ to column j, $j = k + 2, \ldots, n$

Step 1 and each part of step 3 are equivalent to postmultiplying the matrix by elementary column matrices {50}. Therefore, to complete the similarity transformation for row k, it is only necessary to premultiply by the inverses of these (nonsingular) elementary matrices {50}. It is quite easy to see that the zero elements in rows $1, \ldots, k - 1$ remain zero. Therefore, performing this algorithm for $k = 1, \ldots, n - 2$ results in a matrix $B = [b_{ij}]$ in Hessenberg form. The stability of this method with respect to roundoff results from the fact that the m_{kj} in (10.5-13) are all no greater than 1 in magnitude.

The number of multiplications and divisions required is $\frac{2}{3}n^3 + O(n^2)$ while Householder's method for nonsymmetric matrices requires $\frac{4}{3}n^3 + O(n^2)$ operations plus $n - 2$ square roots {50}.

In Sec. 10.6-2 we shall consider a powerful method for calculating all the eigenvalues of a matrix in Hessenberg form. In the remainder of this section, however, we shall consider, first, how we may calculate an eigenvalue and eigenvector of such a matrix and, second, how we may then deflate the Hessenberg matrix B to a matrix of order $n - 1$. We assume throughout the remainder of this section that no $b_{i,i+1}$ is zero, for if so we can then consider a reduced matrix {51}.

The system of equations $(B - \lambda I)\mathbf{x} = 0$ may be written

$$
\begin{aligned}
(b_{11} - \lambda)x_1 + b_{12}x_2 &= 0 \\
b_{21}x_1 + (b_{22} - \lambda)x_2 + b_{23}x_3 &= 0 \\
\cdots\cdots\cdots\cdots\cdots\cdots\cdots\cdots\cdots\cdots\cdots \\
b_{n1}x_1 + b_{n2}x_2 + \cdots\cdots\cdots + (b_{nn} - \lambda)x_n &= 0
\end{aligned}
\qquad (10.5\text{-}14)
$$

Now let us assume a value of λ and set $x_1 = 1$ in the first equation. The first $n - 1$ equations may then be solved recursively for $x_2, \ldots, x_n$. But the last equation will be satisfied only if λ is an eigenvalue (why?). Denote the value of the left-hand side of the last equation by $F(\lambda)$. We shall now show that $F(\lambda)$ is a multiple of the characteristic equation.

The matrix $B - \lambda I$ has the form

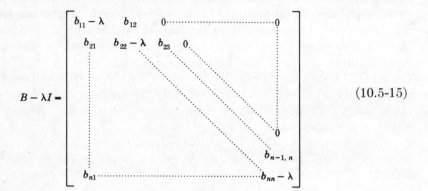

$$B - \lambda I =$$ (10.5-15)

For $i = 2, \ldots, n$ we multiply the ith column by x_i as found above and add this to the first column, thereby obtaining the matrix

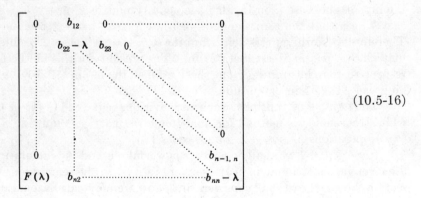

(10.5-16)

We have then

$$|B - \lambda I| = F(\lambda) \prod_{i=1}^{n-1} b_{i,i+1} = cF(\lambda) \tag{10.5-17}$$

where c is nonzero since we have assumed no $b_{i,i+1} = 0$. Since our object is to find a zero of $F(\lambda)$, we may use one of the techniques of Chap. 8 to find this zero. One choice would be the secant method, in which case we would evaluate $F(\lambda)$ for two values of λ, λ_1 and λ_2, and then use (8.3-27) to compute λ_3, etc. Since in fact it is easy to calculate derivatives of

$F(\lambda)$, another good choice is Laguerre's method (Sec. 8.10-4) [Parlett (1964b)].   Note that both these choices are applicable to complex as well as real eigenvalues.

It might seem that the accuracy of this procedure would be severely curtailed if any of the $b_{i,i+1}$ are very small in magnitude because of the necessity of dividing by $b_{i,i+1}$ in the recursion used to solve the first $n - 1$ equations of (10.5-14).   But, in fact, it can be shown that there is little correlation between the accuracy of the method and the magnitude of the $b_{i,i+1}$, $i = 1, \ldots, n - 1$ [see Wilkinson (1959a)].

Having computed an eigenvalue of B by the procedure above, the formal computation of the corresponding eigenvector is easy using (10.5-14).   However, our previous comments on the numerical difficulties involved in the calculation of eigenvectors of tridiagonal matrices are also applicable to the calculation of eigenvectors of matrices in Hessenberg form.

Now suppose we have found a real eigenvalue λ_1.   Let $S_{n-1,n}$ be a plane rotation matrix as defined by (10.4-9) with $p = n - 1$, $q = n$. Let

$$B_\lambda = B - \lambda_1 I \tag{10.5-18}$$

Then the element in the nth row and nth column of $S_{n-1,n}B_\lambda$ is given by

$$- \sin \theta \, b_{n-1,n} + \cos \theta \, (b_{nn} - \lambda_1) \tag{10.5-19}$$

By choosing θ such that $\tan \theta = (b_{nn} - \lambda_1)/b_{n-1,n}$, we may make this element zero.   We then choose a plane rotation matrix $S_{n-2,n}$ such that the element in the nth row and $(n - 1)$st column in $S_{n-1,n}B_\lambda$ is annihilated while the element in the (n,n) position remains zero.   In this way we consider a sequence of plane rotation matrices S_{in}, $i = n - 1, \ldots, 1$ such that

$$T = S_{1n}S_{2n} \cdots S_{n-1,n}B_\lambda = SB_\lambda \tag{10.5-20}$$

has zeros in the last row in positions $2, 3, \ldots, n$ {52}.   That is, each plane rotation matrix S_{in} is chosen so that the $(i + 1)$st element in the last row is annihilated.   Thus T has the form

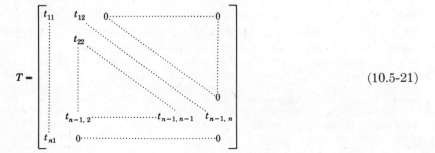

$$\tag{10.5-21}$$

Now we may show $\{52\}$ that, if no $b_{i,i+1}$ in B was equal to zero, then neither is any $t_{i,i+1}$. But

$$\det (T) = (-1)^{n-1} t_{n1} \prod_{i=1}^{n-1} t_{i,i+1} \tag{10.5-22}$$

From (10.5-20), since λ_1 is an eigenvalue of B

$$\det (T) = \det (S) \det (B_\lambda) = 0 \tag{10.5-23}$$

Therefore, $t_{n1} = 0$ and the whole last row is zero.   Then, using the form of the plane rotation matrices, we may show $\{52\}$ that

$$SBS^T = SB_\lambda S^T + \lambda_1 I \tag{10.5-24}$$

has the form

$$SBS^T = \begin{bmatrix} & & & \alpha_{1n} \\ & & & \cdot \\ & B_1 & & \cdot \\ & & & \cdot \\ & & & \alpha_{n-1,n} \\ 0 & \cdots & 0 & \lambda_1 \end{bmatrix} \tag{10.5-25}$$

where B_1 is in Hessenberg form and the α_{jn}'s are some constants.   Since S, the product of the plane rotation matrices, is easily calculated we have therefore developed a method of deflating the supertriangular matrix each time an eigenvalue is found.   However, despite its elegance, this deflation technique is often unstable [see Wilkinson (1962)].

If λ_1 is a complex eigenvalue, then the deflation process may still be carried through using unitary instead of plane rotation matrices $\{55\}$. This, of course, requires the use of complex arithmetic.

The deflation technique itself provides another method for evaluating the characteristic polynomial of B for various values of λ.   If λ_1 in (10.5-18) is any value of λ, not necessarily an eigenvalue, then we can no longer say that t_{n1} in (10.5-21) is zero.   But

$$\det (T) = \det (S) \det (B - \lambda_1 I) = \det (B - \lambda_1 I) \tag{10.5-26}$$

since each plane rotation matrix in (10.5-20) has a determinant of one. Therefore, (10.5-22) gives the value of the characteristic polynomial of B for $\lambda = \lambda_1$.   As above, by evaluating this determinant for a sequence of values of λ, we may find an eigenvalue by the secant or some other method.

Example 10.10   Apply the Gaussian elimination and deflation methods of this section to the matrix of Example 10.9.

Interchanging the second and third columns of the matrix and then eliminating the element in the (1,3) position we obtain the matrix

$$\begin{bmatrix} 2 & 3 & 0 \\ 1 & 1 & 5\!\!/_3 \\ 1 & -1 & 7\!\!/_3 \end{bmatrix} \tag{10.5-27}$$

Then premultiplying by the inverses of the elementary matrices used to derive (10.5-27), we obtain {50}

$$B = \begin{bmatrix} 2 & 3 & 0 \\ 1\!\!/_3 & -5\!\!/_3 & 11\!\!/_9 \\ 1 & 1 & 5\!\!/_3 \end{bmatrix}$$

To calculate an eigenvalue of B let us take as initial approximations $\lambda = 0$ and $\lambda = 1\!\!/_2$. Then using Eqs. (10.5-14) we calculate $F(0) = -18\!\!/_{11}$ and $F(1\!\!/_2) = -75\!\!/_{88}$. Then using the secant method we obtain as the next approximation $\lambda = 24\!\!/_{23}$. Convergence to $\lambda_1 = 1$ is very rapid.

Now suppose we have found $\lambda_1 = 1$. Then

$$B_\lambda = B - \lambda_1 I = \begin{bmatrix} 1 & 3 & 0 \\ 1\!\!/_3 & -8\!\!/_3 & 11\!\!/_9 \\ 1 & 1 & 2\!\!/_3 \end{bmatrix}$$

To deflate this matrix we use (10.5-19) to calculate

$$\sin \theta = 6/\sqrt{157} \qquad \cos \theta = 11/\sqrt{157}$$

Then with

$$S_{23} = \begin{bmatrix} 1 & 0 & 0 \\ 0 & 11/\sqrt{157} & 6/\sqrt{157} \\ 0 & -6/\sqrt{157} & 11/\sqrt{157} \end{bmatrix}$$

we calculate

$$S_{23}B_\lambda = \begin{bmatrix} 1 & 3 & 0 \\ 29/3\sqrt{157} & -70/3\sqrt{157} & \sqrt{157}/9 \\ 9/\sqrt{157} & 27/\sqrt{157} & 0 \end{bmatrix}$$

To annihilate the remainder of the third row we use

$$S_{13} = \begin{bmatrix} \sqrt{\dfrac{157}{238}} & 0 & \dfrac{9}{\sqrt{238}} \\ 0 & 1 & 0 \\ -\dfrac{9}{\sqrt{238}} & 0 & \sqrt{\dfrac{157}{238}} \end{bmatrix}$$

and obtain finally

$$S_{13}S_{23}B_\lambda S_{23}^T S_{13}^T + \lambda_1 I = \begin{bmatrix} 152\!\!/_{157} & 33\sqrt{238}/157 & -27/\sqrt{157} \\ 13{,}514/471\sqrt{238} & 5\!\!/_{157} & \dfrac{2204}{9\sqrt{157}\sqrt{238}} \\ 0 & 0 & 1 \end{bmatrix}$$

It is easy to verify that the 2×2 principal minor has the eigenvalues 3 and -2 as found in Example 10.9. While tedious to apply by hand this technique is easy to mechanize on a digital computer.

10.5-3   Other methods for nonsymmetric matrices

1. *Jacobi-type methods*   The Jacobi method for symmetric matrices was based on the result that any symmetric matrix can be diagonalized by an orthogonal transformation. Theorem 10.11 assures us that any non-symmetric matrix can be triangularized by a unitary transformation. However, it has not been proved that this triangularization always can be accomplished by unitary matrices analogous to the plane rotation matrices of Sec. 10.4-1. In fact, for certain procedures directly analogous to those in Sec. 10.4-1, examples can be given for which the process will not converge. Nevertheless, by successively annihilating the largest, off-diagonal element in one triangle of the matrix or by using the threshold technique, it has been found possible in many cases to triangularize A and thus to find its eigenvalues and eigenvectors {53}.

2. *Direct calculation of the characteristic equation*   We considered two such methods in Sec. 10.1-2. In general, however, the amount of calculation required to compute the characteristic equation directly is substantially greater than the amount of calculation required to first reduce A to some more tractable (i.e., tridiagonal or Hessenberg) form and then to calculate the characteristic equation. In {4} another technique for calculating the characteristic polynomial is considered.

10.6   THE LR AND QR TRANSFORMATIONS

Both of the methods to be considered in this section are applicable to the calculation of eigenvalues of an arbitrary matrix, but they are particularly useful for matrices in tridiagonal or Hessenberg form. The former of the two methods, the LR transformation, is the easier to apply but may be numerically unstable. On the other hand, the second of these two methods, the QR transformation, is extremely stable numerically.

10.6-1   The LR transformation

The basis of the method is the successive triangular decomposition of a sequence of matrices $\{A_k\}$ all of which have the same form as the original matrix (e.g., if A is tridiagonal so is every A_k). The key to this method is the observation that, if A_1 is triangularly decomposed into the product $L_1 U_1$, then, if we multiply L_1 and U_1 in reverse order, the matrix $A_2 = U_1 L_1$ has the same eigenvalues as A_1. This is true because

$$A_2 = U_1 L_1 = L_1^{-1} A_1 L_1 = U_1 A_1 U_1^{-1} \tag{10.6-1}$$

so that A_2 and A_1 are similar.   Now A_2 itself may be triangularly decomposed into $A_2 = L_2U_2$, and in this way, we define a sequence of matrices

$$A_k = L_kU_k = U_{k-1}L_{k-1} \qquad k = 1, 2, \ldots \qquad A_1 = A \qquad (10.6\text{-}2)$$

The following properties of the matrices A_k, L_k, and U_k are of interest to us:

1. All the A_k matrices are similar and therefore have the same eigenvalues.   This follows from (10.6-1).
2. Let

$$P_k = U_kU_{k-1} \cdots U_1 \qquad N_k = L_1L_2 \cdots L_k \qquad (10.6\text{-}3)$$

Then P_k and N_k are upper and lower triangular matrices, respectively.   Since, as in (10.6-1), if all matrices are nonsingular

$$A_{k+1} = L_k^{-1}A_kL_k = U_kA_kU_k^{-1} \qquad (10.6\text{-}4)$$

it follows inductively that

$$A_{k+1} = N_k^{-1}A_1N_k = P_kA_1P_k^{-1} \qquad (10.6\text{-}5)$$

3. Since $L_jU_j = U_{j-1}L_{j-1}$

$$\begin{aligned} N_kP_k &= L_1 \cdots L_{k-1}L_kU_kU_{k-1} \cdots U_1 \\ &= L_1 \cdots L_{k-1}U_{k-1}L_{k-1}U_{k-1} \cdots U_1 \quad (10.6\text{-}6) \end{aligned}$$

By repetition of this process we arrive at

$$N_kP_k = (L_1U_1)^k = A^k \qquad (10.6\text{-}7)$$

The process of deriving the sequence $\{A_k\}$ from A by successive triangular decompositions is called the *LR transformation*.†   We assume in what follows that each U_k matrix has 1's on its main diagonal.   (A precisely similar development is obtained if this is assumed instead for each L_k.)   Our interest here is in the convergence of the sequence $\{A_k\}$. This convergence depends upon the convergence of P_k as stated in

Theorem 10.17   If $\{P_k\}$ converges to a nonsingular matrix P_∞ as $k \to \infty$, then $\lim\limits_{k \to \infty} A_k$ exists and is a lower triangular matrix.

Proof   Since $\{P_k\}$ converges the following limits also exist:

$$\lim_{k \to \infty} U_k = \lim_{k \to \infty} P_kP_{k-1}^{-1} = I \qquad (10.6\text{-}8)$$

$$\begin{aligned} L_\infty = \lim_{k \to \infty} L_k &= \lim_{k \to \infty} U_k^{-1}A_{k+1} \\ &= \lim_{k \to \infty} P_{k-1}A_1P_k^{-1} = P_\infty A_1P_\infty^{-1} \qquad (10.6\text{-}9) \end{aligned}$$

† Its discoverer, Rutishauser (1955), used the mnemonic left-right (LR) whereas, in keeping with the notation of Chap. 9, we use lower-upper.

Therefore,

$$A_\infty = \lim_{k \to \infty} A_k = \lim_{k \to \infty} L_k U_k = L_\infty \tag{10.6-10}$$

exists and is lower triangular, which proves the theorem.

An investigation of the convergence of P_k in general is beyond the scope of this book; see Rutishauser (1958). Suffice it to say that the method converges for a large class of matrices which includes all symmetric, positive definite matrices, many matrices with distinct real eigenvalues, and many matrices with real eigenvalues which satisfy neither of these two conditions. When some of the eigenvalues are complex the convergence properties of the LR transformation are more difficult to state (clearly A_∞ cannot be triangular), but the method may often be used even in this case to find the eigenvalues. We note that when the eigenvalues are real and distinct, the diagonal of L_∞ contains the eigenvalues in decreasing order of magnitude from left to right.

The application of the LR transformation to tridiagonal matrices is worth considering in some detail. We consider first the type of tridiagonal matrix that arises in Lanczos's method. Suppose that

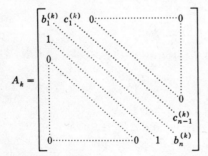

$$\tag{10.6-11}$$

Then, if we define

$$
\begin{aligned}
q_j^{(k)} &= b_j^{(k)} - \epsilon_{j-1}^{(k)} && j = 1, \ldots, n; \epsilon_0^{(k)} = 0 \\
\epsilon_j^{(k)} &= c_j^{(k)}/q_j^{(k)} && j = 1, \ldots, n - 1
\end{aligned}
\tag{10.6-12}
$$

we may easily verify that $A_k = L_k U_k$ where

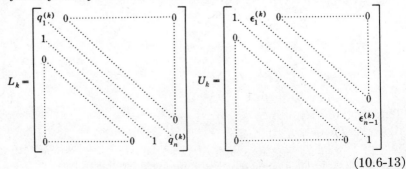

$$\tag{10.6-13}$$

Moreover, it is easy to verify that $A_{k+1} = U_k L_k$ has the same tridiagonal form as A_k. Therefore, starting with the matrix T in (10.5-8) the LR transformation defines a sequence of tridiagonal matrices of the same form. We assume, of course, that no $q_j^{(k)}, j = 1, \ldots, n - 1$ vanishes.

If we use (10.6-13) to compute the elements of A_{k+1} and also rewrite (10.6-12) with k replaced by $k + 1$ we have

$$b_j^{(k+1)} = q_j^{(k)} + \epsilon_j^{(k)} = q_j^{(k+1)} + \epsilon_{j-1}^{(k+1)} \qquad j = 1, \ldots, n$$
$$\epsilon_0^{(k+1)} = \epsilon_n^{(k)} = 0 \qquad (10.6\text{-}14)$$

$$c_j^{(k+1)} = \epsilon_j^{(k)} q_{j+1}^{(k)} = \epsilon_j^{(k+1)} q_j^{(k+1)} \qquad j = 1, \ldots, n - 1 \qquad (10.6\text{-}15)$$

From these we get the recurrence relations

$$q_j^{(k+1)} = q_j^{(k)} + \epsilon_j^{(k)} - \epsilon_{j-1}^{(k+1)} \qquad j = 1, \ldots, n \qquad \epsilon_0^{(k+1)} = \epsilon_n^{(k)} = 0$$
$$\epsilon_j^{(k+1)} = \epsilon_j^{(k)} q_{j+1}^{(k)} / q_j^{(k+1)} \qquad \begin{array}{l} j = 1, \ldots, n - 1 \\ k = 1, 2, \ldots \end{array} \qquad (10.6\text{-}16)$$

which are precisely the recurrence relations of the *quotient-difference algorithm* which was mentioned in Sec. 8.10-3. To use these relations most conveniently we set up the table

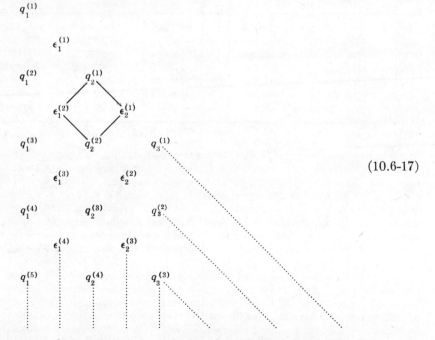

$$(10.6\text{-}17)$$

The upper diagonal may be calculated by using (10.6-12) to decompose the original matrix $A = A_1$. Then (10.6-16) may be used to compute successive diagonals of the table. Each of the recurrence relations involves four entries in the table, for example, those shown joined by solid lines.

For this reason the recurrence relations (10.6-16) are called *rhombus rules*. The relations (10.6-16) enable us to calculate the decompositions of the matrices A_k, $k \geqq 2$ without ever calculating the A_k themselves. If the method converges, it follows from Theorem 10.16 that $\lim\limits_{k \to \infty} q_j^{(k)} = \lambda_j$ and $\lim\limits_{k \to \infty} \epsilon_j^{(k)} = 0$. In fact for matrices of the type (10.6-11) the method always converges for distinct real eigenvalues, and for multiple or complex eigenvalues, the table (10.6-17) may still be used to extract the eigenvalues [see Henrici (1958)].

Example 10.11   Use the *LR* transformation to find the eigenvalues of the matrix T of Example 10.9.   With

$$T = \begin{bmatrix} -1 & 6 & 0 \\ 1 & 8\!/\!3 & -28\!/\!9 \\ 0 & 1 & 1\!/\!3 \end{bmatrix}$$

we may use (10.6-12) to compute the first diagonal of the quotient-difference table. Then using (10.6-16) we get the following table for representative values of k:

k	$q_1^{(k)}$	$\epsilon_1^{(k)}$	$q_2^{(k)}$	$\epsilon_2^{(k)}$	$q_3^{(k)}$
1	-1.0000000	-6.0000000	8.6666666	$-.35897436$	$.69230769$
3	$.42857140$	15.238106	-14.641678	$.01882468$	$.95617524$
10	3.3231963	$-.51762097$	-1.8052116	$-.00052252$	1.0001569
20	3.0052706	$-.00877450$	-1.9964972	$-.00000049$	$.99999979$
30	3.0000934	$-.00015211$	-1.9999427	-4.8×10^{-10}	$.99999963$
40	3.0000037	$-.00000264$	-2.0000025	-4.7×10^{-13}	$.99999963$
49	3.0000020	6.9×10^{-8}	-2.0000034	9.1×10^{-16}	$.99999963$

After 49 iterations no further changes take place in $q_1^{(k)}$, $q_2^{(k)}$, $q_3^{(k)}$ although $\epsilon_1^{(k)}$ and $\epsilon_2^{(k)}$ continue to decrease. All computations were done with floating-point arithmetic using eight digits in the fractional part. The following comments are relevant:

1. Although 49 iterations were required, each iteration requires a very small amount of calculation. A similar example with a 3×3 positive definite symmetric matrix with 5 in each diagonal position and 1's on both subdiagonals requires 64 iterations to converge. Nevertheless, the slowness of the convergence suggests the desirability of a technique for accelerating the convergence. Such a technique is considered at the end of Sec. 10.6-2.

2. For this method to be useful, it must be stable with respect to the buildup of roundoff error. Although the method is stable for this example, triangular decomposition is not always numerically stable. If some of the divisors in the triangular decomposition are small, substantial magnification of error may occur, and in particular, the decomposition may fail to exist if a divisor is zero. One way to avoid this instability might be to modify the *LR* algorithm so that the decomposition is performed using positioning for size. However, convergence has not been proved for this technique. Another way to avoid the instability of this algorithm is to replace the triangular decomposition by a stable factorization. Such a factorization is the subject of the next section.

When the tridiagonal matrix is symmetric, as in the case of Givens's and Householder's methods, the quotient-difference algorithm may again be used to obtain a symmetric triangular decomposition algorithm. Suppose that

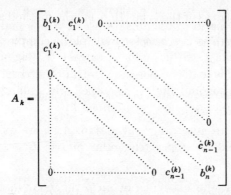

$$A_k = \qquad\qquad\qquad\qquad\qquad\qquad (10.6\text{-}18)$$

In order to preserve symmetry, we should like to decompose A_k into $L_k L_k^T$ where

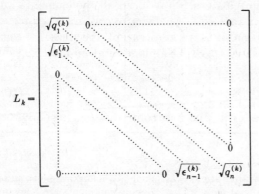

$$L_k = \qquad\qquad\qquad\qquad\qquad\qquad (10.6\text{-}19)$$

If A_k is not positive definite then some of the elements of L_k will be imaginary even though all the $q_j^{(k)}$ and $\epsilon_j^{(k)}$ are real.   Nevertheless, Eqs. (10.6-16) correctly give $q_j^{(k+1)}$ and $\epsilon_j^{(k+1)}$ in the decomposition of $A_{k+1} = L_k^T L_k$ into $L_{k+1} L_{k+1}^T$ {57}.   The initial decomposition of $A = A_1$ into $L_1 L_1^T$ is obtained using the equations {57}

$$q_j^{(1)} = b_j^{(1)} - \epsilon_{j-1}^{(1)} \qquad j = 1, \ldots, n \qquad \epsilon_0^{(1)} = 0$$
$$\epsilon_j^{(1)} = [c_j^{(1)}]^2 / q_j^{(1)} \qquad j = 1, \ldots, n-1 \qquad\qquad\qquad (10.6\text{-}20)$$

When A_1 is positive definite then this algorithm always converges, in which case as before $\lim_{k \to \infty} q_j^{(k)} = \lambda_j$ and $\lim_{k \to \infty} \epsilon_j^{(k)} = 0$.   Moreover, since the triangular decomposition of a positive definite matrix is stable numerically even without positioning for size (see Chap. 9, Probs. 13, 14), the LR transformation is stable for this case.

10.6-2   The QR transformation

We have noted previously in this chapter that methods for the calculation of eigenvalues which make use of orthogonal transformations tend to be numerically stable. It would be desirable, therefore, to have a method analogous to the LR transformation which makes use of orthogonal transformations rather than triangular decomposition. Such a method is the QR transformation.

The basis of this method is to decompose an arbitrary matrix A into a product QU where Q is orthogonal and U is upper triangular.† The assurance that this can be accomplished is contained in

> **Theorem 10.18**   For an arbitrary real matrix A, there exists an orthogonal matrix Q and an upper triangular matrix U such that $A = QU$.

Proof   We prove first the existence of an orthogonal matrix S_1 such that S_1A has zeros in its first column except on the diagonal. To do this we need only refer back to (10.5-20) and (10.5-21). There, with a sequence of plane rotation matrices, we reduced all the elements but one in the last row of a matrix to zero. Analogously, we may reduce all the elements in the first column of A to zero except the diagonal element. For example, let $A = [a_{ij}]$ and let S_{n1} be a plane rotation matrix as defined by (10.4-9) with $p = 1$, $q = n$ and

$$\tan \theta_n = a_{n1}/a_{11} \tag{10.6-21}$$

Then the element in the nth row and first column of $S_{n1}A$ is equal to zero. As in Sec. 10.5-2, if

$$M_{i-1} = S_{i1}M_i \qquad i = n, \ldots, 2 \qquad M_n = A \tag{10.6-22}$$

where, in S_{i1}, $\tan \theta_i$ is determined by an equation analogous to (10.6-21) using elements of M_i, then it follows that M_1 has zero elements in the first column below the diagonal {58}. Therefore $S_1 = S_{21}S_{31} \cdots S_{n1}$ is our desired orthogonal matrix.

Next we work on column two using $S_{n2}, \ldots, S_{32}$. This reduces all the elements in this column below the diagonal to zero without changing those already zero in column one. Continuing in this way, we arrive finally at an upper triangular matrix

$$U = \left(\prod_{i=1}^{n-1} \prod_{j=i+1}^{n} S_{ji} \right) A = Q^T A \tag{10.6-23}$$

with the matrices S_{ji} ordered as implied by the discussion above. This

† Francis (1961), the originator of this method, used R as a mnemonic for right triangular.

completes the proof.   We leave a consideration of the uniqueness of the decomposition to a problem $\{58\}$.

Analogously to (10.6-2) we now define

$$A_k = Q_k U_k = U_{k-1}Q_{k-1} \qquad k = 1, 2, \ldots \qquad A_1 = A \qquad (10.6\text{-}24)$$

where Q_k is orthogonal and U_k is upper triangular.   Then, since

$$A_k = U_{k-1}Q_{k-1} = Q_{k-1}^T A_{k-1} Q_{k-1} \qquad\qquad (10.6\text{-}25)$$

all the matrices A_k are similar.   Equations analogous to (10.6-3) to (10.6-7) are also easily derivable for this method $\{59\}$.

Analogously to Theorem 10.17 it is true that, if the product $Q_1 Q_2 \cdots Q_k$ converges as $k \to \infty$, then A_k converges to an upper triangular matrix with the eigenvalues of A on the diagonal in decreasing order of magnitude. Although a general discussion of the convergence of the QR transformation is beyond our scope, we may say that the convergence properties of this method are very similar to those of the LR transformation.

It is, of course, true that the decomposition of A into QU is in general both quite time-consuming [requiring $O(n^3)$ operations] and substantially more time-consuming than triangular decomposition.   But if A is tridiagonal, the QR transformation can be done quite rapidly $\{60\}$, although not so rapidly as the triangular decomposition using the quotient-difference algorithm.   Moreover, we may show that, if A is symmetric and tridiagonal, then so is every A_k $\{56\}$.   Of more importance is the result that, if A is in upper Hessenberg form, in which case the number of operations required to decompose A into QU is $O(n^2)$, then every A_k is in upper Hessenberg form $\{56\}$.

Example 10.12   Use the QR transformation to find the eigenvalues of the matrix B in Example 10.10.

We perform the calculations on

$$A = B^T = \begin{bmatrix} 2 & \tfrac{1}{3} & 1 \\ 3 & -\tfrac{5}{3} & 1 \\ 0 & 11\tfrac{1}{9} & \tfrac{5}{3} \end{bmatrix}$$

in order to have a matrix in upper Hessenberg form.   The following table indicates the convergence of the method:

k	$a_{11}^{(k)}$	$a_{22}^{(k)}$	$a_{33}^{(k)}$
1	2.0	-1.6666667	1.6666667
5	3.1781374	-2.2260322	1.0478949
10	2.9486278	-1.9471270	.9984996
15	3.0063596	-2.0064061	1.0000468
20	2.9991547	-1.9991527	.9999984
25	3.0001104	-2.0001098	.9999999

The rate of convergence is very similar to that for the LR transformation in Example 10.11, although each iteration of the QR transformation requires substantially more computation.

Both the LR and QR transformations as described here converge quite slowly in general. However, the convergence to $\lambda = 1.0$ in both Examples 10.11 and 10.12 was quite rapid. This was in fact no accident, and the reason for it forms the basis of an acceleration and deflation scheme which we shall now describe.

Let the eigenvalues of A be real, distinct, and ordered such that

$$|\lambda_1| > |\lambda_2| > \cdots > |\lambda_n| \tag{10.6-26}$$

Let us further assume that A is in upper Hessenberg form (which includes the case of tridiagonal matrices). Then it can be shown for either transformation [see Rutishauser (1958) for the LR case] that usually the element $a_{i,i-1}^{(k)}$, $i = 2, \ldots, n$ on the subdiagonal of A_k converges to zero like $(\lambda_i/\lambda_{i-1})^k$. In particular, if λ_n/λ_{n-1} is the smallest of these ratios, then, as in Examples 10.11 and 10.12, $a_{n,n-1}^{(k)}$ will converge to zero most rapidly and $a_{nn}^{(k)}$ will converge to λ_n most rapidly. This suggests that when $a_{n,n-1}^{(k)}$ has become sufficiently small, we could deflate the matrix A_k since, except for the diagonal term, the last row is essentially zero.

However, λ_n/λ_{n-1} is by no means always the smallest of the ratios λ_i/λ_{i-1}, and even when it is, the smaller the ratio the better. This suggests the following acceleration scheme which we consider here for the QR transformation: Let ν_k be an approximation to λ_n. Then in place of A_k we consider

$$A_k - \nu_k I = Q_k U_k \tag{10.6-27}$$

and

$$A_{k+1} = U_k Q_k + \nu_k I = Q_k^T A_k Q_k \tag{10.6-28}$$

With ν_{k+1} a new approximation to λ_n, we may again use (10.6-27) with k replaced by $k + 1$. If ν_k is chosen as that eigenvalue of the lower right 2×2 principal submatrix which is closest to $a_{nn}^{(k)}$, then this procedure has the effect in general of replacing the linear convergence $(\lambda_n/\lambda_{n-1})^k$ by quadratic convergence $(\lambda_n/\lambda_{n-1})^{2k}$ [Parlett (1964a)]. Together with the deflation technique described above, this acceleration technique greatly improves the computational properties of the LR and QR transformations. When there are multiple or complex eigenvalues acceleration and deflation techniques are still possible; for some of the details see Parlett (1964a).

The great advantage of the QR over the LR transformation is that, because of the use of plane rotation matrices throughout, it is very stable numerically. Therefore, because of the advantages discussed in Sec. 10.5-2 of reduction to Hessenberg form over reduction to tridiagonal form by Lanczos's method, a good general purpose scheme for calculating the eigenvalues of a nonsymmetric matrix A is the following:

1. Reduce A to Hessenberg form using the Gaussian elimination scheme of Sec. 10.5-2.
2. Use the QR transformation on the reduced matrix to calculate the eigenvalues.

For symmetric matrices, Householder's method followed by the QR transformation is a good general-purpose method. However, if the matrix is known to be positive definite, in which case the LR transformation is numerically stable, then Householder's method followed by the LR transformation is to be preferred.

10.7   MISCELLANEOUS TOPICS

1. *Errors in computed eigenvalues*   We consider here the effect of perturbations of the elements of a matrix A on the eigenvalues of A (cf. Sec. 8.13). Let A be a matrix with distinct eigenvalues $\lambda_1, \ldots, \lambda_n$, eigenvectors $x_1, \ldots, x_n$, and left eigenvectors $y_1, \ldots, y_n$. If δA is a perturbation of A, then the eigenvectors of $A + \delta A$ may be written

$$\mathbf{x}_i + \sum_{\substack{j=1 \\ j \neq i}}^{n} \epsilon_{ij} \mathbf{x}_j \tag{10.7-1}$$

and the eigenvalues may be written $\lambda_i + \delta\lambda_i$. Then, ignoring all products of perturbations, we may derive {63}

$$\delta\lambda_i \approx \mathbf{y}_i^T \delta A \mathbf{x}_i / \mathbf{y}_i^T \mathbf{x}_i \tag{10.7-2}$$

If the elements of δA are all less than ϵ in magnitude and if all $\mathbf{x}_i$ and $\mathbf{y}_i$ have magnitude 1, then approximately {63}

$$|\mathbf{y}_i^T \delta A \mathbf{x}_i| \leq n\epsilon \tag{10.7-3}$$

and, in particular, if A is symmetric

$$|\delta\lambda_i| \leq n\epsilon \tag{10.7-4}$$

The above enables us to measure the inherent errors in the computed eigenvalues of A. However, if A is ill-conditioned in the sense that small values of δA may cause large changes in $\delta\lambda_i$, then the assumption that the products of perturbations can be neglected is not valid. The above analysis is also not valid when there are multiple eigenvalues.

2. *Complex matrices*   When A has complex elements one approach to the problem of calculating its eigenvalues and eigenvectors is to reduce

the problem to one involving real matrices.   Let

$$A = B + iC \tag{10.7-5}$$

and consider

$$(B + iC)\mathbf{x} = \lambda\mathbf{x} \tag{10.7-6}$$

Multiplying (10.7-6) by $-i$ we get

$$(C - iB)\mathbf{x} = -\lambda i\mathbf{x} \tag{10.7-7}$$

Equations (10.7-6) and (10.7-7) may be combined to read

$$\begin{bmatrix} B & -C \\ C & B \end{bmatrix} \begin{bmatrix} \mathbf{x} \\ -i\mathbf{x} \end{bmatrix} = \lambda \begin{bmatrix} \mathbf{x} \\ -i\mathbf{x} \end{bmatrix} \tag{10.7-8}$$

Therefore, an eigenvalue of A is also an eigenvalue of the matrix

$$D = \begin{bmatrix} B & -C \\ C & B \end{bmatrix} \tag{10.7-9}$$

but this technique doubles the order of the matrix, and it would therefore be better to treat the complex matrix A directly.

When A is Hermitian, with minor modifications, all of what has been said in this chapter on real symmetric matrices remains true.   In particular, if orthogonal matrices are replaced by unitary matrices, all the methods which use orthogonal matrices remain valid.   For non-Hermitian matrices the situation is somewhat more complicated, but nevertheless the power method and deflation may be applied to complex as well as real matrices and again, where orthogonal matrices are used for nonsymmetric matrices as in the QR transformation, we need only use unitary matrices in the complex case.   Thus it is reasonable to say that the eigenvalue problem for complex matrices does not differ in principle from that of real matrices.   With minor modifications and the use of complex arithmetic, most of this chapter is applicable to complex as well as real matrices.

3. *Generalized eigenvalue problems*   We consider here the system

$$A\mathbf{x} = \lambda B\mathbf{x} \tag{10.7-10}$$

where A and B are matrices of order n.   When either A or B is nonsingular, (10.7-10) may be replaced by a system of the form (10.1-2) by computing the inverse of the nonsingular matrix.   When both A and B are singular, the problem becomes substantially more difficult, although $\lambda = 0$ is always an eigenvalue in this case.

BIBLIOGRAPHIC NOTES

The literature on the calculation of eigenvalues and eigenvectors is almost as vast as that on simultaneous linear equations.   However, the field is changing so rapidly that fully up-to-date general sources are comparatively rare.   The best general source for the material of this chapter is the book by Wilkinson (1965).   Other good sources are Bodewig (1959), Fadeeva (1959), and Householder (1953).   A good summary comparing various methods is given by White (1958).   An extensive survey of the theoretical aspects of the calculation of eigenvalues and eigenvectors as well as an excellent bibliography is contained in Householder (1964).

10.1   The material in this section is all classical.   Good sources are Bodewig (1959) and Householder (1953), both of which contain extensive bibliographies.

10.2–10.3   Our major source for the material of these sections is Bodewig (1959).   Much of the material can also be found in Fadeeva (1959).   Wilkinson's technique can be found in Wilkinson (1955).   The Rayleigh quotient appears in a number of areas of numerical analysis; see, for example, Kopal (1955).   The paper by Hotelling (1933) is the source of his method of deflation; all the deflation techniques considered are discussed in Bodewig (1959); see also White (1958).

10.4   There is a large literature on the Jacobi method.   For a discussion emphasizing computational aspects, see Greenstadt (1960).   Corbató (1963) gives an algorithm for searching for the largest off-diagonal element.   Pope and Tompkins (1957) discuss the threshold Jacobi method {33}.   An error analysis is given by Goldstine, Murray, and Von Neumann (1959).   Wilkinson (1962) analyzes the errors in the Jacobi method as well as those in other methods based on orthogonal transformations. For original papers on the other methods of this section, see Givens (1954) and Householder and Bauer (1959).   The use of the method of bisection is considered by Wilkinson (1959a).   Householder's method, especially in its computational aspects, is carefully explained by Wilkinson (1960).   Wilkinson (1958b) illustrates the problems involved in computing the eigenvectors of tridiagonal matrices.

10.5   The biorthogonalization technique is due to Lanczos (1950).   Wilkinson (1958a) discusses some computational aspects of the method.   The use of Gaussian elimination to reduce a matrix to Hessenberg form is due to Wilkinson (1959b).   The technique to find the eigenvalues of such a matrix is due to Hyman (1957).   Wilkinson (1959a) discusses some computational aspects of Hyman's and other methods.   The deflation technique was first considered by Givens (1958).   See Greenstadt (1955) for a discussion of the Jacobi method for nonsymmetric matrices.   White (1958) considers all these methods and contains an extensive bibliography.

10.6   The LR transformation method is due to Rutishauser (1955).   The best paper on this method in English is by Rutishauser (1958).   The quotient-difference algorithm is also due to Rutishauser (1954).   The best paper on it in English is by Henrici (1958).   The QR transformation is due to Francis (1961).   Parlett (1964a) gives an excellent exposition of both transformations.

10.7   The discussion of errors is taken from Wilkinson (1959c); for an extensive and excellent discussion of errors in eigenvalue computations see Wilkinson (1964).

BIBLIOGRAPHY

Birkhoff, G., and S. Maclane (1953): *A Survey of Modern Algebra*, rev. ed., The Macmillan Company, New York.

Bodewig, E. (1959): *Matrix Calculus*, 2d ed., Interscience Publishers, Inc., New York.

Corbató, F. J. (1963): On the Coding of Jacobi's Method for Computing the Eigenvalues and Eigenvectors of Real Symmetric Matrices, *J. Assoc. Comput. Mach.*, vol. 10, pp. 123–125.

Fadeeva, V. N. (1959): *Computational Methods of Linear Algebra* (translated by C. D. Benster), Dover Publications, Inc., New York.

Francis, J. G. F. (1961): The QR Transformation—A Unitary Analogue to the LR Transformation, *Comput. J.*, vol. 4, pp. 265–271, 332–345.

Givens, W. (1954): *Numerical Computation of the Characteristic Values of a Real Symmetric Matrix*, Report ORNL 1574, Oak Ridge National Laboratory.

Givens, W. (1958): Computation of Plane Unitary Rotations Transforming a General Matrix to Triangular Form, *J. Soc. Indust. Appl. Math.*, vol. 6, pp. 26–50.

Goldstine, H. H., F. J. Murray, and J. Von Neumann (1959): The Jacobi Method for Real Symmetric Matrices, *J. Assoc. Comput. Mach.*, vol. 6, pp. 59–96.

Greenstadt, J. (1955): A Method for Finding Roots of Arbitrary Matrices, *MTAC*, vol. 9, pp. 47–52.

Greenstadt, J. (1960): The Determination of the Characteristic Roots of a Matrix by the Jacobi Method in *Mathematical Methods for Digital Computers* (A. Ralston and H. S. Wilf, eds.), John Wiley & Sons, Inc., New York.

Henrici, P. (1958): The Quotient-Difference Algorithm in *Further Contributions to the Solution of Simultaneous Linear Equations and the Determination of Eigenvalues*, vol. 49, National Bureau of Standards Applied Mathematics Series.

Hotelling, H. (1933): Analysis of a Complex of Statistical Variables into Principal Components, *J. Educ. Psychol.*, vol. 24, pp. 417–441, 498–520.

Householder, A. S. (1953): *Principles of Numerical Analysis*, McGraw-Hill Book Company, New York.

Householder, A. S. (1964): *The Theory of Matrices in Numerical Analysis*, Blaisdell Publishing Company, Inc., New York.

Householder, A. S., and F. L. Bauer (1959): On Certain Methods for Expanding the Characteristic Polynomial, *Numer. Math.*, vol. 1, pp. 29–37.

Hyman, M. (1957): *Eigenvalues and Eigenvectors of General Matrices*, presented at the 12th Annual Meeting of the Association for Computing Machinery, June, 1957, Houston, Tex.

Kopal, Z. (1955): *Numerical Analysis*, John Wiley & Sons, Inc., New York.

Lanczos, C. (1950): An Iteration Method for the Solution of the Eigenvalue Problem of Linear Differential and Integral Operators, *J. Res. Nat. Bur. Standards*, vol. 45, pp. 255–282.

Ortega, J. M., and H. F. Kaiser (1963): The LL^T and QR Methods for Symmetric Tridiagonal Matrices, *Comput. J.*, vol. 6, pp. 99–101.

Parlett, B. (1964a): The Development and Use of Methods of LR Type, *SIAM Rev.*, vol. 6, pp. 275–295.

Parlett, B. (1964b): Laguerre's Method Applied to the Matrix Eigenvalue Problem, *Math. Comput.*, vol. 18, pp. 464–485.

Pope, D. A., and C. Tompkins (1957): Maximizing Functions of Rotations, *J. Assoc. Comput. Mach.*, vol. 4, pp. 459–466.

Rutishauser, H. (1954): Der Quotienten-Differenzen-Algorithmus, *Z. Angew. Math. Phys.*, vol. 5, pp. 496–507.

Rutishauser, H. (1955): Une méthode pour la determination des valeurs propres d'une matrice, *C. R. Acad. Sci. Paris*, vol. 240, pp. 34–36.

Rutishauser, H. (1958): Solution of Eigenvalue Problems with the LR Transformation in *Further Contributions to the Solution of Simultaneous Linear Equations and the Determination of Eigenvalues*, vol. 49, National Bureau of Standards Applied Mathematics Series.

White, P. A. (1958): The Computation of Eigenvalues and Eigenvectors of a Matrix, *J. Soc. Indust. Appl. Math.*, vol. 6, pp. 393–437.

Wilkinson, J. H. (1955): The Use of Iterative Methods of Finding the Latent Roots and Vectors of Matrices, *MTAC*, vol. 9, pp. 184–191.

Wilkinson, J. H. (1958a): The Calculation of Eigenvectors by the Method of Lanczos, *Comput. J.*, vol. 1, pp. 148–152.

Wilkinson, J. H. (1958b): The Calculation of the Eigenvectors of Codiagonal Matrices, *Comput. J.*, vol. 1, pp. 90–96.

Wilkinson, J. H. (1959a): Error Analysis of Floating-point Computation, *Numer. Math.*, vol. 2, pp. 319–340.

Wilkinson, J. H. (1959b): Stability of the Reduction of a Matrix to Almost Triangular and Triangular Forms by Elementary Similarity Transformations, *J. Assoc. Comput. Mach.*, vol. 6, pp. 336–359.

Wilkinson, J. H. (1959c): The Evaluation of Zeros of Ill-conditioned Polynomials, *Numer. Math.*, vol. 1, pp. 150–166, 167–180.

Wilkinson, J. H. (1960): Householder's Method for the Solution of the Algebraic Eigenproblem, *Comput. J.*, vol. 3, pp. 23–27.

Wilkinson, J. H. (1962): Error Analysis of Eigenvalue Techniques Based on Orthogonal Transformations, *J. Soc. Indust. Appl. Math.*, vol. 10, pp. 162–195.

Wilkinson, J. H. (1964): *Rounding Errors in Algebraic Processes*, Prentice-Hall, Inc., Englewood Cliffs, N. J.

Wilkinson, J. H. (1965): *The Algebraic Eigenvalue Problem*, Oxford University Press, Fair Lawn, N. J.

PROBLEMS

Section 10.1

1. (*a*) Let x_i and y_j be, respectively, a right and left eigenvector of a matrix A. Prove that x_i and y_j are orthogonal if they correspond to distinct eigenvalues.

(*b*) Therefore, prove that the (right) eigenvectors of a symmetric matrix corresponding to distinct eigenvalues are orthogonal.

2. (*a*) Prove Theorems 10.1 and 10.2.

(*b*) Use Theorem 10.1 to prove Theorem 10.4 in the case where A is symmetric.

(*c*) Prove Theorem 10.4 when A has a number of independent eigenvectors equal to its order. [Ref.: Birkhoff and Maclane (1953), pp. 306–307, and Bodewig (1959), pp. 59–60.]

3. Derive an algorithm for computing the coefficients of a polynomial of degree n given the sums of the first n powers of its zeros.

*4. Danilevsky's method: Let $A = [a_{ij}]$ be a matrix of order n.

(*a*) Suppose $a_{n,n-1} \neq 0$. Let M_{n-1} be the identity matrix of order n with its $(n-1)$st row replaced by $-a_{n1}/a_{n,n-1}$, $-a_{n2}/a_{n,n-1}$, . . . , $1/a_{n,n-1}$, $-a_{nn}/a_{n,n-1}$. Show that M_{n-1}^{-1} is the identity with its $(n-1)$st row replaced by the nth row of A.

(*b*) Show that $M_{n-1}^{-1}AM_{n-1}$ has zeros in the nth row except in the $(n-1)$st column where there is a 1.

(*c*) Show that, by applying this technique $n-1$ times, we may, if the element to the left of the diagonal term is not zero at any stage, reduce A to a similar matrix B of

the form

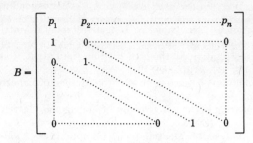

(*d*) Show that the characteristic equation of B is

$$P(\lambda) = (-1)^n(\lambda^n - p_1\lambda^{n-1} - p_2\lambda^{n-2} - \cdots - p_n) = 0$$

(*e*) Show that the number of multiplications and divisions required to calculate the characteristic equation is $(n - 1)(n^2 + n)$.

(*f*) Suppose the process has proceeded to the stage where the $k + 1$ to n rows have been reduced to the desired form. Suppose also that the element in the $(k, k - 1)$ position is zero but that for some $j < k - 1$ the term in the (k,j) position is not zero. How can the process be continued?

(*g*) Suppose now that the elements in the (k,j) positions for all $j < k$ are all zero. What can be done in this case? [Ref.: Fadeeva (1959), pp. 166–176.]

5. Let A be the matrix (cf. Example 10.9)

$$\begin{bmatrix} 2 & -2 & 3 \\ 1 & 1 & 1 \\ 1 & 3 & -1 \end{bmatrix}$$

(*a*) Use Gerschgorin's theorem to find a domain in which the eigenvalues must lie.

(*b*) Repeat part *a* using A^T in place of A.

(*c*) Let S be a diagonal matrix of order 3 with elements 1, 2, 2 on the diagonal. Calculate $B = SAS^{-1}$ and apply Gerschgorin's theorem to B^T.

(*d*) Generalize part *c* by indicating what happens to A when a diagonal matrix S with α in its last m positions and 1's in the remaining positions is used to effect a similarity transformation on A.

(*e*) With $m = 2$, what value of α minimizes the total length of the domain on the real axis in which Gerschgorin's theorem says the eigenvalues of A must lie?

6. (*a*) Prove that two similar matrices have the same trace.

(*b*) Let $T = [t_{ij}]$ be a matrix with complex elements. Prove that tr $(TT^*) = \| U \|_E^2$ where U has elements $|t_{ij}|$.

7. (*a*) Let A and B be two matrices such that AB is defined. Let the ranks of A and B be $r(A)$ and $r(B)$. Prove that

$$r(AB) \leqq \min [r(A),r(B)]$$

(*b*) Thus deduce that, if A is nonsingular, then

$$r(AB) = r(B)$$

(*c*) Finally deduce that two similar matrices have the same rank.

*8. Generalized eigenvectors:

(a) Show that the number of eigenvectors that a matrix A has corresponding to an eigenvalue λ_i is equal to the number of different elementary divisors (10.1-45) in which λ_i appears.

(b) Suppose A has an elementary divisor of order ν corresponding to λ_i. Show that there exists a solution $\mathbf{x}_\nu$ of the system

$$(A - \lambda_i I)^\nu \mathbf{x} = 0$$

such that

$$(A - \lambda_i I)^{\nu-1} \mathbf{x}_\nu \neq 0$$

(c) If we define

$$(A - \lambda_i I)^j \mathbf{x}_\nu = \mathbf{x}_{\nu-j} \qquad j = 1, \ldots, \nu - 1$$

show that

$$(A - \lambda_i I)^j \mathbf{x}_j = 0 \qquad j = 1, \ldots, \nu - 1$$

(The vectors $\mathbf{x}_j, j = 1, \ldots, \nu$ are called *generalized eigenvectors* of rank j corresponding to λ_1. The vector $\mathbf{x}_1$ is an eigenvector.)

(d) Prove that the vectors $\mathbf{x}_j, j = 1, \ldots, \nu$ are linearly independent.

Section 10.2

9. (a) Where does the derivation of the power method fail if A has nonlinear elementary divisors?

(b) Show that the matrix

$$A = \begin{bmatrix} 6 & 2 & 2 \\ -2 & 2 & 0 \\ 0 & 0 & 2 \end{bmatrix}$$

has nonlinear elementary divisors.

(c) Do 10 iterations of the power method on this matrix using $(1,1,1)$ as the starting vector. Does the method seem to be converging?

10. Suppose the dominant eigenvalue of A is complex so that

$$|\lambda_1| = |\bar{\lambda}_1| > |\lambda_3|$$

(a) Show that the eigenvector corresponding to $\bar{\lambda}_1$ is the conjugate of that corresponding to λ_1.

(b) Deduce then that the Schwarz constants approach a limit analogous to that of Eq. (8.10-45) in the Bernoulli iteration.

(c) Finally display equations analogous to (8.10-46) and (8.10-47) for the magnitude and argument of λ_1.

11. (a) Suppose the dominant eigenvalue λ_1 of A is multiple and that the power method has been used to compute λ_1 and a corresponding eigenvector $\mathbf{x}_1$. In order to compute another eigenvector corresponding to λ_1, is it sufficient to choose an initial vector $\mathbf{v}_0$ which is orthogonal to $\mathbf{x}_1$? Why? Is it necessary that $\mathbf{v}_0$ be orthogonal to $\mathbf{x}_1$? Why?

(b) From this deduce a technique to calculate all the eigenvectors corresponding to a given eigenvalue.

(c) If it is not known a priori what the multiplicity of the eigenvalue is, what will happen when all the eigenvectors for a given eigenvalue have been found?

(d) Apply this technique to find all the eigenvectors corresponding to the dominant eigenvalue of

$$A = \begin{bmatrix} 7\frac{1}{8} & 2\frac{5}{8} & -1\frac{3}{4} \\ \frac{7}{8} & 5\frac{3}{8} & 1\frac{3}{4} \\ -1\frac{3}{4} & 5\frac{1}{4} & 4\frac{1}{2} \end{bmatrix}$$

12. The matrix B in part c of Prob. 4 is called the *companion matrix* of the polynomial $P(x)$ in part d of that problem.

(a) Show why the power method applied to the companion matrix is precisely equivalent to Bernoulli's method applied to $P(x)$.

(b) What operation applied to the companion matrix corresponds to Graeffe's method?

13. (a) Let $f(x)$ be a function of x with a Maclaurin expansion $F(x)$. If A is a square matrix, define $f(A) = F(A)$. What are the eigenvalues of $f(A)$? (Cf. Theorem 10.1.)

(b) Consider the iteration

$$\mathbf{v}_{m+1} = f(A)\mathbf{v}_m \qquad m = 1, 2, \ldots$$

where $\mathbf{v}_1$ is arbitrary. Generalize Theorem 10.13 for this iteration.

(c) If γ is a good approximation to an eigenvalue λ_1 of A, why should $f(x) = 1/(x - \gamma)$ be a good function to use in part b? But what happens if this function is actually used?

(d) But deduce from part c that, for computational purposes, using

$$f(A) = A^k + \gamma A^{k-1} + \cdots + \gamma^{k-1}A + \gamma^k I \qquad k \geq 1$$

should produce more rapid convergence than using A if λ_1 is the dominant eigenvalue. [Ref.: Bodewig (1959), pp. 322–323.]

14. (a) Use the technique of the previous problem with $k = 2$ and $\gamma = 2$ to find the dominant eigenvalue of the matrix of Example 10.1.

(b) Show the connection between the technique of the previous problem and Wilkinson's method.

15. (a) What does the iteration of Prob. 13b converge to if $f(x) = e^x$? If $f(x) = e^{-x}$?

(b) Show how $f(x) = e^{-x}$ might be used to determine if a matrix is positive definite.

16. (a) Derive (10.2-13) from (10.2-12).

(b) Apply the δ^2 process to the calculation of Example 10.2 with $m = 5$. Using the results of Example 10.4, explain whether or not this result is just fortuitous.

17. (a) If the eigenvalues of A are all positive, show that the optimal value of p in Wilkinson's method is $(\lambda_2 + \lambda_n)/2$.

(b) What is the optimal choice for p in Example 10.1 given the results of Example 10.4?

18. (a) Explain why you would expect the Rayleigh quotient to generally give better results than the δ^2 process.

(b) Show that the method of steepest descent in Sec. 9.8-2 involves the use of a reciprocal Rayleigh quotient at each stage. Thus give a geometrical interpretation of the Rayleigh quotient.

19. (a) Use the power method to calculate the dominant eigenvalue and corresponding eigenvector of

(i) $\qquad A_1 = \begin{bmatrix} 7 & 3 & -2 \\ 3 & 4 & -1 \\ -2 & -1 & 3 \end{bmatrix}$

(ii) $\qquad A_2 = \begin{bmatrix} 3 & -4 & 3 \\ -4 & 6 & 3 \\ 3 & 3 & 1 \end{bmatrix}$

Stop each iteration when three decimal places of the eigenvalue have stabilized.

(b) Use the power method to calculate the dominant real or complex (cf. Prob. 10) eigenvalue of

(i) $\qquad B_1 = \begin{bmatrix} 5 & 30 & -48 \\ 3 & 14 & -24 \\ 3 & 15 & -25 \end{bmatrix}$

(ii) $\qquad B_2 = \begin{bmatrix} 4\frac{9}{8} & -13\frac{1}{8} & -4\frac{3}{4} \\ 1\frac{1}{8} & -1\frac{7}{8} & -\frac{9}{4} \\ -\frac{1}{2} & \frac{7}{2} & 3 \end{bmatrix}$

(iii) $\qquad B_3 = \begin{bmatrix} 1\frac{5}{8} & -6\frac{9}{8} & -1\frac{7}{4} \\ -\frac{5}{8} & \frac{7}{8} & -\frac{5}{4} \\ \frac{1}{8} & -\frac{3}{8} & 1\frac{7}{4} \end{bmatrix}$

Stop each iteration when three decimal places of the magnitude of the eigenvalue have stabilized.

20. (a) Use the δ^2 process, where applicable, to get an improved value of the eigenvalue for each part of the previous problem.

(b) Use Wilkinson's method with $p = 2$ to speed up the convergence of the power method for the matrix A_1 of the previous problem.

(c) Use the Rayleigh quotient to get an improved value of the eigenvalue for A_1 and A_2 in the previous problem.

Section 10.3

21. (a) Let A be nonsingular with no nonlinear elementary divisors and let x_i be an eigenvector of A corresponding to λ_i. For this matrix prove Theorem 10.14 by considering $x_i - \alpha x_1$ where α is a constant to be determined.

(b) Why does the proof fail when A is singular or when A has nonlinear elementary divisors? If A has no nonlinear elementary divisors, can W_1 have nonlinear elementary divisors?

22. (a) Verify (10.3-6). (b) Derive (10.3-10). (c) Verify (10.3-14).

*23. Let the matrix W_1 be defined as in (10.3-2). Let w_i be an eigenvector of W_1 (other than x_1) which corresponds to an eigenvalue λ_i.

(a) If $\lambda_i \neq \lambda_1$, show that $x_i = (A - \lambda_1 I)w_i$ is an eigenvector of A corresponding to λ_i.

(b) Use this result to show that

$$x_i = (\lambda_i - \lambda_1)w_i + \lambda_1(v^T w_i)x_1$$

(c) Thus verify (10.3-17) and deduce that, if A has a nonlinear elementary divisor corresponding to λ_1, then some w_i corresponding to λ_1 will not satisfy the first condition in (10.3-17).

24. (a) Show that in Hotelling's deflation the eigenvectors of W_1 and A are the same when there are no nonlinear elementary divisors.

*(b) Let A be any matrix with nonlinear elementary divisors corresponding to some eigenvalue λ. Prove that there are corresponding right and left eigenvectors which are orthogonal.

25. Use the results of Example 10.4 to calculate the eigenvectors of A corresponding to the two subdominant eigenvalues.

*26. Suppose the dominant eigenvalue of A is complex.

(a) What matrix should be used in place of W_1 in (10.3-19) in Hotelling's deflation so that the deflated matrix has zero eigenvalues corresponding to both the conjugate dominant eigenvalues?

(b) Let x_1 correspond to λ_1 and $\bar{x}_i$ correspond to $\bar{\lambda}_1$. Show that, if similarity deflation is applied to A using λ_1 and x_1, then

$$y = -2i n + e_1$$

is an eigenvector of C where n is the imaginary part of x_1 and e_1 is the first column of I.

(c) Thus deduce a second similarity deflation which in effect removes both dominant conjugate eigenvalues. [Ref.: Bodewig (1959), pp. 366–367.]

27. (a) Given a simple eigenvalue λ_1 and the corresponding left and right eigenvectors y_1 and x_1, show how you would compute α_1 in (10.2-1) from a given v_0.

(b) By defining

$$s_m = v_m - \alpha_1 \lambda_1^m x_1$$

derive a method of vector deflation similar to that of (10.3-1). Show that the same problem of loss of significance applies to this method as to that using (10.3-1).

28. Use the Schwarz numbers

$$y^T A^m v_1 = y^T v_m$$

where y is any vector to derive two methods of *scalar deflation* corresponding to the vector deflations of (10.3-1) and the preceding problem. Are there loss-of-significance problems with scalar deflation also?

29. Use annihilation to calculate the subdominant eigenvalues of the matrix A of Example 10.1. Note what happens if the eigenvalues already found are not periodically reannihilated.

30. (a) Use the results of Prob. 19 to calculate the remaining eigenvalues and eigenvectors in those cases in which the dominant eigenvalue is real by (i) Hotelling's deflation; (ii) Wielandt's deflation; (iii) similarity deflation.

(b) When the dominant eigenvalue is complex, show how similarity deflation may be used to find the remaining eigenvalue and eigenvector immediately.

Section 10.4

*31. Derive the relations (10.4-16) and (10.4-17).

32. Give a formal proof of the convergence of the Jacobi method to a diagonal matrix similar to A in the case where the off-diagonal element of greatest magnitude is annihilated at each stage. Why isn't this proof sufficient to show that the method converges for any choice of a nonzero off-diagonal element at each stage?

*33. The threshold Jacobi method:

(a) With v_0 given by (10.4-4) define $\gamma_1 = \sqrt{v_0}/\sigma$ where σ is a positive number called the *threshold constant*. If $\sigma \geqq n$ show that there is at least one off-diagonal element in the original matrix A greater than or equal to γ_1 in magnitude.

(b) If all off-diagonal elements of magnitude greater than or equal to γ_1 are annihilated, show that the remaining sum of squares of the off-diagonal elements is no greater than $(1 - 2/\sigma^2)v_0$.

(c) Define $\gamma_{i+1} = \gamma_i/\sigma$, $i = 1, 2, \ldots$. Then at the ith stage of the method, all elements of magnitude greater than or equal to γ_i will be annihilated. Let $\{\gamma_{i_j}\}$ be the subsequence of $\{\gamma_i\}$ such that at the i_j stage at least one element is annihilated. Deduce that, after i_m stages, the sum of squares of the off-diagonal elements is no greater than $(1 - 2/\sigma^2)^m v_0$.

(d) Suppose we set an accuracy requirement that the final sum of squares of the off-diagonal elements should be less than $\rho^2 v_0$ where ρ is some constant. Show that this requirement will be satisfied if the final threshold γ_F is such that $\gamma_F \leqq (\rho/n)\sqrt{v_0}$. [Ref.: Greenstadt (1960).]

34. Do three stages of the threshold Jacobi method, in which at least one element is annihilated, for the matrix of Example 10.1 using $\sigma = 3$.

35. (a) Show that the sequence of orthogonal transformations defined by (10.4-29) annihilates the elements $a_{24}, a_{25}, \ldots, a_{2n}$ and does not affect the zeros in the first row obtained using (10.4-27).

(b) Thus deduce that the sequence of transformations (10.4-30) does indeed reduce A to the form B in (10.4-31).

36. (a) Derive (10.4-33).

(b) Show that, if any c_i in (10.4-31) is zero, then the determinant of B may be written as the product of the determinants of two smaller tridiagonal matrices.

(c) Prove that the sequence defined by (10.4-33) is a Sturm sequence if no $c_i = 0$.

(d) Verify (10.4-35) when $i = 2$.

37. (a) Derive the relationship between the eigenvectors of B in (10.4-31) and those of A.

(b) If λ_1 is an eigenvalue of B, display an algorithm to compute the corresponding eigenvector of B.

(c) If λ_1 is a multiple eigenvalue, how can this algorithm be used to get all the eigenvectors corresponding to λ_1? [Ref.: Wilkinson (1958b).]

***38.** (a) Show that the matrix P defined by (10.4-37) is symmetric and orthogonal.

(b) Use (10.4-40) to (10.4-42) to show that A_k has zeros in the same positions in its first $k - 2$ rows and columns as does A_{k-1}.

(c) Show that, with the elements of $\mathbf{v}$ chosen as in (10.4-44) and (10.4-45), A_k has zeros in the desired positions in the $(k - 1)$st row and column and that (10.4-36) is satisfied.

39. Let $\mathbf{y}$ be an eigenvector of A_{n-1} given by (10.4-40).

(a) Show that the corresponding eigenvector $\mathbf{x}$ of A is given by

$$\mathbf{x} = P_2 P_3 \cdots P_{n-1}\mathbf{y}$$

How would you calculate $\mathbf{x}$ given $\mathbf{y}$?

(b) Compare this result with that of Prob. 37a to show that about half as much computation is required to compute the eigenvectors of A in Householder's method as in Givens's method. Assume that both $\mathbf{v}_k$ and $2\mathbf{v}_k$ are available from the computation of the eigenvalues (cf. Example 10.8).

(c) Derive the equation for A_k given in Example 10.8.

***40.** (a) Verify that the total number of operations required in Givens's method to reduce the matrix to tridiagonal form is of the order of $\frac{4}{3}n^3$ and that $(n - 2)(n - 1)/2$ square roots must be calculated.

(*b*) Verify that the corresponding figures for Householder's method are $\frac{2}{3}n^3$ operations and $2n - 4$ square roots if the scheme of Example 10.8 is used.

(*c*) Show, however, that the $v_k^{(k)}$ need not be calculated explicitly and that, therefore, only $n - 2$ square roots are required. [Ref.: Wilkinson (1960).]

41. Carry through the computation of Example 10.8 using the minus instead of the plus sign in (10.4-44). Keep five decimals in all computations. Compare the results with those of Example 10.8 and explain the differences.

42. (*a*) Use the Jacobi method as described in Sec. 10.4 to find the eigenvalues of A_1 and A_2 of Prob. 19*a*. Carry through five rotations. Why are the results for A_1 better than those for A_2?

(*b*) Use Givens's method to tridiagonalize A_1 and A_2 and then calculate the characteristic equation.

(*c*) Use Householder's method to tridiagonalize A_1 and A_2 and then calculate the characteristic equation.

Section 10.5

43. (*a*) Use Lanczos's method to tridiagonalize the matrix of Example 10.1. Then calculate the characteristic equation and check that its roots are those found in Example 10.4.

(*b*) How many operations are required in the application of Lanczos's method to a symmetric matrix of order n to reduce the matrix to tridiagonal form?

44. (*a*) Apply Lanczos's method to the matrix

$$A = \begin{bmatrix} 5 & 1 & -1 \\ -5 & 0 & 1 \\ 1 & 0 & 1 \end{bmatrix}$$

using $\mathbf{x}_1^T = (.6, -1.4, .3)$ and $\mathbf{y}_1^T = (.6, .3, -.1)$.

(*b*) Repeat the calculations of part *a* using $\mathbf{y}_1^T = \mathbf{x}_1^T = (.6, -1.4, .3)$. Then calculate the characteristic equation. [Ref.: Wilkinson (1958a).]

***45.** (*a*) Suppose at some stage in Lanczos's method $\mathbf{x}_j = \mathbf{0}$. Show that the modifications of the biorthogonalization process given on p. 503 do in fact lead to two biorthogonal sets of vectors.

(*b*) Show that this procedure results in a matrix T in (10.5-8) whose characteristic equation is easily factored into the product of two polynomials.

(*c*) Deduce from this that, when $\mathbf{x}_j = \mathbf{0}$ and $P_{j-1}(A) \neq 0$, then $P_{j-1}(\lambda)$ is a divisor of the characteristic polynomial.

(*d*) What modifications must be made if $\mathbf{y}_j = \mathbf{0}$ or both $\mathbf{x}_j$ and $\mathbf{y}_j$ are zero? [Ref.: Wilkinson (1958a).]

46. (*a*) Calculate the eigenvectors of the matrix T in Example 10.9.

(*b*) Use the results of part *a* to calculate the eigenvectors of A.

47. (*a*) Show that, if the eigenvalues of A are distinct and $\mathbf{x}_j = \mathbf{0}$ for $j \leq n$ in Lanczos's method then $\mathbf{x}_1$ has no component in the direction of one or more eigenvectors of A.

(*b*) Using $\mathbf{x}_1^T = \mathbf{y}_1^T = (1, 0, 0)$ with the matrix of Example 10.9, show that $\mathbf{x}_3 = \mathbf{0}$.

(*c*) Use the results of the previous problem to show that, in fact, $\mathbf{x}_1$ has no component in the direction of one of the eigenvectors of A.

(*d*) Calculate the eigenvalues of A in Example 10.9 using the starting vectors of part *b* and the modifications of the biorthogonalization process on p. 503.

*48. Let A be an arbitrary matrix and let x_1 and y_1 be arbitrary vectors. Define two sequences of vectors

$$\mathbf{x}_{i+1} = A\mathbf{x}_i - \sum_{j=1}^{i} c_{ij}\mathbf{x}_j$$

$$i = 1, 2, \ldots$$

$$\mathbf{y}_{i+1} = A^T\mathbf{y}_i - \sum_{j=1}^{i} c_{ij}\mathbf{y}_j$$

(a) Show that

$$\mathbf{x}_{i+1} = P_i(A)\mathbf{x}_1$$
$$\mathbf{y}_{i+1} = P_i(A^T)\mathbf{y}_1$$

where $P_i(A)$ is a polynomial of degree i in A.

(b) Thus deduce that

$$\mathbf{y}_{i+1}^T\mathbf{x}_j = \mathbf{y}_j^T\mathbf{x}_{i+1}$$

(c) Let the c_{ij} be chosen so that $\mathbf{y}_{i+1}^T\mathbf{x}_{i+1}$ is a minimum. Show that this requires that

$$0 = -\mathbf{y}_j^T\mathbf{x}_{i+1} - \mathbf{y}_{i+1}^T\mathbf{x}_j \qquad j = 1, \ldots, i$$

(d) From parts b and c deduce that this minimum requirement means that the vectors $\mathbf{x}_i$ and $\mathbf{y}_i$ must form a biorthogonal sequence.

(e) Deduce then that those c_{ij} which give the minimum are given by

$$c_{ij} = \mathbf{y}_j^T A\mathbf{x}_i/\mathbf{y}_j^T\mathbf{x}_j$$

(f) Then deduce that $c_{ij} = 0, j < i - 1$.

(g) Finally deduce that these sequences of biorthogonal vectors are precisely those of Lanczos's method. Because of the requirement of part c, Lanczos's method is therefore often called the method of minimized iterations. [Ref.: Lanczos (1950).].

49. Let A be an arbitrary matrix and let x_1 and y_1 be arbitrary vectors. Define two sequences of vectors

$$\mathbf{x}_{i+1} = A\mathbf{x}_i - \sum_{j=1}^{i} c_{ij}\mathbf{x}_j \qquad \mathbf{y}_{i+1} = A^T\mathbf{y}_i - \sum_{j=1}^{i} d_{ij}\mathbf{y}_j$$

where

$$c_{ij} = \mathbf{y}_j^T A\mathbf{x}_i/\mathbf{y}_j^T\mathbf{x}_j \qquad d_{ij} = \mathbf{x}_j^T A^T\mathbf{y}_i/\mathbf{y}_j^T\mathbf{x}_j$$

(a) Show that the sequences $\mathbf{x}_j, j = 1, \ldots, i + 1$ and $\mathbf{y}_j, j = 1, \ldots, i + 1$ are biorthogonal if the sequences without $\mathbf{x}_{i+1}$ and $\mathbf{y}_{i+1}$ are biorthogonal.

(b) Show that we would expect the c_{ij} and d_{ij} for $j < i - 1$ to be very small but that retaining these quantities will improve the biorthogonality of the two sequences.

(c) Show that this method leads to a matrix equation of the form (10.5-8) where the matrix T is supertriangular with 1's on the diagonal below the main diagonal.

50. (a) Display the elementary column matrices used in the reduction of a matrix A to Hessenberg form by Gaussian elimination with positioning for size.

(b) Display the inverses of the matrices of part a.

(c) Verify that the number of multiplications and divisions required for this method is $\frac{2}{3}n^3 + O(n^2)$ as opposed to $\frac{4}{3}n^3 + O(n^2)$ for Householder's method.

(d) Use this Gaussian elimination technique to derive the matrix B in Example 10.10. [Ref.: Wilkinson (1959b).]

51. Suppose an element $b_{i,i+1}$ above the principal diagonal in Fig. 10.2 is zero.
(a) Show that B may be written

$$B = \begin{bmatrix} B_1 & 0 \\ B_3 & B_2 \end{bmatrix} \} \; i \text{ rows}$$

where B_1 and B_2 are both in Hessenberg form.

(b) Show how the eigenvectors of B may be found from those of B_1 and B_2.

*52. (a) Display the form of the plane rotation matrix which annihilates the element in the nth row and column of B_λ in (10.5-18).

(b) Generalize this result to obtain the form of S_{in}, the plane rotation matrix which annihilates the element in the $(i+1)$st column of the last row of $S_{i+1,n}S_{i+2,n}$ $\cdots S_{n-1,n}B_\lambda$. Show that the already produced zeros in this row remain zero and that the matrix remains in Hessenberg form.

(c) Use the result of part b to show that if no $b_{i,i+1}$ is zero in B_λ, then no $t_{i,i+1}$ in (10.5-21) is zero.

(d) Verify (10.5-24) and (10.5-25).

53. (a) If all the eigenvalues of a matrix are real, does it follow from Corollary 10.3 of Sec. 10.1 that the matrix can be triangularized using a sequence of plane rotation matrices of the type (10.4-9)? Why? If the eigenvalues are real, is it always possible to annihilate any given off-diagonal element by an orthogonal transformation using plane rotation matrices?

(b) What modifications must be made in (10.4-11) to (10.4-15) for nonsymmetric matrices?

(c) Use plane rotation matrices to annihilate successively the largest element in the upper triangle of the matrix of Example 10.9. Do six iterations. [Ref.: Greenstadt (1955).]

54. Use Lanczos's method to tridiagonalize the matrices of Prob. 19b using, in all cases, $\mathbf{x}_1^T = \mathbf{y}_1^T = (1,0,0)$. How do you explain what happens with B_1?

55. (a) Calculate the eigenvalues of the matrices of Prob. 19b by supertriangularizing, using the secant method to find a real eigenvalue, and then deflating as in Sec. 10.5-2.

(b) Show how unitary instead of plane rotation matrices could be used to carry through the deflation if the eigenvalue found by the secant method is complex.

Section 10.6

56. (a) Let $A = [a_{ij}]$ be a band matrix; that is, $a_{ij} = 0$ for $|i - j| > m$ for some $m < n - 1$. Prove that the LR transformation applied to A results in a sequence of matrices A_k all of which are band matrices with the same value of m.

(b) Prove that the QR transformation applied to a symmetric band matrix results in a sequence of band matrices with the same value of m.

(c) Show that, if A is in upper Hessenberg form, then the QR transformation results in a sequence of matrices A_k each of which is in upper Hessenberg form. [Ref.: Rutishauser (1958), p. 71, and Francis (1961).]

57. (a) Verify that Eqs. (10.6-16) correctly relate L_k and L_{k+1} as given by (10.6-19).

(b) Verify that (10.6-20) correctly gives the initial decomposition of A into $L_1 L_1^T$.

58. (a) Show that M_1 as given by (10.6-22) has zero elements below the diagonal in column one.

(b) Thus deduce that U in (10.6-23) is upper triangular.

(c) Prove that, if A is nonsingular and U is constrained to have nonnegative diagonal elements, then the decomposition of A into QU is unique.   [Ref.: Francis (1961).]

*59. (a) Derive the equations analogous to (10.6-3) to (10.6-7) for the QR transformation.

(b) State and prove the theorem analogous to Theorem 10.17 for the QR transformation.

*60. (a) If A is a symmetric tridiagonal matrix, show that there exist plane rotation matrices $P_1, \ldots, P_{n-1}$ such that

$$U_1 = P_{n-1} \cdots P_1 A = Q_1^T A$$

is upper triangular.

(b) Derive an algorithm to compute the elements $\cos \theta_j$ and $\sin \theta_j$ of P_j, $j = 1, \ldots, n-1$.

(c) Show that U_1 has nonzero elements only on the main diagonal and on the two diagonals above the main diagonal.   Derive an algorithm for the computation of the elements of U_1.

(d) Finally derive an algorithm to compute the elements of $A_2 = U_1 Q_1$.   (The algorithms of parts b, c, and d can be combined to form one compact algorithm for the QR transformation for symmetric tridiagonal matrices.)   [Ref.: Ortega and Kaiser (1963).]

61. (a) Apply the LR and QR transformations to the two tridiagonal matrices obtained in Prob. 42b.

(b) Apply both transformations to the tridiagonal matrices obtained in Prob. 54. When either method fails to converge to a triangular matrix, explain why.   Can the resulting matrices be used to find the eigenvalues in any case?

62. Apply the LR transformation directly to the matrices of Prob. 19a, and compare these results with those of part a of the previous problem.

Section 10.7

63. (a) Verify (10.7-2) to (10.7-4).

(b) Let λ and $\mathbf{x}$ be approximations to an eigenvalue and eigenvector of a symmetric matrix A.   If $\mathbf{r} = A\mathbf{x} - \lambda\mathbf{x}$, show that there exists an eigenvalue λ_i of A such that

$$|\lambda_i - \lambda|^2 \leq \mathbf{r}^T\mathbf{r} = \epsilon^2$$

(c) By considering $A = \begin{bmatrix} a & \epsilon \\ \epsilon & a \end{bmatrix}$, $\lambda = a$, and $\mathbf{x}^T = (1,0)$, show that no useful bound on the error in the eigenvector can be obtained.   [Ref.: Wilkinson (1959c, 1964).]

64. (a) Suppose B in (10.7-10) is positive definite.   Show that there exists a positive definite matrix P and a diagonal matrix D such that the generalized eigenvalue problem may be reduced to

$$C\mathbf{y} = \lambda\mathbf{y}$$

where

$$PD^{-1}\mathbf{y} = \mathbf{x} \qquad C = D^{-1}P^TAPD^{-1}$$

(b) Suppose A and B in (10.7-10) are both singular.   Show that the characteristic equation

$$|A - \lambda B| = 0$$

has no constant term or term in λ^n.

ANSWERS AND HINTS
TO THE PROBLEMS

Chapter 1

1. (a) 2.05265, 2.05375; (b) 10.7015, 10.7125; (c) 18.74486, 18.77916; (d) 131.3565, 133.4410.

2. (a) .00005; (b) 6.493.

3. (a) Add, then round; (b) consider $(x \pm \epsilon_x)/(y \pm \epsilon_y)$.

4. (a) You *know* only by computing the true value; (b) retain all digits in sum and use this as dividend.

5. (a) $\sum_{i=1}^{n} \epsilon_i f_i / y_i$; (c) $a_e y^{a-1}$.

6. (a) Product: $E \approx .01715$; same as results from 1c.
Quotient: $E \approx 1.0421$; from 1d, 1.0504.

7. (a) $E \approx .000026$; (b) $E \approx .0057$.

8. (a) (i) $E \approx -.00208$; (ii) $E \approx .00013$; (iii) $E \approx .00068$; (iv) $E \approx .04262$; (b) (i) $E \approx -.00348$; (ii) $E \approx .00019$; (iii) $E \approx .00102$; (iv) $E \approx .04954$.

9. (a) $(-1 + \sqrt{.99})t < \Delta t < (\sqrt{1.01} - 1)t$; (b) $E \leq .00163$, $RE \leq .00025$.

10. (b) Show that relevant region in ϵ_1, ϵ_2 plane is triangular; (c) use change of variable $s \to u - t$.

11. (b) $\dfrac{x^2}{2} - \tfrac{3}{2}x + \tfrac{9}{8}$ on $[\tfrac{1}{2}, \tfrac{3}{2}]$; $\tfrac{3}{4} - x^2$ on $[0, \tfrac{1}{2}]$.

13. (b) $n \geq 16$, Pr. $\approx 2.1 \times 10^{-7}$.

14. (b) $\delta_i < \tfrac{1}{2} \times 10^{-d}$; (c) $\epsilon_i = \alpha \epsilon_{i-1} + \delta_i$; (f) $\epsilon_n = \sum_{j=0}^{n} \alpha^{n-i} \delta_j$ and use (1.4-7).

15. Minimize $\dfrac{1}{2} \sum_{i=1}^{n} \alpha_i^2 + \lambda \left(\sum_{i=1}^{n} \alpha_i - \alpha \right)$.

16. Average value of leading digits less than 5.

17. (a) 4768763453; (b) $E = -.48 \times 10^{-5}$; (c) $|E| \leq .985 \times 10^{-5}$.

19. (a) To add (a_1, a_2) to (b_1, b_2): (i) $c_1 = a_1 + b_1$; (ii) $c_2 = a_2 + b_2$; (iii) Overflow?, Yes $\to$ (iv), No $\to$ END; (iv) $c_1 = c_1 + 10^{-d}$.

(b) (i) $c_1 = a_1 + b_1$; (ii) $c_2 = a_2 + b_2$; (iii) Overflow?, Yes $\rightarrow$ (iv), No $\rightarrow$ (vii); (iv) Positive?, Yes $\rightarrow$ (v), No $\rightarrow$ (vi); (v) $c_1 = c_1 + 10^{-d}$, Go to (vii); (vi) $c_1 = c_1 - 10^{-d}$; (vii) Signs of c_1, c_2 same?, Yes $\rightarrow$ END, No $\rightarrow$ (viii); (viii) c_1 positive?, Yes $\rightarrow$ (ix), No $\rightarrow$ (xi); (ix) $c_1 = c_1 - 10^{-d}$; (x) $c_2 = c_2 + \frac{1}{2} + \frac{1}{2}$, Go to END; (xi) $c_1 = c_1 + 10^{-d}$; (xii) $c_2 = c_2 - \frac{1}{2} - \frac{1}{2}$.

Chapter 2

1. (a) $P(x) = x$; max error $\pi/2 - 1$ at $x = \pi/2$; (b) $P(x) = (1/\pi^3)(96 - 24\pi)x + (1/\pi^2)(8\pi - 24)$; max error .158 at $x = \pi/2$; (c) $P(x) = (1/\pi^4)(384\pi - 1152)x + (1/\pi^3)(384 - 120\pi)$; max error .226 at $x = 0$.

2. (a) Suppose there is only one zero; show rotation of line reduces error.

5. (a) Use induction; (b) $n = 1$: $3t/(3 + t^2)$; max error .0354 at $x = 1.0$; $n = 2$: $(15t + t^3)/(15 + 6t^2)$; max error .0235 at $x = 1.0$; (c) $t - t^3/3$; max error .1187 at $x = 1.0$; $t - t^3/3 + t^5/5$; max error .0813 at $x = 1.0$.

6. $a = -1$, $b = -2$, $c = -2$; max error .2817 at $x = 1.0$.

7. (a) $|E| < x^7/7!$; (c) $3 \times 10^{-10}/2 + 10^{-20}/4$; (d) 3×10^{-10}; (e) yes.

8. (a) 6; (b) 9.

9. (a) $P_1(x) = (x - a_2)/(a_1 - a_2)$; $P_2(x) = (x - a_1)/(a_2 - a_1)$; independence means approximation found once and for all; (b) $x^2 - (a_1 + a_2)x - a_1 a_2$; no dependence on a and b because approximation exact for linear polynomials.

10. (b) Consider $x_{n+1} - 1$ and $x_{n+1} - a$; (c) show that $\sqrt{a} - x_{n+1} = (1/2x_n)(\sqrt{a} - x_n)^2$.

11. (a) $y = (x - a)/(b - a)$; (b) $B_1(x) = 2x/\pi$; $B_2(x) = 4(1 - \sqrt{2})x^2/\pi^2 + 2\sqrt{2}x/\pi$; $B_3(x) = 8x^3/\pi^3 + 6\sqrt{3}(1 - 2x/\pi)x^2/\pi^2 + 3x(1 - 2x/\pi)^2/\pi$; (c) 432.

13. (a) Note that $\phi(t)$ and $\psi(t)$ are *even*, continuous functions of period 2π; (b) for $V(t)$ consider $\phi_1(t) = [F(t - \pi/2) + F(-t - \pi/2)]/2$ and $\psi_1(t) = \{[F(t - \pi/2) + F(-t - \pi/2)] \sin t\}/2$; (c) consider $F(t) \sin^2 t$ and $F(t) \cos^2 t$.

14. (a) Since $F(t) = \phi(t)$ and $\psi(t) = 0$, part a of the previous problem serves as the whole proof; (b) $F(t) = (\pi/2)(1 - \cos t)$ in both cases; plot the error to see why any $\cos 2t$ term would increase the maximum error.

15. $n = 2$: $\frac{1}{4}(3 - x^2)$; $n = 3$: $\frac{1}{10}(8 - 3x^2)$; $n = 4$: $\frac{1}{80}(3x^4 - 30x^2 + 67)$.

16. Result is (2.2-1) with $\delta_0 = 1$, $m = N - 1$, $n = 1$, $A_{i1}(x) = -(x - x_1)^i/i!$, $a_{i1} = x_1$.

17. No, because all $A_{0j}(x) = 0$.

19. First use operator to approximate $F(y) = \int_a^b f(x,y)\, dx$; then use it to approximate $\int_c^d F(y)\, dy$.

20. (a) Use $f(x_i) = z(x_i)$ and $f'(x_i) = z'(x_i) = F[x_i, z(x_i)]$; (b) Replace x_1, x_0 by, respectively, x_{n+1}, x_n.

Chapter 3

1. (a) Taylor-series formula better in neighborhood of x_1; (b) $-.510480$; $\ln x$ one of few functions whose derivatives are easily calculable.

2. (a) Just use fact that formula is exact for x^k, $k < n$; (b) $j = 1$: 1 at a_1; $j = 2$: 1 at a_2; $j = 3$: 1 at a_3; for small values of n roundoff not serious.

3. (a) Extrema of $p_3(x)$ at $a_2 \pm h/\sqrt{3}$; $h^3 f'''(x) < 9\sqrt{3} \times 10^{-d}$; (b) $\approx 120 \times 10^{-d}/1.14$; (c) $n = 3$: $\sin x$: $h < 1.15 \times 10^{-3}$; e^x: $h < .27 \times 10^{-3}$; $\sin 100x$: $h < 1.15 \times 10^{-5}$; $n = 5$: $\sin x$: $h < 10^{-2}$; e^x: $h < 1.25 \times 10^{-2}$; $\sin 100x$: $h < 10^{-4}$.

4. (b) $(23x^3 - 63x^2 - 234x + 324)/162$.

5. (a) Example 3.1: .564634; Example 3.2: .514136; (b) Example 3.1: .540375; Example 3.2: .495133.

6. (a) (i) $|J_p''| < .37$; $|E| < 4.7 \times 10^{-4}$; (ii) $|J_p'''| < .15$; $|E| < 10^{-5}$; with roundoff error in linear interpolation error could be greater than 5×10^{-4}; therefore, use three-point formula. (b) .1951, .1384, .0828, .0288, $-.0232$, $-.0729$, $-.1200$, $-.1641$, $-.2051$, $-.2426$. (c) Can use linear interpolation; results: .5725, .5622, .5480, .5300, .5087, .4840, .4562, .4257, .3925, .3572. (d) Six.

7. (a) .1837, .5712, .3683; (b) $-.0001$, .5191, .4318; (c) $-.1154$, .4595, .4635; (d) $-.2280$, .3719, .4837.

8. Use induction and (3.3-5).

9. Use (3.3-5).

10. $\Delta = (1 - \nabla)^{-1} - 1$; $\delta = \Delta/(\Delta + 1)^{1/2} = \Delta/E^{1/2}$.

11. (b) For any closed path by replacing portions of the path that are three sides of a rhombus by the fourth side and portions that are two-sided by the other two sides until a single rhombus is left. (d) Using results of parts b and c any such path can be deformed into any other without introducing any new contribution.

12. (a) Two adjacent errors in second difference give rise to ϵ_1, $\epsilon_2 - 2\epsilon_1$, $\epsilon_1 - 2\epsilon_2$, ϵ_2 pattern; in third difference ϵ_1, $\epsilon_2 - 3\epsilon_1$, $3\epsilon_1 - 3\epsilon_2$, $3\epsilon_2 - \epsilon_1$, $-\epsilon_2$. When other differences are near zero, the two end values in the pattern may be used to estimate ϵ_1 and ϵ_2. Then the other values may be used to test the hypothesis that the errors have the supposed pattern and/or to get more precise values of ϵ_1 and ϵ_2; any two interacting errors give rise to *some* characteristic pattern. The problem is to deduce the correct pattern in a particular case.
(b) $1791930 \to 1791924$, $1267432 \to 1267619$, $1162645 \to 1162655$; third differences need to be calculated; latter two errors interact but first of two dominates in overlapping pattern.
(c) $.0649 \to .0643$, $.0870 \to .0840$; in the third difference the two errors interact.

13. (a) Calculate the first six or eight differences; from the pattern it is not hard to deduce that desired entry is given by $(-1)^{k-1}[2^{2k-1} - (2k!)(\frac{1}{2} + \epsilon)/(k!)^2]$; the correctness of this can be proved by induction. (b) With $\epsilon = -\frac{1}{2}$ the error in the $2k$ difference is given by $(-1)^{k-1}2^{2k-1}$; but the difference pattern in part a could have all the signs reversed so the important fact is the magnitude 2^{2k-1}; therefore, must find that positive value of ϵ in part a which results in difference of magnitude 2^{2k-1}; results for $k = 1, \ldots, 6$ are $\frac{3}{2}$, $1\frac{3}{6}$, $2\frac{7}{10}$, $22\frac{1}{70}$, $44\frac{9}{126}$,

$181\frac{7}{462}$. (c) $\epsilon_{max} = -\frac{1}{2} + 4^k \Big/ \binom{2k}{k}$.

14. (a) Use an interpolation formula with $m = \rho$ for each entry. (b) If series converges, then remainder must go to zero. (c) Use (3.3-8) for $\Delta_1^j f_0$ and then (3.3-11) for $f(x + k\rho h)$. (d) $\Delta_1 = E^\rho - 1 = (1 + \Delta)^\rho - 1 = \rho\Delta(1 + (\rho - 1)(\Delta/2)\{1 + (\rho - 2)(\Delta/3)[1 + (\rho - 3)\Delta/6]\})$; $\Delta_1^2 = \rho^2\Delta^2[1 + (\rho - 1)\Delta + (7\rho - 11)\Delta/12]$; $\Delta_1^3 = \rho^3\Delta^3[1 + 3(\rho - 1)\Delta/2]$; $\Delta_1^4 = \rho^4\Delta^4$; (e) $\rho = \frac{1}{2}$: .1952, .1383, .0827, .0287, $-.0233$, $-.0729$, $-.1200$, $-.1641$, $-.2051$, $-.2427$; $\rho = \frac{1}{3}$: .2047, .1477, .0919, .0376, $-.0148$, $-.0648$, $-.1123$, $-.1570$, $-.1985$, $-.2386$; $\rho = -\frac{1}{3}$: .1856, .1291, .0737, .0200, $-.0317$, $-.0809$, $-.1275$, $-.1711$, $-.2116$, $-.2486$; near the end of the table backward differences would be better.

15. (a) (i) Use binomial theorem; (b) replace $\binom{i}{j}\binom{j}{r}$ by $\binom{i - r}{j - r}\binom{i}{r}$.

16. (a) Consider ΔE^{-1}; result is $y(m) = \Sigma(m + j - 1)_j \nabla^j f_0$. (b) For Gauss's forward consider $\Delta^2 E^{-1}$; result is $y(m) = \Sigma(m + j - 1)_{2j}\delta^{2j}f_0 + (m + j)_{2j+1}\delta^{2j+1}f_{1/2}$; for Gauss's backward result is $y(m) = \Sigma(m + j)_{2j}\delta^{2j}f_0 + (m + j)_{2j+1}\delta^{2j+1}f_{-1/2}$. (c) Stirling: $2k$th term: $m^2(m^2 - 1) \cdots [m^2 - (k - 1)^2]\delta^{2k}f_0/(2k)!$; $(2k + 1)$st term: $m^2(m^2 - 1) \cdots (m^2 - k^2)\mu\delta^{2k+1}f_0/(2k + 1)!$; Bessel: 2kth term: $m(m^2 - 1)$ $\cdots [m^2 - (k - 1)^2](m - k)\mu\delta^{2k}f_{1/2}/(2k)!$; $(2k + 1)$st term: $m(m^2 - 1) \cdots$ $[m^2 - (k - 1)^2](m - k)(m - \frac{1}{2})\delta^{2k+1}f_{1/2}/(2k + 1)!$

18. (a) Min at $m = \frac{1}{2}$, max at $m = 0, 1$; (b) $B_4 - cB_2 = f(m) = [m(m - 1)/2][(m + 1)(m - 2)/12 - c]$; max at $m_1 = \frac{1}{2}$, min at $m_{2,3} = \frac{1}{2} \pm (\frac{5}{4} + 6c)^{1/2}$; set $f(m_1) = -f(m_{2,3})$; get $576c^2 + 144c + 7 = 0$; one root $c = -.18394$ is near average value of B_4/B_2 which is $-.1805$.

19. (a) Newton forward: Analogous to (3.3-4) $h^n m(m - 1) \cdots (m - k)f^{(k+1)}(\xi)/k!$; (b) Stirling ended with 2k difference: $h^{2k+1}m(m^2 - 1) \cdots (m^2 - k^2)f^{(2k+1)}(\xi)/(2k + 1)!$; Bessel ended with 2k difference: $\{h^{2k+1}m(m^2 - 1) \cdots [m^2 - (k - 1)^2](m - k)/(2k + 1)!\}[(m + k)f^{(2k+1)}(\xi_1) + (m - k - 1)f^{(2k+1)}(\xi_2)]$.

20. (a)

Difference	Newton	Gauss
2	.9, .8, .7	.6, .7, .5
5	.9, .8, .7, .6, .5, .4	.6, .7, .5, .8, .4, .9

(b) Error should be between -8.0×10^{-5} and -3.7×10^{-7}; calculated error is -7.0×10^{-6}.

21. (a) (i) Through second difference; (ii) through seventh difference. (b) In both cases coefficients of differences are small.

22. (a) Use $m = (x - a_0)/h$ in (3.3-11); (b) use induction; (d) use ratio test; (e) asymptotic even when $e^{ah} < 2$ because of roundoff; see Sec. 3.3-2-3.

23. (a) 3; (b) 3; (c) 4.

24. (a) Newton forward, $m = -.3$; .1837, .5712, .3683. (b) Stirling, $m = .05$; $-.0001$, .5191, .4318. (c) Bessel, $m = .4$; $-.1154$, .4594, .4635. (d) Newton backward, $m = .1$; $-.2280$, .3719, .4838.

25. (a) Use induction.

(b)

.40	$-.916291$			
		2.23144		
.50	$-.693147$		-1.8303	
		1.68236		1.684
.70	$-.356675$		-1.1568	
		1.33531		
.80	$-.223144$			

(c) By repeated application of definition in part a; (d) use first result of part c; (e) result follows since $E(a_k) = 0, a_k = 1, \ldots, n$; (f) as $a_i \to a, f[a_1, \ldots, a_k] \to f^{(k-1)}(a)/(k - 1)!$; (g) $-.509977$; (h) use induction.

26. (a) Use (3.6-1) as in Sec. 3.6; additional entries: $a_{n+1} - x$, $y_{n+1}(x)$, $y_{n,n+1}(x)$, $\ldots, y_{1,2,\ldots,n+1}(x)$. (b) $-.616144$.

27. (a) .1837, .5712, .3683; (b) $-.0001$, .5191, .4318.

28. (a) 806.16264; (b) 771.42567; true value is 771.41025; large derivatives of $\tan x$ near $\pi/2$ cause of large error in part a.

29. 2.4048; true value 2.4048.

30. (a) $\bar{x} = 1.5677$; (b) $\sin \bar{x} = .9999950$; true value of $\bar{x}$ is 1.5676; if $f'(x) \neq 0$ on $[x_1, x_2]$ process will converge for any $f(x)$.

31. Set $t_j(x) = mx + n$ and use (3.8-7); proceed similarly for $s_j(x)$ using (3.8-9).

32. Use $J_1(x) = J_0'(x)$; results: .1838, $-.0001$, $-.1154$, $-.2280$.

33. (a) For Lagrangian show $y(a_j) = 0, j = 1, \ldots, n$ and that $y(x)$ is polynomial of degree $n - 1$; for Hermite by differentiating first row show also that $y'(a_j) = 0$, $j = 1, \ldots, n$. (b) Differentiate first row $1, 2, \ldots, r_i$ times and set $x = a_i$.

34. (a) Show $\Delta = 0$ when $a_j = a_i$; (b) sum of powers in each term of determinant is $\sum\limits_{1}^{n-1} j = n(n-1)/2$ and coefficient of each of these terms is 1.

35. (a) $l_j(x) = \Delta(1,a_1, \ldots ,a_{j-1},x,a_{j+1}, \ldots ,a_n)/\Delta(1,a_1, \ldots ,a_n)$; (b) consider the Vandermonde determinant for $n + r$ tabular points, then differentiate with respect to $a_{n+1}, \ldots , a_{n+r}$ successively, setting $a_{n+j} = a_j$ after differentiation.   (c) Proceed just as in part b.

36. (a) Use Rolle's theorem and result that multiplicity of a multiple zero is reduced by one by differentiation.   (b) Let $P(x) = \pi(x - a_i)^{r_i+1}$, consider $F(z) = f(z) - y(z) - [f(x) - y(x)][P(z)/P(x)]$, and proceed as in Lagrangian case.

37. (a) Merely omit first derivative rows in (3.9-5).

38. (a) $f(x_j) = \Sigma c_i u_i^{x_j}, j = 1, \ldots , n$; (b) $c_1 = 2.229$, $c_2 = -1.079$, $c_3 = 1.200$.

39. (b) (i) Horizontal: .8034, .8303, .8566, .8823; vertical: .8451.   (ii) Vertical: .8566, .8478, .8392, .8310; horizontal: .8448; for diagonal points just interpolate in single variable along the diagonal.

Chapter 4

1. (a) Compare coefficients of $(d^m/dx^m)[f(x)/p_n(x)]/(x - a_{n+1})^{k-m+1}$ on both sides of equation.   (b) Use induction.   (c) Use argument similar to that used to prove Theorem 4.1.   (d) Use $F(z) = f(z) - y(z) - [f^{(k)}(x) - y^{(k)}(x)][p_n(z)/p_n(x)]$; differentiate k times and show that result has $n - k$ zeros in interior of interval; then differentiate k more times and use Rolle's theorem.

2. (a) $f'(a_0) = (1/h)(\Delta f_0 - \frac{1}{2}\Delta^2 f_0 + \frac{1}{3}\Delta^3 f_0 - \frac{1}{4}\Delta^4 f_0 + \frac{1}{5}\Delta^5 f_0)$; $f^{iv}(a_0) = (1/h^4)(\Delta^4 f_0 - 2\Delta^5 f_0)$.
(b) $f'(a_0) = (1/h)(\nabla f_0 + \frac{1}{2}\nabla^2 f_0 + \frac{1}{3}\nabla^3 f_0 + \frac{1}{4}\nabla^4 f_0 + \frac{1}{5}\nabla^5 f_0)$; $f^{iv}(a_0) = (1/h^4)(\delta^4 f_0)$.

5. Get two linear equations for a, b; result $y'' + y = x$; $y = \sin x + y$.

6. (a) Find value of h which minimizes $h^{2n-2}e_1^2 + r_1^2/h^2$.

7. (a) $h = 1.0$: ≈ -100; $h = .1$: -1.0000; $h = .01$: $-.9900$; true value $-.9901$.
(b) Determining factor is large value of $f'(x)$ as $x \to -1$; M_n depends strongly on h.

8. (a) $f'_{-2} = (1/12h)(-25f_{-2} + 48f_{-1} - 36f_0 + 16f_1 - 3f_2) + h^4 f^v(\eta_{-2})/5$; $f'_{-1} = (1/12h)(-3f_{-2} - 10f_{-1} + 18f_0 - 6f_1 + f_2) - h^4 f^v(\eta_{-1})/20$; $f'_0 = (1/12h)(f_{-2} - 8f_{-1} + 8f_1 - f_2) + h^4 f^v(\eta_0)/30$.   (b) $h_{opt} = (45\epsilon/M_5)^{1/5}$; $M_5 \approx 4! \times 2^5 = 768$; with $\epsilon = 5 \times 10^{-10}$, $h_{opt} \approx .01$; $1/x \approx 1.999999766$ at $x = .5$.

9. First derivative: .6: 1.79576; .7: 1.73138.   Second derivative: .6: $-.6438$; .7: $-.7167$.

10. (a) Factor out $H_j a_j^i$.   (b) Linear system has no solution; implicit assumption of part a is that solution of linear system exists.

11. Argument with weight function is precisely analogous.

12.

	Calculated value				True value
	$n = 2$	$n = 3$	$n = 4$	$n = 5$	
(a)	1.263	3.975	2.047	3.089	2.6516353
(b)	.0128	.0116	.0102	.0099	.0099010304
(c)	.0927	.3019	.2111	.1432	$\frac{1}{6}$
(d)	.9122	1.0898	1.0823	1.0827	1.08294
(e)	2.052	2.144	2.199	2.235	2.40394

13. (a) Perform successive integration by parts on the orthogonality integral.   (b) Any other set of boundary conditions on $U_r(x)$ satisfying part a give a $U_r(x)$

differing from that given by conditions of part b by a polynomial of degree $r - 1$, but this leaves $\phi_r(x)$ unchanged.

14. (a) In orthogonality integral write ϕ_r^2 as $\phi_r[A_r x^r + q_{r-1}(x)]$; (b) integrate by parts.

15. Proof is precisely similar to that of Theorem 4.2.

16. (a) Show that x^j can be expressed as a linear combination of $\phi_k(x)$, $k < j$. (b) Multiply both sides by $\phi_i(x)$, $i \leq r - 1$, and integrate. (c) Consider coefficients of x^r in recurrence relation. (e) Use induction; if $A_r > 0$ for all r then show at zero of ϕ_1 that ϕ_2 and ϕ_0 have opposite signs; from this get result for $n = 1$; similarly, use inductive hypothesis to get general result.

17. (b) Use telescoping of series on right-hand side.

18. (a) $\phi_r(x) = [k!/(r - k)!](1/x^k)(d^r/dx^r)[x^{r+k}(1 - x)^r]$.
(b) $\gamma_r = (r!)^2(k!)^2/\{(2r + k + 1)[(r + k)!]^2\}$ (use gamma-function integral); $A_r = (-1)^r(2r + k)!k!/[(r + k)!]^2$.
(c) $H_j = (2n + k + 2)n!k!/\{[(n + k + 1)!]^2\phi_{n+1}(a_j)\phi_n'(a_j)\}$.

19. (b) For γ_r successively integrate by parts; (c) show $\alpha_r = (2r + 1)/(r + 1)$, $b_r = 0$, $b_{r-1} = -r/(r + 1)$.

20. (b) For γ_r successively integrate by parts.

21. (b) For γ_r use result of Prob. 12a of Chap. 1.

22. (b) Legendre: $2/[nP_{n-1}(a_j)P_n'(a_j)]$; Laguerre: $-[(n - 1)!]^2/L_n'(a_j)L_{n-1}(a_j)$; Hermite: $2^n(n - 1)!\sqrt{\pi}/[H_n'(a_j)H_{n-1}(a_j)]$. (c) Legendre: $2(1 - a_j^2)/\{(n + 1)^2[P_{n+1}(a_j)]^2\}$; Laguerre: $(n!)^2 a_j/[L_{n+1}(a_j)]^2$; Hermite: $2^{n+1}n!\sqrt{\pi}/[H_{n+1}(a_j)]^2$.

23.

	Calculated value				True value
	$n = 2$	$n = 3$	$n = 4$	$n = 5$	
(a)	.00990057	.00990098	.00990098	.00990096	$1/101 \approx .00990099$
(c)	.7979	.7815	.7819	.7840	$\pi/4 \approx .783598$
(d)	.4178	.2412	.3710	.2784	$\frac{1}{3}$
(f)	1.3475	1.3820	1.38033	1.3803904	$\sqrt{\pi}\,e^{-1/4} \approx 1.3803884$
(b)	Bound:	$e^{-10}/10$			
(e)	Bound:	$e^{-75}/3$			

24. (b) For A_n use induction.

25. (a) Show coefficient of x^n in $J_n(x;1,1)$ is $2/(n + 2)$ times that in $P_{n+1}'(x)$ by using Probs. 19 and 24. (b) Express $(1 - x^2)p_{n-1}(x) = \sum_{j=0}^{n+1} A_j P_j(x)$; express $(1 - x^2)J_n(x;1,1) = 2[xP_{n+1}(x) + P_{n+2}(x)] + (1 - x^2)p_{n-1}(x)$; show $A_j = 0, j = 0, \ldots, n - 1$ using orthogonality relationships for J_n, P_{n+1}, and P_{n+2}; for $j = n$, $n + 1$ show $\int(1 - x^2)J_n P_j\,dx = 2\int(xP_{n+1} - P_{n+2})\,dx$. (c) $H_j = -2/[(n + 2)P_{n+1}''(a_j)P_{n+2}'(a_j)]$; $E = n![(n + 1)!]^2(n + 2)!2^{2n+3}/\{(2n + 3)[(2n + 2)!]^2(2n)!\}$; abscissas are zeros of $P_{n+1}'(x)$.

26. (d) Since a polynomial of degree r in $\cos\theta$ is a linear combination of $\cos k\theta$, $k = 0, \ldots, r$; (e) Use $\cos k\theta = 2\cos(k - 1)\theta \cos\theta - \cos(k - 2)\theta$.

28. By change of variable $\theta = \cos^{-1} x$.

29.

	Calculated value				True value
	$n = 2$	$n = 3$	$n = 4$	$n = 5$	
(a)	2.3884	2.4041	2.40394	2.40394	2.40394
(b)	1.8138	1.3711	1.6274	1.5028	1.570796

30. (a) Show that $S_r(x) = T'_{r+1}(x)$. (b) $\gamma_n = \pi/2$; $S_{n+1}(a_j) = \cos j\pi$; $S'_n(a_j) = (n+1)/\sin^2 [j\pi/(n+1)]$.

31. (b) $\gamma_n = 2/(4n+1)$; $A_n = (4n)!/\{2^{2n}[(2n)!]^2\}$;
$p'_n(a_j)p_{n+1}(a_j) = (4n+3)P'_{2n}(\alpha_j)P_{2n+1}(\alpha_j)/[2(2n+2)]$.
(c) $\gamma_n = 2/(4n+3)$; $A_n = (4n+2)!/\{2^{2n+1}[(2n+1)!]^2\}$;
$p'_n(a_j)p_{n+1}(a_j) = (4n+5)P'_{2n+1}(a_j)P_{2n+2}(a_j)/[2(2n+3)a_j^2]$.

32. (b) $\gamma_n = \pi/2$; $A_n = 2^{2n}$; $p'_n(a_j)p_{n+1}(a_j) = T'_{2n+1}(a_j)T_{2n+2}(a_j)/a_j$.

33. (a) Calculated result: $.531099$; $|E| < 3.1 \times 10^{-6}$. (b) Calculated result: 3.42164; $|E| < 6.7 \times 10^{-5}$.

34. (a) $y = \cosh \theta$. (b) $th'(t) = (p+1)[f(t) - h(t)]$; $h(0) = f(0)$; $h'(0) = (p+1)f'(0)/(p+2)$; $h''(0) = (p+1)f''(0)/(p+3)$.

35. (a) Because of the singularity at $x = y$. (b) Let $F(y) = \int_0^y [f(x)\,dx/(y-x)^{1/2}]$; approximate $F(h)$, $F(2h)$, $\ldots$, $F(1)$ using (4.9-18); then differentiate numerically.
(c) $g(y) = 2(d/dy) \int_0^{\pi/2} f(y \sin^2 \theta) \sin \theta\, d\theta$; no singularity in integrand now.

36. (b) Consider zeros with odd multiplicity as in Theorem 4.2.

37. (a) Use technique of Prob. 13; (b) apply Leibniz's rule to $\phi_{n-1}(x)$, use result of Prob. 25 and fact that $2^{n-2}(n-2)!(x^2-1)J_{n-2}(x;1,1) = (d^{n-2}/dx^{n-2})(x^2-1)^{n-1}$.

38. $\phi_{n-2}(x) = [1/(x^2-1)](d^{n-2}/dx^{n-2})\{[n/2^{n-1}(n-2)!](x^2-1)^{n-1}\}$.

39. $\phi_1(x) = P'_2(x)$; zero at $x = 0$; $H_1 = \frac{4}{3}$, $H_2 = H_3 = \frac{1}{3}$; expect Lobatto with $n = 3$ to be Simpson by symmetry and because they have same order of accuracy; for this reason expect no other Lobatto to be like Newton-Cotes.

40.

Calculated value (Radau, Lobatto)

	$n = 2$	$n = 3$	$n = 4$	$n = 5$	True value
(a)	-62.35	-28.99	-21.90	-21.001	-20.931036
(b)		1.889	1.93347	1.933427	1.933420

Caloulated value (Legendre)

	$n = 2$	$n = 3$	$n = 4$	$n = 5$
(a)	-9.76	-18.68	-20.71	-20.921
(b)		1.93339	1.933417	1.933422

41. All terms on left-hand side of (4.10-33) are positive; negative a_i's can only decrease right hand side.

42. (a) Starting from $(n!)^{1/(n-1)} \geqq [nn!]^{1/n}$ get (4.10-35); for (4.10-36) replace n by $n-1$ in foregoing. (b) Show

$$\int_{-\infty}^{\infty} e^{-x^2}x^k\, dx = \{(k-1)!/[(k/2-1)!2^{k-1}]\} \int_{-\infty}^{\infty} e^{-x^2}\, dx$$

to get (4.10-37, 4.10-38); proceed in fashion similar to part a to get (4.10-39).

43. (a) For n even inequality is $n/(n-1) \geqq [(n-1)/(n+1)]^{(n-2)/2}$ which is always satisfied; similarly for n odd, $[n/(n-2)]^{(n-1)/(n-3)} > 1$ is always satisfied.
(b) Abscissas will be symmetrically placed with respect to center of interval; left-hand side of (4.10-31) will be alternately zero and nonzero as k is odd or even; with n even center point is not abscissa; last equation has nonzero left-hand side; with n odd get reverse; systems, therefore, fall naturally into two groups.

44. (b) First integrate with respect to u, then exponentiate. (c) Expand logarithm in series and integrate term by term. (d) On right-hand side of $p_n(u)$ in part b all powers of u except 0 through n must vanish since $p_n(u)$ is polynomial of degree n in u.

45. (a) $n = 2$: $\pm 1/\sqrt{3}$; $n = 3$: 0 and $\pm 1/\sqrt{2}$. (b) $n = 2$: .483; $n = 3$: .404; true value: .378.

46. (a) In (4.11-11) 2^{2n+1} becomes m^{2n+1} and there are m 2nth derivatives. (b) Using

$$\text{Table 4.1:} \int_a^b f(x)\,dx \approx (h/6) \sum_{j=0}^{m/3-1} \{5f[a + (3h/2)(1 + .774597 + 2j)] + 8f[a +$$

$(3h/2)(1 + 2j)] + 5f[a + (3h/2)(1 - .774597) + 2j)]\}$; $h = (b - a)/m$; $E = 81mh^7 f^{vi}(\eta)/224{,}000$.

47.

Calculated value

	$n = 1$			$n = 2$			
	$m = 2$	$m = 4$	$m = 8$	$m = 2$	$m = 4$	$m = 8$	*True value*
(a,b)	1.6	2.4	2.6416	1.26	2.70	2.71	2.6516353
(c)	2.027	2.107	2.177	2.052	2.147	2.219	2.40394

48. Abscissas are symmetrically placed in interval and, if center of interval is $x = 0$, the integral of x^{n+1} is zero.

49. (a) Use fact that $p_{n+1}(x)$ is odd with respect to center of interval. (b) Let $y = x + h$ in I_{j-1} integral. (c) Integrand of $q(x)$ alternates in sign on $[a_j, a_{j+1}]$, but because $|I_{j-1}| \geqq |I_j|$ integral remains of constant sign.

50. (a) $\int_{a_{n-1}}^{a_n} f^{(n+1)}(\xi) p_{n+1}(x)\,dx = f^{(n+1)}(\eta) \int_{l_{n-1}}^{a_n} p_{n+1}(x)\,dx$. (b) Write $f(x) =$

$$\sum_{j=0}^{n} l_j(x) f(a_j) + p_{n+1}(x) f^{(n+1)}(\xi)/(n + 1)!;$$ express p'_{n+1} in $l_j(x)$ in terms of p_n and

p'_n; subtract term in $j = n$ from both sides and proceed as in Theorem 4.1. (c) Note $\int_{a_0}^{a_{n-1}} p_n(x)\,dx = 0$. (d) Note $\int_{a_0}^{a_{n-1}} x p_n(x)\,dx = \int_{a_0}^{a_{n-1}} (x - a_n) p_n(x)\,dx$.

51. (a) Lobatto quadrature exact for $f(x)$; moreover, from Lobatto get $\int_{-1}^{1} f(x)\,dx = 0$ since abscissas are zeros of $P'_m(x)$; therefore, $\Sigma H_j f(a_j)$ in given quadrature formula is zero from which result follows. (b) $(2 - n)/n$ smallest abscissa after -1. (c) For n even set $2m - 1 = n + 1$ and consider inequality $(2 - n)/n < \beta_1$; for n odd set $2m - 1 = n$.

52. (a) Use an argument based on symmetry; (b) n even: $(1/n!) f^{(n)}(\xi) \int_{a_0}^{a_n} x p_{n-1}(x)\,dx$.

53. (a) Show resulting determinant when solved for $\int f(x)\,dx$ is exact for polynomials of proper degree. (b) Cotes numbers are solutions of (4.5-1) with $j = 1$ replaced by $j = 0$ and a_j's set equal to equidistant abscissas; A_n is matrix of coefficients in this system of linear equations. (c) Show that $S_n A_n = I$.

(d) $S_1 = \begin{bmatrix} \frac{1}{2} & -1 \\ \frac{1}{2} & 1 \end{bmatrix}$; $\quad S_2 = \begin{bmatrix} 0 & -\frac{1}{2} & \frac{1}{2} \\ 1 & 0 & -1 \\ 0 & \frac{1}{2} & \frac{1}{2} \end{bmatrix}$

(e) If $\boldsymbol{\alpha}$ is vector of α_k's then $S_2\boldsymbol{\alpha}$ is vector (H_0, H_1, H_2).

54. (a) In Lagrangian formula use abscissas $a_j = x + jh$, $j = \pm 1, \ldots, \pm k$; express $p_{2n}(x)$ in terms of j; solve for $h^{2k} f^{(2k)}(\xi)$. (b) Subtract $4h/45$ times formula of part a with $k = 2$.   (c) Add $h/140$ times formula of part a with $k = 3$.   (d) Subtract $9h/700$ times formula of part a with $k = 3$.

55. (a) $I \approx I_2 + m_1^4(I_2 - I_1)/(m_2^4 - m_1^4)$.   (b) $m = 4$: 1.1; $m = 8$: 1.0987251.   (c) 1.098640.

56. Derivation of extrapolation assumes constant derivative; when derivative is constant get monotonic convergence.

57. (a) Derive (4.12-12) from (4.12-25).   (b) Proceed just as in part a.   (c) Assume true for $T_{m,k}$ and use induction.   (d) $T_{m,k}$ uses $2^m + 1$ points on each of 2^k subintervals but Newton-Cotes formulas with these numbers of points have different error terms.

58. (a) From (4.12-27) and (4.12-28) show $c_{m+1,j} = [1/(4^{m+1} - 1)][4^{m+1}c_{mj} - c_{m,j-1}]$

and use (4.12-31) to get same relation.   (b) Show $\displaystyle\sum_{j=1}^{\infty} 2/(4^j - 1)$ converges and thus deduce product converges; derive bound using $\Sigma(1 + a_j) \leq e^{\Sigma a_j}$.   (c) Show $c_{mm} \to 0$; then replace j by $m + 1 - j$ in recurrence relation of part a and use induction.

59. (a) Use (4.12-28) to express $T_{m,k}$ in form of sum of ordinate values.   (b) Consider any term in z^i from expansion of numerator of (4.12-31); corresponding to this there is a sequence of terms in z^{i+1} which are $\frac{1}{4}$, $\frac{1}{16}$, $\frac{1}{64}$, $\ldots$, etc., as great as z^i term in magnitude; since $\displaystyle\sum \frac{1}{4^i} \leq \frac{1}{3}$ get result.   (c) Using parts a and b and fact that signs of c_{mj} alternate, get $d_{jm} > 0$; since $|c_{m1}| < \frac{1}{3}|c_{m0}|$, get $\frac{1}{3}c_{m0} < d_{jm} < c_{m0}$; c_{m0} is minimum for $m = 0$ (and equals $\frac{4}{9}$) and is maximum as $m \to \infty$.

60. $T_{1,j} = \phi_{j+1,j+2}$; $T_{2,j} = \phi_{j+1,j+2,j+3}$; etc.

61.

	$T_{1,0}$	$T_{2,0}$	$T_{3,0}$	$T_{4,0}$	$T_{5,0}$	True value
(a)	.549	2.278	2.584	2.654	2.65186	2.6516353
(b)	.0022	.0078	.00977	.009895	.0098970	.0099010304
	6.0×10^{-6}	.0204	.1784	.1683	.16659	$\frac{1}{6}$
	1.333	1.077	1.084	1.0831	1.08296	1.08291

62. (a) $n = 1$: $H_0 = \frac{4}{15}$, $H_1 = \frac{2}{5}$; $n = 2$: $H_0 = \frac{4}{105}$, $H_1 = \frac{16}{35}$, $H_2 = \frac{6}{35}$.
(b) $n = 1$: $H_0 = \frac{4}{3}$, $H_1 = \frac{2}{3}$; $n = 2$: $H_0 = \frac{4}{5}$, $H_1 = \frac{16}{15}$, $H_2 = \frac{2}{15}$.
(c) Calculated values: Prob. 33, $n = 1$: .4828, $n = 2$: .5319; Example 4.6, $n = 1 = 2$: 2.6666667.

63. (a) Use integration by parts.   (b) $\displaystyle\int_a^b p_n(x)\, dx = H_0[p_n(b) - p_n(a)]$;

$\displaystyle\int_a^b x p_n(x)\, dx = H_0[b p_n(b) - a p_n(a)]$.   (c) $H_j = \displaystyle\int_a^b l_j(x)\, dx - H_0\{[p_n(b)/(b - a_j)p_n'(a_j)] - [p_n(a)/(a - a_j)p_n'(a_j)]\}$.   (d) For $k = 0, 1, \ldots, n - 1$ use result of part c; for $k = n$, $n + 1$ use result of part b; for $k > n + 1$ write $x^k = x^{k-2}(x - a)(x - b) + (a + b)x^{k-1} - abx^{k-2}$ and use induction.   (e) Same argument as Theorem 4.2; $n = 1$: $H_0 = \mp 1/\sqrt{3}$, $H_1 = h$, $a_1 = \alpha = h(1 \pm \sqrt{3})/2$; in composite formulas interior end points of intervals drop out.

65. Remember to apply quadrature formula in (4.14-3) to error in (4.14-2).

66. (b) Integrate by parts.

67. (b) When $x = \frac{1}{2}$, left-hand side of (4.15-2) becomes $t/(e^{t/2} + 1)$.   (c) $B_{2k}(1 - x) = B_{2k}(x)$ and $B_{2k+1}(1 - x) = -B_{2k+1}(x)$ since $B_{2k+1} = 0$.   (d) If $B_{2k+1}(x)$ has five zeros, $B_{2k}(x) + B_{2k}$ has four from (4.15-8), then from (4.15-7) $B_{2k-1}(x)$ has at least three zeros in the interior of $[0,1]$ which means five in $[0,1]$; but $B_3(x)$ has only three zeros.

68. (*a*) By part *d* of previous problem can apply second law of mean to (4.15-15); (*b*) since $B_{2m+1}(x)$ is odd.

69. (*b*) $B_{2k+2}''(0) = (2k+2)(2k+1)B_{2k}$. (*c*) Since $B_{2k}'(0) = 0$ from (4.15-7) sign of $B_{2k}(x)$ is sign of $B_{2k}''(0)$. (*d*) Consider sum formula with m and $m+1$; because of part *c* first neglected term in $m+1$ case less than error in m case.

70. (*b*) Show $t/(e^{t/2} - e^{-t/2}) = 2(t/2)/(e^{t/2} - 1) - t/(e^t - 1)$; (*c*) use parts *a* and *b* together; (*d*) use fact that $B_{2k}(x)$ has maximum value at $x = \frac{1}{2}$.

71. Proceed just as in (4.15-17); $\int_{x_0}^{x_0+nj} f(y)\,dy = h \sum_{j=0}^{n-1} f[x_0 + (j + \frac{1}{2})h] + (h/24)[\Delta f_0 - \Delta f_{n-1}] + \cdots$

72. (*a*) Use (4.15-17) noting that $E_m = 0$ for polynomials of degree $2m$ or less and differences of order greater than $2m$ are zero.

(*b*) $\int_{x_0}^{x_0+nj} f(y)\,dy = h(\frac{1}{2}f_0 + \cdots + \frac{1}{2}f_n) + (h/12)(\mu\delta f_0 - \mu\delta f_n) + \cdots$

73. (*a*) Successive approximations are $\frac{1}{2}$, .583, .575, .5790, .5748, .5823, and then results get worse because of poor asymptotic convergence. (*b*) Using terms through B_4 get .5772156; good asymptotic convergence.

74. (*a*) 2.6515656; (*b*) 2.6598039; poor asymptotic convergence of Euler-Maclaurin formula causes corrections to give worse result than without.

75. (*c*) $(d^i/dx^i)(x)_n\big|_{x=0} = j!\alpha_{nj}/n!$; from (4.1-15) $(d^i/dx^i)(x)_n = j! \sum_{k=j}^{n} S_k^{(j)} \Delta^k(x)_n/k!$;

at $x = 0$ only term left in sum is $k = n$.
(*d*) Use $x^{(n+1)} = x^{(n)}(x - n)$

n	$S_n^{(0)}$	$S_n^{(1)}$	$S_n^{(2)}$	$S_n^{(3)}$	$S_n^{(4)}$	$S_n^{(5)}$	$s_n^{(0)}$	$s_n^{(1)}$	$s_n^{(2)}$	$s_n^{(3)}$	$s_n^{(4)}$	$s_n^{(5)}$
1	0	1					0	1				
2	0	−1	1				0	1	1			
3	0	2	−3	1			0	1	3	1		
4	0	−6	11	−6	1		0	1	7	6	1	
5	0	24	−50	35	−10	1	0	1	15	25	10	1

76. (*a*) Since $x^{(k)}$ is a polynomial of degree k in x, $x^k = x^{(k)} +$ polynomial of degree $k - 1$. (*b*) Use (4.15-21).

77. (*a*) $\tilde{S} = 0^{(-2)}/2$. (*b*) $S = \frac{1}{2} - \sum_{2}^{\infty} (3x^2 + 1)/[x(x^2 - 1)(x^2 + 1)^2]$.

(*c*) Use $\tilde{S} = \sum_{1}^{\infty} (x - 1)^{(-4)} = 0^{(-3)}/3 = \frac{1}{18}$; then $S = \frac{1}{18} - \sum_{1}^{\infty} (6x^3 + 11x^2 + 6x)/[x^5(x + 1)(x + 2)(x + 3)]$; four terms of $\Sigma 1/x^4$ gives 1.0788; four terms of new series gives 1.0818; true value 1.0823.

Chapter 5

1. (*a*) If—construct as in (5.1-3); only if—show that if highest-order derivative must appear on some right-hand side, then can't construct as in (5.1-3). (*b*) $y' = u_1$; $z' = v_1$; $u_1' = u_2$; $u_2' = \sin y - u_1 v_1 - xy^2 z u_2$; $v_1' = -(y^3 u_2 + v_1^{3/2} u_1 - e^{yz})/u_1$.

2. (*a*) $Y(x_0 + h) - Y(x_0) - \cdots - h^m Y^{(m)}(x_0)/m! = h^{m+1}Y^{m+1}(\xi)/(m + 1)!$.
(*b*) Compute $y^{(i)}$, $i = 2, 3, 4$ from differential equation; computed values; .2: 1.0204, .4: 1.0860; true values; .2: 1.020408, .4: 1.086957.

3. Show can solve for y_{n+1}.

4. (a) $306a = -413b + 468$, $34c = 13b - 20$, $153d = -5b + 9$, $34e = -b + 12$, $51f = 31b + 36$, $34g = 37b - 36$; for $b = \frac{2}{3}$, $a = \frac{17}{27}$, $c = -\frac{1}{3}$, $d = \frac{1}{27}$, $e = \frac{1}{3}$, $f = \frac{19}{9}$, $g = -\frac{1}{3}$. (b) $8a = -19b + 27$, $8c = 11b - 19$, $24e = -b + 9$, $f = b$, $8g = 19b - 27$, $12d = 5b - 9$; for $b = 1$, $a = 1$, $c = -1$, $e = \frac{1}{3}$, $f = 1$, $g = -1$, $h = -\frac{1}{3}$. $d = -\frac{1}{3}$

5. (a)

j	a_j	b	c	d	e
0	1	$\frac{55}{24}$	$-\frac{59}{24}$	$\frac{37}{24}$	$-\frac{3}{8}$
1	1	$\frac{8}{3}$	$-\frac{5}{3}$	$\frac{4}{3}$	$-\frac{1}{3}$
2	1	$\frac{21}{8}$	$-\frac{9}{8}$	$\frac{15}{8}$	$-\frac{3}{8}$
3	1	$\frac{8}{3}$	$-\frac{4}{3}$	$\frac{8}{3}$	0

6. If $\int G(s)\,ds \neq 0$ let $y(s)$ be such that $y(s) > 0$ on $[a,b]$ and $\int y(s)G(s)\,ds = 0$; if $\int G(s)\,ds = 0$ then any $y(s)$ such that $\int y(s)G(s)\,ds \neq 0$ will do.

7. Change order of integration from $\int_a^b \int_a^x F(s,x)\,ds\,dx$ to $\int_a^b \int_s^b F(s,x)\,dx\,ds$.

8. (a) $n = 1$: $G(s) = (b - s)(a - s)/2$ is of constant sign on $[a,b]$; $\int G(s)\,ds = -h^3/12$; $n = 2$: on $[0,h]$, $G(s) = s^4/4 - hs^3/3 < 0$, on $[h,2h]$, $G(s) = (2h - s)^3(h/6 - s/4) < 0$; $\int G(s)\,ds = -h^5/90$. (b) $\alpha \leq \frac{1}{2}$; $E = [(1 - 3\alpha^2)/3]\,f''(\xi)$; at $\alpha = 1/\sqrt{3}$ formula is Gaussian two-point formula and order of accuracy is 3.

9. (b) Interchange order of integration, expand denominator, and integrate term by term. (c) $G(s) = \frac{1}{2}(1 - s)^2$, $s > 0$ and $\frac{1}{2}(1 + s)^2$, $s < 0$; $E = \frac{1}{3}f''(\xi)$.

10. (a) $b < \frac{9}{5}$, $G(s) < 0$; $b > 12$; $G(s) > 0$; $G(s)$ could change sign twice in interval (x_i, x_{i+1}). (b) Use $y = x^6$; $E = (-216 + 86b)h^6 Y^{vi}(\eta)/17 \times 6!$.

11. (a) $j = 3$, yes, $E = 14h^5 Y^v(\eta)/45$; $j = 2$, yes, $E = 141h^5 Y^v(\eta)/240$; $j = 1$, yes, $E = 16h^5 Y^v(\eta)/45$; $j = 0$, yes, $E = 251h^5 Y^v(\eta)/720$. (b) $a_1 < 1$, $G(s) < 0$; $a_1 > 9$, $G(s) > 0$; $E = (-9 + 5a_1)h^5 Y^v(\eta)/360$.

12. (a) Stability equations are

$$r_1^{p+1}(1 + hK_{11}b_{-1}) + r_2^{p+1}(hK_{12}b_{-1}) = \sum_{i=0}^{p} [(a_i - hK_{11}b_i)r_1^{p-i} - hK_{12}b_i r_2^{p-i}]$$

and

$$r_1^{p+1}(hK_{21}b_{-1}) + r_2^{p+1}(1 + hK_{22}b_{-1}) = \sum_{i=0}^{p} [-hK_{21}b_i r_1^{p-i} + (a_i - hK_{22}b_i)r_1^{p-i}];$$

in general these two coupled equations are very difficult to solve. (b) Set $h = 0$; get uncoupled equations of form (5.4-14).

13. (b) As $h \to 0$ first column of numerator determinant becomes all 1's and ith column becomes all y_0's; therefore, determinant is zero.

14. (a) For equation $y' = 0$, $y(0) = 0$, $y_k = \sum_{i=0}^{p} hr_i^k$ is solution of (5.2-5) as in proof of Theorem 5.1; if complex roots are $Re^{\pm i\theta}$, y_k has term $w_k = hR^k \cos k\theta$; then $(w_k^2 - w_{k+1}w_{k-1})/\sin^2 \theta = h^2 R^{2k}$; for convergence $w_k^2 - w_{k+1}w_{k-1}$ must $\to 0$; therefore, $R^{2k} \to 0$. (b) Let $w_k = hkr^k$ and proceed as in part a. (c) For all types of roots show $y_n \to 0$ as $n \to \infty$.

15. (b) $y_{n+1} = y_n + hy_n'$.

16. (a) By induction; take absolute value of both sides of (5.4-25). (b) Use fact that $\Sigma a_i = 1$. (c) Use second equation of (5.2-6). (d) $e_n = cr_0^n + E/Kh\sigma$; if $c = \lambda - E/Kh\sigma$ then $e_0 = \lambda$ and $e_i > \lambda$, $i = 1, \ldots, p$.

17. (a) If $z = re^{i\theta}$, $|r| < 1$, show real part of w is negative. (c) Since $n = p + 1$, $c_i = -a_{i-1} + hKb_{i-1}$. (d) Need $d_0 > 0$, $d_1 > 0$, $d_1d_2 - d_0d_3 > 0$, $d_3 > 0$; for $hK = 0$ get $-.6 \leq b \leq 1$. (e) $b = 0$, $0 \leq hK < \frac{8}{3}$; $b = \frac{1}{2}$, $0 \leq hK \leq \frac{24}{17}$;

this result determines stability if stability is defined as in Remark 3 after Definition 5.2; the range of positive hK for which a method is relatively stable will be smaller than the above ranges.

18. (a) Consider $\sum_{p=0}^{n-1} \Big[\Big(\sum_{r=0}^{n-p-1} c_r x_{p+r} \Big)^2 - \Big(\sum_{s=0}^{n-p-1} c_{n-s} x_{p+s} \Big)^2 \Big]$; by manipulation get quadratic form with coefficients A_{rs}; by comparing polynomial with coefficients c_j with (5.4-14) get $c_j = -a_{j-1}$. (b) $A_{00} = A_{22} = (63 + 2b - b^2)/64$; $A_{01} = A_{12} = A_{21} = A_{10} = (-9 + 10b - b^2)/8$; $A_{11} = (11 - 10b + 5b^2)/4$. (c) $c_j = -a_{j-1} + Khb_{j-1}$. (d) Get higher powers of hK than in previous problem, but paper by Emanuel indicates how these higher powers can be avoided.

19. (a) With $p = 3$ and using method of Prob. 17 with $hK = \lambda$ get $d_4 = 10\lambda/9$, $d_3 = (20 + 32\lambda)/9$, $d_2 = (64 + 24\lambda)/9$, $d_1 = (164 - 24\lambda)/9$, $d_0 = (16 - 30\lambda)/9$; from this get $0 \leq \lambda \leq \frac{8}{15}$. (b) Consider convergence only; get $d_0 = 2 - 2b$, $d_1 = (-3 + 11b)/4$, $d_2 = (27 - 3b)/4$, $d_3 = 0$; find no b for which principal minors all have same sign.

20. (a) Since $r_0 = 1 - Kh + O(h^2)$. (b) Merits: guarantees no absolute increase of error and it is comparatively easy to compute when a method is stable; limitations: doesn't relate error to true solution and ignores $K > 0$ case.

21. (a) $h < 3$. (b) $-7h^6 Y^{vi}(\xi)/540 = -5203e^{-\xi}/540$. (c) $b = 0$: $h < \frac{8}{3}$; $b = 1$: $h < 3$; $b = 0$: $T = 4096e^{-\xi}/1215$, $b = 1$: $T = 243e^{-\xi}/90$. (d) Show that the kth derivative of y, where $y' = f(x,y)$, contains a factor $\partial f/\partial y$ raised to the $k - 1$ power.

22. (a) Integrate from 0 to h. (b) $p = 0$: $h^2 Y''(\eta)/2$; $p = 1$: $5h^3 Y'''(\eta)/12$; $p = 2$: $3h^4 Y^{iv}(\eta)/8$.

23. (a) Integrate from $-h$ to 0. (b) $Y^{(p+2)}(\eta) \int_{-h}^{0} x(x + h) \cdots (x + ph) \, dx/(p + 1)!$. (c) $p = 0$: $y_{n+1} = y_n + hy'_{n+1}$, $T = -h^2 Y''(\eta)/2$; $p = 1$: $y_{n+1} = y_n + (h/2)(y'_{n+1} + y'_n)$, $T = -h^3 Y'''(\eta)/12$; $p = 2$: $y_{n+1} = y_n + (h/12)(5y'_{n+1} + 8y'_n - y'_{n-1})$, $T = -h^4 Y^{iv}(\eta)/24$.

24. (a) Integrate from $-h$ to h. (b) $\int_{-h}^{h} x(x + h) \cdots (x + ph) Y^{(p+2)}(\eta) \, dx/(p + 1)!$; integrand changes sign. (c) $p = 0$ and 1: $y_{n+1} = y_{n-1} + 2hy'_n$, from Table 4.7 with $n = 2$, $T = h^3 Y'''(\eta)/3$; $p = 2$: $y_{n+1} = y_{n-1} + (h/3)(7y'_n - 2y'_{n-1} + y'_{n-2})$.

25. (a) In (3.8-14) set $f(x) = y(x)$, $x = x_{n+1}$, $a_j = x_{n-j+1}$; since $n = p + 1$ and $r = q - s + 1$ result follows. (b) $p = 2$, $q = 1$, $s = 0$. (c) $y_{n+1} = 9y_n + 9y_{n-1} - 17y_{n-2} + h(-18y'_{n-1} - 6y'_{n-2})$; $T = 3h^5 Y^v(\eta)/10$.

26. Modifier equation is $\bar{y}_{n+1}^{(0)} = y_{n+1}^{(0)} + \frac{9}{10}[y_n - y_n^{(0)}]$.

27. (a) Show result is exact for $y = x^5$. (b) If predictor-corrector pair is of order n, show exact for x^{n+1}.

28. (a) $a_0 = 1 - a_1 - a_2$, $b_{-1} = (9 - a_1)/24$, $b_0 = (19 + 13a_1 + 8a_2)/24$, $b_1 = (-5 + 13a_1 + 32a_2)/24$, $b_2 = (1 - a_1 + 8a_2)/24$. (b) Let $n = 0, -1, -2$ and solve for C_3; then by factoring out $(r - 1)$ from (5.4-14) show $\rho_1 + \rho_2 = -(a_1 + a_2)$ and $\rho_1 \rho_2 = a_2$. (c) Need $|1 + a_1 + 2a_2| \geq 1$; in Table 5.2 $a_1 = 0$ and $\frac{9}{17}$ satisfy condition. (d) $(a_0^2 + a_1^2 + a_2^2)^{1/2}$. (e) Use $y = x^5$ to get $T = (-19 + 11a_1 - 8a_2)h^5 Y^v(\eta)/720$.

29. (a) $d_0 = 2(1 - a) - hK(1 + a)/3$, $d_1 = 2(a + 1) + hK(1 - a)$, $d_2 = hK(1 + a)$. (b) $d_0 > 0$ implies $hK \leq (6 - 6a)/(1 + a)$, $d_1 > 0$ and $d_2 > 0$ do not restrict Kh for $K > 0$. (c) $a = 4 - \sqrt{13}$; $a_0 = \sqrt{13} - 3$, $a_1 = 4 - \sqrt{13}$, $b_{-1} = (\sqrt{13} + 1)/12$, $b_0 = (10 - 2\sqrt{13})/3$, $b_1 = (19 - 5\sqrt{13})/12$.

30. (a) Predictor error: $14h^5 Y^v(\eta)/45$; corrector error: $-h^5 Y^v(\eta)/90$. (b) $h^6 Y^{vi}(\eta)/20$. (c) $\bar{y}_{n+1}^{(0)} = y_{n+1}^{(0)} + 34(y_n - y_n^{(0)})/27$.

31. (b) For (5.5-1) integrate Lagrangian formula based on x_n and x_{n+1} from 0 to h; for (5.5-2) integrate formula based on x_n and x_{n-1} from $-2h$ to h. (c) No, only if method has order $p + 1$ can Lagrangian formula be used.

32. (b) Show $(d^{r+i}/dx^{r+i})[x^r(h-x)^r]\Big|_0^h = (r+j)!/[j!(r-j)!]$; get $\displaystyle\sum_{j=0}^{r-1}(-1)^i\{(r+j)!/[j!(r-j)!]\}[(-1)^r y^{(r-i)}(h) - (-1)^i y^{(r-i)}(0)] + \int_0^h y'(x)\,dx$; set $k = r - j$.
(c) Use expression in part a, apply the second law of the mean and then integrate by parts r times.

33. (a) Use Newton's backward formula with $m = 1$. (b) If r differences are retained $h^{r+1}Y^{(r+1)}(\eta)$. (c) Method requires more past values than ordinary predictor to get same accuracy; but it requires one less evaluation of $f(x,y)$; further disadvantage is that no error estimate available.

34. (b) $y_0' = (-11y_0 + 18y_1 - 9y_2 + 2y_3)/6h$; $y_1' = (-2y_0 - 3y_1 + 6y_2 - y_3)/6h$; $y_2' = (y_0 - 6y_1 + 3y_2 + y_3)/6h$; $y_3' = (-2y_0 + 9y_1 - 18y_2 + 11y_3)/6h$; errors: $-h^4/4$, $h^4/12$, $-h^4/12$, $h^4/4$, respectively. (e) Not a special case of general operator since (x_2, y_2) is not a solution point.

35. (a) Method best when $f(x,y)$ is polynomial in x and y. (b) Show A_k is proper coefficient in Taylor series.

36. (a) $y(.01) \approx 1.010101$, $y(.02) \approx 1.020408$, $y(.03) \approx 1.030927$; true values: $1.01010101\ldots$, $1.02040816\ldots$, $1.03092781\ldots$ (b) $y(.1) \approx 1.111$, $y(.2) \approx 1.248$, $y(.3) \approx 1.417$.

37. (b) Only for first equation is $G(s)$ of constant sign.

38. (b) Consider $f(x,y)$ such that $f_y = 0$ and $Df_y = 0$.

39. (a) From (5.6-39), $w_2 \neq 0$; from (5.6-43), $w_3 \neq 0$. (b) By induction; suppose k_M has a term $c(f_y)^{M-2}D_2 f$; then from $\beta_{M+1,M}(k_M - h_n f_n)(\partial/\partial y)$ term, k_{M+1} has term $\bar c(f_y)^{M-1}D_2 f$.

40. (b) From (5.6-39) use $\alpha_2 w_2 = \frac{1}{2}$. (c) Use (5.6-43).

41. (b) $\alpha_2 = 0$ means fourth equation of (5.6-43) cannot be satisfied. (c) $\alpha_2 = \alpha_3 = \frac{2}{3}$, $w_1 = \frac{1}{4}$, $w_2 = \frac{3}{4} - w_3$, $\beta_{31} = \frac{2}{3} - 1/4w_3$, $\beta_{32} = 1/4w_3$; $\alpha_3 = 0$, $\alpha_2 = \frac{2}{3}$, $w_2 = \frac{3}{4}$, $w_1 = \frac{1}{4} - w_3$, $\beta_{31} = -\beta_{32} = 1/4w_3$.

43. (a) To show $\alpha_4 = 1$ proceed as follows; number equations in (5.6-29) from (1) to (8) and perform following manipulations [$\alpha_4(4)$ means α_4 times Eq. (4)]: (9): $\alpha_4(4) - (7)$; (10): (6) $- \alpha_2(4)$; (11): eliminate w_4 between (8) and (10); (12): eliminate β_{32} between (9) and (11); (13): $\alpha_2\alpha_4(2) - (\alpha_2 + \alpha_4)(3) + (4)$; then from (12) and (13) get $\alpha_4 = 1$. (b) $\alpha_2 = 0$, (8) cannot be satisfied; for $\alpha_3 = 1$ (4) and (7) are incompatible since $\alpha_4 = 1$. (c) $\alpha_2 = \alpha_3 = \frac{1}{2}$, $w_1 = w_4 = \frac{1}{6}$, $w_2 = \frac{2}{3} - w_3$, $\beta_{32} = 1/6w_3$, $\beta_{42} = 1 - 3w_3$, $\beta_{43} = 3w_3$; $\alpha_2 = 1$, $\alpha_3 = \frac{1}{2}$, $w_1 = \frac{1}{6}$, $w_3 = \frac{2}{3}$, $w_2 = \frac{1}{6} - w_4$, $\beta_{32} = \frac{1}{8}$, $\beta_{42} = -1/12w_4$, $\beta_{43} = 1/3w_4$; $\alpha_3 = 0$, $\alpha_2 = \frac{1}{2}$, $w_2 = \frac{2}{3}$, $w_4 = \frac{1}{6}$, $w_1 = \frac{1}{6} - w_3$, $\beta_{32} = 1/12w_3$, $\beta_{42} = \frac{3}{2}$, $\beta_{43} = 6w_3$.

44. (a) $\alpha_2 = \frac{1}{2}$ implies β_{32} is infinite unless $\alpha_3 = \frac{1}{2}$; $6\alpha_2\alpha_3 - 4(\alpha_2 + \alpha_3) + 3 = 0$ implies β_{42} and β_{43} are infinite. (b) When β_{32} is infinite $w_3 = 0$; when β_{42} and β_{43} are infinite $w_4 = 0$. (c) If w_4 term is omitted last equation of (5.6-29) will never be satisfied; if w_3 term omitted arrive at similar contradiction.

45. (a) x^2: $R - K$ exact, (5.5-11): $-h^3/6$; y: $R - K$: $h^3 y_n/6 + 0(h^4)$, (5.5-11): $-h^3 Y(\eta)/12$. (b) x^4: $R - K$: $\approx 10^{-2}h^5$; (5.5-33): $-.6h^5$; y: $R - K$: $-h^5 y_n/120 + 0(h^6)$, (5.5-33): $-h^5 Y(\eta)/40$. (c) In the Runge-Kutta cases at most one term in (5.6-33) is nonzero; y is probably a better test than x^m since in practice f_y will generally not be zero.

46. (a) Each $(k_n - h_n f_n)$ starts with an h^2 term; therefore, cross products start with h^4; together with multiplicative factor h have at least h^5. (b) Since no cross-products, equations for v_i, γ_{ij} same as those for w_i, β_{ij}. (c) Yes; result of part a holds in general.

47. Use $y' = z$, $z' = F(x,y,z)$; if F independent of y', $k_i = h_n \left(z_n + \sum_{j=1}^{i-1} \beta_{ij} m_j \right)$,

$$m_i = h_n F \left(x_n + \alpha_i h_n, y_n + \sum_{j=1}^{i-1} \beta_{ij} k_j \right).$$

48. (a) At least five in order to retain fourth-order accuracy; $y(x_n - \tfrac{3}{2}h)$, $y(x_n - \tfrac{1}{2}h)$. (b) Use y_{n-2}, y_{n-4}, y_{n-6}, etc.; y_{n-1} through y_{n-6}.

49. (a)

	Calculated values			True values		
	$x = .1$	$x = .2$	$x = .3$	$x = .1$	$x = .2$	$x = .3$
A	.904837	.818734	.740838	.904837	.818731	.740818
B	.000050	.000800	.004050	.000050	.000789	.003931
C	.900625	.804667	.714625	.900623	.804631	.714430
D	1.020116	1.081866	1.189450	1.020134	1.082182	1.191380

(b) $y_0 = 1$, $y_1 = 1 - x$, $y_2 = 1 - x + x^2/2$, etc., getting at each stage term of expansion of e^{-x}. (c) .904837, .818733, .740837.

(d)

	(i)			(ii)		
	$x = .1$	$x = .2$	$x = .3$	$x = .1$	$x = .2$	$x = .3$
A	.905000	.819025	.741218	.904833	.818723	.740808
B	.000044	.000784	.003948	.000046	.000781	.003919
C	.900644	.804742	.714676	.900625	.804632	.714427
D	1.020030	1.081819	1.190529	1.020131	1.082174	1.191357

	(iii)		
	$x = .1$	$x = .2$	$x = .3$
A	.904838	.818731	.740818
B	.000050	.000790	.003931
C	.900624	.804631	.714430
D	1.020134	1.082183	1.191378

50. (a) Estimated errors: Milne: $\approx -8 \times 10^{-8}$, Hamming: $\approx -18 \times 10^{-8}$.

51. (a) Milne's method satisfies criterion of Prob. 28c, Hamming's does not but the differences between the two are not great; $(a_0^2 + a_1^2 + a_2^2)^{\frac{1}{2}}$ is 1 for Milne, approximately $\tfrac{9}{8}$ for Hamming; not surprising differences don't show up in Table 5.6. (b) Show truncation error very small. (c) Increasing interval will decrease total error as roundoff dominates truncation and it will speed up computation.

52. Results at $x = 1.0$ using 10-digit floating-point arithmetic ($d = 10$, $m = 8$):

	A	B	C	D
(a)	.36769539	.36883001	.29081685	5.9839745
(b)	.35623574	.32688895	.27727846	4.6883179
(c)	.36778742	.36821519	.29131811	5.6775766
(d)	.36787955	.36787700	.29099004	5.8555604
(e)	.36787888	.36785361	.29100297	5.8636981
True value	.36787944	.36787944	.29098835	5.8510379

Solution of D is $y = (2/\cos^2 x) - 1$; as x increases derivatives of y grow very rapidly.

53. (a) $y_{n+1}^{(0)}, z_{n+1}^{(0)}, \bar{y}_{n+1}^{(0)}, \bar{z}_{n+1}^{(0)}, [\bar{y}_{n+1}^{(0)}]', [\bar{z}_{n+1}^{(0)}]', y_{n+1}, z_{n+1}$. (b) Since $z = y'$, $\bar{z}_{n+1}^{(0)} = [\bar{y}_{n+1}^{(0)}]'$. (c) Each component of the solution vector would be compared with a convergence factor (which might be different for different components); if any component failed the test that component (or perhaps all the components) would be corrected again.

54. (a) $a_0 = 2 + 2a_2$, $a_1 = -(1 + 2a_2)$, $b_{-1} = \frac{1}{12}$, $b_0 = (10 - a_2)/12$, $b_1 = (1 - 10a_2)/12$, $b_2 = -a_2/12$; with $a_2 = 0$ get (5.8-5). (b) Three roots are $+1$, $+1$, a_2; therefore, $a_2 = 0$ gives third root as small as possible. (d) Predictor: $h^6 Y^{vi}(\eta)/15$; corrector: $-h^6 Y^{vi}(\eta)/240$. (e) Modifier: $\bar{y}_{n+1}^{(0)} = y_{n+1}^{(0)} + \frac{16}{17}[y_n - y_n^{(0)}]$; $T \approx [y_{n+1}^{(0)} - y_{n+1}]/17$.

55. (a) Predictor: $a_1 = -1$, $a_0 = 2$, $b_1 = 0$, $b_0 = -1$; corrector: $a_1 = -1$, $a_0 = 2$, $b_{-1} = b_1 = \frac{1}{2}$. (b) Predictor error: $h^4 Y^{iv}(\eta)/12$; corrector error: $-h^4 Y^{iv}(\eta)/24$; modifier: $\bar{y}_{n+1}^{(0)} = y_{n+1}^{(0)} + \frac{2}{3}[y_n - y_n^{(0)}]$; $T \approx [y_{n+1}^{(0)} - y_{n+1}]/3$.

56. (b) Use Hermite formula with $a_1 = x_n$, $a_2 = x_{n-1}$; (c) $T \approx [y_{n+1} - y_{n+1}^{(0)}]/30$.

57. (a) Write (5.8-8) as $y_{n+1} = y_n + h\Sigma b_i y'_{n-i} + h^2 \Sigma \bar{b}_i y''_{n-i}$; let K, M be characteristic values of f_y, f_{xy}; then get $r^{p+1}[1 + hKb_{-1} - h^2(K^2 + M\bar{b}_{-1})] = r^p + \displaystyle\sum_{0}^{p}[-hKb_i +$

$h^2(K^2 + M)\bar{b}_i]r^{p-i}$. (b) Only root of convergence equation is $r = 1$. (c) Equation of part a has a single root only for all hK.

58. Results at $x = 1.0$: Hamming: .36787901; (5.8-5): .36788116; true value: .36787944; Hamming's method better mainly because starting values have error of opposite sign to that produced by this method but (5.8-5) produces same sign error as starting values; therefore, at $x = .6$ errors are 2×10^{-8} and 63×10^{-8}, respectively.

59. Results at $x = 1.0$: A: .36787963, B: .36788031, C: .29098801, D: 5.8497670; could have started at $x = .2$.

Chapter 6

1. (a) Coefficients for $m = 5$:

9.0000	0	3.7500	0	2.7656	0
0	3.7500	0	2.7656	0	2.3876
3.7500	0	2.7656	0	2.3876	0
0	2.7656	0	2.3876	0	2.2080
2.7656	0	2.3876	0	2.2080	0
0	2.3876	0	2.2080	0	2.1145

(b) Coefficients for $m = 5$:

9.0000	0	1.1250	0	1.4121	0
0	3.7500	0	1.2890	0	1.6351
1.1250	0	2.8476	0	1.5159	0
0	1.2890	0	2.6184	0	1.7516
1.4121	0	1.5159	0	1.2890	0
0	1.6351	0	1.7516	0	2.5937

2. (a) Show that the ith component of $\mathbf{f} - Q\mathbf{a}^{(m)}$ is given by (6.2-2). (b) Form is positive definite since $Q^T Q$ is positive definite. (c) Consider $[\mathbf{f} - Q\mathbf{a}^{(m)}]^T(\mathbf{f} - Q\mathbf{a}^{(m)})$. (d) Only first term in part c affected by choice of $\mathbf{a}^{(m)}$.

3. (a) $g_{jk} = 0$ if $j + k$ is odd. (c) Yes; can decouple if $\phi_j(x)$ are, respectively, odd and even.

4. (a) Use $a_i = i$, $b_k = k - 1$. (b) Use $a_i = 1, 2, \ldots, i - 1, i + 1, \ldots, n$; $b_j = 0, \ldots, j - 2, j, \ldots, n - 1$. (d) $h_n^{ij} = (-1)^{i+j} \Delta_n^{ij}/\Delta_n$. (f) Upper triangle of H_5^{-1} is

25	−300	1050	−1400	630
	4800	−18900	26880	−12600
		79380	−117600	56700
			179200	−88200
				44100

5.

	a_0	a_1	a_2	a_3
$m = 3$:	2.0001004	2.2501083	.0313056	.0020859
$m = 4$:	2.0000374	2.2501083	.0318428	.0020859
$m = 5$:	2.0000374	2.2507475	.0318428	−.0005568

	a_4	a_5	Det
$m = 3$:			14.13
$m = 4$:	−.0005233		−1.269
$m = 5$:	−.0005233	.0020571	.0252

6. (a)

	a_0	a_1	a_2	a_3
$m = 3$:	2.0105356	2.2513600	.0208705	.0008340
$m = 4$:	2.0105472	2.2513600	.0209302	.0008340
$m = 5$:	2.0105472	2.2512948	.0209302	.0006904

	a_4	a_5	Det
$m = 3$:			198.7
$m = 4$:	−.0001209		341.5
$m = 5$:	−.0001209	.0002625	420.1

(b)

	a_0	a_1	a_2	a_3
$m = 3$:	2.0001004	2.2501090	.0313056	.0020850
$m = 4$:	2.0000368	2.2501090	.0318488	.0020850
$m = 5$:	2.0000368	2.2507514	.0318488	−.0005710

	a_4	a_5
$m = 3$:		
$m = 4$:	−.0005291	
$m = 5$:	−.0005291	.0020674

Difference between 5 and 6b accounted for by differing roundoff errors in solution of two systems; expect 6b to be better since system is much better conditioned; low-order coefficients are quite inaccurate (see Prob. 20).

7. (c) In 7a let $v_i = u_{i-1}$ and $u_i = v_i$

8. (a) Calculate $(1 + x)^{p+m}$

9. (a) $(i - N - 1)^{(i)} = j! \binom{i - N - 1}{j} = j! \left[\dfrac{(i - j) - (N + 1 - j)}{j} \right]$; (b) Convert to factorial notation; (c) Use result that $\binom{i - j}{k} = (i - j)^{(k)}/k!$; (d) Show $\Delta^i i^{(i+k)} = (j + k)! i^{(k)}/k!$

10. Express $(j + k)^{(i)}$, $N^{(k)}$ and $\binom{N - k}{j - k}$ in terms of factorials.

11. (a) Use the orthogonality property of the $p_j(i,N)$, then use (6.4-12) and sum by parts. (b) Show $c_j = (2j)!/[(j!)^2 N^{(i)}]$ and then use (6.4-21) to derive the first equality; for the second equality use $(j + i)^{(j)} = \Delta(j + i)^{(j+1)}/(j + 1)$ and sum by parts. (c) Show limits in sum in part b can be changed to j to N; then let $k = i - j$ and use result that $(2j + k)^{(2j)} = \Delta(2j + k)^{(2j+1)}/(2j + 1)$.

12. (a) ϵ_j is coefficient of s^j. (b) Each Gram polynomial contains only even or only odd powers. (c) From (6.4-39) $\beta_j = \gamma_j \epsilon_{j-1}^2/(\gamma_{j-1}\epsilon_j^2)$.

13. (a) Consider zeros of odd multiplicity and use argument similar to that used to prove Theorem 4.2. (b) Show that if $p_n^{(n)}(x) = (x - x_1) \cdots (x - x_n)$ then all conditions are satisfied; show uniqueness of $p_n^{(n)}(x)$ by considering another such polynomial $q_n^{(n)}(x)$ and using orthogonality to show that $p_n^{(n)}(x) - q_n^{(n)}(x) \equiv 0$.

14. (a) Let $p_{J+1}(s,2L) = s^{J+1} + \displaystyle\sum_{p=0}^{J} \alpha_j s^j$; multiply both sides by $p_k(s,2L)$, $k \leq J$ and sum over the $2L$ points; thereby get $\alpha_k = -\Sigma p_k(s_i,2L)s_i^{J+1}/\gamma_k$; recurrence relation technique is simpler. (b) $p_0(x) = 1$; $p_1(x) = x - .7$; $p_2(x) = (x - .7)^2 - .04$; $p_3(x) = (x - .7)[(x - .7)^2 - .04] - .03(x - .7)$; $p_4(x) = (x - .7)^2[(x - .7)^2 - .07] - \dfrac{.18}{7}[(x - .7)^2 - .04]$.

15. (a) Use (6.4-46) and show limiting recurrence relation is that for Legendre polynomials. (b) $y(x) = \displaystyle\sum_{j=0}^{m} b_j P_j(s)$ where $b_j = 2\displaystyle\int_{-1}^{1} f(s)P_j(s)\, ds/(2j + 1)$.

16. (a) $b_0 = 2.0131444$, $b_1 = 2.2516466$, $b_2 = .01826140$, $b_3 = .0005471$, $b_4 = -.0000498$, $b_5 = .0000538$.

	a_0	a_1	a_2	a_3
$m = 3$:	2.0001006	2.2501095	.0313053	.0020843
$m = 4$:	2.0000366	2.2501095	.0318505	.0020843
$m = 5$:	2.0000366	2.2507520	.0318505	−.0005721

	a_4	a_5
$m = 3$:		
$m = 4$:	−.0005310	
$m = 5$:	−.0005310	−.0020677

As expected, approximations are closer to those of Prob. 6 than Prob. 5.

(b) m:	0	1	2	3	4
δ_m:	19.013	.00118	$.176 \times 10^{-5}$	$.248 \times 10^{-6}$	$.227 \times 10^{-6}$
σ_m:	2.377	.00017	$.29 \times 10^{-6}$	$.50 \times 10^{-7}$	$.54 \times 10^{-7}$

Therefore, $M = 3$.

18.

	$x = .3$	$x = .4$	$x = .5$	$x = .6$	$x = .7$
(a)	3.1193	4.2952	5.7495	7.5091	9.5786
(b)	3.1174	4.2965	5.7509	7.5046	9.5814
(c)	3.1180	4.2960	5.7500	7.5040	9.5820

19. (a) $p_0(x) = 1$; $p_1(x) = 2.5x - 1.25$; $p_2(x) = (300x^2 - 300x + 55)/28$; $p_3(x) = (5000x^3 - 7500x^2 + 3160x - 330)/84$; $p_4(x) = (70,000x^4 - 140,000x^3 + 93,500x^2 - 23,500x + 1716)/168$. (b) Using only $p_4(x)$ terms, since others are all small, get $\sigma_{\Delta a_4}^2 \approx .00203$, $\sigma_{\Delta a_4} \approx .045$, $\sigma_{\Delta a_3}^2 \approx 10^{-4}$, $\sigma_{\Delta a_3} \approx 10^{-2}$. (c) Estimates very conservative because main contribution to error comes from $p_4(x)$ but b_4 is exact (see Example 6.1); when data interval in x is small it is preferable not to convert to s because multiplications by large numbers will magnify errors.

20. (a) Estimate of σ^2 from residuals is 5×10^{-8}; get $\sigma_{\Delta b_0} = .75 \times 10^{-4}$; $\sigma_{\Delta b_1} = 1.15 \times 10^{-4}$; $\sigma_{\Delta b_2} = 1.2 \times 10^{-4}$; $\sigma_{\Delta b_3} = 10^{-4}$. (b) $s = 4x$; $f(s) = e^{s/16} + \frac{1}{2}s + 1 \approx 2.013021 p_0(s) + 2.251758 p_1(s) + .018229 p_2(s) + .000686 p_3(s)$; therefore, $\Delta b_0 = -1.23 \times 10^{-4}$, $\Delta b_1 = 1.11 \times 10^{-4}$, $\Delta b_2 = -.32 \times 10^{-4}$, $\Delta b_3 = 1.39 \times 10^{-4}$; all within expected bounds. (c) $p_0(s) = 1$; $p_1(s) = s$; $p_2(s) = (3s^2 - 20)/28$; $p_3(s) = (5s^3 - 59s)/84$; from (6.6-8) get $\sigma_{\Delta a_0} = 1.25 \times 10^{-4}$; $\sigma_{\Delta a_1} = 5.2 \times 10^{-4}$; $\sigma_{\Delta a_2} = 2 \times 10^{-4}$; $\sigma_{\Delta a_3} = 3.8 \times 10^{-4}$; using Prob. 6 get $\Delta a_0 = -1.0 \times 10^{-4}$, $\Delta a_1 = -1.1 \times 10^{-4}$, $\Delta a_2 = -.56 \times 10^{-4}$, $\Delta a_3 = 5.2 \times 10^{-4}$; all within expected bounds.

21. (a) $x = .1s + .7$; $b_0 = -.3919$, $b_1 = .9478$, $b_2 = .4202$, $b_3 = .0238$, $b_4 = -.0001$; then calculating σ_m^2 get $M = 3$ as best least-squares approximation. (b) $b_0 = -.3919$, $b_1 = 3.1737$, $b_2 = 8.4033$, $b_3 = 3.9667$, $b_4 = -.2651$; again get $M = 3$.

(c)

x:	.4	.5	.6	.7
Residual from (a):	-2.0×10^{-4}	3.7×10^{-4}	-4.7×10^{-5}	-3.4×10^{-4}
Residual from (b):	4.1×10^{-3}	3.2×10^{-3}	1.4×10^{-3}	-3.7×10^{-4}

.8	.9	1.0
1.9×10^{-4}	2.3×10^{-4}	-1.0×10^{-4}
-1.3×10^{-3}	-2.6×10^{-3}	-4.4×10^{-3}

Part a approximation appears better as expected; see next to last paragraph of Sec. 6.5.

(d) $\sigma_{\Delta b_0} \approx 1.4 \times 10^{-4}$, $\sigma_{\Delta b_1} \approx 2.1 \times 10^{-4}$, $\sigma_{\Delta b_2} \approx 2.0 \times 10^{-4}$, $\sigma_{\Delta b_3} \approx 1.5 \times 10^{-4}$; $T_3(s) = .024 p_3(s) + .420 p_2(s) + .948 p_1(s) - .392 p_0(s)$; therefore, all errors within expected limits.

22. (a) $s = Lp_1(s)$; $s^2 = [(2L + 1)Lp_2(s) + L(L + 1)]/3$; $s^3 = [L(L - 1)(2L - 1)p_3(s) + L(3L^2 + 3L - 1)p_1(s)]/5$; $s^4 = 2L(L - 1)(2L - 1)(2L - 3)p_4(s)/35 + L(2L - 1)(6L^2 + 6L - 5)p_2(s)/21.$

		f_{-3}	f_{-2}	f_{-1}	f_0	f_1	f_2	f_3
(a)	$y_1(-3)$	$\frac{13}{28}$	$\frac{5}{14}$	$\frac{1}{4}$	$\frac{1}{7}$	$\frac{11}{28}$	$-\frac{3}{7}$	$-\frac{5}{28}$
	$y_1(-2)$	$\frac{5}{14}$	$\frac{2}{7}$	$\frac{3}{14}$	$\frac{1}{7}$	$\frac{1}{14}$	0	$-\frac{1}{14}$
	$y_1(-1)$	$\frac{1}{4}$	$\frac{3}{14}$	$\frac{5}{28}$	$\frac{1}{7}$	$\frac{3}{28}$	$\frac{1}{14}$	$\frac{1}{28}$
	$y_1(0)$	$\frac{1}{7}$	$\frac{1}{7}$	$\frac{1}{7}$	$\frac{1}{7}$	$\frac{1}{7}$	$\frac{1}{7}$	$\frac{1}{7}$
(b)	$y_3(-2)$		$\frac{69}{70}$	$\frac{2}{35}$	$-\frac{3}{35}$	$\frac{2}{35}$	$-\frac{1}{70}$	
	$y_3(-1)$		$\frac{2}{35}$	$\frac{27}{35}$	$\frac{12}{35}$	$-\frac{8}{35}$	$\frac{2}{35}$	
	$y_3(0)$		$-\frac{3}{35}$	$\frac{12}{35}$	$\frac{17}{35}$	$\frac{12}{35}$	$-\frac{3}{35}$	
(c)	$y_3(-3)$	$\frac{13}{14}$	$\frac{4}{21}$	$-\frac{2}{21}$	$-\frac{2}{21}$	$\frac{1}{42}$	$\frac{2}{21}$	$-\frac{1}{21}$
	$y_3(-2)$	$\frac{4}{21}$	$\frac{19}{42}$	$\frac{8}{21}$	$\frac{1}{7}$	$-\frac{2}{21}$	$-\frac{1}{6}$	$\frac{2}{21}$
	$y_3(-1)$	$-\frac{2}{21}$	$\frac{8}{21}$	$\frac{19}{42}$	$\frac{2}{7}$	$\frac{1}{21}$	$-\frac{2}{21}$	$\frac{1}{42}$
	$y_3(0)$	$-\frac{2}{21}$	$\frac{1}{7}$	$\frac{2}{7}$	$\frac{1}{3}$	$\frac{2}{7}$	$\frac{1}{7}$	$-\frac{2}{21}$
(d)	$y_5(-3)$	$\frac{923}{924}$	$\frac{1}{154}$	$-\frac{5}{308}$	$\frac{5}{231}$	$-\frac{5}{308}$	$\frac{1}{154}$	$-\frac{1}{924}$
	$y_5(-2)$	$\frac{1}{154}$	$\frac{74}{77}$	$\frac{15}{154}$	$-\frac{10}{77}$	$\frac{15}{154}$	$-\frac{3}{77}$	$\frac{1}{154}$
	$y_5(-1)$	$-\frac{5}{308}$	$\frac{15}{154}$	$\frac{233}{308}$	$\frac{25}{77}$	$-\frac{75}{308}$	$\frac{15}{154}$	$-\frac{5}{308}$
	$y_5(0)$	$\frac{5}{231}$	$-\frac{10}{77}$	$\frac{25}{77}$	$\frac{131}{231}$	$\frac{25}{77}$	$-\frac{10}{77}$	$\frac{5}{231}$

24. (a) $y_1(-1) = f(-1) - \frac{1}{6}\delta^2 f_0$, $y_1(0) = f(0) + \frac{1}{3}\delta^2 f_0$. (b) $y_3(-2) = f(-2) - \delta^4 f_0/70$, $y_3(-1) = f(-1) + 2\delta^4 f_0/35$, $y_3(0) = f(0) - 3\delta^4 f_0/35$; $y_5(-3) = f(-3) - \delta^6 f_0/924$, $y_5(-2) = f(-2) + \delta^6 f_0/154$, $y_5(-1) = f(-1) - 5\delta^6 f_0/308$, $y_5(0) = f(0) + 5\delta^6 f_0/231$.

25. (a) $\{y_i^{(k)}\}$ form a bounded sequence; therefore, there is a convergent subsequence; this subsequence must converge to straight line; but once get straight line no change thereafter; therefore, complete sequence converges to straight line; in general this is not same straight line as would be obtained with n-point linear smoothing. (b) 405, 422, 439, 455, 470, 486, 502, 519, 539, 562, 589, 618, 651, 684, 718, 751, 784, 816, 850, 886, 925, 968, 1013, 1060, 1107, 1154.

26. (a) $-.94335$, $-.99997$, $-.71322$, $-.72802$, $-.26810$, $.21620$, $.99991$; (b) -6.5×10^{-4}, -2.9×10^{-5}, 1.3×10^{-4}, 1.9×10^{-5}, -1.6×10^{-4}, -2.0×10^{-4}, 9.1×10^{-5}.

28. (a) Use formula for sum of geometric series; (b) take real and imaginary parts.

29. (a) In (6.8-1) and (6.8-2) replace $(2L + 1)/2$ by L and $2L + 1$ by $2L$. (b) In (6.8-5), (6.8-6), and (6.8-18) replace $2L + 1$ by $2L$ and $2L$ by $2L - 1$. (c) $a_L = (1/L)\Sigma \bar{f}_i \cos (ij\pi/L)$; $\sin Lx = 0$ at all x_i.

30. (a) $\sigma^2_{\Delta a_k} = 2\sigma^2/(2L + 1)$, $k \neq 0$, $\sigma^2_{\Delta a_0} = 4\sigma^2/(2L + 1)$; $\sigma^2_{\Delta b_k} = 2\sigma^2/(2L + 1)$, all k. (b) $\sigma^2_m = \left(\sum_{i=1}^{m} R_i^2\right)/2(L - m)$. (c) With $m = 2$, $\delta^2_m = 1.4968 \times 10^{-6}$, $\sigma^2_m = .3742 \times 10^{-6}$; $\sigma_{\Delta a_0} \approx 4 \times 10^{-4}$, $\sigma_{\Delta a_k} = \sigma_{\Delta b_k} \approx 2 \times 10^{-4}$.

31. (b) Consider $\sin \frac{1}{2}(x_i - x)\left[\frac{1}{2} + \sum_{j=1}^{L} \cos j(x_i - x)\right]$, multiply out and get telescoping series.

(c) $y_L(x) = (1/2L) \sum_{i=0}^{2L-1} \left[\frac{1}{2}\sin L(x_i - x)\cos \frac{1}{2}(x_i - x)/\sin \frac{1}{2}(x_i - x)\right]f_i$.

32. (a) Show (6.8-27) is exact when $f(x) = 1$, write (6.8-27) for $f(x) = 1$, multiply by $f(x)$, and subtract from (6.8-27) as in text. (b) For x_i near x denominator terms are smallest; $\sin (L + \frac{1}{2})(x_i - x)$ oscillates rapidly; if $f(x)$ changes slowly there is cancellation for those x_i not near x; even for rapidly changing $f(x)$ terms with x_i near x are most important.

33. (a) $a_j = (1/\pi)\int_0^{2\pi} f(x) \cos jx\, dx$; use $h = 2\pi/(2L + 1)$ and note that $f(0) = f(2\pi)$; similarly for b_j. (b) All derivative terms drop out because of periodicity, but this does *not* mean that error term is zero.

34. (a) $a_0 = .0003$, $a_1 = .0002$, $a_2 = .0000$, $a_3 = 1.0002$, $b_1 = 1.0000$, $b_2 = -.0002$, $b_3 = .0001$. (b) -1.5×10^{-4}, 2.8×10^{-4}, -1.1×10^{-4}, 1.5×10^{-4}, -1.6×10^{-4}, -2.8×10^{-5}, 6.8×10^{-5}. (c) 1.69×10^{-7}, -6.6×10^{-4}; roundoff causes negative result from second form of (6.8-18).

35. (a) $y_m(x) = [1/(2L + 1)]\sum_{i=0}^{2L} f_i + [2/(2L + 1)]\sum_{i=0}^{2L}\sum_{j=1}^{m} \{\cos [2\pi ij/(2L + 1)]\cos jx + \sin [2\pi ij/(2L + 1)]\sin jx\}\bar{f}_i$. (b) (i): Let $\alpha_1 = \cos 2\pi/5$, $\alpha_2 = \cos 4\pi/5$, $\beta_1 = \sin 2\pi/5$, $\beta_2 = \sin 4\pi/5$; then $y_1(x_0) = \frac{1}{5}(3\bar{f}_0 + (1 + 2\alpha_1)\bar{f}_1 + (1 + 2\alpha_2)\bar{f}_2 + (1 + 2\alpha_2)\bar{f}_3 + (1 + 2\alpha_1)\bar{f}_4)$, $y_1(x_1) = \frac{1}{5}[(1 + 2\alpha_1)\bar{f}_0 + 3\bar{f}_1 + [1 + 2(\alpha_1\alpha_2 + \beta_1\beta_2)]\bar{f}_2 + [1 + (\alpha_1^2 - \beta_1^2)]\bar{f}_3 + [1 + 2(\alpha_1^2 - \beta_1^2)]\bar{f}_4]$, $y_1(x_2) = \frac{1}{5}[(1 + 2\alpha_2)\bar{f}_0 + [1 + 2(\alpha_1\alpha_2 + \beta_1\beta_2)]\bar{f}_1 + 3\bar{f}_2 + [1 + (\alpha_1^2 - \beta_1^2)]\bar{f}_3 + [1 + 2(\alpha_1\alpha_2 - \beta_1\beta_2)]\bar{f}_4]$.

36. (a) Because results of Prob. 34 indicate that $m = 1$ does not give good approximation (since $a_3 \approx 1$); (b) 1.0006, $-.1192$, 1.5987, $.2115$, $-.6567$, $-.3512$, -1.6827.

37. $\frac{2}{2L + 1} a_0 = \sum_{i=0}^{2L} \bar{f}_i = \frac{2L + 1}{2} A_0 + \sum_{j=1}^{\infty} A_j \sum_{i=0}^{2L} \cos jx_i + \sum_{j=1}^{\infty} B_j \sum_{i=0}^{2L} \sin jx_i$; then use result of Prob. 28c. (b) Again use Prob. 28c.

38. (b) $c_k = (1/2\Omega)\int_{-\Omega}^{\Omega} F_1(\lambda)e^{-(i\pi k\lambda/\Omega)}\, d\lambda$; then use expression for $f(t)$ as inverse

Fourier transform. (c) Calculate $\int_{-\infty}^{\infty} P(\lambda)e^{2\pi i\lambda x}\,d\lambda$. (d) Substitute series for $F(\lambda)$ in part b into inverse transform, interchange summation and integration and then use part c.

Chapter 7

2. (a) (i) $q_6(y) = y\{y[(y^2 - 3)(y^2 + y + 2) + 8] + 9\} + 12$ where $y = x - 1$; (ii) $q_5(y) = (y^2 - 5)[(y^2 - 5)(y + 1) + 2] + 43$ where $y = x + 2$. (b) The degree of (7.2-8) may still be even after one synthetic division, but after two it will surely be odd.

3. (b) $(x^2 - 1)[(x^2 + 39)(x + 11) - 382] + 91$.

4. (b)

(m,k):	(2,2)	(3,2)	(3,3)	(4,3)	(4,4)	(5,4)
Poly. eval.:	6	7	8	9	10	11
Cont. frac.:	4	5	6	7	8	9
(m,k):	(5,5)	(6,5)	(6,6)			
Poly. eval.:	12	13	14			
Cont. frac.:	10	11	12			

5. (a) $p = \frac{1}{2}(A - 1)$; $a = B' - 2q$ with $B' = B - p(p + 1)$; $r + s = C' - q$ with $C' = C - pB'$; $r = q^2 + D'q + D''$ with $D' = -B' + p$, $D'' = D - pC'$; $-2q^3 - q^2(1 - B' + 2D') - q(-B'D' + 2D'' - C') + B'D'' - E = 0$.
(b) Express $P(x)$ in terms of a, b, c, d, e, f and match coefficients using equations of part a. (c) $y = x(x + 3)$, $w = (y - 7)(x + 3)$, $P = (w + y + 15)(w + 16) - 27$; this solution corresponds to root $q = 2$ of $2q^3 - 8q^2 + 2q + 12 = 0$; corresponding to two other real roots there are two other solutions.

6. Show valid for $n = 2^k$ for any k; then for $2^k \leq n < 2^{k+1}$ use induction; to get code word for $r + 1$ from that for r start from right changing each SX to S until come to first S; change this to SX; then show new code word results in one higher power of x than old.

7. By long division; then let $q_j = b_{k-j}/b_k$; calculate s_j's from $\sum\limits_{i=0}^{k} b_i s_{r-i-1} = a_r$,

$r = m, \ldots, k + 1$ with $s_j = 0, j > m - k - 1$; calculate p_j's from $\sum\limits_{i=0}^{k} b_i s_{r-i-1}$

$+ p_{k-r} = a_r, r = 0, \ldots, k$ with $s_j = 0, j < 0$. (b) $D_0 = p_0, C_1 = p_1 - p_0 q_1$; degenerate case if $C_1 = 0$. (c) $\bar{q}_{j+1} + \bar{p}_j = q_j, j = 1, \ldots, k - 1$; $\bar{p}_k = q_k$; $p_0 \bar{q}_{j+1} + p_0 \bar{p}_j + (p_1 - p_0 q_1)\bar{q}_j = p_j, j = 1, \ldots, k - 1; (p_1 - p_0 q_1)\bar{q}_k + p_0 \bar{p}_k = p_k$; calculate $\bar{p}_k, \bar{q}_k, \bar{p}_{k-1}, \bar{q}_{k-1}$, etc.

8. (a) In place of $C_0 x$ have $x\left(\sum\limits_{j=0}^{m-k-1} s_j x^j\right)$. (c) $m > k + 1$: k divisions, $m - k$ multiplications; $m < k$: $m + 1$ divisions, $k - m$ multiplications. (d) $2 + 3/[x - 1 + 2/(x - 2)]$.

9. With d = division, same time (2,2) and (3,3), $d = 2$, (5,5), $d = 1\frac{1}{2}$; rational faster (2,2) and (3,3), $d \geq 2\frac{1}{4}$, (4,4), $d \geq 1\frac{1}{2}$, (5,5), $d \geq 1\frac{3}{4}$; continued fraction faster in all other cases.

10. (b) (7.3-5) with $s = 0$ is $c_2 b_0 + c_1 b_1 = 0$ but $c_1 = 0$ and $b_0 = 1, c_2 = -\frac{1}{2}$.

11. Consider $f(x) - [P_{m-1}^{(m-1,k)}(x) + DxP_{m-1}^{(m-1,k-1)}(x)]/[Q_k^{(m-1,k)}(x) + DxQ_{k-1}^{(m-1,k-1)}(x)]$ and show that D can be chosen so that this is $f(x) - R_{mk}(x)$; $D = d_N^{(m-1,k)}/d_{N-1}^{(m-1,k-1)}$; $E = d_N^{(m,k-1)}/d_{N-1}^{(m-1,k-1)}$.

12. (b) $R_{33}(z) = (a_0 + a_1z + a_2z^2 + a_3z^3)/(1 + b_1z + b_2z^2 + b_3z^3)$ where $a_0 = 1, a_1 = -3665 \times 10!/A, a_2 = 19,197 \times 8!/A, a_3 = -14,615 \times 6!/A, b_1 = 229 \times 10!/A, b_2 = 297 \times 8!/A, b_3 = 127 \times 6!/A$ with $A = 59 \times 12!$.

(c) $D_0 = -14,615/127 \approx -115.1$; rest of continued fraction must add to D_0 to get result less than 1 in magnitude.   (d) $d_7 = 45,469/(38,940 \times 14!)$.

13. (a) $b_1 = 10!(229 - 76\xi)/\lambda, b_2 = 8!(297 - 42\xi)/\lambda, b_3 = 127 \times 6!,$
$a_3 = 6!(-14,615 + 16,632\xi)/\lambda$ where $\lambda = 12!(59 - 34\xi)$.

(b) $c_0 = -\xi, D_0 = (-2352\xi^2 + 33,264\xi - 14,615)/127$.

(c) $d_7 = (45,469 + 9336\xi)/[(59 - 34\xi)660 \times 14!]$.   (d) $\xi \approx +.45, +13.69$; latter value gives smaller value of d_7.

14. (a) For the interior arguments use induction.   (b) Any permutation of arguments can be changed back to $x_1, \ldots, x_k$ by interchanging interior arguments, end arguments, and first two arguments.

15. (b)

.3	−1.203973				
	.347606				
.4	−.916291	1.073065			
	.448141		1.769896		
.5	−.693147	1.300036		2.288830	
	.548483		2.174429		2.535369
.6	−.510826	1.484544		2.469300		3.116367
	.648715		2.580621		2.923609
.7	−.356675	1.639831		2.640794	
	.748890		2.980236		
.8	−.223144	1.774279			
	.849019				
.9	−.105361				

16. (a) $f(x) = f(x_1) + (x - x_1)/\rho_1(x,x_1) = f(x_1) + (x - x_1)/\{\rho(x_1,x_2) + (x - x_2)/[\rho_2(x,x_1,x_2) - \rho_0(x_1)]\}$ etc,   (b) When $x = x_i$ continued fraction from $x - x_i$ on is zero.   (c) Convergents are $-.693147, -.620219, -.616209$; true value $-.616186$.

17. (a) From definition of $\rho_1(x_1,x_2)$.   (b) Last equality follows from definition of partial derivative.   (c) $1/(\partial/\partial x)\rho_{j-1}(x, \ldots ,x) = (1/j)/(d/dx)\rho_{j-1}(x, \ldots ,x) = jR_1R_{j-1}f(x)$.

18. (a) Use Prob. 17c.   (b) $r_{2n}(0) = (2n + 1); r_{2n+1}(0) = 2/(n + 1)$; convergents of $\ln .54$: $-.46, -.597403, -.612593, -.615714$.   (c) $r_{2n}(0) = (-1)^{n+1}2, r_{2n+1}(0) = (-1)^n(2n + 1)$; convergents of e: $1, 2, 3, 2.75, 271143$.

19. (a) Show $Q^2(z)y(z)$ has degree $n - 1$; show $F(z)$ has $n + 1$ zeros; take nth derivative of $F(z)$ and use Rolle's theorem.   (b) $p_n(x) \to (x - a)^n$; rest is unchanged.   (c) In both cases approximation has same functional value and same first $n - 1$ derivatives as $f(x)$ at $x = 0$.

20. (b)

(m,k):	(4,0)	(3,1)	(2,2)	(1.3)	(0,4)
d_5:	$\frac{1}{120}$	$-\frac{1}{480}$	$\frac{1}{720}$	$-\frac{1}{480}$	$\frac{1}{120}$

21. (a) $\sin x$: $R_{5,0}(x) = x - x^3/6 + x^5/120, R_{3,2}(x) = (x - 7x^3/60)/(1 + x^2/20),$
$R_{1,4}(x) = x/(1 + x^2/6 + 7x^4/360)$; $\cos x$: $R_{4,0}(x) = 1 - x^2/2 + x^4/24, R_{2,2}(x) = (1 - 5x^2/12)/(1 + x^2/12), R_{0,4}(x) = 1/(1 + x^2/2 + 5x^4/24)$.   (b) Take remainder y of $x/2\pi$; if $y \,\varepsilon\, [\pi,2\pi]$ consider $y - 2\pi$; then reduce to interval $[-(\pi/2),\pi/2]$; if magnitude of y less than $\pi/4$ compute $\sin y$; otherwise compute $\cos (\pi/2 - y)$;

then adjust sign; algorithm for cosine similar; the Padé approximation is more accurate the smaller the argument. (c) Magnitude of errors at $\pm\pi/4$: $R_{5,0}(x)$: 3.6×10^{-5}; $R_{3,2}(x)$: 3.8×10^{-5}; $R_{1,4}(x)$: 3.3×10^{-4}; $R_{4,0}(x)$: 3.2×10^{-4}; $R_{2,2}(x)$: 4.5×10^{-4}; $R_{0,4}(x)$: 1.4×10^{-2}.

22. (a) $R_{2,2}(x) = 1 + 12/(x - 6 + 12/x)$.

(b)

	$R_{4,0}$	$R_{3,1}$	$R_{2,2}$	$R_{1,3}$	$R_{0,4}$
Cont. fract. (M/D):	$3/0$	$2/1$	$0/2$	$2/2$	$3/1$
Rat. fnct. (M/D):	$3/0$	$3/1$	$2/1$	$3/1$	$3/1$

(c) (i) $R_{2,2}$ by continued fraction; (ii) $R_{2,2}$ by continued fraction or $R_{4,0}$; (iii) $R_{4,0}$.

23. (a) Use $y = \frac{1}{2}(x + 1)$; $T_r^*(x) = T_r(2x - 1) = \cos\, r\theta$. (b) $T_{r+1}^*(x) = (4x - 2)T_r^*(x) - T_{r-1}^*(x)$; $T_0^*(x) = 1$; $T_1^*(x) = 2x - 1$; $T_2^*(x) = 8x^2 - 8x + 1$; $T_3^*(x) = 32x^3 - 48x^2 + 18x - 1$; $T_4^*(x) = 128x^4 - 256x^3 + 160x^2 - 32x + 1$; $T_5^*(x) = 512x^5 - 1280x^4 + 1120x^3 - 400x^2 + 50x - 1$; $T_6^*(x) = 2048x^6 - 6144x^5 + 6912x^4 - 3584x^3 + 640x^2 - 72x + 1$. (c) $T_r^*(x)/2^{2r-1}$ has smallest magnitude on $(0,1)$ of all polynomials of degree r with leading coefficient 1; proof same as for Theorem 7.1.

24. (a) Use recurrence relation and induction on i; consider only even $i - j$. (b) Proceed as in part a.

25. (a) Use (7.5-1).

26. (a) $\bar{c}_0 \approx 2.532132$; $\bar{c}_1 \approx 1.130318$; $\bar{c}_2 \approx .271498$; $\bar{c}_3 \approx .044382$; $\bar{c}_4 \approx .006017$. (b) Coefficients: 1.000584; .997172; .494859; .177528; .048137; maximum error on $[-1,1]$: -1.0×10^{-3} at -1.

27. (a) Use change of variable $x = \sin\,\theta$ and integrate term by term. (b) $c_0 \approx 2.532118$, $c_1 \approx 1.130317$, $c_2 \approx .271484$; $c_3 \approx .044336$, $c_4 \approx .005469$. (c) Coefficients: 1.000044; .997309; .499216; .177344; .043752; maximum error on $[-1,1]$: 6.2×10^{-4} at $+1$.

28. (a) For $\sin\,x$: $c_{2k} = 0$; $c_{2k+1} = 2(-1)^k J_{2k+1}(1)$; for $\cos\,x$: $c_{2k+1} = 0$; $c_{2k} = 2(-1)^k J_{2k}(1)$; $\sin\,x \approx .999980x - .166504x^3 + .008000x^5$; $\cos x \approx .999958 - .499244x^2 + .039632x^4$; maximum error on $[-(\pi/4),\pi/4]$: $\sin x$: 2.8×10^{-6}; $\cos x$: 4.2×10^{-5}. (b) $T_{3,2}(x) = [.890848T_1(x) - .027874T_3(x)]/[1 + .025556T_2(x)] = (1.000027x - .114420x^3)/(1 + .052452x^2)$; maximum error on $[-(\pi/4),\pi/4]$: 3.9×10^{-6}. (c) $T_{2,2}(x) = [.760245 - .196714T_2(x)]/[1 + .043107T_2(x)] = (1.000069 - .411152x^2)/(1 + .090098x^2)$; maximum error on $[-(\pi/4),\pi/4]$: 6.9×10^{-5}.

29. $T_{3,1}(x) = (.999877 + .756693x + .256442x^2 + .042212x^3)/(1 - .243945x)$; maximum error on $[-1,1]$: 3.1×10^{-4}; $T_{1,3}(x) = (1.000068 + .247144x)/(1 - .753525x + .252980x^2 - .040644x^3)$; maximum error on $[-1,1]$: 4.2×10^{-4}.

30. (a) $C_{N,0}(x) = R_{N+2,0}(x) - d_{N+2}\alpha^{N+2}T_{N+2}(x/\alpha)/2^{N+1}$. (b) $C_{5,0}(x) = .999995x - .166601x^3 + .008119x^5$; maximum error on $[-(\pi/4),\pi/4]$: 6.3×10^{-7}. (c) $C_{4,0}(x) = .999990 - .499703x^2 + .040382x^4$; maximum error on $[-(\pi/4),\pi/4]$: 1.1×10^{-5}.

31. (a) $C_{2,2}(x) = (2281 + 1128x + 180x^2)/(2281 - 1152x + 192x^2)$; maximum error on $[-1,1]$: 1.4×10^{-3} at $+1$. (b) $C_{2,2}(x) = (2281 + 1152x + 192x^2)/(2281 - 1128x + 180x^2)$; maximum error on $[-1,1]$: -1.1×10^{-3} at $+1$; choice of second and fourth rational functions doesn't matter since $\gamma_2 = \gamma_4 = 0$.

32. (a) Using $R_{0,0}, R_{1,0}, R_{1,1}, R_{2,1}, R_{3,1}$: $C_{3,1}(x) = (1487 + 1128x + 384x^2 + 64x^3)/(1487 - 360x)$; using $R_{1,2}, R_{3,1}$: $C_{1,3}(x) = (1487 + 384x)/(1487 - 1128x + 384x^2 - 64x^3)$; maximum errors on $[-1,1]$: $C_{3,1}(x)$: 5.4×10^{-4}; $C_{1,3}(x)$: 1.9×10^{-3}. (b) Only requires computation of γ_1; not necessarily equal to $C_{3,2}(x)$. (c) $xC_{1,1}(x^2) = [(1 + \gamma_1)x - 7x^3/60]/(1 + \gamma_1 + x^2/20)$ where $\gamma_1 = 3\pi^4/716,800$; maximum error

on $[-(\pi/4),\pi/4]: 8.3 \times 10^{-6}$.   (d) $C_{1,1}(x^2) = (1 + \gamma_1 - 5x^2/12)/(1 + \gamma_1 + x^2/12)$ where $\gamma_1 = \pi^4/81,920$; maximum error on $[-(\pi/4),\pi/4]$: 1.2×10^{-4}.

33. (a) $y = x - .505$; $R_{2,2}(y) = (.710634 + .831642y - .200409y^2)/(1 + .180184y + .029733y^2)$; maximum error for $x \, \varepsilon \, [.01,1]$: $-.172$ at .01.   (b) $C_{2,2}(y) = (1.04357 + 1.31879y - .20041y^2)/(1.46850 + .40869y + .02973y^2)$;   maximum   error   for $x \, \varepsilon \, [.01,1]$: $-.168$ at .01.

34. (a) Use shifted Chebyshev polynomials.   (b) $C_{2,2}^*(x) = (1.211504 + .646267x + .125000x^2)/(1.211507 - .565104x + .083333x^2)$; maximum error on $[0,1]$: 1.2×10^{-3} at 1.

35. (a) From differential equation get $D + 1$ equations; from initial conditions n equations.   (b) $D - m + n$ τ_i's give $D + n + 1$ total   unknowns.   (c) Using $L(y) = y' - y$, $y(0) = 1$ get $y(x) = 1 + 1824x/1825 + 928x^2/1825 + 256x^3/1825 + 128x^4/1825$; maximum error on $[0,1]$: 9.9×10^{-5}.

36. Use partial fractions.

37. (a) Choose $R_{mk}^{(i)}(x)$ such that $r_{mk}^{(i)} = r + 1/i$.   (b) Let $|R_{mk}^{(i)}(x)| < G$ on $[a,b]$; choose any $m + 1$ points $\xi_1, \ldots, \xi_{m+1}$ in (a,b); then $|P(\xi_i)/Q(\xi_i)| \le G + \max\limits_{[a,b]} f(x)$;

since Q normalized $|P(\xi_i)|$ is bounded; polynomial of degree m bounded at $m + 1$ fixed points is such that all its coefficients are bounded; therefore, convergent subsequence exists.   (c) $R(x) = f(x) + R^{(i)}(x) - f(x) + R(x) - R^{(i)}(x)$; therefore, $|R| < f + |R^{(i)} - f| + |R - R^{(i)}|$; $R = \lim\limits_{i \to \infty} R^{(i)}$ except perhaps at finite number

of points where denominator is zero; except at these points $|R| < \max f + r_i + \epsilon_i$ where $\epsilon_i \to 0$ as $i \to \infty$; therefore, $|R(x)|$ is bounded except at a finite number of points; therefore, $R^{(i)}(x)$ converges uniformly to R.   (d) $\max \; |f - R| \le \max \; |f - R_i| + \max \; |R_i - R| \le r$, therefore, $\bar{r} \le r$ but $\bar{r} \ge r$ also since r is assumed minimum.

38. (a) Since $\Delta = [f - R^{(2)}] - [f - R^{(1)}]$ and α_i's are extrema of $f - R^{(2)}$.   (b) Use properties of $R^{(2)}$ to deduce that $\Delta(\alpha_{i-1})$ and $\Delta(\alpha_{i+k+1})$ have same sign if k is even, different signs if k odd.   (c) Apply result of part b.   (d) Show degree of numerator of Δ no greater than $L_2 - 2$.

39. (a) Each step of each proof is unchanged by the introduction of $s(x)$.   (b) Multiply rational functions in (7.9-2) and (7.9-3) by $s(x)$.

40. Best constant approximation is $\frac{1}{2}$; show that no ratio of linear approximations could be better.

41. (a) $R_{1,1}(x) = (1 + \frac{1}{2}x)/(1 - \frac{1}{2}x)$.   (b) $C_{1,1}(x) = (^{17}\!/_{16} + \frac{1}{2}x)/(^{17}\!/_{16} - \frac{1}{2}x)$; extrema at -1.0, $-.43$, $.59$, 1.0.   (c) $R_{1,1}^*(x) \approx (1.017024 + .517541x)/(1.0 - .439785x)$ after two iterations; maximum error .020972.

Chapter 8

1. (b) $g' = 1/y'$; $g'' = -y''/(y')^3$; $g''' = [-y'''y' + 3(y'')^2]/(y')^5$.

2. (a) If $C > 1$ then a small error would tend to grow if order is 1; if order greater than 1 then $|\epsilon_{i+1}| \approx C|\epsilon_i|^p$ will be smaller than $|\epsilon_i|$ if $|\epsilon_i|$ is sufficiently small even if $C > 1$; need "or equal" part for case where $\epsilon_{i+1} = (1 - 1/i)\epsilon_i$.   (b) No; for any C, $|\epsilon_{i+1}| > C|\epsilon_i|^p$ if $p < 1$ and $|\epsilon_i|$ sufficiently small.

3. Set $S_i = \rho^i$ in homogeneous part; get $\rho = p_i$; then get particular solution.

4. (a) 25 for $f(x)$; 5 more for $f'(x)$; if evaluations of elementary functions are saved $f'(x)$ will usually be easy to calculate.   (b) Since evaluation of $f(x)$ is of no use for $f'(x)$ the relative costs are $(n - 1)/(n - 2)$.

5. (a) Assume contrary and use fact that sequence of iterates is bounded.   (b) Use a geometric argument.

6. $3\pi/4$, $5\pi/8$, $9\pi/16$, $19\pi/32$, $39\pi/64$, $77\pi/128$.

7. (b) Plausibility because $\gamma_{i+1} \approx (1 + \sqrt{5})\gamma_i/2$.

8. (a) (i) $x_7 = .517747$; (ii) $x_7 = .515201$; true value: $.51775737$. (b) $x_7 = .85705674$; true value: $.85705677$. (c) Equation in y is $y \cot y = \ln y - \ln \sin y$; with $y_1 = 1$, $y_2 = 2$, $y_7 = 1.3372355$, true value: 1.3372356, true value of x is $.3181316$.

9. (a) Use (8.4-7) to calculate Y'_{i-1}; from this get (8.4-10); similarly, use (8.4-11) to calculate D'_{i-1}. (b) Use induction, (8.4-10) and (8.4-12).

10. (b) $I_{m0}(x) = x - \sum_{j=0}^{m} Z_j(x)$. (c) Use recurrence relation in expression for I'_{m0} and get telescoping series.

11. (a) Use error term in (8.4-6) and (8.4-7). (b) Expand $f(x)$ and $f'(x)$ in Taylor series about α. (c) $\nu_2 = -A_2$; $\nu_3 = -2A_2^2 + 2A_3$; $\nu_4 = -3A_4 + 7A_2A_3 - 4A_2^3$.

12. (a) $I_{m0}(x_i) = \alpha - (-1)^{m+1}Y_{m+1}(\alpha)\epsilon_i^{m+2} + O(\epsilon_i^{m+3})$; result expected because I_{m0} has order $m + 2$. (c) Define $I_{-1,0} = x_i = \alpha - \epsilon_i$. (d) $\tau_{10} = 0$; $\tau_{20} = A_2$; $\tau_{30} = 2A_2^2 - 2A_3$; $\tau_{40} = 3A_4 - 7A_2A_3 + 4A_2^3$; $\tau_{11} = \tau_{21} = 0$; $\tau_{31} = A_3 - 2A_2^2$; $\tau_{41} = -3A_4 + 12A_2A_3 - 9A_2^3$; $\tau_{12} = \tau_{22} = \tau_{32} = 0$; $\tau_{42} = A_4 - 5A_2A_3 + 5A_2^3$.

13. (a) $f(x_{i+1}) = f(x_i) + (x_{i+1} - x_i)f'(x_i)$.
(b) $f(\alpha) = f(x_i) + (\alpha - x_i)f'(x_i) + \frac{1}{2}(\alpha - x_i)^2 f''(\xi)$.

14. (a) $C_1 = [f''(\alpha)/2f'(\alpha)]^{(1+\sqrt{5})/2}$; $C_2 = [f''(\alpha)/2f'(\alpha)]$. (b) Get $[(1 + \sqrt{5})/2]^I = 2^J$; $I/J = \ln 2/\ln [(1 + \sqrt{5})/2]$.

16. (b) For x_2 the errors are less than 7×10^{-3}; since the methods are fourth order the errors in x_3 are approximately C times the fourth power of the error in x_2. (c) $H_2 = Y_2$ for I_{10}; $H_2 = Y_2 - Y_1^2$ for I_{01}; $C_{10} = (n - 1)(2n - 1)/6\alpha^2$; $C_{01} = (n^2 - 1)/12\alpha^2$; $C_{10}/C_{01} \to 4$ as $n \to \infty$; I_{10}: $x_2 = 1.4375$, $x_3 = 1.4142166$; I_{20}: $x_2 = 1.4285714$, $x_3 = 1.4142139$.

17. (a) (i) $x_6 = .51775740$; (ii) method diverges, try $x_1 = .25$; (iii) $x_4 = .51775737$. (b) (i) $x_9 = .85705679$; (ii) $x_6 = .85705679$; (iii) $x_3 = .85705679$; for faster convergence in all three cases try $x_1 = .25$.

18. (a) Newton: $x_{11} = 1.5882040$; Halley: $x_7 = 1.5849805$; true value: 1.5848933. (b) Use $f(x) = 1/x - a$ for reciprocal of a; $x_{11} = .0999966$; Halley's method can't be used because it needs division. (c) Draw the graph of $1/x - 10$.

19. (a) True value: 1.2572742; (i) $x_5 = 1.2572742$; (ii) $x_3 = 1.2572742$; (iii) $x_4 = 1.2572742$. (b) True value: $.3311944$; (i) $x_7 = .3311944$; (ii) $x_6 = .3311944$; (iii) $x_6 = .3311944$.

20. (a) Use Theorem 8.1; $G^{(j)}(\alpha) = 0$, $j = 1, \ldots, p - 1$ if $U(\alpha)$ is bounded; $G^{(p)}(\alpha) \neq 0$ if $U(\alpha) \neq -F^{(p)}(\alpha)/p!$.

21. Show $\epsilon_{i+1} = [1 - Cf'(x_i)]\epsilon_i + O(\epsilon_i^2)$.

22. (a) Use second equation to compute $(x_{i+1} - \alpha)f'(x_i)/(y_i - \alpha)$. (b) Use first equation and error in Newton-Raphson method. (c) Order is 3; to get from x_i to x_{i+1} need two function evaluations, one derivative; more efficient than Newton-Raphson if $\theta_1 < .71$; more efficient than secant if $\theta_1 < .28$. (d) $x_4 = .51775738$.

23. (a) Expand f/f' in powers of ϵ_i and manipulate remaining expression so that powers through third vanish. (c) Let Kiss iteration function be K; show that $I_{02} - K$ is $O(u_1^4)$.

24. (a) Proceed as in derivation of (8.3-17). (b) Solve $\gamma_{i+1} = \gamma_i + \gamma_{i-1} + \gamma_{i-2}$, $\gamma_0 = \gamma_1 = \gamma_2 = 1$; positive root of $r^3 - r^2 - r - 1 = 0$ is 1.839. (c) 2.732.

25. (a) $x_{i+1} = (f(x_{i-1})f(x_{i-2})/\{[f(x_i) - f(x_{i-1})][f(x_i) - f(x_{i-2})]\})x_i$
$+ (f(x_i)f(x_{i-2})/\{[f(x_{i-1}) - f(x_i)][f(x_{i-1}) - f(x_{i-2})]\})x_{i-1}$
$+ (f(x_i)f(x_{i-1})/\{[f(x_{i-2}) - f(x_i)][f(x_{i-2}) - f(x_{i-1})]\})x_{i-2}$.

(b) $x_{i+1} = \{1/[f(x_i) - f(x_{i-1})]^3\}\{[3f(x_i) - f(x_{i-1})][f(x_{i-1})]^2x_i - [3f(x_{i-1}) - f(x_i)][f(x_i)]^2x_{i-1}\} - \{[f(x_i)f(x_{i-1})]/[f(x_i) - f(x_{i-1})]^3\}[f(x_{i-1})/f'(x_i) + f(x_i)/f'(x_{i-1})]$.
(c) Part a with $x_1 = 0$, $x_2 = 1$, $x_3 = 2$, get $x_9 = .51775736$; part b with $x_1 = 0$, $x_2 = 1$, get $x_6 = .51775733$.

26. (a) Since $f'(x) \neq 0$, $f(x)$ has different signs at x_{i-n}, x_i; therefore, polynomial which goes through $f(x_{i-j})$, $j = 0, \ldots, n$ must have zero in interval but need not be unique. (b) Set $x = \alpha$ in (8.5-1) and use mean-value theorem.

27. (a) Use a two-point Lagrangian formula; (b) Use a one-point Hermite formula.

28. (a) In three-point Lagrangian formula set $x = x_{i+1}$ and solve for $(x_{i+1} - x_i)/(x_i - x_{i-1})$. (c) Same difference equation as in Prob. 24b; order is 1.84. (d) With $x_1 = 0$, $x_2 = 1$, $x_3 = 2$, get $x_8 = .51775738$.

29. (c) (8.5-25) is of form (8.5-8) with $n = 2$, $r_1 = r_2 = 1$.

30. (a) $x_{i+1} = x_i - f_i/\bar{f}'_i$ where $\bar{f}'_i = (2x_i - x_{i-1} - x_{i-2})f_i/(x_i - x_{i-1})(x_i - x_{i-2}) + (x_i - x_{i-2})f_{i-1}/(x_{i-1} - x_i)(x_{i-1} - x_{i-2}) + (x_i - x_{i-1})f_{i-2}/(x_{i-2} - x_i)(x_{i-2} - x_{i-1})$.
(b) If F_1 is Newton-Raphson and F_2 is function of part a, then $\epsilon_{i+1} = \alpha - F_2 = \frac{1}{2}f''(\xi)\epsilon_i^2/f'_i - f_if_i'''(x_i - x_{i-1})(x_i - x_{i-2})/6f'_i\bar{f}'_i$; dominant term is in $\epsilon_i\epsilon_{i-1}\epsilon_{i-2}$.
(c) With $x_1 = 0$, $x_2 = 1$, $x_3 = 2$, get $x_9 = .51775738$; no square roots needed.

31. (c) Use induction. (d) If $r \neq 1$, $(1/r - 1)_{m+1} \neq 0$.

32. (a) With $m = 0$ in (8.6-10) get $\epsilon_{i+1} \approx (1 - 1/r)\epsilon_i$. (b) $x_{10} = .5121$, $x_{20} = .51766$.

33. (a) $x_8 = .51775737$; (b) $x_6 = .51775737$.

34. (a) $f(x)$ has same sign on both sides of root. (b) Suppose x_1 and x_2 are such that $f(x_1) = f(x_2)$.

35. $x_{i+1} = -x_i^2/(1 - x_i)$; therefore, $x_i < 0$, $i = 2, 3, \ldots$; but magnitude of x_{i+1} less than that of x_i

36. (a) $x_{i+1} - x_i = F(x_i) - x_i$ which approaches zero as $x_i \to \alpha$.
(b) $|x_{i+1} - x_i|/|x_{i+1}|$.

37. (a) $x_{i+1} = 19x_i/20 + 1/20x_i^{19}$; show that if $x_i > 1$ then $x_{i+1} < x_i$ and $x_{i+1} > 1$.
(b) $x_2 = .75$, $x_3 = 1.125$, $x_8 = 1.0000039$.

38. (a) Compute $\alpha - x_{i+2}$, $\alpha - x_{i+1}$; then from $\epsilon_{i+2} = (1 - 1/r)\epsilon_{i+1} + 0(\epsilon_i^2)$ get $\epsilon_{i+2}/\epsilon_{i+1} \approx 1 - 1/r$. (b) Five iterations are enough to determine $r = 3$; then using (8.6-13) with $x_1 = 0$ get $x_7 = .51775738$.

39. (a) Use $F_i[x^{(1)}, x^{(2)}, y^{(1)}, y^{(2)}] = y^{(i)} - f_i[x^{(1)}, x^{(2)}]$, $i = 1, 2$. (b) Get two simultaneous equations for $x_{i+1}^{(1)} - x_i^{(1)}$ and $x_{i+1}^{(2)} - x_i^{(2)}$. (c) $\frac{1}{2}d^2\mathbf{g}(\boldsymbol{\xi} - \mathbf{y}_i)$; components have form of products of two components of $\mathbf{y}_i$; therefore, components of $\boldsymbol{\epsilon}_{i+1}$ have form of sum of products of components of $\boldsymbol{\epsilon}_i$. (d) Definition: Order p if lim $|\boldsymbol{\epsilon}_{i+1}|/|\boldsymbol{\epsilon}_i|^p = C \neq 0$; use result of part c to get order of 2 for (8.8-10).

40. $e^x \cos y = x$; $e^x \sin y = y$; $x_5^{(1)} = .3181316$, $x_5^{(2)} = 1.3372354$.

41. (a) Does not converge. (b) Converges to $x_4 = .35725$, $y_4 = 2.78575$.

42. (a) $z = ax + by + c$ where $a = D_a/D$, $b = D_b/D$, $c = D_c/C$ with $D_a = |f_{i-k}^{(1)}, y_{i-k}, 1|$, $D_b = |x_{i-k}, f_{i-k}^{(1)}, 1|$, $D_c = |x_{i-k}, y_{i-k}, f_{i-k}^{(1)}|$, $D = |x_{i-k}, y_{i-k}, 1|$; second plane similar replacing superscript 1 by 2 to get $z = dx + ey + f$. (b) $x_{i+1} = (cd - af)/(ae - bd)$, $y_{i+1} = (bf - ce)/(ae - bd)$; fails if points are collinear. (c) After 10 iterations $x = .317692$, $y = 1.338849$; there is no always convergent analog of false position in more than one dimension.

43. (a) $\pi_0 + \pi_1 = 1$, $\pi_0 f_i + \pi_1 f_{i-1} = 0$; solve to get secant. (b) $f_k(\mathbf{x}_{i+1}) = (G_k, \mathbf{x}_{i+1} - \boldsymbol{\alpha}) + \frac{1}{2}(\mathbf{x}_{i+1} - \boldsymbol{\alpha})^T Q_k(\mathbf{x}_{i+1} - \boldsymbol{\alpha})$ and $\mathbf{x}_{i+1} - \boldsymbol{\alpha} = \Sigma\pi_j(\mathbf{x}_{i-j} - \boldsymbol{\alpha})$. (c) $f_k(\mathbf{x}_{i-j}) = (G_k, \mathbf{x}_{i-j} - \boldsymbol{\alpha}) + (\mathbf{x}_{i-j} - \boldsymbol{\alpha})^T Q_k(\mathbf{x}_{i-j} - \boldsymbol{\alpha})$; can't infer quadratic convergence because behavior of π_j's is unknown. (d) After five iterations $x = .3181320$, $y = 1.3372355$; rule is reasonable because in a sense it removes worst approximation.

44. (a) Draw a picture. (b) After four iterations $x = .3181315$, $y = 1.3372356$.

45. Use partial fractions.

46. (a) $f_m(x)$ is greatest common divisor of f and f'; therefore, find multiplicity of zero in $f_m(x)$ and add 1. (b) If $f(a) = 0$, $f(a + \epsilon)$ has same sign as $f'(a)$; if $f(b) = 0$, $f(b - \epsilon)$ has opposite sign of $f'(b)$; if zeros are multiple then each $f_i(x) = 0$.

47. (a) Yes; Cauchy index, $V(a)$ and $V(b)$ unchanged. (b) Sturm if $f_m(x)$ does not vanish; if $f_m(x)$ does vanish generalized Sturm sequence with $p(x) = f_m(x)$; for rational function let numerator and denominator be $f(x)$ and $g(x)$, respectively.

48. (a) 1 positive, 1 negative; (b) 1.

49. (a) On Γ, $\bar{z}^{-1} = z$. (b) Suppose $T[f(\xi)] = 0$; but this implies from part a that $|\bar{a}_0| = |a_n|$, which implies $T[f(0)] = 0$. (c) On Γ, $|T[f(z)]| = |f(z)|(|a_n| - |\bar{a}_0|) < 0$; therefore, $\bar{a}_0 f(z)$ and $T[f(z)]$ have same number of zeros inside Γ by Rouche's theorem. (d) Use Rouche's theorem again. (e) From parts c and d. (f) Suppose $T^h < 0$; then f, T^1, . . . , T^{h-1} have same number, say m, zeros inside Γ; T^h has $d_{h-1} - m$ inside Γ where d_{h-1} is degree of T^{h-1}; but $d_h \geqq d_{h-1} - m$; therefore, $m \geqq d_{h-1} - d_h > 0$; if all $T^h > 0$ then all have same number of zeros as T^{k-1} which has none.

50. (a) Show each adjacent pair of circles intersect outside of $R \leqq |z| \leqq 2R$. (b) $[3/2 \cos (\pi/8)][R + \frac{2}{5}R + (\frac{2}{5}R)^2 + \cdots] = 5R/2 \cos (\pi/8)$.

51. (a) First step ended by zero at $\pm 3i/2$; second step ended by zero at 2. (b) $T[f(z)] \equiv 0$; try $R = 1 + \delta$.

52. True value: $.2878155 + 1.4160932i$ (see Prob. 60e).

53. (b) $a_j^{(r)} = (-1)^{n-i} S_{n-j}(a_1^{2r}, \ldots, a_n^{2r}) = (-1)^{n-i} \Sigma_c \alpha_{i_1}^{2r} \times \cdots \times \alpha_{i_{n-j}}^{2r}$
   (c) Magnitude of dominant term in $s_{n-j}^{(r)}$ is $(\rho_1 \cdots \rho_j)^{2r}$ when (8.10-18) holds; for general case consider dominant terms in $a_{n-\mu_j}^{(r)}$ and $a_{n-\mu_j+1}^{(r)}$.

54. (a) If $z + pz + \rho^2$ is a factor then $qb_0 = a_0$; zeros are $\rho e^{\pm i\theta}$; $(z - \rho e^{i\theta})(z - \rho e^{-i\theta}) = z^2 - 2\rho \cos \theta + \rho^2$; therefore, $p^2 = 4\rho^2 \cos^2 \theta \leqq 4q$; if $a_0 = qb_0$ and $p^2 \leqq 4q$ then $z^2 + pz + q$ is a factor and both zeros have magnitude $\rho = \sqrt{q}$.

55. Roots of $|a_2^{(r)}/a_4^{(r)}|$ form sequence 5.025, 5.014, 4.9998, 5.00000; roots of $|a_0^{(r)}/a_2^{(r)}|$ give .4975, .4986, .50002, .500000; true zeros are $2 \pm i$ and $\frac{1}{2} \pm \frac{1}{2}i$.

56. (a) Long division. (c) Equate coefficients of like powers of z in part b. (d) Since $u_m = s_m$.

57. (a) Add terms of the form $c_{ij}k^j \alpha_i^k$, $j = 0, \ldots, m_i$ where m_i is the multiplicity of α_i. (b) In (8.10-40) factor out all terms in α_1.

58. (b) $\beta_1^2 = \lim (1/\lambda_k \lambda_{k+1})[(\lambda_{k+1} - \lambda_k)/(\lambda_k - \lambda_{k-1})]$; $2\beta_1 \cos \phi_1 = \lim (1/\lambda_{k+1})[(\lambda_{k+1} - \lambda_{k-1})/(\lambda_k - \lambda_{k-1})]$.

59. (a) Using u_{11} to u_{14}, $\beta_1 = 2.23607$, $\phi_1 = .46365$. (b) Using u_{97} to u_{100}, $\beta_1 = 1.54980$, $\phi_1 = -.58205$.

60. (a) For first equation of (8.10-57) see Prob. 56b; for second equation consider derivative of $f'(x)/f(x)$; other equations verifiable by algebraic manipulations.

(b) Use induction to prove that $n \sum\limits_{i=1}^{n} a_i^2 - \left(\sum\limits_{i=1}^{n} a_i \right)^2$ is nonnegative for any set of

real a_i's. (d) By construction $\Phi(x)$ has one zero in $(x, x^{(1)})$ if $x < x^{(1)}$; by choosing sign to agree with $f'(x_i)$ we assure that $x_{i+1} > x_i$ and that $|x_{i+1} - x_i|$ has minimum magnitude; argument for $x^{(n)} < x$ is similar. (e) (i) $x_6 = 1.5000000$, true value: 1.5; (ii) $x_6 = -1.2878155 + .8578968i$ which is true value to seven decimals; other pair of zeros given in Prob. 52.

61. (a) $f(z) = (z^i + A_{j-1}z^{j-1} + \cdots + A_0)(b_{n-j}z^{n-i} + \cdots + b_0) + B_{j-1}z^{j-1} + \cdots + B_0$; $b_k = a_{k+j} - A_{j-1}b_{k+1} - A_{j-2}b_{k+2} - \cdots - A_0 b_{k+j}$, $k = n - j, \ldots, 0$; $b_{n-j+1} = b_{n-j+2} = \cdots = b_n = 0$; $B_k = a_k - A_k b_0 - A_{k-1}b_1 - \cdots - A_0 b_k$.
(b) Zeros are $+1$, $+1$, $+1$, -1, -1.

62. (a) Use (8.11-4). (b) Common denominator and then mean-value theorem. (c) Set $z_j = \alpha$ in coefficient of $\alpha - z_j$ in part b. (d) $1 + \alpha f'(\alpha)/a_0 < -1$.

63. Let $z_{j-1} = x_{j-1} + iy_{j-1}$ and $b'_k = a_{k+1} - z_{j-1}b'_{k+1}$ with $b'_k = \gamma'_k + i\delta'_k$; then
$\gamma_k = a_{k+1} + x_j\gamma_{k+1} - y_j\delta_{k+1}$, $\delta_k = x_j\delta_{k+1} + y_j\gamma_{k+1}$; $\gamma'_k = a_{k+1} + x_{j-1}\gamma'_{k+1} - y_{j-1}\delta'_{k+1}$,
$\delta'_k = x_{j-1}\delta'_{k+1} + y_{j-1}\gamma'_{k+1}$, $R_j = b_{-1}$, $R_{j-1} = b'_{-1}$.

64. Doesn't converge; expect sensitivity to initial approximation for reasons given in Sec. 8.8.

66. (a) 2.0945515, $-1.0472757 \pm 1.1359399i$; (b) 15.988265, -4.273434, .439079; (c) 1.4476230, -2.0523004, .3023387 $\pm$ .4951598i; (d) .8714384, $-.2492279$, $-.3111053 \pm 2.1230983i$; (e) .0446927 $\pm$ .3633450i, $-1.2393991 \pm .6270835i$, 1.1947065 $\pm$ 1.5621069i.

67. (a) 20.104687; (b) 7.6132307; (c) 2.1.

68. (b) Because $|\epsilon|$ as given by (8.13-5) will not be small. (c) $z_0 = 1$, $|\epsilon| < 10^{-24}$; $z_0 = -5$, $|\epsilon| \approx 6 \times 10^{-8}$; $z_0 = -8$, $|\epsilon| \approx 7 \times 10^{-3}$; $z_0 = -15$, $|\epsilon| \approx 200$.

Chapter 9

1. Any time $a_{ii}^{(i-1)} = 0$ interchange rows and columns until nonzero element in (i,i) position; iteration terminates when this cannot be done or after $n - 1$ stages; at this point status of right-hand sides and number of nonzero coefficients in last nonzero equation give results of theorem and corollary.

2. (a) Sparse if orthogonal polynomials are used; filled otherwise. (b) Number of equations equals number of points in mesh, but equation for each point involves only a few other points of mesh.

3. (a) Use induction. (b) $x_1 = x_2 = 1$. (c) Determinant has constant magnitude 1 but elements of matrix grow. (d) $\epsilon = .018$, $x_1 = -159.2$, $x_2 = 100$; $\epsilon = .02$, $x_1 = 18.8$, $x_2 = -10$; $\epsilon = \frac{1}{55}$, no solution.

4. For (9.3-13) use $\sum_1^{n-1} k = (n-1)n/2$; $\sum_1^{n-1} k^2 = n(n-1)(2n-1)/6$; for

(9.3-14) $M = n - 1 + \sum_{k=1}^{n-1} (n-1)(n-k+1)$.

5. (a) $a_{ij}^{(k-1)} = a_{ij}^{(k-2)} + M_{k-1,i}a_{k-1,j}^{(k-2)}$; then express $a_{ij}^{(k-2)}$ using (9.3-7), etc. (b) Must show $m_{ki} = M_{ki}$; use induction on k and result of part a.

6. (a) $-.0496$ should be $-.0485$. (b) $x_1 = -.1927$, $x_2 = -1.6729$, $x_3 = 2.2328$, $x_4 = -.4470$; true solution: $x_1 = -.18192$, $x_2 = -1.66303$, $x_3 = 2.21723$, $x_4 = -.44670$. (c) $x_1 = -.1817$, $x_2 = -1.6630$, $x_3 = 2.2170$, $x_4 = -.4468$.

7. (a) Solve (9.3-22) for m_{ki} and use induction on k. (b) $x_1 = 4.5856$, $x_2 = -.6312$, $x_3 = 2.7345$; true solution: $x_1 = 4.58669$, $x_2 = -.63152$, $x_3 = 2.73520$.

8. (a) $a_{n+1,j}^{(k)} = a_{n+1,j}^{(k-1)} - a_{n+1,k}^{(k-1)}a_{kj}^{(k-1)}/a_{kk}^{(k-1)}$; use induction on k. (b) Check row determines column of error, check column gives error row.

9. (b) $c_{ij} = \Sigma a_{ik}b_{kj}$; suppose $i < j$; if A, B lower triangular show $c_{ij} = 0$. (c) Consider $A^{-1}A$ and show desired elements of A^{-1} are zero.

10. (a) $y_i = b_i - \sum_{j=1}^{i-1} l_{ij}y_j$, $i = 1, \ldots, n$; $x_i = (1/u_{ii})\left(y_i - \sum_{j=i+1}^{n} u_{ij}x_j\right)$, $i = n, \ldots, 1$.

11. (a) Let $B = [b_{ij}] = A_n^{-1}A_n$; show $b_{ii} = 1$, $i \neq n$, $b_{nn} = 1$; $b_{ij} = 0$, $i > j$; $b_{ij} = 0$, $i < j \neq n$; $b_{in} = 0$. (c) A_n is normalized and A_n^{-1} contains no large elements. (d) Use $B_{31} = A_{31} + \frac{1}{2}E_{31,31}$ where $E_{31,31}$ has 1 in (31,31) position and zero elsewhere; then calculate $B_{31}^{-1}B_{31}$; differences in B_{31}^{-1} and A_{31}^{-1} are as large as 2^{-3}. (e) At each stage only elements of last column are changed. (f) Show each stage of elimination doubles (31,31) element. (g) At second stage largest element is in last column.

12. (b) If there exist $x_2, \ldots, x_n$ such that right-hand side of part a is negative, then choose x_1 such that second term on left is zero. (c) $a_{ii}^{(1)} = a_{ii} - a_{i1}^2/a_{11}$; also largest element of positive definite matrix lies on diagonal. (d) Since each matrix is positive definite. (e) $a_{11} = 2 \times 10^{-6}$, $a_{21} = a_{12} = 1.3 \times 10^{-3}$, $a_{22} = .9$.

13. (a) Compute LL^T. (b) Induction on i. (c) $n^3/6 + n^2 + 11n/6$. (d) Partial positioning would destroy symmetry; largest element at each stage is on diagonal. (e) $x_1 = 4.5878$, $x_2 = 2.7360$, $x_3 = -.6319$.

14. (a) Let $\mathbf{c} = (l_1, \ldots, l_{n-1})$; then $l_1 l_{11} = a_1$ gives l_1; $l_1 l_{21} + l_2 l_{22} = a_2$ gives l_2, etc.; $\mathbf{c}^T \mathbf{c} + l_{nn}^2 = a_{nn}$ gives l_{nn}. (b) Since $a_{nn} < 1$ from part a all l_i and l_{nn} are less than 1 in magnitude. (c) Results of parts a, b may be applied at each stage of algorithm.

15. (b) $x_1 = .7315$, $x_2 = -2.1887$, $x_3 = -.6554$; true solution: $x_1 = .73152$, $x_2 = -2.18886$, $x_3 = -.65439$; for low-order systems roundoff using single precision not usually significant.

16. (a) $l_{21} = -.9182$, $l_{31} = .2806$, $l_{32} = -.4051$, $u_{11} = .9411$, $u_{12} = -.0175$, $u_{13} = .1463$, $u_{22} = -.4404$, $u_{23} = .2054$, $u_{33} = .9063$; no scaling needed. (b) $p_1 = 3$, $p_2 = 2$, $p_3 = 3$.

17. True solution: $x_1 = 1.95539$, $x_2 = .10568$, $x_3 = 1.45557$, $x_4 = -.94924$.

18. (a) Euclidean: (iii) use scalar Schwarz inequality, (iv) express $\|A\|\,\|B\| - \|AB\|$ as a sum of squares; spectral: (iii) use Theorem 9.2 to find $\mathbf{x}$ such that $\|A + B\| = \|(A + B)\mathbf{x}\|$, then use triangle inequality and Theorem 9.2 again, (iv) use Theorem 9.2 again. (c) (iv), can only say $\|AB\| \leqq n\|A\|\,\|B\|$; counterexample is product AA^T where A has first row all 1's, rest zero.

19. (a) From (ii) $\|B\| = \|-B\|$; write $A = (A + B) - B$.

20. (a) Trace is negative of coefficient of λ^{n-1} in characteristic equation. (b) $\|A\|_S^2 = \max [\lambda_i(AA^T)] \leqq \Sigma\lambda_i(AA^T) = \|A\|_E^2$.

21. (b) $\|\mathbf{b}\|^2 \|\mathbf{a}\| = \|\mathbf{ab}^T\mathbf{b}\| \leqq \|\mathbf{ab}^T\|\,\|\mathbf{b}\|$. (d) Since AA^T is symmetric its norm is magnitude of largest eigenvalue.

22. (a) Consider $L\mathbf{y} = \mathbf{b} + \Delta\mathbf{b} + \Delta\mathbf{s}$; use induction to show that the solution of this system is $\mathbf{y} + \Delta\mathbf{c}$ where $\mathbf{y}$ is the solution of (9.3-34).

23. Calculation equation for $a_{43}^{(3)} = 0$ is $a_{33}^{(2)} - [a_{33}^{(2)}/a_{43}^{(2)}]_{\text{true}} a_{43}^{(2)} + \epsilon_{43}$ where $\epsilon_{43} \leqq \frac{1}{2} \times 10^{-d}$; similarly for $a_{44}^{(3)}$ and $b_4^{(3)}$. (b) $k = 1$ to $k = 2$ brings $\frac{1}{2} \times 10^{-d}$ factor into every element of last two rows except in first column; $k = 0$ to $k = 1$ brings $\frac{1}{2} \times 10^{-d}$ into every element of last three rows; add all contributions to get result. (c) jth row has entries $1, 2, 3, \ldots, j-1, j-1, \ldots, j-1$.

24. (a) Inverse by rows: $-.16194$, 1.00902, $-.10784$, $.51468$, -2.03801, -2.06231, 1.10330, $.10080$, $.44699$; (b) $\|\mathbf{x}_c - \mathbf{x}_t\| \approx 2.2 \times 10^{-2}$.

25. (a) Upper triangle of inverse by rows: -2.22291, $.20574$, -1.03891, 2.05389, 1.38996, $.21704$, $-.43611$, $.68163$, $.73332$, $-.80208$; (b) $\|\mathbf{x}_c - \mathbf{x}_t\| \approx 6.5 \times 10^{-2}$.

26. $\|A\|_E$ is between 1 and n; use (9.5-2).

27. (a) $x_1 = x_2 = x_3 = x_4 = 1$. (b) $x_1 = .0444$, $x_2 = 1.5761$, $x_3 = 1.2411$, $x_4 = .8571$; system is badly ill-conditioned. (c) First iteration: $x_1 = 1.3954$, $x_2 = .7621$, $x_3 = .8987$, $x_4 = 1.0607$; after four iterations: $x_1 = .9713$, $x_2 = 1.0174$, $x_3 = 1.0073$, $x_4 = .9956$.

28. (a) $\frac{1}{2}(1 \pm \sqrt{5})$. (b) Show sum of eigenvalues is $\lambda_1^{n+1} + \lambda_2^{n+1}$ and product is $(-1)^{n+1}$. (c) $\|A_n\|\,\|A_n^{-1}\| = (1 + \sqrt{5})^{n+1}/(1 - \sqrt{5})^{n+1} \approx (2.6)^{n+1}$.

29. (a) Reciprocal: $x_{i+1} = x_i(2 - ax_i)$. (b) $C_{i+1} = I - AB_{i+1} = I - AB_i(I + C_i) = C_i(I - AB_i) = C_i^2$. (c) For then $C_i \to 0$ and $B_i \to A^{-1}$. (d) $B_i\mathbf{b} \to A^{-1}\mathbf{b} = \mathbf{x}_t$; $B_3\mathbf{b} = (^{31}\!/_{32}, ^{63}\!/_{32}, ^{31}\!/_{32})$; need for matrix products at each stage is bad computationally.

30. (a) Solve for b_{ii} in the ith equation. (b) Let $B = A - \lambda I$; $|a_{ii} - \lambda| \leqq \displaystyle\sum_{k \neq i} |a_{ik}|$. (c) Since $B = -(L + U)$ diagonal terms of B are zero.

32. (b) For second part use $\boldsymbol{\epsilon}_i = \mathbf{x}_t - \mathbf{x}_i$ in definition of $\mathbf{r}_{i+1}$. (c) Consider change from $\boldsymbol{\epsilon}_i$ to $\boldsymbol{\epsilon}_{i+1}$ component by component; show each change reduces Q by $-[r_{i+1}^{(j)}]^2/a_{jj}$. (d) Q's form a decreasing sequence which converges to zero; therefore, $Q(\boldsymbol{\epsilon}_1) > 0$ for any $\boldsymbol{\epsilon}_1$.

33. (a) $(I - L)^{-1} = I + L + L^2 + \cdots$. (b) $B_J = -L - U$; $B_G = -(I + L)^{-1}U$ is nonnegative from part a.

34. (a) Jacobi: $\rho = \frac{1}{4}$; Gauss-Seidel: $\rho = \frac{1}{16}$. (b) Result is $(1\frac{9}{20}, \frac{5}{2}, 1\frac{9}{20})$; iteration for second component is not converging monotonically yet. (c) Result is $(1,2,1)$ and is just fortuitous.

35. (a) .999991. (b) $x^{(1)} = .39473$, $x^{(2)} = .62470$. (c) After first iteration still have $x^{(1)} = .33116$, $x^{(2)} = .70000$; reason is severe ill condition of matrix.

36. (a) The order in which the equations are considered varies from one iteration to the next. (b) Jacobi: $\|\mathbf{r}_2\| \approx 2.35$; Gauss-Seidel: $\|\mathbf{r}_2\| \approx 1.65$; relaxation: $\|\mathbf{r}_4\| = 1.75$; $\|\mathbf{r}\|$ reasonable criterion since matrix is well-conditioned.

37. Take $i_1, \ldots, i_k$ equations and solve for $x_{i_1}, \ldots, x_{i_k}$. (b) Choose one residual from each A_i. (c) $\mathbf{x}_2^T = (0, \frac{5}{3}, \frac{5}{3}, 0)$; $\mathbf{x}_3^T = (1\frac{1}{12}, \frac{5}{3}, \frac{5}{3}, 1\frac{1}{12})$; $\mathbf{x}_4^T = (1\frac{1}{12}, 7\frac{1}{36}, 7\frac{1}{36}, 1\frac{1}{12})$; true solution: $(1,2,2,1)$.

39. (a) $B_i = (1 + \omega_i)B - \omega_i I$; $C_i = (1 + \omega_i)C$. (b) $\rho[K_i(B)] = \max \ \lambda_j[K_i(B)]$; since $K_i(B)$ is sum of powers of B get result. (d) $K_i(1) = 1$; $K_i(x) = \pi(x - \gamma_j)/\pi(1 - \gamma_j)$; want $K_i(x)$ to be minimum on $[x_0, x_1]$; therefore, make change of variable to $[-1,1]$ and use Chebyshev polynomials. (e) Since zeros of $K_i(x)$ are γ_j's. (f) Must recompute ω_i's again in order to minimize $\rho[K_{i+1}(B)]$.

40. (a) $\mathbf{x}_4^T = (1\frac{5}{16}, 1\frac{5}{16}, 1\frac{5}{16}, 1\frac{5}{16})$; (b) $\mathbf{x}_4^T = (1\frac{27}{128}, 1\frac{27}{128}, 2\frac{55}{256}, 2\frac{55}{256})$; (c) $(1,1,1,1)$.

41. (a) $\rho(B) = \frac{1}{2}$; (b) $\rho(B) = \frac{1}{4}$. (c) Yes, Gauss-Seidel converged more rapidly.

42. (a) $\partial Q/\partial x_j = \Sigma a_{jk}x_k - b_j$. (b) Follows from (9.8-3).

43. (a) $R = \Sigma r_i^2$. (b) From (9.8-3) $Q(\mathbf{x} + \Delta\mathbf{x}) - Q(\mathbf{x}) = \frac{1}{2}\Delta\mathbf{x}^T A \Delta\mathbf{x} + \Delta\mathbf{x}^T(A\mathbf{x} - \mathbf{b})$; can be given plus or minus sign by choosing $\Delta\mathbf{x}^T$ properly if $A\mathbf{x} - \mathbf{b}$ not zero.

45. (a) $A\mathbf{x} = \mathbf{b}$ becomes $D\mathbf{y} = \mathbf{c}$ where $\mathbf{y} = P\mathbf{x}$, $\mathbf{c} = P\mathbf{b}$ and $D = PAP^T$ is diagonal. (b) The Gauss-Jordan reduction is not a similarity transformation.

46. (b) Consider $R(\mathbf{x}_i + \alpha_i A^T\mathbf{r}_i)$ and set partial derivative with respect to α_i equal to zero. (c) $R(\mathbf{x}_{i+1}) - R(\mathbf{x}_i) = -(\mathbf{r}^T A A^T\mathbf{r})/(A A^T\mathbf{r})^T A A^T\mathbf{r}$.

47. (a) $\mathbf{x}_5^T = (.9960, 1.0024)$; slow convergence caused by ill condition. (b) Converges still more slowly.

48. (a) $\mathbf{x}_3^T = (-19.79, -5.68, -2.09, 8.35)$; method does not converge because matrix is not positive definite. (b) $\mathbf{x}_4^T = (.38, .41, .87, 1.20)$; convergence is slow because of ill condition, but it is sure. (c) $\mathbf{x}_2^T = (1,1,1,1)$ because hyperellipsoid is hypersphere.

49. (a) Compute $Q(\mathbf{x}_i + \alpha_i\mathbf{v}_i)$ and take partial derivative with respect to α_i. (b) $Q(\mathbf{x}_{i+1}) - Q(\mathbf{x}_i) = -(\mathbf{v}_i^T\mathbf{r})^2/2\mathbf{v}_i^T A\mathbf{v}_i$.

50. (a) Use induction; suppose true for $\leq i$, then $\beta_{i+1,k} = -\mathbf{v}_k^T A_{i-1}/\mathbf{v}_k^T A_k = -a_{k,i+1}^{(k-1)}/a_{kk}^{(k-1)} = m_{k,i+1}$ from (9.3-26); then $\mathbf{v}_{i+1} = \mathbf{e}_{i+1} + \Sigma m_{k,i+1}\mathbf{v}_k$. (b) $\mathbf{v}_j^T A\mathbf{v}_j = a_{jj}^{(j-1)}$; $\mathbf{v}_j^T\mathbf{b} = a_{j,n+1}^{(j-1)}$. (c) From (9.3-8) $D\mathbf{x}_t = \mathbf{s} - U\mathbf{x}_t$; $\mathbf{x}_t = (I + D^{-1}U)D^{-1}\mathbf{s}$. (d) From part b $(D^{-1}\mathbf{s})^T = (\alpha_1, \ldots, \alpha_n)$; therefore, from part c, $\mathbf{x}_t$ is a linear combination of vectors with the α_i's the coefficients; the vectors must then be the $\mathbf{v}_j$'s.

51. (a) Must show $\mathbf{v}_j^T\mathbf{r}_1 = \mathbf{v}_j^T\mathbf{r}_j$; from (9.8-33) show $\mathbf{r}_j$ is a linear combination of $\mathbf{r}_1$ and $A\mathbf{v}_k$, $k < j$. (b) From (9.8-21) $\mathbf{u}_j = \mathbf{r}_j$ is a linear combination of $\mathbf{v}_j$, $j \leq k$.

52. (a) Use induction. (b) Use $\mathbf{r}_{i+1}^T A\mathbf{v}_k = (1/\alpha_k)\mathbf{r}_{i+1}^T(\mathbf{r}_k - \mathbf{r}_{k+1})$.

53. (a) $\mathbf{v}_i^T\mathbf{r}_i = \mathbf{r}_i^T\mathbf{r}_i$ since $\mathbf{v}_i$ is a linear combination of $\mathbf{r}_j$, $j \leq i$; use third equation of (9.8-33) for β_i.

54. Use Prob. 49.

55. $A\mathbf{v}_i$ requires n^2 multiplications; all other computations require $O(n)$.

56. (a) From Prob. 53a, $\beta_i > 0$; let $i < j$; then $\mathbf{v}_i^T\mathbf{v}_j = \mathbf{v}_i^T\mathbf{r}_j + \beta_{j-1}\mathbf{v}_i^T\mathbf{v}_{j-1} = \beta_{j-1}\mathbf{v}_i^T\mathbf{v}_{j-1}$ from Prob. 53b; continue until get $\beta_{j-1}\beta_{j-2} \cdots \beta_i\mathbf{v}_i^T\mathbf{v}_i$.

(b) $\boldsymbol{\epsilon}_{i+1}^T\mathbf{v}_i = \left(\sum_{j=i+1}^{n} \alpha_j\mathbf{v}_j \right)^T\mathbf{v}_i$; $\alpha_j > 0$ from Prob. 53a. (c) $\boldsymbol{\epsilon}_i = \boldsymbol{\epsilon}_{i+1} + \alpha_i\mathbf{v}_i$; $\boldsymbol{\epsilon}_i^T\boldsymbol{\epsilon}_i = \boldsymbol{\epsilon}_{i+1}^T\boldsymbol{\epsilon}_{i+1} + 2\alpha_i\boldsymbol{\epsilon}_{i+1}^T\mathbf{v}_i + \alpha_i^2\mathbf{v}_i^T\mathbf{v}_i$; last two terms are both positive.

57. (a) $A\mathbf{v}_1, \ldots , A\mathbf{v}_{k-1}$. (b) Use induction. (c) Direction taken at each stage is projection of error vector on space of remaining A-conjugate vectors.

58. (a) (i) After 10 iterations $x^{(1)} = .34227$, $x^{(2)} = .02339$, $x^{(3)} = 2.19604$; (ii) after three iterations $x^{(1)} = .36713$, $x^{(2)} = -.01164$, $x^{(3)} = 2.23961$. (b) (i) $x^{(1)} = -.45545$, $x^{(2)} = .33294$, $x^{(3)} = 1.50056$, $x^{(4)} = -.71409$; (ii) $x^{(1)} = -.45566$, $x^{(2)} = .33429$, $x^{(3)} = 1.50507$, $x^{(4)} = -.71712$.

59. (a) Let $U^{-1} = [s_{ij}]$; $s_{kk}u_{kk} = 1$; $\displaystyle\sum_{i=k}^{j} s_{ki}u_{ij} = 0$, $k = j - 1, j - 2, \ldots , 1$.

(b) For L^{-1}, $k - j$ multiplications for each r_{kj}; $\displaystyle\sum_{k=2}^{n} \sum_{j=1}^{k-1} (k - j) = \tfrac{1}{6}n^3 + O(n^2)$, similarly for U^{-1}, $L^{-1}U^{-1}$ requires $\tfrac{1}{3}n^3 + O(n^2)$.

60. (a) $[\mathbf{x}^{(1)}, \ldots ,\mathbf{x}^{(n)}] = A^{-1}I$. (b) $\tfrac{1}{3}n^3$ for triangular decomposition; to solve $L\mathbf{y} = \mathbf{e}_i$ note that last $n - i$ components of $\mathbf{y}$ are zero; really have $i \times i$ triangular system which requires $\tfrac{1}{2}i^2 + O(i)$ operations; so all $L\mathbf{y} = \mathbf{e}_i$ solutions require $\tfrac{1}{6}n^3$; $U\mathbf{x} = \mathbf{y}$ requires $n(\tfrac{1}{2}n^2)$; total is n^3. (c) Each $\mathbf{e}_i$ in part a may be considered a column of I.

61. (b) Let $U^{-1} = [s_{ij}]$; start with last column of A; $a_{jn}^{-1} = s_{jn}, j = 1, \ldots , n$; given columns $j + 1, \ldots , n$ get column j. (c) $\tfrac{1}{3}n^3$ for LU; $\tfrac{1}{6}n^3$ for U^{-1}; $\tfrac{1}{2}n^3$ for algorithm of part b; n^3 total.

62. (b) $\displaystyle\sum_{k=i}^{n} u_{ik}a_{kj}^{-1} = 0$, $i < j$, $\displaystyle\sum_{k=i}^{n} u_{ik}a_{ki}^{-1} = 1$; $\displaystyle\sum_{k=j}^{n} a_{ik}^{-1}l_{kj} = 0$, $i > j$. (c) Calculate last row of A^{-1}, last column, next to last row, next to last column, etc.

63. $A = LL^T, A^{-1} = (L^{-1})^TL^{-1}$; $\tfrac{1}{6}n^3$ for L, $\tfrac{1}{6}n^3$ for L^{-1}, $\tfrac{1}{6}n^3$ for $(L^{-1})^TL^{-1}$; $\tfrac{1}{2}n^3$ total.

64. (a) $\mathbf{u}^T\mathbf{u} = (2\alpha/\mu^2)(\alpha - \mathbf{a}^T\mathbf{v}) = 1$. (b) In $I - \sigma\mathbf{v}_1\mathbf{v}_2^T$ multiply first row by $v_1^{(j)}/v_1^{(1)}$ and subtract from jth row; then add $v_1^{(k)}/v_1^{(1)}$ times kth column to first column. (c) First column of U_1A is $U_1A_1 = (I - 2\mathbf{u}_1\mathbf{u}_1^T)A_1 = \alpha\mathbf{e}_1$. (d) At each stage reduce one column to desired form, leaving previous columns unchanged in form. (e) Inversion: $V^{-1}U = A^{-1}$; linear equations: $UA\mathbf{x} = V\mathbf{x} = U\mathbf{b}$, determinants: $\det A = (-1)^{n-1} \det V$.

65. (b) $C_{k+1} = (C_k^{-1} + \mathbf{u}_{k+1}\mathbf{v}_{k+1}^T)^{-1}$. (c) $C_0 = D^{-1}$; then $C_m = B^{-1}$.

66. (a) Use induction on k; for $k + 1$ and i and $j < k$, $a_{ij}^{(k+1)} = 0$ from definition; for $i = k$, $a_{kj}^{(k+1)} = a_{kj}^{(k)} - a_{kj}^{(k)} = 0$; similarly for $a_{ik}^{(k+1)}$. (b) Must show $b_{ij} = \delta_{ij} + \displaystyle\sum_{k=1}^{n} u_k^{(i)}v_k^{(j)}$. (c) $C_0 = I$; as before get $C_n = B^{-1}$.

67. (a) Substitute (9.9-10)–(9.9-13) into (9.9-5) and then verify that $AA^{-1} = I$. (b) With K and M given by (9.9-8) and (9.9-9) the analogs of (9.9-12) and (9.9-13) are $L = -KQS^{-1}$ and $N = S^{-1} - S^{-1}RL$; after substitution in (9.9-5) again can verify that $AA^{-1} = I$.

68. For true inverse see Prob. 24.

69. For true inverse see Prob. 25.

Chapter 10

1. (a) Show $\mathbf{y}_j^T A \mathbf{x}_i = \lambda_i \mathbf{y}_j^T \mathbf{x}_i = \lambda_j \mathbf{y}_j^T \mathbf{x}_i$.

2. (a) Show $A^k \mathbf{x}_i = \lambda_i^k \mathbf{x}_i$ for 10.1; for 10.2 consider $\mathbf{x}_i^* A \mathbf{x}_i$ and its conjugate transpose. (b) $f(A)$ has eigenvalues $f(\lambda_i)$; that is, all zeros; only symmetric matrix with all zero eigenvalues is null matrix. (c) $f(A)\mathbf{x}_i = \mathbf{0}$ where $\mathbf{x}_i$ is any eigenvector; thus for any $\mathbf{x}$, $f(A)\mathbf{x} = \mathbf{0}$ since eigenvectors span space.

3. From (8.10-42) given $u_1, \ldots, u_n$ get $a_{n-1}, \ldots, a_0$ successively.

4. (b) Consider $\Sigma m_{nr}^{-1} a_{rs} m_{rs}$. (c) Show each step does not affect zeros from previous steps. (d) Use induction. (e) Postmultiplication by M_{j-1} requires nj multiplications; premultiplication by M_{j-1}^{-1} also requires nj; M_j itself requires n; sum from $j = 1$ to $n - 1$. (f) Exchange $(k - 1)$st and jth rows and columns. (g) Express characteristic equation as product of two determinants, one already in form B.

5. (a) Domain covered by circles with centers at $x = 2, 1, -1$ and radii 5, 2, 4, respectively. (b) Centers at 2, 1, -1, radii 2, 5, 4. (c) By rows B is 2, -1, $\frac{3}{2}$; 2, 1, 1; 2, 3, -1; centers 2, 1, -1; radii 4, 4, $2\frac{1}{2}$. (d) $n - m \times n - m$ principal minor unchanged; lower right $m \times m$ minor unchanged; rest of lower triangle multiplied by α, upper triangle multiplied by $1/\alpha$. (e) $\alpha = \sqrt{5}$.

6. (a) Compute diagonal elements of $P^{-1}AP$. (b) Compute diagonal elements of TT^*.

7. (a) Consider linear transformations represented by matrices. (c) $B = PAP^{-1}$; $r(B) \leq r(AP^{-1}) \leq r(A)$ but also $r(A) \leq r(B)$.

8. (a) Consider $(A - \lambda_i I)\mathbf{x} = \mathbf{0}$; let $\mathbf{y} = P^{-1}\mathbf{x}$ where P^{-1} is such that $P^{-1}AP$ is Jordan canonical matrix; then $(J - \lambda_i I)\mathbf{y} = \mathbf{0}$; rank of $J - \lambda_i I$ is n less the number of different elementary divisors in which λ_i appears. (b) Change variable to get $(J - \lambda_i I)^\nu \mathbf{y} = \mathbf{0}$; let νth component of $\mathbf{y}$ be nonzero; satisfies equation but $(J - \lambda_i I)^{\nu-1}\mathbf{y} \neq \mathbf{0}$. (c) $(A - \lambda_i I)^i \mathbf{x}_j = (A - \lambda_i I)^i (A - \lambda_i I)^{\nu-i}\mathbf{x}_\nu$. (d) Consider $(A - \lambda_i I)^{\nu-1}$ times linear combination of $\mathbf{x}_j$.

9. (a) (10.2-1) not possible since there are not n eigenvectors. (b) $\lambda = 4$ is double eigenvalue with one eigenvector. (c) After 10 iterations $\lambda \approx 4.41$; convergence is very slow; after 50 iterations $\lambda \approx 4.08$.

10. (b) Consider $\mathbf{y}^T \mathbf{v}_m$ and let $\lambda_1 = \beta_1 e^{i\phi_1}$. (c) $\beta_1^2 = \lim [(\mathbf{y}^T \mathbf{v}_m)^2 - (\mathbf{y}^T \mathbf{v}_{m+1})(\mathbf{y}^T \mathbf{v}_{m-1})]/[(\mathbf{y}^T \mathbf{v}_{m-1})^2 - (\mathbf{y}^T \mathbf{v}_m)(\mathbf{y}^T \mathbf{v}_{m-2})]$; $2\beta_1 \cos \phi_1 = \lim [(\mathbf{y}^T \mathbf{v}_m)(\mathbf{y}^T \mathbf{v}_{m-1}) - (\mathbf{y}^T \mathbf{v}_{m+1})(\mathbf{y}^T \mathbf{v}_{m-2})]/[(\mathbf{y}^T \mathbf{v}_{m-1})^2 - (\mathbf{y}^T \mathbf{v}_m)(\mathbf{y}^T \mathbf{v}_{m-2})]$.

11. (a) No, $\mathbf{v}_0$ must also have component in direction of other eigenvectors; no, merely need some nonzero component in direction of another eigenvector. (b) Keep taking $\mathbf{v}_0$ orthogonal to previously found eigenvectors; may fail if no component in direction of some eigenvector. (c) Will get new eigenvalue and eigenvector. (d) $\lambda = 8$; $\mathbf{x}_1^T = (1,1,1)$; $\mathbf{x}_2^T = (1,7,10)$.

12. (a) Characteristic equation of B given in Prob. 4d; with u_m defined as in (8.10-38) and with components of $\mathbf{x}$ initial values for (8.10-38), first component of $P^k \mathbf{x}$ is u_{n+k}. (b) Squaring companion matrix squares eigenvalues.

13. (a) $F(\lambda_i)$ where λ_i's are eigenvalues of A. (b) If $|f(\lambda_1)|$ is dominant, $\lim [f(A)]^m \mathbf{v}_0/[f(\lambda_i)]^m = \alpha_1 \mathbf{x}_1$. (c) $f(\lambda_1)$ is large but series for $1/(x - \gamma)$ converges slowly. (d) This is equivalent to using first $k + 1$ terms of expansion of $x^{k+1}/(x - \gamma)$.

14. (a) Using $A^2 + 2A + 4I$ after 15 iterations get 15.5071 where for true eigenvalue $\lambda^2 + 2\lambda + 4 = 15.5070$. (b) In Wilkinson's method $k = 1$.

15. (a) e^{λ_1} where λ_1 is the largest eigenvalue algebraically; $e^{-\lambda_n}$ where λ_n is the smallest eigenvalue algebraically. (b) If result is less than 1 then λ_n is positive and matrix is positive definite.

16. (b) 1.4801215; result is fortuitous.
17. (a) Want to maximize ratio of $\lambda_1 - p$ to eigenvalue of second greatest magnitude. (b) .732.
18. (a) Because of the $2m$ in (10.2-16) as opposed to the m in (10.2-11). (b) Use (9.8-16); Rayleigh quotient is reciprocal of distance along gradient which minimizes Q in (9.8-2).

19.

	Eigenvalue	Eigenvector
A_1	9.6055509	$(1.0, .6056, -.3944)$
A_2	8.86988	$(-.6043, 1.0, .1509)$
B_1	-4.0	$(1, \tfrac{1}{2}, \tfrac{1}{2})$
B_2	$3 \pm i$	$(8 \pm i, 2 \pm i, -1 \pm i)$
B_3	4.0	$(1, 0, -\tfrac{1}{2})$

20. (a) A_1: $m = 8$ gives 9.6055502, whereas tenth iterate is 9.6055530; δ^2 process also applicable to A_2, B_1, B_3. (b) Converges to 7.6055509 in 11 instead of 13 iterations.
21. (a) If $\alpha = (\lambda_1/\lambda_i)(\mathbf{v}^T\mathbf{x}_i)$ then $\mathbf{x}_i - \alpha\mathbf{x}_1$ is an eigenvector of W_1 corresponding to λ_i. (b) If A is singular, λ_i can be zero; if A has nonlinear elementary divisors there is not an eigenvector for every eigenvalue; if A is singular, W_1 can have a nonlinear elementary divisor corresponding to the zero eigenvalue.
22. (a) Show $(\mathbf{u}\mathbf{e}_1^T)(\mathbf{u}\mathbf{e}_1^T) = 0$.
23. (a) $A(A - \lambda_1 I)\mathbf{w}_i = \lambda_i A\mathbf{w}_i - \lambda_1(A - \lambda_1\mathbf{x}_1\mathbf{v}^T)\mathbf{w}_i = \lambda_i(A - \lambda_1 I)\mathbf{w}_i$; show $(A - \lambda_1 I)\mathbf{w}_i \neq \mathbf{0}$ if $\lambda_1 \neq \lambda_i$. (b) Use (10.3-2). (c) If $\lambda_i = \lambda_1$ and $(A - \lambda_1 I)\mathbf{w}_i = \mathbf{0}$, then $A\mathbf{w}_i = \lambda\mathbf{w}_i$; if A has nonlinear elementary divisor corresponding to λ_1, then for some $\mathbf{w}_i$ corresponding to λ_1, $(A - \lambda_1 I)\mathbf{w}_i \neq \mathbf{0}$.
24. (a) Use (10.3-17) to show that $\mathbf{y}_1^T\mathbf{w}_i = 0$. (b) Let A be in Jordan form; show that there exist solutions of $(A - \lambda I)\mathbf{x} = \mathbf{0}$ and $\mathbf{y}^T(A - \lambda I) = \mathbf{0}$ such that $\mathbf{x}$ has non-zero components only where $\mathbf{y}$ has zero components and vice versa.
25. $\mathbf{x}_2 \approx (-.6369, -.8058, 1.0)$, $\mathbf{x}_3 \approx (1.0, -.9517, -.1300)$
26. (a) $W_1 = A - \lambda_1\mathbf{x}_1\mathbf{y}_1^T - \bar{\lambda}_1\bar{\mathbf{x}}_1\bar{\mathbf{y}}_1^T$. (b) $C = T^{-1}AT$; $T^{-1}A\mathbf{x}_1 = \lambda_1 T^{-1}\mathbf{x}_1$; then $\mathbf{y}_1 = T^{-1}\mathbf{x}_1 = \mathbf{x}_1 - (\mathbf{x}_1 - \mathbf{e}_1)x_1^{(1)} = \mathbf{e}_1$ is an eigenvector of C; $\bar{\mathbf{y}}_1 = T^{-1}\bar{\mathbf{x}}_1 = \bar{\mathbf{x}}_1 - (\mathbf{x}_1 - \mathbf{e}_1) = -2i\mathbf{n} + \mathbf{e}_1$. (c) Let C_1 be C with its first column removed; C_1 has eigenvector $-2i\mathbf{n}$; let $C_2 = (I - \mathbf{v}\mathbf{e}_1^T)C_1(I - \mathbf{v}\mathbf{e}_1^T)$ where $\mathbf{v} = \mathbf{z} - \mathbf{e}_1$ and $\mathbf{z}$ is above eigenvector of C_1 normalized to have first component 1.
27. (a) Use fact that left and right eigenvectors corresponding to distinct eigenvalues are orthogonal. (b) $\mathbf{s}_m$ has no component in $\mathbf{x}_1$ direction but as $m \to \infty$ it becomes difference of two nearly equal quantities.
28. First method: $\mathbf{y}^T\mathbf{v}_{m+1} - \lambda_1\mathbf{y}^T\mathbf{v}_m$; second method: $\mathbf{y}^T\mathbf{v}_m - \alpha_1\lambda_1^m\mathbf{y}^T\mathbf{x}_1$; same loss of significance problems.
30. Remaining eigenvalues and eigenvectors of matrices of Prob. 19 are:

	Eigenvalue	Eigenvector	Eigenvalue	Eigenvector
A_1	2.39445	$(-.8685, .1315, 1.0)$	2.0	$(1, -1, 1)$
A_2	4.72956	$(.8689, .3743, 1.0)$	-3.59946	$(-.8616, -.6715, 1.0)$
B_1	-1.0	$(1, 1, \tfrac{3}{4})$	-1.0	$(1, 0, \tfrac{1}{8})$
B_2	1.0	$(\tfrac{1}{2}, -\tfrac{1}{2}, 1)$		
B_3	4.0		-1.0	$(1, \tfrac{1}{3}, 0)$

Any linear combination of eigenvectors of B_1 corresponding to -1.0 is eigenvector; eigenvalue 1.0 of B_2 found by technique of Prob. 26; B_3 has nonlinear elementary divisor corresponding to 4.0 eigenvalue.

31. $\tan 2\theta_k = \lambda/\mu$; use double-angle identities to get $2\sin\theta_k\cos\theta_k = (\lambda/\mu)(2\cos^2\theta_k - 1)$ and $\cos^2\theta_k\sin^2\theta_k = (\lambda^2/4\nu^2)$; choose sign so as to maximize magnitude of $\cos\theta_k$.

32. Method must converge since off-diagonal norm is monotonically decreasing and bounded below by zero; prove convergence to diagonal matrix by assuming contrary; obtain contradiction by showing that sequence of off-diagonal norms cannot converge to nonzero quantity if largest off-diagonal element chosen at each stage; sequence of norms could conceivably converge to nonzero limit for some choice of sequence of nonzero elements.

33. (a) Average of square of off-diagonal elements is $v_0/n(n-1) > \gamma_1^2$. (b) Each annihilation reduces square of off-diagonal norm by at least $2\gamma_1^2$. (c) Use induction and result of part b. (d) Final off-diagonal norm $v_F \leq n(n-1)\gamma_F^2 \leq \dfrac{\rho^2(n)(n-1)}{n^2} v_0$.

34. $\gamma_1 \approx .54$; one annihilation at first stage after which diagonal elements are 2.0, 0.0, 2.0; $\gamma_2 \approx .18$; one annihilation; diagonal elements 2.530, 0.0, 1.470; $\gamma_3 \approx .06$; two annihilations; diagonal elements 2.53649, $-.0166472$, 1.48016.

35. (a) Use (10.4-12) to show t_{13} and t_{1i} remain zero during $(3,i,2)$ transformation. (b) In general show $t_{ji}, j = 1, \ldots, i-1$ remain zero.

36. (a) Use induction. (c) $f_n(\lambda)$ is a constant; if $f_{n-i}(\lambda) = 0$ then $f_{n-i-1}(\lambda) = -c_i^2 f_{n-i+1}(\lambda)$. (d) $f_{n-2}(\lambda) = (\lambda - b_2)(\lambda - b_1) - c_1^2; r_1 = b_1; f_{n-2}(\lambda)$ is negative at r_1 and positive at $\pm \infty$.

37. (a) If $\mathbf{x}$ eigenvector of A, $\mathbf{y}$ of B then $\mathbf{x} = S_1 \cdots S_k \mathbf{y}$. (b) Let $x^{(1)} = 1$; $x^{(2)} = (\lambda - b_1)/c_1; x^{(i+1)} = (-1/c_i)[c_{i-1}x^{(i-1)} + (b_i - \lambda)x^{(i)}]; i = 2, \ldots, n-1$. (c) From Theorem 10.15 it follows that, if λ_1 is multiple, then some $c_i = 0$; get eigenvector from each of smaller tridiagonal matrices and set other components equal to zero.

38. (b) Show first that $P_k^T A_{k-1}$ has same first $k-1$ rows as A_{k-1}. (c) $\displaystyle\sum_{j=k}^n [v^{(j)}]^2 =$

$$[1/(2\sqrt{S})]\left\{\sqrt{S} \pm g_{k-1,k} + [1/(\sqrt{S} \pm g_{k-1,k})] \sum_{j=k+1}^n (g_{k-1,j})^2\right\} = [1/(2\sqrt{S})][1/$$

$(\sqrt{S} \pm g_{k-1,k})](2S \pm 2g_{k-1,k}\sqrt{S})$; compute $\displaystyle\sum_{r=1}^n \sum_{s=1}^n p_{k-1,r}g_{rs}p_{sj}, j = k+1, \ldots,$ n; use $p_{sj} = 0, s < k; -2v_k^{(s)}v_k^{(i)}, s > k \neq j; 1 - 2v_k^{(j)}v_k^{(i)}, s = j$ and (10.4-43) to show sum is zero for all $j > k$.

39. (b) Householder's method: $n^2 + 0(n)$; Givens's: $2n^2 + O(n)$. (c) $P_k^T A_{k-1} P_k = (I - 2\mathbf{v}_k\mathbf{v}_k^T)(A_{k-1} - 2\mathbf{w}_k\mathbf{v}_k^T)$.

40. (a) For each $(j, i, j-1)$ the ith and jth rows and columns are affected; for $(j, i, j-1)$ need $4(n-j) + 15$ operations (using symmetry); sum from $i = j+1$ to $n, j = 2$ to $n-1$ to get result; one square root needed for each $(j, i, j-1)$. (b) $M = (n-k+2)(n-k+1)$ multiplications for $\mathbf{w}_k$; for $\mathbf{w}_k\mathbf{v}_k^T$ and $\mathbf{v}_k\mathbf{q}_k^T$, $n^2/2$ each plus $O(n)$ using symmetry; sum from $k = 2$ to $n-1$. (c) In $\mathbf{v}_k\mathbf{v}_k^T$ every element contains factor of $[v_k^{(k)}]^2$; therefore, need only $[v_k^{(k)}]^2$; still true if scheme of Example 10.8 used.

41. $v_2^{(2)} = .22975, v_2^{(3)} = -.97326; \mathbf{w}_2^T = (-.25688, -.01357, -1.88908); \mathbf{q}_2^T = (-.25688, -.43526, -.10271); A_2$ by rows 1.0, 1.11804, $-.00002$; 1.11804, 1.40000, $-.55004$; $-.00002$, $-.55004$, 1.60024.

42. (a) Diagonal terms after five rotations: A_1: 9.6055522, 1.9999997, 2.3944482; A_2: -3.5994607, 8.8698995, 4.7295617; results for A_1 better because diagonal of A_1 is more dominant than A_2. (b) $A_1: b_1 = 7, b_2 = 69\frac{1}{13}, b_3 = 31\frac{1}{13}, c_1 = \sqrt{13}$, $c_2 = \frac{1}{13}; f_0(\lambda) = \lambda^3 - 14\lambda^2 + 47\lambda - 46; A_2: b_1 = 3, b_2 = 33\frac{3}{25}, b_3 = 142\frac{2}{25}$, $c_1 = 5, c_2 = 8\frac{1}{25}; f_0(\lambda) = \lambda^3 - 10\lambda^2 - 7\lambda + 151$. (c) Same as part b except for roundoff.

43. (a) $b_1 = 2.0$, $b_2 = 1.8$, $b_3 = .2$; $c_1 = .3125$, $c_2 = .36$; $f_0(\lambda) = \lambda^3 - 4\lambda^2 + 3.6875\lambda + .0625$. (b) If $x_1 = y_1$, $n^3 + O(n^2)$; if $x_1 \neq y_1$, $2n^3 + O(n^2)$.

44. (a) $\mathbf{x}_2^T = (\frac{1}{2}, -\frac{5}{6}, \frac{1}{2})$, $\mathbf{y}_2^T = (\frac{3}{5}, \frac{1}{5}, -\frac{4}{15})$; $\mathbf{x}_2^T \mathbf{y}_2 = 0$ so method fails. (b) $b_1 = 2.00415$, $b_2 = 2.00956$, $b_3 = 1.98629$; $c_1 = .23235$, $c_2 = .76750$; $f_0(\lambda) = \lambda^3 - 6\lambda^2 + 11\lambda - 6$.

45. (a) Show $\mathbf{y}_k^T \mathbf{x}_{j+1} = 0$ and $\mathbf{x}_k^T \mathbf{y}_{j+1} = 0$ for $k \leq j$. (b) Equation with $k = j$ in (10.5-7) has no $\mathbf{x}_j$ on right-hand side; this produces 0 in T matrix; show c_{j-1} appears in no term of characteristic equation; therefore, equation can be factored. (c) $P_{j-1}(\lambda)$ is determinant of upper left-hand factor of $T - \lambda I$. (d) $\mathbf{y}_j = \mathbf{0}$, interchange meanings of $\mathbf{x}_j$ and $\mathbf{y}_j$; both zero, set $c_{j-1} = 0$ in both equations and generate $\mathbf{x}_{j+1}$ and $\mathbf{y}_{j+1}$.

46. (a) $\lambda_1 = 3$, $\mathbf{v}_1^T = (\frac{3}{2}, 1, \frac{3}{8})$; $\lambda_2 = -2$, $\mathbf{v}_2^T = (-6, 1, \frac{3}{4})$; $\lambda_3 = 1$, $\mathbf{v}_3^T = (3, 1, \frac{3}{2})$. (b) $\mathbf{y}_1^T = (1,1,1)$, $\mathbf{y}_2^T = (4\frac{5}{7}, \frac{3}{4}, -6)$, $\mathbf{y}_3^T = (-1, 1, 1)$.

47. (a) Let $\mathbf{x}_1 = \displaystyle\sum_{i=1}^{n} a_i \mathbf{y}_i$ where the $\mathbf{y}_i$'s are eigenvectors. (c) $(1,0,0) = \frac{1}{2}(\mathbf{y}_1^T - \mathbf{y}_3^T)$.

(d) $b_1 = 2$, $b_2 = 2$ and with $\mathbf{x}_3^T = (0,3,2)$, $b_3 = -2$; $c_1 = 1$.

48. (b) $\mathbf{y}_{i+1}^T \mathbf{x}_j = \mathbf{y}_1^T P_i(A) P_{j-1}(A) \mathbf{x}_1 = \mathbf{y}_1^T P_{j-1}(A) P_i(A) \mathbf{x}_1 = \mathbf{y}_j^T \mathbf{x}_{i+1}$. (c) $\mathbf{y}_{i+1}^T \mathbf{x}_{i+1} = $

$$\left(A^T \mathbf{y}_i - \sum_{j=1}^{i} c_{ij} \mathbf{y}_j \right)^T \left(A \mathbf{x}_i - \sum_{j=1}^{i} c_{ij} \mathbf{x}_j \right); \text{ take partial with respect to } c_{ij}. \quad (d) \text{ If}$$

no $\mathbf{y}_j$ or $\mathbf{x}_j$ equals zero the result is immediate. (e) $\mathbf{y}_{i+1}^T \mathbf{x}_{i+1} = \mathbf{y}_i^T A^T A \mathbf{x}_i - \Sigma c_{ij} \mathbf{y}_j^T A \mathbf{x}_i - \Sigma c_{ij} \mathbf{y}_i^T A \mathbf{x}_j + \Sigma c_{ij}^2 \mathbf{y}_j^T \mathbf{x}_j$; take partial with respect to c_{ij} and use part a. (f) Use equations in part a.

49. (a) Compute $\mathbf{y}_k^T \mathbf{x}_{i+1}$ and $\mathbf{x}_k^T \mathbf{y}_{i+1}$, $k \leq i$. (b) Show that if $\mathbf{x}_j$ and $\mathbf{y}_j$ sequences were truly biorthogonal then c_{ij} and d_{ij} for $j < i - 1$ would be zero. (c) If $T = [t_{ij}]$, $t_{ij} = c_{ij}$, $i \leq j$.

50. (a) Matrix to interchange columns p and q, $C = [c_{ij}]$; $c_{ii} = 1, i \neq p, q, c_{pq} = c_{qp} = 1$, $c_{ij} = 0$ otherwise; matrix to add m times column p to column q, $M = [m_{ij}]$; $m_{ii} = 1$, $m_{pq} = m$, $m_{ij} = 0$ otherwise. (b) $C^{-1} = C$, $M^{-1} = [n_{ij}]$; $n_{ij} = m_{ij}$ except $n_{pq} = -m$. (c) For row k there are $n - k - 1$ row and column additions each requiring $2n - 2k - 1$ multiplications; sum $(n - k - 1)(2n - 2k - 1)$ from $k = 1$ to $n - 2$; for Householder's method asymmetry doubles number of operations.

51. (b) If $\mathbf{v}^T$ is an eigenvector of B_2, then $(\mathbf{0}^T, \mathbf{v}^T)$ is an eigenvector of B; if $\mathbf{w}^T$ is an eigenvector of B_1 then $(\mathbf{w}^T, \mathbf{z}^T)$ is an eigenvector of B where $\mathbf{z}$ is a solution of $(B_2 - \lambda I)\mathbf{z} = B_3 \mathbf{w}$ where λ is the eigenvalue of B_1 corresponding to $\mathbf{w}$.

52. (a) $S_{n-1,n} = [s_{ij}]$; $s_{jj} = 1, j \leq n - 2$; $s_{jj} = \cos \theta$, $j = n - 1, n$; $s_{n-1,n} = -s_{n,n-1} = \sin \theta$; all other $s_{ij} = 0$. (b) $s_{jj} = 1$, $j \neq i$ or n; $s_{jj} = \cos \theta$, $j = i, n$; $s_{in} = -s_{ni} = \sin \theta$; all other $s_{jk} = 0$; (j,n) element, $j = i + 2, \ldots, n$ remains zero since $\sin \theta$ multiplies 0 in Hessenberg form and $\cos \theta$ multiplies 0 in (j,n) position. (c) $t_{i,i+1} = \cos \theta \, b_{i,i+1}$ but $\cos \theta = 0$ only if $b_{i,i+1} = 0$.

53. (a) No, all that is assured is existence of orthogonal matrix Q. (b) $t_{pq}^{(k)} = [t_{pp}^{(k-1)} - t_{qq}^{(k-1)}] \sin \theta \cos \theta + \cos^2 \theta \, t_{pq}^{(k-1)} - \sin^2 \theta \, t_{qp}^{(k-1)}$; $\tan \theta = (t_{pp}^{(k-1)} - t_{qq}^{(k-1)} \pm \{[t_{pp}^{(k-1)} - t_{qq}^{(k-1)}]^2 - 4t_{pq}^{(k-1)} t_{qp}^{(k-1)}\}^{1/2})/2t_{qp}^{(k-1)}$. (c) Diagonal elements: 3.0000028, .9999707, −1.9999739.

54. B_1: $b_1 = 5, b_2 = -10$; $\mathbf{x}_3 = \mathbf{y}_3 = \mathbf{0}$; therefore, choose $\mathbf{x}_3 = (0,8,5)$, $\mathbf{y}_3 = (0,-1,1)$ get $b_3 = -1$; $c_1 = -54, c_2 = 0$; $f_0(\lambda) = \lambda^3 + 6\lambda^2 + 9\lambda + 4$, minimal polynomial is $\lambda^2 + 5\lambda + 4$. B_2: $b_1 = 6.125$, $b_2 = .36087$, $b_3 = .51413$; $c_1 = -17.14063$, $c_2 = -1.31447$; $f_0(\lambda) = \lambda^3 - 7\lambda^2 + 24\lambda - 18$. B_3: $b_1 = 1.875$, $b_2 = .57838$, $b_3 = 4.54662$; $c_1 = 4.85938, c_2 = -.62034$; $f_0(\lambda) = \lambda^3 - 7\lambda^2 + 8\lambda + 16$.

55. (a) B_1: Hessenberg form by rows: 5, -48, 0; $\frac{9}{8}$, -10, 0; 3, -24, -1 and eigenvalues are immediate without further computation; B_2: Hessenberg form by rows: $^{49}\!\!\frac{}{8}$, $-^{131}\!\!\frac{}{8}$, 0; $^{1097}\!\!\frac{}{1048}$, $^{181}\!\!\frac{}{1048}$, $-^{6760}\!\!\frac{}{17161}$; $-\frac{1}{2}$, $\frac{7}{2}$, $^{92}\!\!\frac{}{131}$; B_3: Hessenberg form by rows: $^{15}\!\!\frac{}{8}$, $-^{69}\!\!\frac{}{8}$, 0; $-^{311}\!\!\frac{}{552}$, $^{127}\!\!\frac{}{184}$, $^{800}\!\!\frac{}{1587}$; $\frac{1}{8}$, $-\frac{3}{8}$, $^{102}\!\!\frac{}{23}$.
(b) $\cos\theta$ elements replaced by $\bar c$ and c; $\sin\theta$ and $-\sin\theta$ replaced by $\bar s$ and $-s$ where c and s are such that (10.5-19) is satisfied and $|c|^2 + |s|^2 = 1$.

56. (a) In $A = LU$, $u_{ij} = 0$, $j - i > m$, $l_{ij} = 0$, $i - j > m$; therefore, UL has all elements with $|i - j| > m$ equal to zero. (b) If $A = QU$ has elements with $i - j > m$ equal to zero, then elements of Q with $i - j > m$ are zero; thus elements of UQ with $i - j > m$ are zero; since $A_{k+1} = Q_k^T A_k Q_k$ each A_k is symmetric. (c) Each Q_k is an upper Hessenberg matrix.

57. (a) Compute $L_k^T L_k$ and $L_{k+1} L_{k+1}^T$.

58. (a) Show zeros at each stage remain zero at later stages. (b) Show zeros in each column unaffected at later stages. (c) Suppose $A = Q_1 U_1 = Q_2 U_2$; then $U_1 U_2^{-1} = Q_1^T Q_2$ and $(U_1 U_2^{-1})^{-1} = (U_1 U_2^{-1})^T$; thus $U_1 U_2^{-1}$ is diagonal and orthogonal; since diagonal elements are positive $U_1 U_2^{-1} = I$.

59. (a) Let $P_k = U_k U_{k-1} \cdots U_1$, $N_k = Q_1 Q_2 \cdots Q_k$; then $A_{k+1} = Q_k^T A_k Q_k = U_k A_k U_k^{-1}$; $A_{k+1} = N_k^T A_1 N_k = P_k A_1 P_k^{-1}$; $N_k P_k = (Q_1 U_1)^k = A^k$. (b) Statement analogous except for change from lower to upper triangular; proof: $Q_k = N_{k-1} N_k^{-1}$; $\lim Q_k$ exists and is nonsingular; $U_\infty = N_\infty^T A_1 N_\infty$; therefore, $A_\infty = U_\infty$.

60. (a) Each P_j annihilates one subdiagonal element. (b) Let A have $a_1, \ldots, a_n$ on diagonal, $b_1, \ldots, b_{n-1}$ on subdiagonal; $\cos\theta_j = p_j/(p_j^2 + b_j^2)^{1/2}$, $\sin\theta_j = b_j/(p_j^2 + b_j^2)^{1/2}$ where $p_j = \cos\theta_j a_j - \sin\theta_{j-1}\cos\theta_{j-2} b_{j-1}$. (c) Let U_1 have r_j on diagonal, q_j on first superdiagonal, t_j on second; $r_j = \cos\theta_j p_j + \sin\theta_j b_j$; $q_j = \cos\theta_j \cos\theta_{j-1} b_j + \sin\theta_j a_{j+1}$; $t_j = \sin\theta_j b_{j+1}$. (d) Let A_2 have $a_j^{(2)}$ on diagonal, $b_j^{(2)}$ on subdiagonal; $a_j^{(2)} = \cos\theta_{j-1}\cos\theta_j r_j + \sin\theta_j q_j$; $b_j^{(2)} = \sin\theta_j r_{j+1}$.

61. (a) A_1: After 10 iterations eigenvalues by LR: 9.60555, 2.04630, 2.34027, by QR: 9.60555, 2.19353, 2.20091; after 25 iterations by LR: 9.60555, 2.26204, 2.11707, by QR: 9.60555, 2.39261, 2.00184. A_2: after 10 iterations by LR: 8.85293, 21.04718, -8.10398, by QR: 8.86988, 4.46548, -3.33536; after 25 iterations by LR: 8.86990, 4.63906, -3.66970, by QR: 8.86990, 4.72949, -3.59939. (b) B_1: LR all correct to five decimals after 11 iterations; QR after 11 iterations -4.00000, -1.09499, $-.90501$, convergence to double eigenvalue at -1 is very slow; for B_2 get convergence only to 1.0 because of complex eigenvalues; complex eigenvalues are given by 2×2 principal minor of U_∞; for B_3 convergence is rapid to -1.0 but very slow for double eigenvalue 4.0.

62. A_1: after 25 iterations, 9.60555, 2.38835, 2.00610; A_2: after 25 iterations, 8.86990, 4.72164, -3.59154.

63. (a) Consider $(A + \delta A)(\mathbf{x}_i + \Sigma\epsilon_{ij}\mathbf{x}_j)$; multiply resulting equation by $\mathbf{y}_i^T$. (b) Let $\mathbf{x} = \Sigma\alpha_i \mathbf{v}_i$; $\mathbf{v}_i$ are orthonormal set of eigenvectors; get $\epsilon^2 = \Sigma|\lambda_i - \lambda|^2 |\alpha_i|^2$; assume result false and get contradiction. (c) $\mathbf{r}^T = (0, \epsilon)$ but true eigenvectors are $(1, 1)$, $(1, -1)$.

64. (a) U exists such that $U^T B U = D > 0$. (b) Constant term is $\det(A)$: coefficient of λ^n is $\det(B)$.

INDEX